T3-BNY-850

Structural Mechanics Software Series

Volume IV

Structural Mechanics Software Series

Volume IV

Edited by
N. Perrone
W. Pilkey

Technical Editor
B. Pilkey

University Press of Virginia
Charlottesville

THE UNIVERSITY PRESS OF VIRGINIA

First published 1982

ISSN: 0146-2059
ISBN: 0-8139-0918-X

Printed in the United States of America

PREFACE

In this volume of the Software Series some new additions and changes are being effected. The Structural Mechanics Software Series is now being published with the cooperation of the Computer Technology Division of the American Society of Mechanical Engineers (ASME). Although publication will still be accomplished at the University of Virginia through the University Press of Virginia, ASME is expected to play a significant cooperative role in developing chapters for this series as well as in recommending directions in technical areas to be covered.

Prospective readers and contributors are encouraged to interact through the auspices of ASME or the editors. The editors welcome feedback from users and readers of the Software Series and are planning to conduct an informal poll to assess the usefulness of the volumes in their current form. We would appreciate your cooperation with this effort.

Computer-aided design and computer-aided manufacturing (CAD/CAM) are key areas with which structural mechanics software has an important and direct impact. Chapters related to CAD-CAM are especially welcomed and planned for inclusion in future volumes.

In this volume a wide spectrum of subjects is treated, ranging from general sources of programs to the evaluation of a specific program (NASTRAN). Transportation-related problems, civil engineering, fracture, plastic analysis, code evaluation methods, and other areas are addressed.

June 1981

Nicholas Perrone

Structural Mechanics Program
Office of Naval Research,
Code 474
800 N. Quincy St.
Arlington, Virginia 22217

Walter D. Pilkey

Applied Mechanics Division
Department of Mechanical and
Aerospace Engineering
University of Virginia
Charlottesville, Virginia 22901

CONTRIBUTORS

John E. Akin
Department of Engineering Science
and Mechanics
University of Tennessee
Knoxville, Tenn. 37919

Harry Armen
Grumman Aerospace Corporation
Bethpage, New York 11714

Michael Chi
CHI Associates, Inc.
Arlington, Virginia 22201

John H. Conoway
Digital Equipment Corporation
200 Forest Street
Marlboro, Massachusetts 01752

B. R. Dewey
Department of Engineering Science
and Mechanics
University of Tennessee
Knoxville, Tenn. 37919

H. H. Fong
Swanson Service Corporation
Huntington Beach, California 92646

Arnold J. Gilchrist
Senior Dynamics Engineer
Wyle Laboratories
Colorado Springs, Colorado 80915

J. A. Hadden
Battelle
Columbus Laboratories
Columbus, Ohio 43201

J. W. Jones
Swanson Service Corporation
Huntington Beach, California 92646

Albert S. Kobayashi
Department of Mechanical Engineering
University of Washington
Seattle, Washington 98195

C. S. Krishnamoorthy
Department of Civil Engineering
Indian Institute of Technology
Madras 600 036
India

Robert E. Nickell
Applied Science & Technology
3344 North Torrey Pines Court
La Jolla, California 92037

Alan B. Palazzolo
Allis Chalmers Corporation
Advanced Technology Center
Engineering Development and
Computer Applications
Milwaukee, Wisconsin 53201

Alan B. Pifko
Grumman Aerospace Corporation
Bethpage, New York 11714

Walter D. Pilkey
Department of Mechanical and
Aerospace Engineering
University of Virginia
Charlottesville, Virginia 22901

N. T. Tsai
Offce of Freight Systems
Freight Service Division
Federal Railroad Administration
Department of Transportation
400 7th Street, S.W.
Washington, D.C. 20590

John Tucker
CHI Associates, Inc.
Arlington, Virginia 22201

Bo Ping Wang
Department of Mechanical and
Aerospace Engineering
University of Virginia
Charlottesville, Virginia 22901

CONTENTS

Part I

SOURCES OF INFORMATION AND PROGRAMS

Computerized Sources of Abstracts of the Engineering Literature

INTRODUCTION

Following is a list of three major commercial services through which the customer can have access to a variety of data bases. Each service is described, and then the data bases available on-line through the service are listed and described.

DIALOG

Address: Lockheed Information Systems
Orgn. 5208, Building 201
3251 Hanover Street
Palo Alto, CA 94304
(800) 277-1960 Continental U.S.
(800) 982-5838 in California
(415) 493-4411 outside U.S.A.

This system has no initiation fees and no minimum monthly charges. At the present time there are 81 data bases on-line, of which they say 22 are of interest to people working in some phase of transportation. Of these 22 data bases, eight would probably be of some interest to people concerned with technical and engineering information. These eight are listed below, along with a short description of what is available in the data base and the rates for both on-line usage and for off-line printouts.

A special feature offered by the DIALOG system is the Private File Service. This service allows a user to put an established data base or to build a new personal data base on the DIALOG system. The user then has access to his files on an interactive basis using the DIALOG retrieval system. DIALOG guarantees the security and confidentiality of the file, and will update the file as frequently as is desired. Records can be printed off-line and mailed to the user, or typed on-line.

COMPENDEX

Coverage: January 1970 - present
File size: 817,000 records, monthly updates
Prepared by: Engineering Index, Inc., New York, N.Y.
Description: The COMPENDEX data base is the machine-readable version of the Engineering Index (Monthly/Annual), which provides the engineering and information communities with abstracted information from the world's significant engineering and technological literature. The EI data base provides worldwide coverage of approximately 2500 journals, publications of engineering societies and organizations, papers from the proceedings of conferences, and selected government reports and books. Cost: $65 per on-line computer hour, 15¢ per full record printed off-line, 10¢ per full record typed on-line.

COMPREHENSIVE DISSERTATION ABSTRACTS

Coverage: 1861 - present. File size: 648,000 citations, monthly updates. Prepared by: Xerox University Microfilms, Ann Arbor, MI.
Description: COMPREHENSIVE DISSERTATION ABSTRACTS is a definitive subject, title, and author guide to virtually every American dissertation accepted at an accredited institution since 1861, when academic doctoral degrees were first granted in the United States. In addition, CDA serves to disseminate citations for thousands of Canadian dissertations and an increasing number of papers accepted in institutions abroad. Professional (e.g., M.D., L.L.D.) and honorary degrees are not included. All subject areas are covered.

Individual degree-granting institutions submit copies of dissertations or lists of dissertations completed to University Microfilm International (UMI). Citations for these dissertations are included in the data base and in University Microfilms International printed publications: Dissertation Abstracts International (DAI), American Doctoral Dissertations (ADD), and Comprehensive Dissertation Index (CDI).

Cost: $55 per on-line computer hour
12¢ per full record printed off-line

CONFERENCE PAPERS INDEX

Coverage: 1973 - present
File size: 715,000 records, monthly updates
Prepared by: Data Courier, Inc., Louisville, KY
Description: CONFERENCE PAPERS INDEX provides access to records of more than 100,000 scientific and technical papers presented at over 1,000 major regional, national, and international meetings each year. CONFERENCE PAPERS INDEX provides a centralized source of information on reports of current research and development from papers presented at conferences and meetings; it provides titles of the papers as well as the names and addresses (when available) of the authors of these papers. Also included in this data base are announcements of any publications issued or planned for issuance from the meetings and of available preprints, reprints, abstract booklets, and proceedings volumes as well

as dates of availability, costs, and ordering information. Primary subject areas covered include the life sciences, chemistry, physical sciences, geosciences, and engineering.

Cost: $75 per on-line computer hour
15¢ per full record printed off-line

INSPEC

Coverage: 1969 - present
File size: 1,404,000 citations, monthly updates
Prepared by: The Institution of Electrical Engineers, Savoy Place, London WS2R OBL, England
Description: The Science Abstracts family of abstract journals, indexes, and title bulletins commenced publication in 1898. Today it forms the largest English-language data base in the fields of physics, electrotechnology, computers, and control. The on-line INSPEC file corresponds to the printed <u>Physics Abstracts</u>, <u>Electrical and Electronics Abstracts</u>, and <u>Computer and Control Abstracts</u>. Foreign language source material is also included, but abstracted and indexed in English.

Journal papers, conference proceedings, technical reports, books, patents, and university theses are abstracted and indexed for inclusion in the INSPEC data bases. The total number of journals scanned is approximately 2000; over 200 of these are abstracted completely.

Cost: $55 per on-line computer hour
15¢ per full record printed off-line

ISMEC

Coverage: 1973 - present
File size: 98,000 citations, monthly updates
Prepared by: Data Courier, Inc., Louisville, KY
Description: ISMEC (Information Service in Mechanical Engineering) indexes significant articles in all aspects of mechanical engineering, production engineering, and engineering management from approximately 250 journals published throughout the world. In addition, books, reports, and conference proceedings are indexed. The primary emphasis is on comprehensive coverage of leading international journals and conferences on mechanical engineering subjects. The principal areas covered are mechanical, nuclear, electrical, electronic, civil, optical, medical, and industrial process engineering; mechanics; production processes: energy, and power; transport and handling; and applications of mechanical engineering.

Cost: $75 per on-line computer hour
15¢ per full record printed off-line

NTIS

Coverage: 1964 - present
File size: 765,000 citations, biweekly updates
Prepared by: National Technical Information Service, NTIS, U.S. Department of Commerce, Springfield, Virginia
Description: The NTIS data base consists of government-sponsored research, development, and engineering, plus analyses prepared by federal agencies,

their contractors, or grantees. It is the means through which unclassified, publicly available, unlimited distribution reports are made available for sale from such agencies as NASA, DDC, DOE, HEW, HUD, DOT, Department of Commerce, and some 240 other units. State and local government agencies are now beginning to contribute their reports to the file.

The NTIS data base includes material from both the hard and soft sciences, including substantial material on technological applications, business procedures, and regulatory matters. Many topics of immediate broad interest are included, such as environmental pollution and control, energy conversion, technology transfer, behavioral/societal problems, and urban and regional planning.

Cost: $35 per on-line computer hour
10¢ per full record printed off-line

SCISEARCH

Coverage: January 1974 - present
File size: 2,970,000 citations, monthly updates
Prepared by: Institute for Scientific Information, Philadelphia, PA
Description: SCISEARCH is a multidisciplinary index to the literature of science and technology prepared by the Institute for Scientific Information (IST). It contains all of the records published in Science Citation Index (SCI) and additional records from the Current Contents series of publications that are not included in the printed version of SCI. SCISEARCH is distinguished by two important and unique characteristics. First, journals indexed are carefully selected on the basis of several criteria, including citation analysis, resulting in the inclusion of 90 percent of the world's significant scientific and technical literature. Second, citation indexing is provided, which allows retrieval of newly published articles through the subject relationships established by an author's reference to prior articles. SCISEARCH covers every area of the pure and applied sciences.

The ISI staff indexes all significant items (articles, reports of meetings, letters, editorials, correction notices, etc.) from about 2600 major scientific and technical journals. Beginning January 1, 1976, all items from Current Contents - Engineering, Technology, and Applied Science have been included each month. This expanded coverage adds approximately 58,000 items per year to the SCISEARCH file.

Cost for citations from 1978 to present:

$120 per on-line connect hour 20¢ per full record printed off-line,	nonsubscribers
$30 per on-line connect hour 10¢ per full record printed off-line,	subscribers

Cost for citations from 1974 to 1978:

$130 per on-line connect hour 20¢ per full record printed off-line,	nonsubscribers
$40 per on-line connect hour 10¢ per full record printed off-line,	subscribers

SSIE CURRENT RESEARCH

Coverage: last two years, e.g., 1978 - present
File size: 299,000 citations, monthly updates
Prepared by: Smithsonian Science Information Exchange, Washington, D.C.

Description: SSIE (SMITHSONIAN SCIENCE INFORMATION EXCHANGE) CURRENT RESEARCH is a data base containing reports of both government and privately funded scientific research projects, either currently in progress or initiated and completed during the most recent two years. SSIE data are collected from the funding organizations at the inception of a research project and provide a source for information on current research long before first or progress reports appear in the published literature. SSIE CURRENT RESEARCH encompasses all fields of basic and applied research in the life, physical, social, and engineering sciences.

Project descriptions are received from over 1,300 organizations that fund research including federal, state, and local government agencies; nonprofit associations and foundations; and colleges and universities. A small amount of material is provided from private industry and foreign research organizations, while 90 percent of the information in the data base is provided by agencies of the federal government.

Research projects in SSIE CURRENT RESEARCH include work in progress in the electronics, physics, materials science, engineering, and mathematics.

Cost: $90 per on-line computer hour
20¢ per full record printed off-line

TRIS

Coverage: 1968 – present
File size: 145,000 records, monthly updates
Prepared by: U.S. Department of Transportation and Transportation Research Board, Washington, D.C.
Description: TRIS provides transportation research information in air, highway, rail, and maritime transport, mass transit, and other transportation modes. Subjects included are regulations and legislation; energy, environmental, and safety concerns; materials, design, construction and maintenance technology; and operations, traffic control, and communications. The data base records can be either abstracts of documents and data holdings or resumes of research projects. Among the transportation research information services contributing to TRIS are the Highway Research Information Service (HRIS), the Maritime Research Information Service (MRIS), the Railroad Information Service (RRIS), the Air Transportation Research Information Service (ATRIS), and the Urban Mass Transportation Research Information Service (UMTRIS). Use is restricted to U.S. and Canada passwords only.
Cost: $40 per on-line connect hour
10¢ per full record printed off-line

ORBIT

Address: System Development Corporation (SDC)
2500 Colorado Avenue
Santa Monica, California 90406
(213) 829-7511

and

7979 Westpark Drive
McLean, Virginia 22101
(703) 790-9850 in Virginia
(800) 336-3313 outside of Virginia

also

(800) 352-6689 in California
(800) 421-7229 continental USA except California

There are no start-up fees or minimum charges if you wish to use this service. The data bases available through SDC in many cases overlap those available on the DIALOG system. The technically oriented data bases are listed below, along with pertinent information which is unique to this system. Data bases not available from the DIALOG system are abstracted. A private data base service is available; customers can have their personal data bases installed on the SDC computers and then access the files using the ORBIT system.

COMPENDEX

Coverage: January 1970 - present
Cost: $65 per on-line computer hour
10¢ per full record printed off-line
6¢ per full record typed on-line

Conference Papers Index

Coverage: 1973 - present
Cost: $75 per on-line computer hour
15¢ per full record printed off-line

INSPEC and INSP6976

Coverage: INSPEC: 1970 - present
INSP6976: 1969 - 1976
Cost: $55 per on-line computer hour
15¢ per full record printed off-line

ISMEC

Coverage: 1973 - present
Cost: $65 per on-line computer hour
12¢ per full record printed off-line

NTIS

Coverage: January, 1970 - present
Cost: $45 per on-line computer hour
8¢ per full record printed off-line

SAE Abstracts

Coverage: January, 1965 - present
File size: Approximately 800 citations per year

Prepared by: Society of Automotive Engineers, Inc.
Description: Worldwide coverage of papers concerned with self-propelled vehicles gathered from industry, government, and academic sectors as well as research and private organizations. Subject coverage includes aircraft, missiles, and spacecraft, ground support equipment, passenger cars, military equipment, aircraft propulsion, electric vehicles, energy conversion, fuels and lubricants, manufacturing and production, transportation systems, emissions, safety, noise, management, testing, and instrumentation.
Updating: Quarterly, approximately 200 citations
Cost: $80 per on-line computer hour
15¢ per citation for off-line printing

Safety Scientific Abstracts

Coverage: 1975 - present
File size: Approximately 15,000 citation per year
Prepared by: Cambridge Scientific Abstracts
Description: Broad, interdisciplinary coverage of literature related to the science of safety; a relatively new field devoted to identifying, evaluating, and eliminating or controlling hazards. Major subject categories are: general safety; industrial and occupational safety; transportation safety; aviation and aerospace safety; environmental and ecological safety; and medical safety. Topics covered include: pollution, fire, waste disposal, prediction and reporting of natural disasters, legislative regulations and their impact, urban development, radiation, drug dosages, criminal acts (e.g., arson, child abuse), epidemics, pesticides, education, prevention, and psychological factors related to safety.
Updating: Bimonthly, approximately 3000 citations
Cost: $75 per on-line computer hour
15¢ per citation for off-line printing

SSIE

Coverage: Fiscal year 1974 to present date
Cost: $110 per on-line computer hour
25¢ per full record printed off-line

BRS

Address: Bibliographic Retrieval Services, Inc.
Corporation Park, Bldg. 702
Scotia, New York 12302
(518) 374-5011

This is a relatively new data base service, which was started in 1976. The on-line searching capabilities are the current three- to five-year portions of the data bases. Earlier years will searched and processed off-line at the user's request, and be available for on-line printing the next day. In the past year the number of data bases on-line through BRS has increased greatly. It may also be of interest that they have recently been acquired by Information Handling Services.

Charges are computed in a unique manner on this system. The user must make an annual committment for a minimum level of use. Based on this figure, an hourly fee of from $16 to $30 is charged for the use of the BRS system. On top of this hourly charge, some files also have royalty charges. There are also printout costs associated with some data bases. The hourly charges listed below are the royalty charges only.

Books Info.

File size: More than 800,000 books in print or in press
Prepared by: Brodart Inc.
Description: Contains citations and prices on books whether in print or press.
Cost: $10 per on-line computer hour royalty
5¢ per page printed out off-line

Comprehensive Dissertation Index

Royalty: 50% of user connect hour rate

Index to Code of Federal Regulations

Prepared by: Information Handling Services

Index to State Publications

Coverage: 1976 to present
Prepared by: Information Handling Services
Description: This is an index to all state publications produced in all 50 states plus P.R. and the Virgin Islands
Cost: $20 per hour royalty

INSPEC

NTIS

SCI

Cost: This file is priced separately fron the normal BRS scheme, as no subscription fee is charged, and the hourly fee is different for SCI subscribers and nonsubscribers.
$30 per hour for SCI subscribers
$120 per hour for non-SCI subscribers
10¢ offline

SSIE

Cost: $30 per hour royalty
10¢ per record off-line

ADDITIONAL DATA BASES AND CUSTOM SEARCH SERVICES

What follows is a list of individualized or custom data search services. Some of these may overlap the sources available on the interactive services described in the previous section, but in this section information is given on how each service will do a personalized search for a customer.

NTIS (National Technical Information Service)

NTIS will do a custom search of its own data base if a customer requests one. The charge is $125 per search and includes up to 100 abstracts. The search is screened by someone in the appropriate field to remove false hits. The serivces are available to anyone.

NTIS can also be searched through one's own terminal using the data base services of DIALOG, ORBIT (SDC), and BRS.

For a custom search contact

National Technical Information Service
U.S. Department of Commerce
5285 Port Royal Road
Springfield, Virginia 22161

or call:

(703) 557-4642 and ask for an information specialist

Railroad Research Information Service (RRIS)

This is a computer-based information service active since 1972 and operated by the Transportation Research Board with financial support from the Federal Railroad Administration. RRIS can give transportation administrators, engineers, economists, planners, and researchers access to information concerning ongoing and completed railroad and railroad-related research activities. In addition to coverage of all phases of railroading from worldwide sources through exchange agreements, there are a large number of references to all types of rail transit and to the various advanced guideway systems. About 2500 citations are added annually. A file, updated twice a year, is maintained of current research projects giving the project description, objectives, sponsor, principal investigator, and other information. Abstracts of reports, pertinent technical papers, and articles are stored in the RRIS file along with descriptions of computer programs from railroad and other sources (such as the Federal Railroad Administration and the Association of American Railroads).

The RRIS file is available for searches of information related to an inquiry. The basic charge for doing a search (batch mode) is $50 plus 25¢ per citation. This includes screening of the search by RRIS subject specialists. Requests may be made by phone, letter, or visit.

In addition the RRIS data base may be searched on-line through the Lockheed DIALOG Information Retrieval Service. This method of access is handled entirely through Lockheed and is only available to its users in the United States and Canada. RRIS citations are updated in Lockheed file 63 on a monthly basis. Phone 800-227-1960 or 800-982-5838 (California only).

RRIS also prints the Railroad Research Bulletin biannually. This abstract bulletin contains all of the new references that have been added to the RRIS data base during the preceding six months. The Bulletin can be obtained through annual subscription or by single-copy purchase.

For more information write to:

Mr. F. N. Houser, Manager
Railroad Research Information Service
Transportation Research Board
2101 Constitution Avenue
Washington, D.C. 20418

Telex 710-822-9589
Telephone 202-389-6611

SSIE (Smithsonian Science Information Exchange)

This data base consists of resumes of current and past technical research projects sponsored by the Smithsonian and other government branches. The information is available on-line through DIALOG and ORBIT (SCD). The SSIE will do custom searches with specialists checking the validity of the search, for $60. This fee gives up to 50 projects, each described and summarized on a single sheet. Additional hits can be had for $0.25 each (if they exist).

For more information contact

Smithsonian Science Information Exchange (SSIE)
Smithsonian Institution
1730 Main Street, N.W.
Washington, D.C. 20036

Telephone 202-381-4211

TRIS (Transportation Research Information Service)

This data base was loaded onto a computer by Battelle-Columbus and was maintained and updated by Battelle until it was turned over to the Department of Transportation on April 6, 1979. The system will probably be made publicly available on DIALOG, the Lockheed System, but final arrangements have not yet been completed. It has not been decided how or if custom searches will be done. It should be noted, however, that TRIS is one of the bases searched by the Railroad Research Information Service when they do their custom searches. For futher information about TRIS and its present status and availability, contact

Don Johnson
Information and Management Branch
Research and Specia Programs Administration
U.S. Department of Transportation
Washington, D.C. 20590

Telephone 202-426-0975

or visit: Room 513, 2100 Pennsylvania Avenue, N.W., Washington, DC.

Program Dissemination Centers and Users Groups

INTRODUCTION

Computers, because of their ever increasing capabilities coupled with their lower and lower costs, are becoming more common as office tools for the engineer, as well as everyone else. The groups that have been formed for software dissemination and sharing are also proliferating. These range from the local groups, which meet on an ad hoc basis to solve and share problems as well as software, to the more formal groups which have national meetings and programs. Although the membership structures and/or dissemination goals may vary, a member has benefits such as reduced-cost software and/or updates and technical help with program problems when he belongs to these groups. What follows is a list of cooperative users groups and software dissemination services which would be of the most interest to the engineer.

AASHTO Subcommittee on Computer Technology

Contact: Mr. Kenneth Close, HMS-40, Secretary
Federal Highway Administration
400 7th Street, S.W.
Washington, D.C. 20590

In 1973 the American Association of State Highway and Transportation Officials established the AASHTO Committee on Computer Technology to replace the Committee on Data Processing.

The purposes of the committee are: to develop, improve, and promote the use of data-processing techniques in transportation engineering, management, and fiscal control; to investigate advances in the use of computers in allied fields; to promote the application of appropriate new methods to transportation programs; to keep current a catalog of computer programs applicable to the transportation field; and to disseminate this information to member departments. The committee has annually compiled and distributed the Computer System Index, a catalog of programs developed by AASHTO members. Through this index, members are able to exchange knowledge, programs, and experience. The exchange is between user and originator, and the user's experience is not formally passed back to the committee or other members. The subcommittee publishes proceedings of these seminars. Copies of the Computer System Index and the Proceedings of the subcommittee meetings are available from:

American Association of State Highway and Transportation
444 North Capital Street, N.W.
Washington, D.C. 20001

Aerospace Structures Information and Analysis Center (ASIAC)

Contact: AFWAL/FIBR(ASIAC)
Wright-Patterson AFB
Dayton, Ohio 45433

ASIAC is sponsored by the Flight Dynamics Laboratory to provide quick response and in-depth literature searches, data retrieval, and state-of-the-art solutions to structural problems. ASIAC maintains a library of aerospace structures related computer programs that are not available from other program dissemination organizations. These services are available to government agencies and to their contractors upon written request with a valid need. A newsletter is published containing topics of interest to the structures community. For specific information, contact Mr. Gordon R. Negaard at (513) 255-6688.

Automated Procedures for Engineering Consultants (APEC)

Contact: Mrs. Doris J. Wallace
Executive Director
Automated Procedures for Engineering Consultants
Fourth and Ludlow Streets
Dayton, Ohio 45402

APEC is a nonprofit association of member firms who pool their resources and work together in volunteer cooperative efforts to develop computer programs for use in building design. A membership fee and annual dues are assessed to all members, who are then eligible to license any software in the APEC library at a shared cost of program development.

APEC programs are "designed by engineers, for use by engineers." Member firms volunteer personnel with specialized expertise and talents to serve on Technical Committees which are responsible for researching the market and defining the capabilities and scope of proposed program development efforts for review, comment, and input of all member firms. Endorsement of proposed efforts is confirmed by precommittments of financial support prior to entering into formal contractural agreements for development which are required to incorporate APEC's FORTRAN Programming and Documentation Standards.

Complete documentation, including listings and flow charts, and with specific methodology fully identified, is provided with each Program license. Workshops are held periodically to provide a "hands-on" experience in the application of APEC programs. Maintenance is provided through technical Program Development Committees and through the services of a Program Technical Adviser and a Data Processing Adviser.

Members of APEC obtain the use of quality programs specifically tailored to their needs at a low shared cost of development because of the unique system of efforts volunteered by engineers from the world's leading design firms. Additional benefits include education and promotion in the professional use of computers to aid design, plus an unusually free and cooperative exchange of ideas and experiences with design and management problems.

APEC publishes numerous items including documentation and abstracts for all their programs.

Programs written in FORTRAN IV for IBM/1130, 370/OS, and DOS. They are available on GE and CDC Networks. Programs include: HCC-III, a heating/cooling load calculation; ESP-I, an energy simulation program; SUPER-DUCT II, for duct design; PIPING for piping design; Lighting-II, for lighting design and cost analysis; HCCJR, a heating/cooling load calculation program; SPECS, specification editing computer systems; and STD90, which is based on ASHRAE Standard 90-75.

COMMON

Contact: Mr. David G. Lister
Administrative Director, COMMON
435 N. Michigan Avenue
Chicago, Illinois 60611

COMMON, a users group for IBM computers, was formed in 1962. Its membership consists of users of Systems 3, 32, 34, 38, 1130, 1800, 51XX, and 7. The principal objective is to advance the effective usage of equipment among users of IBM computers and data-processing machines. The organization promotes the free interchange of information about the machines and the techniques of use.

Computer Software Management and Information Center (COSMIC)

Contact: COSMIC
112 Barrow Hall
University of Georgia
Athens, Georgia 30602
(404) 542-3265

The Computer Software Management and Information Center (COSMIC), an integral part of the National Aeronautics and Space Administration's Technology Utilization Program, has been operated by the University of Georgia since its beginning in 1966. COSMIC functions as the collection, evaluation, and dissemination center for over 1500 computer programs developed by NASA, NASA contractors, and other agencies.

Program areas include engineering, manufacturing, transportation, communications, natural resources, energy conservation, information management, and, of course, computer technology. For example, COSMIC is the dissemination point for NASTRAN, NASA's Structural Analysis program. First developed for space vehicles, NASTRAN is used by industry to design automobiles, aircraft, oil drilling towers, and much more.

Further information on COSMIC and available programs may be obtained by contacting a COSMIC representative. A catalog of the programs on this system is published.

Cooperating Users of Burroughs Equipment (CUBE)

Contact: Mr. Thomas S. Grier
CUBE Secretary
Burroughs Corporation
Second Avenue at Borroughs
Detroit, Michigan 48232

CUBE was founded because of the need of computer users to exchange ideas as well as software and to communicate among themselves and with the vendor. The common link shared by CUBE members is their use of computers manufactured by Burroughs Corporation. Users of all Burroughs computers, B1700/B1800 through B7800, are eligible to join CUBE.

Program exchange among CUBE members takes two forms. For users of the smaller and medium systems, the catalog of abstracts provides the name and address of the originating member to contact for further discussion and negotiation at the time of the exchange. For users of the larger systems (B6700 through B7800), tapes of the desired programs may be obtained by sending scratch tapes and postage to the CUBE librarian. The programs were donated by members and are available only to other CUBE members. The library of program consists of mathematical subroutines, some language enhancements, and various data-processing and accounting routines.

Digital Equipment Computer Users Society (DECUS)

Contact: Digital Equipment Computer Users Society
One Iron Way
Marlboro, Massachusetts 01752

DECUS was established to advance the effective use of DIGITAL computers; it is a not-for-profit users group, supported in part by Digital Equipment Corporation. Because membership in DECUS is voluntary, no membership fee is charged. In addition to the office in the United States, DECUS maintains offices in Australia, Canada, and Switzerland. As of January 1980, the DECUS Program Library contained 1700 active software packages. These programs are available to members for a nominal service charge. Information on membership and available programs may be requested from the DECUS Publications Office at the address listed above.

Federal Agencies Computer Time-Sharing System (FACTS)

Contact: Mr. Henry A. Borger
Program Manager
Federal Construction Council
Building Research Advisory Board
2101 Constitution Avenue, N.W.
Washington, D.C. 20018

FACTS, a main mechanism of a program for facilitating the use of computers in federal construction agencies, is an extensive library of fully validated, easily utilized computer programs dealing with a wide variety of construction-related engineering problems. The library is available for use by all federal construction agencies, through remote terminals.

The aim of this effort is to solve the two major problems that lead to the underutilization of computers by federal construction agencies. The two problems are:

1. that engineers at most agencies have far too few programs of proven validity available to them.
2. that most programs available in the agencies are written in such a way that they can be used only by engineers who have extensive knowledge of computers or only after the using engineer has been given detailed instructions on the use.

The solutions to these problems are respectively:

1. pooling the programs already available in the various agencies into this consolidated interagency library of programs and subsequently initiating a coordinated interagency effort to develop new programs.
2. using the library system developed by the U.S. Army Corps of Engineers that employs programs in which documentation is an inherent part of the program.

Work associated with the development, adaptation, refinement, and validation of computer programs is carried out on a voluntary basis by participating federal agencies. Work associated with the development of the executive programs for the FACTS library (i.e., the computer programs that serve as librarian) and the preparation of manuals on writing programs for the library and on using the library is carried out by the Office, Chief of Engineers, U.S. Army Corps of Engineers. The library of the General Services Administration (GSA) will be made available to federal agencies through the Center's time-sharing system identified as RAMUS, Remote Access Multi-User System, and the entire program is coordinated by the Federal Construction Council. FACTS has been in operation since July 1974, and there are currently 75 programs in the library; all of these programs have been validated and have the documentation as an inherent part of the program.

The programs in the FACTS library cover a wide variety of subjects dealing with construction engineering; however, the majority deal with hydraulics. Since FACTS is an interactive time-sharing system, no programs are included in the library that require a substantial amount of input data or generate extensive output.

Federal agencies can gain access to FACTS merely by becoming RAMUS subscribers. For details, agencies should write to

General Service Administration
Automated Data Telecommunications Service
1776 Peachtree Street, NW
Atlanta, Georgia 30309

GENESYS LIMITED

Contact: Laurence N. Beckreck
Sales Manager
GENESYS LIMITED
Lisle Street
Loughborough
Leicestershire, LE11 OAY
England

Genesys Ltd. is a wholly-owned subsidiary of the British Government's National Research Development Corporation. The Company is established in the fields of Computer Aided Design for Building and Civil Engineering on an international basis.

The products and service available comprise:

1. GENESYS System and Subsystem library
2. brokerage service for other software
3. hardware/software turnkey systems
4. engineering consultancy and programming

GENESYS is a control program designed to provide an effective interface between computers and the application programs of GENESYS, called Subsystems. Since the control program is largely written in ANSI Stanard Fortran, GENESYS and the range of Subsystems are implemented on a wide range of different computers.

The control program performs two types of operations. For the programmer developing a subsystem, it provides facilities through which a set of commands may be defined to allow users to call up individual program modules of a subsystem. The commands provided for the subsystem form a problem-oriented language. GENESYS also translates the modules of the subsystem from the source language called GENTRAN into FORTRAN, tailored to fit the particular configuration of the run time computer. GENTRAN is almost identical to FOTRAN IV, but with a computer independent set of statements for reference to peripheral devices. Programmers write GENTRAN modules assuming the availability of an infinitely large core storage but are provided with a number of optional statements which override the software virtual storage providing this facility.

Gifts Users Group (GUG)

Contact: H. A. Kamel
Aerospace and Mechanical Engineering
University of Arizona
Tucson, Arizona

The Gifts Users Groups has an international membership, encompassing people in universities, federal agencies, the military, and industry, who use the graphics-oriented finite element program GIFTS. GUG members are supported through regular updates and have the right to free telephone consultation. Exchange of information, program innovations, and enhancements between GUG members is encouraged and implemented through the Interactive Graphics Engineering Laboratory at the University of Arizona. Modest membership fees are charged so that GUG can be self-supporting. An earlier unsupported version, GIFTS 4, is in the public domain. GIFTS 5, distributed through GUG, has been copyrighted.

Highway Engineering Exchange Program (HEEP)

Contact: Mr. James W. Dahlen
Seattle District
Corps of Engineers
P.O. Box C-3755
Seattle, Washington 98124
(206) 764-3742

HEEP was organized with the objectives of promoting the free exchange of computer programs and related concepts among its membership and increasing the effectiveness of computer usage and development. Membership is held by state and provincial highway and transportation departments, major city and county road departments, federal agencies, and institutions of higher education. Associate membership includes civil engineering consultants and equipment and software vendors. The objectives of HEEP are primarily promoted by one national meeting and four to six area meetings held each year; however, the active membership varies depending on agency-imposed travel restrictions.

There is no HEEP library. To accomplish the goal of information interchange, HEEP has cooperated with the AASHTO Committe on Data Processing in publishing a Computer Systems Index. Any cross-agency development efforts have been carried out primarily by indivudal agencies cooperating together. The AASHTO index can be obtained ($10.00 prepaid, plus $1.25 postage and handling) from

American Association of State and Highway and
Transportation Officials
444 North Capital Street, N.W., Suite 225
Washington, D.C. 20001

Honeywell Large Systems Users Association (HLSUA)

Contact: HLSUA Association
815-15th Street, N.W.
Suite 511
Washington, D.C. 20005

The HLSUA was organized to stimulate the development of and to disseminate information concerning techniques for the preparation and operation of electronic data-processing systems for Honeywell computers. The organization operates primarily as a working group concerned with operating systems, program languages, computer utilization, and operational problems of the member organizations.

ICES Users Group

Contact: Frederick E. Hajjar
Executive Director
ICES Users Group, Inc.
P.O. Box 8243
Cranston, Rhode Island 02920

The ICES Users Group is a nonprofit, professional organization which was formed in 1967 for the purpose of free exchange and public dissemination of technological information pertaining to the ICES family of computer programs, the most important of which is STRUDL. The ICES Users Group conducts semiannual meetings, discussion groups, forums, panels, lectures, and other similar programs and publishes the *ICES Journal*, which contains conference papers, information on ICES activities and publications, and instructions on ordering programs. Currently the Group has 525 organization members; among these are 375 private industrial organizations, 90 universities and colleges, and 60 state and federal government agencies. Information about the ICES Users Group can be obtained through the Executive Office of the Director or through the ICES Distribution Agencies currently located in Cambridge, Massachusetts, Ispra, Italy, and Tokyo, Japan.

International Society of Wang Users (ISWU)

Contact: Shirley Leney, Manager
International Society of Wang Users
One Industrial Avenue
Lowell, Massachusetts 01841

The primary objective of this group is to advance the effectiveness of utilization of both data-processing and word-processing systems manufactured by Wang Laboratories, Inc. Membership is open only to those with Wang equipment. Several hundred programs and applications are maintained and distributed. An annual Users Conference is held to give the members an opportunity to meet other Wang Users, who may be in the same industry, have the same equipment, or are trying to accomplish similar tasks. It also allows the members to pose questions to Wang and industry specialists.

International Computer Programs, Inc. (ICP)

Contact: International Computer Programs, Inc. (ICP)
9000 Keystone Crossing
Indianapolis, Indiana 46240

ICP is a private company involved in many software dissemination activities. They deal primarily in aiding commercial software companies with preparing and selling their programs. Among their publications is the ICP Software Directory, which contains a section on Manufacturing and Engineering. The directory consists of abstracts of computer programs that can be purchased or leased. Each abstract contains a description of the program along the complete details of its availability. Since the Directory accepts abstracts free of charge from anyone, it contains an interesting array of structural mechanics programs, many of which are not listed elsewhere.

National Energy Software Center

Contact: Margaret Butler, Director
National Energy Software Center
Argonne National Laboratory
9700 S. Cass Avenue
Argonne, Illinois 60439
(312) 972-7250

The National Energy Software Center collects, reviews, tests, maintains, and distributes a software library which was developed to meet the needs of the Department of Energy and the U.S. Nuclear Regulatory Commission. The library presently consists of over 725 programs, systems, models, and data compilations; approximately 68 of the computer codes relate to structural analysis and engineering design. An organization may become affiliated with the Center as a registered installation, or it may purchase single software packages on a one-time basis. Inquiries concerning the available programs and the procedures for obtaining them should be directed to the Center.

National Information Service for Earthquake Engineering (NISEE)

Contact: NISEE/Computer Applications
519 Davis Hall
University of California
Berkeley, California 94720
(415) 642-5113

NISEE/Computer Applications is a service offering a means by which computer programs related to earthquake engineering can receive wide distribution among both the engineering profession and the academic community. Its activities include dissemination of brief documentation newsletters about recent computer programs and distribution of programs. Program user documentation and a source deck are sent when a program is ordered through NISEE. The distribution is unlimited; royalty or development charges are not allowed; and the programs which are purchased should not be resold for direct profit.

NTIS

Contact: NTIS
U.S. Department of Commerce
5285 Port Royal Road
Springfield, Virginia 22161

NTIS has cataloged the computer programs it has available for distribution into thirty area-specific directories. Each directory costs $35. A total of more than 5400 programs are abstracted in these directories, a large percentage of which are technically oriented. Reports which describe the software and often contain the source code are referenced in the directories. The reports can be purchased in paper or microfiche form from NTIS. Costs are extremely modest.

PAFEC USERS GROUP

Contact: Mr. Alan Jackson
Hatfield Polytechnic
Department of Mechanical Engineering
Hatfield, Herts
England

The user group is an independent organization to report on the use of PAFEC, to critique the features, and to recommend program enhancements. It meets at least twice each year. Members vote on a formal set of questions and recommendations. Anyone may attend the conferences. Each site can have up to two voting representatives; however, there is a $20.00 charge for the second voting representative. The next USA meeting is planned for the summer of 1981.

SAP Users Group

Contact: SAP Users Group
Dept. of Civil Engineering
University of Southern California
Los Angeles, CA 90007
(213) 741-5508

This university research group upgrades and maintains the SAP finite element programs and also distributes IBM versions of the NISEE (Berkeley) programs and BOSOR 4 and 5. They are presently developing SAP 7, a linear and nonlinear program for release in the coming months. This program is an outgrowth of SAP 6, which performs static and dynamic analysis of structural systems. Pre- and postprocessing plot generation auxiliary programs are also available to accompany SAP 6 and 7. These programs are available in IBM, CDC, and VAX versions.

SHARE

Contact: SHARE, Inc.
111 E. Wacker Drive
Chicago, Illinois 60601
(312) 822-0932

This organization, formed in 1955 as an IBM 704 Society, has incorporated into its family of machines the scientific computers from the IBM 700-7000 series and, since 1964, the larger systems from the 360 and 370 lines.

The principal purpose of SHARE is to foster research and development and the exchange and public dissemination of data pertaining to computer science in the scientific tradition. To achieve these ends, SHARE: (1) conducts meetings, discussion groups, forums, panels, lectures, and other similar events; (2) publishes through its SHARE secretary the results of its research, and other publications as appropriate, and makes such publications available to the interested public on a noncommittal and nondiscriminatory basis; and (3) establishes and continually improves standards for communicating computer science research results and programming information to interested members of the public. SHARE currently has over a thousand members.

A program library of approximately two hundred programs is formed by contributions of both domestic and foreign member installations. The programs are available at distribution cost. Complete information on Share's Program Library can be provided by:

SHARE PROGRAM LIBRARY AGENCY
Triangle Universities Computation Center
P.O. Box 12076
Research Triangle Park, North Carolina 27709
(919) 549-0671

Society for Computer Application in Engineering, Planning, and Architecture, Inc. (CEPA)

Contact: Patricia C. Johnson
Executive Director
358 Hungerford Drive
Rockville, Maryland 20850
(301) 762-6070

CEPA, a nonprofit organization, was founded in 1965 by a group of civil engineers. Its principal objective is to further the effective application of computers in engineering, planning, architecture, and related fields. To this end, CEPA provides means for the exchange and cooperative development of computer programs and systems.

Membership is open to organizations utilizing computers in the practice of engineering and related fields and subscribing and contributing to the cooperative purposes and efforts of CEPA. CEPA is supported by the dues of its members.

One of the important facilities offered by CEPA to its memberhsip is the program library. This library consists of between 300 and 400 programs, contributed by members and classified under Bridges, Buildings, Construction, Electricity, Environment/Energy Management, Geometry/Highways, Geotechnical, Graphics, Hardware/Systems Software, Management, Sanitary/Hydraulics, and Traffic/Transit. Typical of the programs included are those in geometry and alignment areas. In structural areas, the library includes bridges, retaining walls, and project management programs.

Members obtain programs based on a point system similar to a bank account. Members are credited with points when a program is contributed, debited points when they request a program. In operating the program library, CEPA acts as a broker between members in providing information on program availability and in keeping an account of point balances. The cost associated with program acquisition is a matter between the owner of the program and the requester. Should a member run out of points, they may be purchased from CEPA, with the funds going to CEPA's general operating fund.

The Structural Members Users Group

Contact: The Structural Members Users Group
P.O. Box 3958, University Station
Charlottesville, Virginia 22903

The Structural Members Users Group distributes and maintain computer programs for the static, stability, dynamic response, and stress analysis of structural members and mechanical elements. The program are available on such national networks as UCS, or they can be purchased for use on an in-house computer. These are general analysis programs for classical structural members with arbitrary mechanical or thermal loading. The members can be of variable cross section with any in-span supports, foundations, and boundary conditions. Composite cross sections can be handled. The member can be modeled with either a continuous or a lumped mass. Static and steady-state displacements and forces, natural frequencies and mode shapes, and buckling loads are calculated. The programs apply to beams, torsional systems, extension systems, cylinders, thick spheres, torsion of thin-walled beams, strings, sectional properties, stress analyses, rotating shafts, circular plates, rectangular plates, gridworks, and discs. These are small, efficient, easy-to-use FORTRAN programs with versions available for all major computers. Pre- and postprocessors permitting interactive use of the programs are available. The programs can be used in batch or time-sharing form with fixed, free, or prompted input formats.

Users Group for CDC 6000 Series Machines (VIM)

Contact: Mr. Thomas Burt
Fluor Corporation
3331 Michelson Drive
Irvine, California 92730

VIM is an organization for users of large-scale CDC computer systems. It currently has 320 institutional members around the world. Control Data Corporation maintains a centralized library of programs; it disseminates programs to members upon request at no charge. To provide information on software in the library, it publishes a program catalog once a year. The programs in the library are contributions from users and Control Data Corporation. For better communication among users, VIM publishes a monthly newsletter and holds conferences twice a year.

Plans for the future include the publication of a catalog, The VIM Software Directory, which will abstract programs available from members and information on how to obtain them. Many of these programs will be available for a nominal fee from the source instead of from CDC. This new cataloging system will probably supersede the present system.

Library of Available Software Series Programs

INTRODUCTION

The following programs were documented in previous volume as part of the library of the Software Series computer programs.

SAP V
UCIN
WHAMS
DISK
TWIST
GRILL
TABS 77
BOSOR
GIFTS
PREMSAP
BEAM
BEAMSTRESS
SHAFT

Some of these programs can be accessed on United Computing Systems (USC), a participating computer network. Usually, connection to the computer requires only a local telephone call. UCS should be contacted directly for information on using the program on their system. Appropriate addreses are listed in this chapter. For information or assistance in using the programs on the netwrok, please contact the local UCS representative.

The following summaries are updated to reflect new capabilities of the programs and the pertinent available information.

BOSOR4

This is a program for the stress, stability, and free vibration analysis of segmented, ring-stiffened, branched shells of revolution and prismatic shells and panels. BOSOR4 performs large-deflection, axisymmetric stress analysis, small-deflection nonsymmetric stress analysis, modal vibration analysis with axisymmetric nonlinear prestress included, and buckling analysis with axisymmetric or nonsymmetric prestress.

Network Availability
United Computing Systems
University Computer Company
TYMSHARE
McDonnel-Douglas Automation, Huntington Beach, California
Control Data Corp., Rockville, MD
Westinghouse Electric, Pittsburgh, PA
Information System Design, Oakland, California
Boeing Computer Service, Seattle, Wash.
Det Norski Veritas (Norway)
CNES (France)
Aeronautical Res. Inst. of Sweden (FFA) (Sweden)
CTR (Italy)
Matematischer Beratungs and Programmierungsdienst (West Germany)
CERN (Switzerland)
Technical Manual
Use the one in Volume I of the Software Series. No other technical manual is adequate.
User Documentation
Volume I of the Software Series
Program Availability
CDC and UNIVAC versions are available from

D. Bushnell 52-33/205
Lockheed Missiles and Space Co.
3251 Hanover St.
Palo Alto, CA 94304

IBM and VAX versions of the program can be purchased from

V. Weingarten
Dept. of Civil Engineering
University of Southern California
University Park
Los Angeles, California 90007

The cost is $600

Assistance in Using the Program on the Networks
Please contact the local representatives of the networks.
Contact for Technical Probelms in Using the Program
D. Bushnell
Lockheed Missiles and Space Co.
Palo Alto Research Lab.
3251 Hanover Street
Palo Alto, California 94304
Phone: (415) 493-4411 Ext. 45491 or 45133

UCIN

The purpose of UCIN is to study the dynamics of crash victims. The model consists of 12 rigid bodies representing the human limbs together with a vehicle cockpit. The twelve bodies of the model are connected together with ball-and-socket joints.

Technical Manual
Available at no cost from
R. L. Huston
Dept. of Mechanical Engineering
University of Cincinnati
Cincinnati, Ohio 45221
User Documentation
Contained in Volume II of the Software Series
Program Availability
The program is available for the cost of the tape, or free if a tape is sent to
R. L. Huston
at the address above.

The cost of a new tape is approximately $15

Contact for Technical Problems in Using the Program
R. L. Huston
Phone: (513) 457-6131

TABS 77

TABS 77 is a special purpose computer program for the elastic three-dimensional static and dynamic analysis of frame and shear wall buildings. For buildings with rigid diaphragms (in-plane), which can be approximated by independent frame and shear walls, the program is very economical and easy to use as compared to a general purpose three-dimensional structural analysis program.

Network Availability
UCS
Technical Manual Availability
National Information Service for Earthquake Engineering (NISEE)
Earthquake Engineering Research Center
519 Davis Hall
University of California
Berkeley, California 94720
Phone: (415) 642-5113

The cost of a manual is $10.00

User Documentation
Contained in Volume II of this Series
Program Availability
National Information Service for Earthquake Engineering

The cost is $150 including manuals.

Assistance in Using the Program on the Network
Please contact the local representatives of the network.
Contact for Technical Problems in Using the Program
For problems arising using the documentation presented in Volume II contact
A. Habibullah
Computers/Structures International
Oakland, California 94609

GIFTS

This is a finite element program with advanced interactive graphics pre- and postprocessors. It has the capability of model generation, display, editing, and verification. Output displays include displacements and stresses. Static analyses are performed using a library of elements suitable for trusses, frames, shells, and solid and elasticity problems.

Network Availability
UCS
Technical Manual
Included with the purchase of the program tape
User Documentation
Documentation is in Volume I of the Software Series and is also included with the pruchase of the program tape.
Program Availability
A tape of the program can be purchased from
H. Kamel
I.G.E.L.
Dept. of Aerospace and Mechanical Engineering
University of Arizona
Tucson, Arizona 85721

The pricing schemes for the program and membership in the GIFTS User's Group (GUG) are:

GIFTS 4A, for U.S. user, unsupported	$600.00
U.S. Government agency, latest standard GIFTS version, unsupported	$1000.00
U.S. GUG member, Initiation fee	$1000.00
Yearly subscription	$2000.00
Foreign user, Initiation fee	$1500.00
Yearly subscription	$3000.00

Assistance in Using the Program on the Network
Contact the local representatives of the network.
Contact for Technical Problems in Using the Program
GIFTS Users Group (GUG)
Phone: (602) 626-1650

BEAM, BEAMSTRESS, SHAFT

The program BEAM is for the flexural analysis of simple and complex beams. It calculates the deflection, slope, bending moment, and shear force for static and steady-state conditions. The critical axial load and mode shape are found for stability. The natural frequencies and mode shapes are computed for free transverse vibrations. The beam can be formed of segments with any mechanical or thermal loading, in-span supports, foundations, and boundary conditions. The user can include any or all of bending, shear deformation, and rotary inertia effects.

The program BEAMSTRESS is for determining the section properties and stresses in an arbitrary, homogeneous, or composite cross section of a straight bar. Properties include cross-sectional area, centroid moments of inertia about any axes, polar moment of inertia, radii of gyration, angle of inclination of principal axes, principal moments of inertia, location of shear center, shear deformation coefficients, torsional constant, and warping constant. For composite cross sections, these cross-sectional properties are calculated as modulus, weighted properties. The stresses include normal stress due to bending moments, axial forces, and constrained warping and shear stress due to torsion, transverse shear forces, and constrained warping.

The program SHAFT is for the flexural unbalanced response and critical speed of a rotating shaft with no cross-coupling coefficients in the bearings. For unbalanced problems, it calculates the component and resultant deflection, slope, bending moment, shear force, and their corresponding phase angles along the shaft. The critical speeds are found for a rotor with or without damping in the bearings. The corresponding modes shapes are also printed out. The shaft can be formed of lumped or continuous mass segments with foundations, any boundary conditions, and any distribution of unbalanced masses. The user can include any or all of bending, shear deformation, and rotary inertia effects.

Network Availability
UCS
Technical Manual
Available from the Structural Members Users Group
These programs belong to a collection of a dozen programs. The technical manuals for all of the programs cost $50.
User Documentation
Contained in Volume I of the Software Series
Program Availability
A tape or deck of the program can be purchased from
The Structural Members Users Group
P.O. Box 3958, University Station
Charlottesville, Virginia 22903

The cost is $750 for all twelve programs, although programs may be purchased individually.

Assistance in Using the Programs
Please contact the local representatives of the network
Contact for technical problems encountered when using the programs
The Structural Members Users Group
Phone (804) 296-4906

DISK, TWIST, GRILL

The program DISK is for the thick elastic solids problems of disks, cylinders, and spheres. These members can be formed of layers of different materials with arbitrary mechanical or thermal loading and boundary conditions.

For a disk it calculates the radial displacement, the radial force per unit circumferential length, and the tangential force per unit radial length for static and steady-state conditions. The natural frequencies and mode shapes are found for radial vibrations. The disk is based on a plane stress assumption. Both applied loadings and responses are axially symmetric.

For the cylinder, DISK calculates the radial displacement, radial stress, tangetial stress, and axial stress for static and steady-state conditions as well as the natural frequencies and mode shapes of radial vibration. The underlying theory for the cylinder employs a plane strain assumption. Applied loadings must be axially symmetrical. The calculated responses are also axially symmetric.

In the case of the sphere, the radial displacement, radial stress, and tangential stress are found for static and steady-state conditions. Also, the natural frequencies and mode shapes are calculated for radial vibration. The applied loading and the resulting responses are spherically symmetric.

The program TWIST is for the torsional analysis of simple and complex torsional systems. It calculates the angle of twist and the twisting moment for static and steady-state conditions. The natural frequencies and mode shapes are computed for three torsional vibrations. The torsion system can be formed of segments with any loading, gears, branches, foundations, and boundary conditions. When applied to extension systems, TWIST finds the axial displacement and force for static and steady state systems. Also, the natural frequencies and mode of longitudinal vibration can be calculated. The extension system can be a sequence of springs and masses or a bar of uniform segments with arbitrary loading, foundations, and boundary conditions.

The program GRILL handles the static analysis of uniform grillages subjected to uniform, hydrostatic (ramp), and concentrated forces. It calculates deflections, slopes, bending moments, and shear forces. In establishing a model, either set of beams of a gridwork may be designated as the girders; the other set is the stiffeners. In GRILL, the stiffeners are simply supported while the girders may be fixed, simply supported, or free ends. Any number of concentrated forces may be placed on the grillage at the intersections of the stiffeners and girders. Only one of each type of the distributed loads (uniform or hydrostatic) may be placed on a particular grillage.

Network Availability
UCS
Technical Manual
Available from the Structural Members Users Group
These programs belong to a collection of a dozen programs, three of which were documented in Volume I of the Software Series.
The technical manuals for all of the programs cost $50.
User Documentation
Contained in Volume II of the Software Series
Program Availability
A tape or deck of the program can be purchased from
The Structural Members Users Group
P.O. Box 3958, University Station
Charlottesville, Virginia 22903
Assistance in Using the Program on the Network
Please contact the local representatives of the network.
Contact for Technical Problems Encountered when Using the Program
The Structural Members Users Group
Phone: (804) 296-4906

Part II

REVIEWS AND SUMMARIES OF AVAILABLE PROGRAMS

Plastic Analysis in General Purpose Programs

Harry Armen

Alan Pifko

Grumman Aerospace Corporation

INTRODUCTION

Advances in science and technology are made typically in response to new performance requirements. The area of computational plasticity is no exception. Increasing demands are being made by both government and private organizations to analyze a wide range of complex structures that must perform safely when subjected to severe environmental and mechanical loading conditions. In these environments the effect of plasticity on the structural response cannot be neglected. An important example occurs in components of nuclear power plants. Accurate determination of stress, strain, and displacement fields in this case is essential for safe structural design.

These requirements have been the motivating force behind the development of general purpose programs for use in plastic analysis of structures. Development of these programs has been the direct result of advances in both structural mechanics and computer sciences. Specifically, advances in finite element methods, made feasible by rapid developments in computer hardware and software, were the foundation from which general purpose computer programs were developed. After more than a decade of development these programs are now widely available and are used for practical analysis and design.

It is the purpose of this paper to review the current capability of available general purpose programs for plastic analysis. Here, a general purpose program is defined as one that can be used to analyze a broad range of structural types and configurations without serious restrictions with respect to problem size. Consideration in this review is limited to situations involving small deflections and small deformations. Consequently, within this context the present work represents an update of Refs. [1] and [2]. In keeping with the original format of Refs. [1, 2], the present paper is composed of three sections as follows:

1. Assumptions and Models for Plastic Behavior. Implicit in the development of any plasticity model are assumptions associated with the behavior of the material. The number and degree of these assumptions affect the generality of the resulting model and its compatibility with actual material behavior. Some assumptions generally employed are listed with a discussion of their implications.

The development of algorithms within the framework of finite element computational techniques for plastic analysis was accomplished indepently of the development of appropriate constitutive relations. Initially, only the simplest plasticity theories were used. However, with the availability of a computational tool that could treat problems more complex than previously practical, analysts could turn their attention toward the development of plasticity theories that more accurately predict the essential features of experimentally observed behavior without the penalities of introducing unrealistic simplifications.

A discussion of several models that incorporate the above assumptions and attempt to overcome some of their restrictions is presented. The models discussed have either been incorporated into available general purpose plastic analysis programs or have been proposed for possible implementation.

2. Review of Solution Procedures. Several alternative algorithms have evolved and are currently being used in programs for plastic analysis. Each of these has computational advantages and liabilities so that the analyst is presented with choices among acceptable procedures. These procedures are reviewed in order to facilitate a rational choice among competing procedures that best suit the needs of a particular problem class.

3. Review of Available Computer Programs. The attributes of a general purpose program for plastic analysis are defined. The capabilities of twelve specific programs surveyed are then listed in tabular form. It is anticipated that this format will allow for a rational assessment of the program capabilities that were reviewed.

ASSUMPTIONS AND MODELS OF PLASTIC BEHAVIOR

> "The tensile test [is] very easily and quickly performed but it is not possible to do much with its results, because one does not know what they really mean. They are the outcome of a number of very complicated physical processes . . . . The extension of a piece of metal [is] in a sense more complicated than the working of a pocket watch and to hope to derive information about its mechanism from two or three data derived from measurement during the tensile test [is] perhaps as optimistic as would be an attempt to learn about the working of a pocket watch by determining its compressive strength."
>
> E. Orowan, F.R.S., Proc. Instn. Mech. Engrs., Vol. 151, 1944, p. 133.

The above quote was used as the opening statement in Ref. [1] on which this review is based and is still applicable here. That is because it is appropriate in our view that any discussion of general purpose programs for plastic analysis should begin with a discussion of those theories that attempt to describe that complex phenomenological process known as plastic deformation. Without a knowledge of the range of validity and required input in terms of material parameters of the theories implemented in a program, any analysis is at best tenuous.

There is not, in our view, any "best" plasticity theory to describe all the known facets of nonlinear material behavior. There are, however, some theories better suited for particular needs than others. It is therefore desirable to be sufficiently familiar with those theories currently available and to be in a position to choose the theory (and program that implements it) that combines mathematical and computational simplicity with a proper representation of experimentally observed behavior.

In the following paragraphs, some of the assumptions made to develop a plasticity theory and some suggested models of plastic behavior are briefly discussed. A more thorough examination of these assumptions and models is to be found in the references cited.

Assumptions of Plastic Behavior

Assumption 1: There exists an initial yield condition which defines the elastic limit of the material in a multiaxial stress state. This assumption is most often used and represents a mathematical convenience that facilitates computational efficiency. Its applicability varies with the material under consideration.

The two popular yield criteria for structural materials are those attributed to von Mises and Tresca. The former implies that yielding begins at an arbitrary material point whenever the combination of stresses is such that the strain energy of distortion per unit volume at the point is equal to the corresponding energy developed in a bar uniaxially stressed to the elastic limit. The Tresca condition states that inelastic action at any point in a body begins only when the maximum shearing stress on some plane through the point reaches a value equal to the maximum shearing stress in a tension specimen.

Assumption 2: Loading surfaces exist that define the limits of elastic and plastic behavior beyond initial yielding; the response after initial yielding differs among various plasticity theories. This postyielding response, called the hardening rule, is described by specifying a subsequent yield surface, termed the "loading surface," which is a convenient mathematical idealization of some macroscopically observed behavior. The "consistency" condition requires that the stress state at any point remain on the loading surface.

Assumption 3: Plastic strain rates are linearly related to their corresponding stress rates by means of a flow rule (the basis of constitutive relations in the treatment of plasticity). A flow rule that is generally used to describe elastic, ideally plastic behavior is the Prandtl-Reuss relation, which is a generalization of the Levy-Mises equations. The Prandtl-Reuss assumption is that the plastic strain increments, $d\varepsilon^p_{ij}$, are proportional to the corresponding stress deviator, σ'_{ij}, where the instantaneous nonnegative value of the constant of proportionality is left to the inventiveness of the user of these equations. The concept of an effective stress or effective plastic strain (generally in terms of one or a combination of their corresponding invariants) is in itself an assumption that is usually introduced to reduce the complexity of a multiaxial situation to one that can be related to uniaxial behavior [3]. Thus, the proportionality parameter can be the ratio of the effective plastic strain increment to the prevailing effective stress.

A more general approach to determining a flow rule is the use of the concept of a plastic potential. The assumption is made that there exists a scalar function of stress, say $f(\sigma_{ij})$, from which the component of plastic strain increments may be determined (e.g., proportional to $\partial f/\partial \sigma_{ij}$). If $f(\sigma_{ij})$ represents the yield surface in stress space, then the above assumption represents a result of Drucker's postulate [4], which states that the work done by an external agency during a complete cycle of loading and unloading must be nonnegative. Furthermore, this assumption leads to an incremental or associated linear flow theory of plasticity, in which the increment of plastic strain (strain rate) is in the direction of the outward normal to the surface represented by $f(\sigma_{ij})$ in stress space, at the current value of stress. A strain rate vector deviating from the outward normal to the yield surface in a direction independent of the stress rate vector constitutes nonassociated flow theories of plasticity. Nonassociated flow theories are particularly suitable for work-softening materials and can reasonably fit the behavior observed in some soils. Associated and nonassociated flow theories are, in general, distinct from the deformation theory of plasticity, in which the total plastic strains are related to the final stress state. According to this latter theory, a relationship between final states of stress and strain exists for any given loading process, while unloading is specified by a separate law.

Assumption 4: Materials are isotropic with respect to initial yielding; whether induced by previous cold-working or as a result of an anisotropic distribution of crystals, most structural materials exhibit some form of initial anisotropy. The von Mises and Tresca criteria assume isotropy with respect to the orientation of the stresses and their sense (tensile or compressive).

Assumption 5: Plastic incompressibility; incompressibility assumptions are generally employed in most nonlinear structural analysis programs. Investigations of the influence of hydrostatic pressure on the plastic response of metals have been considered by Bridgman [5]. Despite some evidence to the contrary [6], most investigations suggest that hydrostatic pressure has little or no effect on the initial and subsequent behavior of metals under quasi-static loading rates. This has been most recently confirmed by Fung et al. [7].

The use of plastic incompressibility requires treating a variable Poisson ratio, i.e., an elastic value, and a value equal to one-half in the plastic range. The treatment of the plastic yielding of nonmetals, such as clay, ice, and concrete, represents an area of investigation in which the effects of hydrostatic pressure are significant. The plasticity theories employed for the treatment of these materials are nonassociated linear flow types.

Assumption 6: Yielding and subsequent response are insensitive to rate of deformation. The nature of the constitutive equations of plasticity for rate-sensitive material behavior has been the subject of several notable investigations (see survey paper [8]). These investigations have shown that limits on dislocation velocity and rate of dislocation density for most structural materials are responsible for the generally observed fact that plastic flow is retarded with increasing strain rate.

Assumption 7: There is elastic unloading and coincidence of yield and loading surfaces. This is an idealization of material behaviour, that implies that unloading from some plastic state to a neighboring state results in a change in the elastic state only. Furthermore, implicit in most analyses are the assumptions that additional plastic strains can occur only upon reloading to a stress state beyond that of the initial unloading, and subsequent behavior (assuming no reverse yielding has occurred) is identical to that which would have been obtained had unloading never occurred.

Assumption 8: The total kinematic strain may be decomposed into elastic and plastic components. This assumption is employed in the linear flow theories of plasticity and is used in developing many of the incremental constitutive equations. The assumption is mathematically convenient when used in conjunction with the concept of a well-defined yield surface and is generally valid for small deformations. In addition, this assumption facilitates the use of a variable Poisson ratio when plastic incompressibility is employed.

In addition to the above assumptions, most successful applications of classical small-strain flow theories of plasticity have been generally limited to situations in which the loading is monotonically increasing and the ratio of the various load components is held constant (proportional loading). Applications of flow theory to problems involving severe changes in stress ratio among the various components of stress, such as occurs during plastic buckling, have been shown to be unconservative because the reduction in the in-plane shear stiffness is generally underestimated. Hutchinson has discussed this problem extensively in [9]. Deformation theory, on the other hand, has been shown to provide consistently better correlation with results for bifurcation problems for plates and shells [10]. This situation illustrates a significant fact that, with few exceptions, appears to have been overlooked in many experimental investigations. While the size, shape, and definition of yield and subsequent loading surfaces are of considerable importance, equal emphasis should be given to a proper description of the plastic hardening modulus under a variety of conditions.

Cyclic loading situations involving reversed plastic flow during which the material response may exhibit cyclic hardening or softening behavior fall into the category of problems of general interest in which classical plasticity theories have met with limited success. Applications of cyclic loading conditions to several problems ranging from membrane-stressed sheets to plates and shells have been presented in Refs. [11, 12]. In these studies, "stabilized" material behavior was assumed.

Finally, most applications of plastic analysis have been limited to isothermal conditions. The influence of elevated temperatures on material response (elastic and inelastic) is generally treated within the framework of theories of viscous strain (creep). For a great many problem areas, ranging from metal-forming processes to the analysis of nuclear reactor components, elevated stress and temperature levels of short duration must be tolerated. In these problems plastic strain development may be quite significant. Thus, nonisothermal plasticity theory is required. Furthermore, it is desirable that such a theory include the effects of temperature on the elastic as well as the plastic properties of the materials.

Models of Plastic Behavior

Following is a brief description of some models for plastic behavior. Several of these models have been developed within the framework of the assumptions mentioned; others have been developed specifically to overcome one or more of the restrictions associated with these assumptions. The primary function of the models is to provide a set of constitutive relations that can be used to describe the response history of nonlinearly deforming media.

Isotropic Hardening

This theory, proposed by Hill [13] and Hodge [14], assumes that during plastic flow the loading surface expands uniformly about the origin in stress space, maintaining the same shape, center, and orientation as the yield surface. Figure 1 illustrates, on the basis of a simplification to a two-dimensional plot, the yield and loading surfaces when the stress state shifts from point 1 to 2. Unloading and subsequent reloading in the reverse direction will result in yielding at the stress state represented by point 3. The path 2-3 will be elastic, and 0-2 is equal to 0-3.

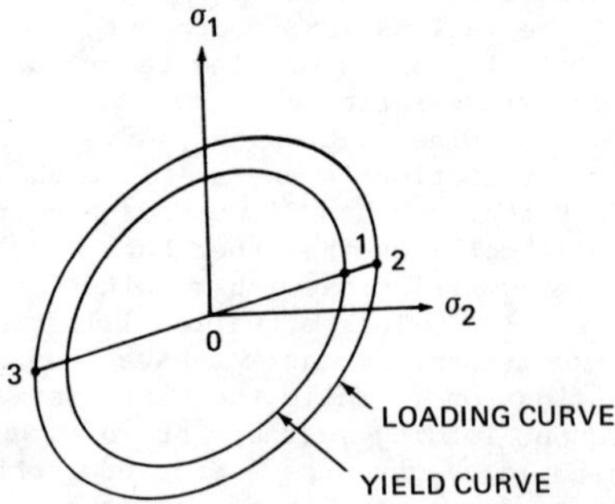

Fig. 1 Isotropic hardening

Isotropic representation of work hardening does not account for the Bauschinger effect exhibited by most structural materials. In fact, contrary to observations, this theory implies that, because of work hardening, the material will exhibit an increase in the compressive yield stress equal to the increase in the tensile yield stress. Furthermore, since plastic deformation is an anisotropic process, it cannot be expected that a theory that predicts isotropy in the plastic range will lead to realistic results when complex loading paths, involving changes in direction of the stress vector in stress space (not necessarily completely reversed), are considered.

Slip Theory

Utilizing the physical concept of slip surfaces in crystals, Batdorf and Budiansky [15] have developed a theory that describes a loading surface that is distorted relative to the yield surface and previous loading surfaces. This theory predicts the formation of corners at the instantaneous stress state on the loading surface during plastic deformation. After some prestrain, the yield locus is the minimum surface through the point of prestrain and the initial yield locus. A representation of the growth of the yield function in going from a stress state at the origin 0 to the final state represented by point 3 is given in Fig. 2. In this figure, the unshaded region is that enclosed by the yield surface, and the various shaded regions indicate the stages (I, II, and III) in the formation of the loading surfaces in going from stress state 0 to 3. Since the stress state is almost always in a corner, the resulting constitutive relation between stresses and strains becomes quite complex. For this reason this theory is rarely selected for application.

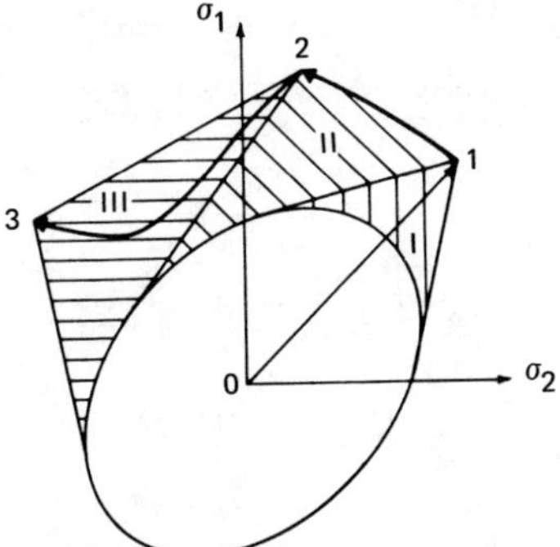

Fig. 2 Slip theory hardening

Piecewise Linear Plasticity

In this representation, the yield surface consists of a finite number of plane surfaces whose intersections constitute corners. The oldest and most widely used piecewise linear yield surface is that associated with the Tresca yield condition. The loading surface is assumed also to consist of plane surfaces, and the subsequent hardening behavior can be classified as:

1. The hardening rule of independent plane loading surface. One of the earliest discussions of this representation of the hardening behavior is given in Ref. [16] and is illustrated in Fig. 3a. As seen from this figure, in which σ_1 and σ_2 are the only nonzero stress components, a loading path, 0-1-2, in any quadrant of the stress plane does not affect the loading surface in the remaining quadrants. Thus, this hardening rule does not take the Bauschinger effect into account.

2. The hardening rule of interdependent loading surface. This type of hardening rule, originally proposed by Hodge [16], is a generalization of the hardening rule described in the previous paragraph. By specifying a dependence between the planes that compose the loading surface, a loading path intersecting any one plane of this surface may effect changes in each of the remaining planes. As illustrated in Fig. 3b, this hardening rule can be used to specify any piecewise linear loading surface and is capable of taking the Bauschinger effect into account.

A special case of the interdependent loading surfaces is considered in Ref. [17]. It is assumed that plastic strain is due to slipping along three independent slip planes, along any one of which the shear is a maximum. Piecewise linear stress-strain relations are written in terms of coefficients representing the hardening behavior of the material.

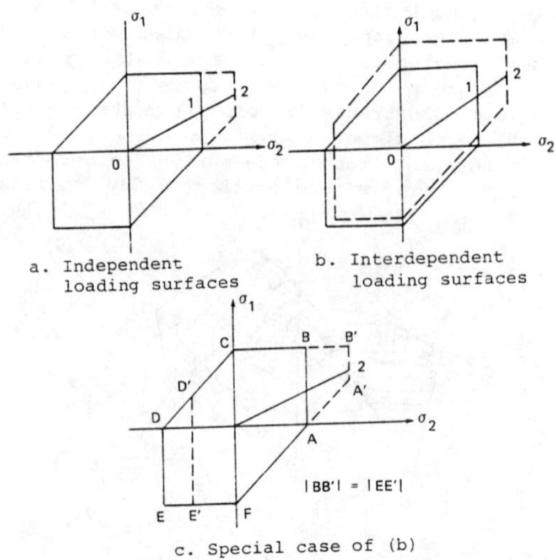

Fig. 3 Piecewise linear hardening

These coefficients are functions of stress and are dependent upon a linear strain-hardening rule employed in the analysis. By specifying the correspondence between various segments of the yield surface and the slip planes, total plastic strains for any loading are computed as the sum of the contributions from the three independent sets of slip planes. It is further assumed that the corresponding segments of the yield surface must maintain a constant elastic range from positive to negative yielding. An illustration of the subsequent loading surfaces determined in this way is shown in Fig. 3c. It is seen from this figure that the Bauschinger effect can be taken into account.

A comprehensive review of the piecewise linear strain-hardening theory of plasticity is presented in Ref. [18].

Kinematic Hardening

The hardening behavior postulated in this theory assumes that during plastic deformation the loading surface translates as a rigid body in stress space, maintaining the size, shape, and orientation of the yield surface. The primary aim of this theory, due to Prager [19, 20], is to provide a means of accounting for the Bauschinger effect. For piecewise linear yield surfaces, kinematic hardening may be considered to be a special case of the hardening rule of interdependent loading surfaces. However, it is not limited to piecewise linear yield surfaces.

An illustration of kinematic hardening, as applied in conjunction with the von Mises yield curve in the σ_1, σ_2 plane, is provided in Fig. 4.

The yield surface and loading surface are shown in this figure for a shift of stress state from point 1 to point 2. The translation of the center of the yield surface is denoted by α_{ij}.

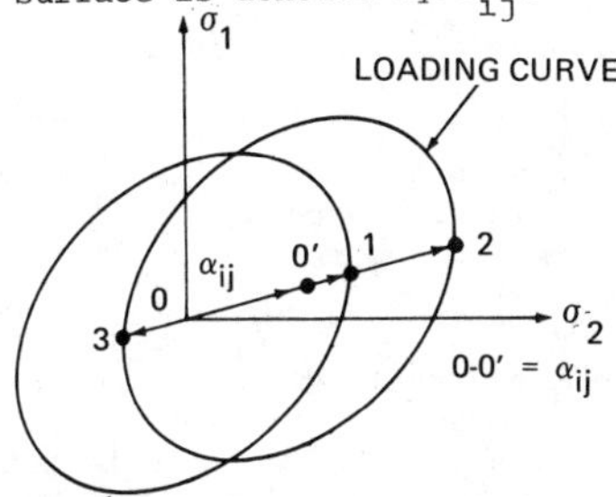

Fig. 4 Kinematic hardening

As a consequence of assuming a rigid translation of the loading surface, kinematic hardening predicts an ideal Bauschinger effect for completely reversed loading conditions. A modification to this theory, proposed by Ziegler [21], eliminates inconsistencies that arise when Prager's original model is used in a subspace of stress. Although originally devised to be used in conjunction with linear strain hardening behavior, this model has been used for materials exhibiting nonlinear hardening [11, 12], and has been further generalized to cyclic loading involving work-hardening and work-softening behavior [22]. A model of combined kinematic and isotropic hardening in which the subsequent loading surfaces expand and translate is presented by Hodge [23].

Mechanical Sublayer and Fields of Work-hardening Moduli Models

A technique to model the arbitrary nonlinear mechanical behavior of a solid by means of a parallel assemblage of elastic ideally plastic solids can be traced to Duwez [24], with extensions by White [25] and Besseling [26]. This modeling concept equates the integrated effect of a network of ideally plastic solids to the actual behavior. An extension of this model, proposed by Mroz [27, 28] to account for the work-hardening behavior of metals under cyclic loading conditions, introduces the notion of a field of work-hardening moduli and the variation of this field during the course of plastic deformation.

In this proposed model, a stress-strain curve of an initially isotropic material is represented by n linear segments of constant plastic moduli, as shown in Fig. 5. In stress space, this approximation can be represented by n hypersurfaces f_0, f_1 ..., f_n, where f_0 is the initial yield surface, and the region between any two successive hypersurfaces defines a region of constant work-hardening modulus.

Figure 6 illustrates these hypersurfaces in the σ_1, σ_2 plane for an initially isotropic material. As seen in this figure, the surfaces f_0, f_1 ..., f_n are similar and concentric, and for simplicity are schematically represented by a family of circles. If we consider proportional loading in the σ_2 direction, and if we assume that the surfaces can experience a rigid translation without experiencing a change of size or orientation, then when the stress state reaches point A on Fig. 6a the surface f_0 will translate until it reaches the circle f_1 at the stress corresponding to point B. The circles f_0 and f_1 translate together until point C is reached, where now f_0, f_1, and f_2 are attached at a common point of contact. For unloading and subsequent reversed loading, when the stress reaches a point corresponding to point E (Fig. 6b), reversed plastic flow occurs and the surface f_0 translates downward along the σ_2 axis until it reaches the surface f_1 at F. Mroz further proposes that the curve of reverse loading in Fig. 5 join the curve OA'B'G that is obtained by symmetry with respect to the origin from OABC. Thus, the curve of reverse loading EFG is uniquely defined by the curve of primary loading, represented by an equation of the form $\sigma = f(e)$. If a new coordinate system $(\sigma, \bar{e})$, with origin at C, is used, we have for the curve CEFG, $\sigma/2 = f(\bar{e}/2)$. This relation is usually referred to as the Masing relation [29], and is a useful rule for describing steady cyclic behavior.

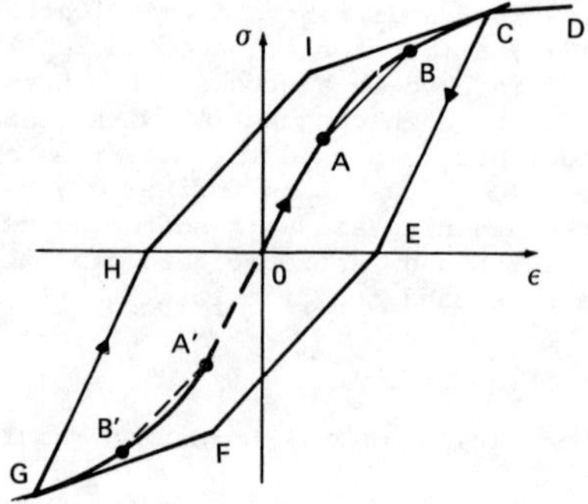

Fig. 5 Representation of typical cyclic stress-strain curve by tangent moduli

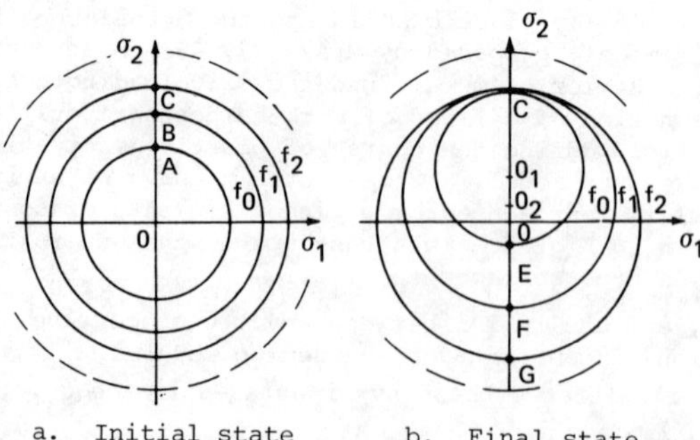

a. Initial state b. Final state

Fig. 6 Representation of hypersurfaces for mechanical sublayer model and Mroz model

In the generalization of this model to nonproportional loading, it is assumed that during translation of the hypersurfaces the individual surfaces do not intersect but consecutively contract and push each other. It should be noted that when f_1 tends to infinity, in which case the work-hardening modulus is constant (the work-hardening curve being represented by a straight line), the theory proposed by Mroz is identical to Prager's kinematic hardening model.

The further generalization of the theory of work-hardening moduli is associated with an expansion or contraction of the surfaces f_0, f_1 ..., f_n so that transitory phenomena (work-stiffening, work-softening, or nonisothermal conditions) can be treated. Thus, the hypersurfaces f_K are not constants but functions of a monotonically increasing scalar parameter during plastic flow. One suggestion for the scalar is presented in Ref. [28].

Two Surface Theories

Eisenberg and Phillips [30] presented an early generalization of conventional plasticity theories to account for the phenomenon of non-coincident yield and reloading stress states. To account for this behavior, a two-surface plasticity theory was proposed involving a yield surface completely enclosed by a prescribed loading surface. The size of the yield surface always remains unchanged. The loading surface on the other hand varies in size, coinciding with the yield surface for elastic behavior and containing the stress point for loading beyond initial yielding. During unloading the yield surface remains unchanged and the loading surface shrinks to accommodate the stress state until it coincides with the yield surface. Upon unloading and subsequent reloading the two surfaces separate.

The incorporation of this behavior, should it be a significant factor for a material under consideration, does not appear to pose any difficulties beyond those normally associated with conventional theories.

A comprehensive and satisfying generalization of the concept of a two-surface plasticity theory was proposed by Dafalias and Popov [31]. In this theory the concept of a bounding surface is introduced. This surface, always enclosing the yield and subsequent loading surface in stress space, is used to model complex loading situations, including cyclic loading involving hardening and softening behavior. This work appears to have been motivated by the general observation of the non-coincidence of the yield and loading stresses previously discussed. The approach to multiaxial loading as presented by Dafalias and Popov is not tied to any hardening law and appears to be sufficiently general and sound to warrant further examination.

A modification of Mroz's fields of work-hardening moduli model has been proposed by Krieg [32]. This modification, similar to the model proposed by Dafalias and Popov [31], replaces all but two of the discrete surfaces specified by a Mroz model with a continuum of intermediate loading surfaces whose distribution is prescribed. The two surfaces are represented by an inner curve, labeled by Krieg as the loading surface, and an outer curve, termed the limit surface. These two surfaces separate the material behavior into three distinct zones: an elastic zone contained within the loading surface, an asymptotic plastic zone outside the limit surface, and a so-called metaelastic zone between the two surfaces. On the basis of a uniaxial stress-strain curve, these zones are joined by a continuous function, generated for a variety of situations including reversed loading. Both the loading and limit surfaces can vary according to a combined kinematic-isotropic hardening behavior. The motion of the loading surface is identical to that assumed by Mroz. For the general multiaxial case the theory requires the retention of three vectors and three scalars, a small increase over the two vectors required for kinematic hardening alone.

Anisotropic Theories

One of the first treatments of the plastic flow of an initially anisotropic metal was suggested by Hill [13]. In this theory an orthotropic yield criterion was assumed to be quadratic in the stress components and to reduce to the von Mises law when the degree of anisotropy was small. In Cartesian coordinates the function, suggested by Hill, takes the following form

$$f(\sigma_k) = N_{ij}\sigma_i\sigma_j - 1 = 0 \tag{1}$$

where the contracted tensor notation is used, i, j, k = 1, 2, ... 6, and the parameters N_{ij} are constants related to the six yield stresses in the principal directions of anisotropy. A consequence of this assumed function is an initial rotation of the von Mises ellipse in the $\sigma_1 - \sigma_2$ space.

Similar anistropic theories have been suggested by several investigators, most notably Jackson, Smith, and Lankford [33], Dorn [34], and Hu [35]. Implicit in Hill's theory are the following assumptions about

Orthotropic anisotropy. The principal axes of anisotropy either coincide with the principal stress axes and the principal strain axes or the transformation between the axes is known.

- The principal axes of anisotropy do not rotate during plastic flow.
- No distinction is made between tensile and comprehensive stresses
- The anisotropic coefficients (N_{ij}) remain unchanged during plastic flow.

A generalization of Hill's equation for anisotropic plasticity, one that combines isotropic and kinematic hardening, is presented by Baltov and Sawczuk [36]. In compact notation this theory assumes a yield condition in the following form

$$f(\sigma_k) = N_{ij}\ (\sigma_i - \alpha_i) - 1 = 0 \tag{2}$$

Unlike previous investigations, the fourth-order tensor of the anisotropic coefficient, N_{ij}, is a prescribed function of the plastic strains, and hence changes during the course of plastic flow. The kinematic hardening parameter, α_i, is also a function of the plastic strains. In a comparison of experimental results for combined tension and torsion it was found that the proposed theory better suited the experimental data than the conventional kinematic hardening theory.

More recently, several investigations have been concerned with defining a strength criterion for orthotropic materials with specific reference to advanced filamentary composites. Generally, a criterion of this type is used to define a "failure surface" in stress space. These failure surfaces may be useful for defining yield surfaces of orthotropic metals. Notable among these proposed theories is the work of Tsai and Wu [37]. The basic assumption associated with this anisotropic strength criterion is a failure surface in the following form

$$f(\sigma_k) = N_i\sigma_i + N_{ij}\sigma_i\sigma_j - 1 = 0 \tag{3}$$

The parameters N_i and N_{ij} are strength tensors of the second and fourth rank respectively and are functions of an appropriate number of independent material strengths. The linear term in the above equation can be used to account for the difference between tensile and compressive induced "failure."

Rate-Sensitive Models

The survey paper of Lee [8] lists some 200 references associated with the investigation and application of dynamic plasticity. Various functional representations and varying degrees of complexity have been proposed. Many of these are impractical for use, either because of their extreme complexity or because they have been simplified beyond the point of usefulness.

The most popular constitutive relation, suggested by Malvern [38], employs the concept of a reference, or static, stress-strain function. The dynamic stress-strain behavior is determined from the static curve in some prescribed manner as a function of the strain rate. For uniaxial conditions this relation is in the following form

$$\frac{\sigma}{\sigma_0} = 1 + \left(\frac{\dot{e}}{D}\right)^{1/n} \tag{4}$$

where n and D are material constants, σ_0 and σ are the static and dynamic yield stresses, respectively, and $\dot{e}$ is the strain rate.

A generalization of the above equation, as suggested by Perzyna [39], replaces the uniaxial strain rate component by the tensor invariant of the plastic deformation rate

$$D_2^p = \left(\dot{e}_{ij}^p\ \dot{e}_{ij}^p\right)/2 \tag{5}$$

Concepts associated with time-independent plastic models may be extended within the framework of the above assumption to treat rate-sensitive yielding. On this basis the rate-dependent loading function may be written in the following form

$$f\left(\sigma_{ij}, \dot{e}_{ij}\right) = \frac{J_2^{\frac{1}{2}}}{k} - \left[1 + \left(\frac{D_2{p}^{\frac{1}{2}}}{D}\right)^{1/n}\right] \tag{6}$$

where J_2 is the second stress invariant, and k is the yield stress in shear.

Another aspect of rate sensitivity, in addition to its effect on yield stress levels, is the variation of the strain-hardening behavior of the material with varying levels of strain rate. In conventional flow theories this dependence must be incorporated in the plastic modulus which will now be a function of strain rate as well as stress level.

Nonisothermal Models

A treatment of structures with a nonisothermal response experiencing simultaneous changes in load and temperature clearly requires a substantial modification of existing isothermal procedures. Without consideration for irreversible thermodynamics and for the uncoupled, quasistatic problem, the treatment of thermoplasticity requires the elastic-plastic constitutive equations to account for the influence of temperature on the elastic coefficients (primarily restricted to Young's modulus), yield stress, plastic hardening coefficient, and rate of thermal expansion.

A theory of nonisothermal deformation of rigid, work-hardening solids is presented by Prager [40]. In this model a general constitutive law for plastic flow is developed that is homogeneous to order one in the rates of temperature, stress, and strain. A yield criterion is chosen to be a function of the state variables of stress, plastic strain, degree of hardening, and temperatures, i.e., $f = f(\sigma, e^p, H, T)$. The degree of hardening (or hardening modulus) term, h, is included in order to provide the material with a "memory" of some previous plastic deformation that will affect subsequent behavior. Conditions for loading, neutral loading, and unloading from some plastic state are represented by the following conditions

$$\frac{\partial f}{\partial \sigma} d\sigma + \frac{\partial f}{\partial T} dT \quad \begin{cases} > 0 & \text{loading} \\ = 0 & \text{neutral loading} \\ < 0 & \text{unloading} \end{cases} \tag{7}$$

If the problem is discretized with respect to space and some monotonically increasing parameter that can be used to prescribe the applied mechanical and thermal history of loading, then an incremental relation between plastic strain, stress, and temperature can be represented by the following linear relation

$$\Delta e^p = C_i \, \Delta\sigma_i + \bar{C}\Delta T \tag{8}$$

where the contracted tensor notation is used and C is the conventional plasticity compliance matrix, modified to account for the effect of temperature on the hardening characteristics of material; $\bar{C}$ is a function of stress and accounts for the influence of temperature-varying yield stresses.

Examples of the treatment of thermoplastic behavior formulated within the framework of finite element methods are presented in Refs. [41] and [42].

Models without a Yield Surface

A theory that attempts to circumvent the ambiguities associated with defining a specific yield surface and prescribing hardening as the subsequent translation, expansion, or distortion of that surface has been proposed by Valanis [43, 44]. In his theory of plasticity, an intrinsic time parameter, independent of external clock time, is chosen to be a monotonically increasing function of deformation. One obtains the stress response by monitoring this history of strain associated with this deformation.

From a physical viewpoint the theory has many advantages. Phenomena such as cross-hardening, noncoincident yield and loading points, and cyclic hardening are capable of being described. On the other hand, the absence of a yield surface does not facilitate the computational effort in a general purpose discrete model analysis. In fact, it may introduce additional effort.

Ideally Plastic Behavior

The plasticity models discussed thus far are used to describe the hardening behavior of materials subsequent to initial yielding. They attempt to describe the process of hardening graphically as an expansion, translation, distortion, etc., of the initial yield surface. For the case of elastic, ideally-plastic behavior the yield surface is assumed to remain unchanged. In Ref. [12], the treatment of multiaxial, ideally plastic behavior requires that the stress increment vector be tangent to the yield surface and the plastic strain increment vector be normal to the loading surface. The condition on the stress rate is the consistency condition ensuring that the stress state remains on the yield surface. This condition provides a linear relationship among the various components of the stress rate. The condition on the strain rate provides a linear relation among the various components of plastic strain rates. The combination of independent increments of stress and plastic strain are subsequently determined as a function of the increment of total strain as outlined in Ref. [12].

Material Description

All the theories described in this section depend on the availability of test data that describe the material behavior beyond yield. These should include the initial yield stress, the change in yield stress with continued plastic flow, and the material hardening behavior. They are analogous to the elastic constants used to characterize the material in the linear range. Unlike the elastic constants, however, these parameters are path-dependent and are significantly more complex to obtain. Yet along with the proper choice of plasticity theory they can play a significant role in determining the accuracy of a numerical analysis. The hardening behavior, for example, for near-proportional monotonic loading is easily obtained. The problem arises in defining the hardening behavior for cyclic loading or unloading followed by nonproportional reloading. In these cases it is not so straightforward to define the subsequent material behavior, particularly when one considers that every point in the plastic range is following a different stress-strain path. In spite of these difficulties, environmental and mechanical loading conditions prevalent in nuclear reactor technology require the specification of plastic hardening coefficients for cyclic loading situations. General recommendations for specific materials using kinematic hardening theory, based on experimental data, are presented by Corum et al. [45]. Briefly stated these are:

1. Use bilinear representation for the actual nonlinear stress-strain curve. In this representation, the plastic properties are characterized by a constant related to the slope of the elastic-plastic segment of the curve and a quantity related to the yield stress. Both of these quantities are a function of the range of strain to be encountered in the problem at hand.

2. For a given analysis the hardening coefficient is assumed to be constant for a given temperature.

3. The initial monotonic stress-strain curve should be used to obtain the bilinear representation for initial loading. The N-cycle stress-strain curve is recommended as an acceptable representation of the "partially-hardened state" (cycling between fixed strain range in a simple tension test will correspond to a variable stress range that will eventually saturate to a constant value). N is the cycle at which a major portion of the cyclic hardening has occurred but well before saturation. This curve is used after the first cycle.

4. A nonlinear representation of the hardening parameter is not recommended except for proportional (radial) loading situations.

Other recommendations for cyclic loading have been made by Morrow and others and summarized in Ref. [46]. They involve introducing the concept of a "cyclic stress-strain curve" to be used to recover cyclic hardening behavior. This curve is defined as the locus of the end points of stabilized stress-strain loops between prescribed strain ranges. It has been found [46] that the single cyclic stress-strain curve contains all the information necessary to construct any cyclic stress-strain loop since the curve seems to be uniquely defined. That is, regardless of the past history of the material, imposing a certain cyclic strain range will produce approximately the same cyclic loop after a sufficient number of cycles to reach a stable state. The cyclic stress strain curve is used in conjunction with the procedure described by Fig. 5. That is, given a curve $\sigma = f(e)$, then reversed loading is defined by $\bar{\sigma} = 2f(\bar{e}/2)$. The variables $(\bar{\sigma},\bar{e})$ refer to a new coordinate system with origin at point C of Fig. 5. The procedure is therefore essentially a one-dimensional description of the model proposed by Mroz. The difference here is that Ref. [46] proposes that f(e) be defined by the cyclic stress-strain curve.

This procedure was tested with a finite element program [47] using kinematic hardening theory. A cyclically loaded circular plate of 2024-0 aluminum alloy was analyzed using three representations for the cyclic hardening behavior;

1. Initial stress-strain curve with shifted origin
2. Morrow et al. model with initial stress-strain data
3. Morrow et al. model with cyclic stress-strain data

Results from Ref. [47] for central deflection are shown in Fig. 7 and demonstrate how different representations for cyclic behavior can seriously affect results for cyclic loading.

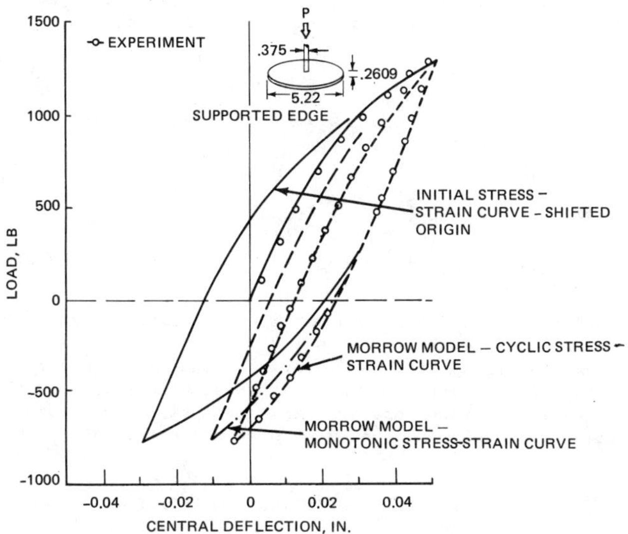

Fig. 7 Central deflection versus load for a cyclically loaded circular plate

Discrete Form of the Constitutive Relations

For flow theories of plasticity, the combination of the flow and hardening rules will provide a relationship (explicit or implicit) between increments of plastic strain and stress in the following matrix form

$$\Delta\varepsilon = C\Delta\sigma \tag{9}$$

where C is an array whose terms reflect the instantaneous states of stress and hardening of the material. Thus the terms of C are dependent upon the particular plasticity theory chosen for use. They also contain parameters for defining the plastic behavior of the material that must be obtained from laboratory tests.

Additional relations are developed by considering the strain generated during the application of an increment of external load to be composed of the sum of elastic and plastic components, as

$$\Delta e^t = \Delta e + \Delta\varepsilon \tag{10}$$

The elastic component of the strain increment Δe is related to the corresponding stress increments as

$$\Delta e = E^{-1}\Delta\sigma \tag{11}$$

where the elements of E^{-1} contain the usual elastic constants.

The combined use of Eqs. (9) through (11) results in the following incremental relations between stress and total strain

$$\Delta\sigma = E_T \Delta e^t \tag{12}$$

where $E_T = \left[C + E^{-1} \right]^{-1}$. The corresponding relation between increments of plastic strain and total strain can be written as

$$\Delta\varepsilon = C E_T \Delta e^t \tag{13}$$

Although Eq. (12) is written symbolically in terms of a matrix inverse, E_T can be obtained explictly.

Equations (12) and (13) are particularly significant since they indicate that incremental stresses and plastic strains can be determined from incremental total strains, quantities that are, in turn, determined from the displacement field by means of kinematic relations that are independent of material behavior. The quantities are obtained at every stress point from the finite element displacement field assumptions.

REVIEW OF SOLUTION PROCEDURES

Static Solution Procedures

In the following it is assumed that the reader is sufficiently familiar with the derivation of the necessary components of the elastic stiffness influence coefficients, formulated within the framework of the displacement method of finite element analysis, that is, the matrix equation relating generalized displacements and loads written in the following matrix notation

$$Ku = P \tag{14}$$

where K is the matrix of conventional elastic stiffness influence coefficients, u is the vector of generalized displacements, and P is the vector of generalized loads. K is the assemblage of all the element stiffness matrices of the grid k, which are defined as

$$k = \int_V B^t E B \, dV$$

where the matrix B maps nodal displacements into element strains.

Basically, the procedure used to solve the small-displacement plasticity problem may be divided into two categories: in one the effects of plasticity are accounted for directly in the stiffness matrix; the second treats plasticity as an effective load that is used in conjunction with the applied mechanical and thermal loads for general equilibrium. The latter is referred to as the residual force or initial strain method, and the former is termed the tangent stiffness method. A derivation of their corresponding equations from virtual work principles, the relationship between the approaches, and a discussion of several variations are presented in Refs. [1, 12, 48, 49].

Fundamentally the two approaches are derived starting from the same energy or virtual work principles so that the governing equations for one approach can be developed directly from the other. The difference in the two methods arises in the solution of the resulting matrix equations.

The governing equation associated with each technique is customarily written in incremental form. The tangent stiffness procedure, for example, uses the following form

$$K_T \, \Delta u = \Delta P \tag{15}$$

where the prefix notation Δ denotes the rate of change of the parameter following it with respect to any monotonically increasing function of time, and K_T represents the matrix of elastic-plastic stiffness influence coefficients. The matrix K_T is the assemblage of all the element stiffness matrices, k_T, where

$$K_T = \int_V B^t \, E_T \, B \, dV$$

The plasticity model chosen for use is contained explicitly in k_T through the matrix E_T. E_T is defined by Eq. (12) and is represented by the usual elastic constants for points that are elastic. The residual force method uses the following matrix relation

$$K\Delta u = \Delta P + \Delta Q \tag{16}$$

where the vector ΔQ is the plastic pseudo-load vector. For this method K is the assembled elastic stiffness matrix and ΔQ is the assemblage of all the element pseudo-load vectors Δq. For the initial strain approach Δq is the product of the initial strain matrix and the increments of plastic strain for each element; $\Delta q = k^* \Delta E$ where

$$k^* = \int_V B^t E \; dV$$

Alternatively, the notion of an initial strain matrix can be discarded and the pseudo-load vector, Δq, developed directly as

$$\Delta q = \int_V B^t E \Delta\varepsilon dV$$

The plasticity model, in this case, enters the analysis through the plastic strains, $\Delta\varepsilon$. Alternatively the pseudo-load vector can be written [49] as

$$\Delta q = \int_V B^t \Delta\sigma' dV$$

where $\Delta\sigma'$ represents the "nonlinear stress increment" which is the difference between the stress increment obtained assuming a completely elastic step and the stress increment obtained from the plastic constitutive relations.

Either Eq. (15), or (16) can be used to solve for an increment of displacement associated with the applied increment of load. The displacement solution is used to obtain total strain increments (from kinematic considerations). Using the elastic-plastic constitutive relations, Eqs. (12) - (13), we can determine increments in stress and plastic strains. This information is used as a basis for going on to the next step, and the process is repeated until the desired history has been obtained. Thus, the solution to the nonlinear response is obtained as a sequence of linear solutions in which either the stiffness or a pseudo-load is introduced in order to maintain equilibrium. The advantages associated with each procedure are listed in the following synopsis:

- The tangent stiffness method permits the use of larger load increments than the residual force method because no approximation need be made for the current increment of plastic strain. Step size is thus limited by the approximations inherent in the assumptions of flow theory of plasticity.
- The residual force method retains the same set of elastic stiffness coefficients throughout the analysis so that calculations associated with forming the stiffness matrix and solving the governing equations need be performed only once. Furthermore, this method may be used for the analysis of materials that exhibit strain-softening behavior, for materials that require a nonassociative flow rule to develop their plastic constitutive relations, and for nonisothermal plasticity problems where the material compliances vary with temperature. In each of these latter situations use of the tangent stiffness approach results in a nonsymmetric stiffness matrix that is generally costlier to deal with than the symmetric case.

The disadvantages associated with each procedure are the mirror images of the above advantages; namely:

- The tangent stiffness method requires a successive reformulation and redecomposition of the stiffness coefficient matrix, K_T. For optimum computational efficiency this set of coefficients should be positive definite, thus precluding materials that exhibit strain softening, or have nonassociative flow rules, or consider plastic material properties that vary with temperature.
- To maintain stability and accuracy, the residual force method requires small load steps to be used in the successive linearization procedure, primarily because a predicted value of the plastic strain increments is used in Eq. (16).

The size of the load increment is an obvious quantity that is commonly used as a basis of comparison between competing successive linearization schemes. However, it is not and should not be construed as the overriding factor. For example, it is generally recognized that by using the tangent stiffness approach greater load increments than those required for a comparable solution using the residual force method are possible. On the surface, this would represent a strong argument favoring the former. It is our experience, however, that the ratio of computational times required for a full decomposition and subsequent solution (as required in the tangent stiffness approach) to the time required to obtain the solution alone (as in the residual force method) can be great enough to offset the gains associated with the larger load increment. The question of which approach is more cost-effective is now not quite so clear.

The methods as outlined above represent the essential ingredients of the computational procedure. In principle, if the step size is "small enough" the methods should always provide accurate solutions. The question arises, however, as to what constitutes "small enough," and can the step size be increased without affecting accuracy? These questions led to the development of the techniques discussed in the remainder of this section.

Computational Enhancements

With either the tangent stiffness or residual force method we can expect the successive linearization procedure to drift from a true equilibrium position for the nonlinear response. This drifting is a combined result of truncation, the successive linearization procedure, and the fact that information not yet available is required for a true solution. In the case of the tangent stiffness method, this information is necessary to form the updated stiffness coefficients K_T; for the residual force method, the value of the plastic strain increment is required to form ΔQ. Several techniques (iterative and noniterative) can be applied to reduce the amount of drifting to tolerable levels. Many of these techniques are reviewed by Tillerson [50]. With respect to both the tangent stiffness and residual force method the simplest corrective procedure involves the introduction of an equilibrium correction term in the incremental procedure.

The equilibrium correction term at the ith step is represented by R_i in the following equation for the tangent stiffness approach

$$R_i = P_{i-1} - f_{i-1} \tag{17}$$

where P_{i-1} and f_{i-1} represent the external and internal forces at the end of the previous step. For the residual force method

$$R_i = Ku_{i-1} - P_{i-1} - Q_{i-1} \tag{18}$$

which can be shown to be

$$R_i = K^* \left(\Delta\varepsilon_{i-1} - \Delta\varepsilon_{i-1}^{PR}\right) \tag{19}$$

or

$$R_i = \int B^t \, E \left(\Delta\varepsilon_{i-1} - \Delta\varepsilon_{i-1}^{PR}\right) dV)$$

where $\Delta\varepsilon_{i-1}^{PR}$ are the predicted incremental plastic strain components at the start of the $(i-1)^{th}$ step. If the system is in equilibrium at the ith step, R_i is a null vector. Otherwise, it must be added to Eq. (15) or Eq. (16) so that the governing equations become

$$K_T \, \Delta u_i = \Delta P_i + R_i \tag{20}$$

or

$$K\Delta u_i = \Delta P_i + \Delta Q_i + R_i \tag{21}$$

where R_i is given by Eqs. (17) or (19), respectively.

This represents a one-step iteration applied between successive load steps, i.e., the equilibrium correction for the ith step is obtained from the equilibrium imbalance of the $(i-1)^{th}$ step. A complete iterative procedure is defined by applying Eq. (20) or (21) successively within each load step until the correction term R_i or some other measure of convergence is satisfied. This can be classified as a Newton method when the tangent stiffness matrix is updated in each iteration or a modified Newton method when the tangent stiffness matrix is constant for all iterations. By definition, iterations with the residual load method are of the modified Newton type since the stiffness matrix is constant throughout the entire procedure. The "initial stress" method of Ref. [49] is an example of an iterative technique using the residual load method.

Using the Newton method may be self-defeating from a computational-efficiency point of view since efficiencies gained by increased step size are nullified by the effort used in reforming the stiffness matrix in each iteration. However, the modified Newton method may be slowly convergent (or divergent) in the presence of strong nonlinearities (for example, plastic collapse). Methods have been developed to accelerate convergence of iterative methods of the modified Newton type and are reported in Refs. [51, 52]. Both methods define a diagonal matrix α_i such that

$$\Delta u_i' = \alpha_i \Delta u_i \tag{22}$$

where Δu_i is obtained from the standard modified Newton approach and α_i modifies this result based on subsidiary calculations that include the current system nonlinearities. Reference [51] refers to this method as the α - constant stiffness method. Recent developments use an iterative quasi-Newton method, Ref. [53], coupled with a search technique used in optimization theory known as the BFGS (Broyden, Fletcher, Goldfarb, and Shanno) update to accelerate convergence. As in Refs. [51, 52], the goal is to accelerate convergence without explicitly changing the stiffness matrix. This is done in Ref. [53] by modifying the stiffness matrix with pre- and postmultiplication by factors obtained from subsidiary relations. Excellent results with this method are reported in Ref. [53].

Iterative techniques enable the load step size to be increased when compared to the one-step procedures, since solution accuracy can be controlled by the number of iterations in each step. However, there is a liability associated with larger steps that can lead to both inaccuracies and a violation of the material constitutive equations. For example, the associative flow rule in incremental plasticity states that the plastic strain increment is proportional to the normal to the loading surface. If the normal at the start and end of the load step differ substantially from each other, use of a constant normal in a one-step procedure can lead to inaccuracies. Krieg [54] and Schreyer, Kulak, and Kramer [55] have performed error analyses for perfectly plastic [54] and strain hardening [55] materials, respectively, for one-step application of the constitutive relations. Based on this analysis, Ref. [54] recommends a one-step radial return method for perfectly plastic materials as a sufficiently accurate method for enforcing consistency with the constitutive equations. Subincrementation techniques that successively apply the constitutive relations "n" times within each increment in total strain appear in Refs. [5], [54], and [56]. The value of "n" can be based on a measure of the initial yield function [48, 45] or on the change in the loading surface normally obtained in a one-step procedure [55].

A two-stage iterative process that can be used in conjunction with the residual force method is described by Vos [57]. This procedure involves the assumption of a fixed normal to the loading surface at the start of the iterative step. This value is held constant until the iterative cycle converges. The normal is then reevaluated at the midpoint of the increment and the iterative procedure continued.

Several other techniques have been suggested and successfully incorporated to enhance calculations for static plastic analysis of structures. These procedures are summarized below.

One is the use of a variable set of inelastic integration points within an element. Examining the governing equations for either the tangent stiffners approach, Eq. (15), or the initial strain approach, Eq. (16), shows that the calculations of the incremental displacements require the evaluation of integrals involving plastic material behavior. Consequently, the accuracy of the solution is dependent on the accuracy of these integrals which are, in turn, dependent on how accurately the plastic behavior is described within an element. A variable representation of the elastic-plastic behavior within an element can be achieved by introducing a variable set of plastic integration points within an element, at which stress and strain histories are monitored. Thus, a judicious choice can be made for the inelastic integration points in order to accurately describe the predicted plastic behavior such as the variation of plastic strain and hence the elastic-plastic boundary within the element. The user is therefore, in effect, modeling for anticipated plastic response. This procedure was followed by Levy et al. [58] for several elastic and elastic-plastic problems.

The use of substructuring techniques is another technique. The objective of these procedures, or static condensation, is to reduce computation costs and to improve the accuracy associated with a nonlinear analysis by eliminating a substantial amount of computations. The method is particularly well suited to the residual load method for treating problems of contained plastic flow, and where the regions of pure elastic behavior and elastic-plastic behavior can be distinguished and estimated with a high level of confidence. In this case, since the stiffness matrix is not updated, a reduced matrix obtained by static condensation is initially formed and then used throughout the plastic analysis. Another associated saving is obtained by recovering stresses and strains only in elements in the reduced set. The substructuring technique can also be used with additional effort and complexity with the tangent stiffness method [59]. A study of substructuring as applied to three particular problems involving small contained regions of plastic flow in which the residual force method is used as presented in Ref. [60]. The results of this study may be summarized by stating that a reduction of an order of magnitude in computing time requirements may be realized per incremental step by incorporating a substructuring option.

Finally, the accuracy and efficiency of any solution to a nonlinear structural analysis problem depends upon a number of other factors, not the least of which is the user's experience in setting the finite element idealization with respect to size, arrangement, and type of elements used. These factors have been discussed by Waltz et al. [61] and Trucke [62] for linear elastic systems and are equally applicable, if not more critical, for elastic-plastic analyses.

Dynamic Solution Procedures

A prerequisite to developing a successful nonlinear dynamic analysis capability is a sound knowledge of the options and pitfalls associated with nonlinear static analysis. Many of the comments concerning efficiency and accuracy discussed in connection with static analyses are directly applicable to nonlinear dynamics. The additional ingredients are the inclusion of an inertial term to the governing equations and the introduction of a time integration scheme to solve the equations of motions. Much attention [63-71] has been given to the development and evaluation of discrete methods to numerically integrate the equations of motion. Little will be added here to the technical content of these references; rather, we will outline the various options and pitfalls that exist with respect to nonlinear dynamic analysis and make some summary and experience-based comments.

At the outset it should be stated that a significant factor affecting time-step size for a dynamic plastic analysis is the plasticity theory. That is, the time step must be such that the assumptions intrinsic to the plasticity theory are not violated. This is in contrast to linear dynamic analysis for which step size is controlled entirely by numerical stability and accuracy considerations.

Basically, the procedures used to solve the equations of motion of both linear and nonlinear dynamic analysis are divided into two categories, direct time integration and modal superposition. Some of the distinctions of the two methods are discussed below.

Direct Integration Procedures

The coupled equations of motion for an undamped discrete system can be written as

$$M\Delta\ddot{u} + \Delta f = \Delta P + R \tag{23}$$

where M is the mass matrix, Δf and ΔP the incremental internal and external force vectors, respectively, and R the residual load vector. Indices are omitted from Eq. (23), but it is implied that the equation is written for the i + 1 increment, i.e., in passing from t_i to t_{i+1}. The two unknowns in Eq. (23) are the incremental vector of internal forces, Δf, and the incremental acceleration vector, $\Delta\ddot{u}$. The mass matrix may be formulated on the basis of a "consistent" or lumped mass approach, the distinction between the two being whether the mass is represented by means of finite element interpolation functions or is directly discretized by lumping components at nodes. The former approach leads to a banded matrix while the latter leads to a diagonal matrix. Which approach to use depends on the integration scheme employed in the analysis [72]. Two approaches to the solution of Eq. (23) can be taken, each affecting the form of the equation to be solved in a sequence of time steps. In the first type, referred to as explicit, Δf is obtained entirely from previous information so that elements of the mass matrix are the only coefficients of the unknowns (accelerations or displacements). In the second type, termed implicit, the mass and stiffness matrices are combined to form coefficients of the unknowns. The choice of which method to use is clearer for linear problems than for nonlinear ones, with implicit methods overwhelmingly used for structural dynamics and explicit methods for problems where high-frequency response is significant, as in the treatment of wave propagation effects.

Explicit integrators are generally conditionally stable [63] with the critical time step inversely proportional to the highest frequency in the discrete model. Implicit integrators are generally unconditionally stable and tend to filter out the higher-frequency response. This allows for larger time steps, the choice of which is controlled by the modes necessary to predict the essential features of the response. For linear problems using a constant time step, both methods lead to coefficient matrices that are constant through the entire response spectrum.

The complicating factor for nonlinear problems is a consequence of the change in stiffness due to plasticity. The operational choices of which method to use in this case are not unlike the choices between using the tangent stiffness or initial strain approaches for static nonlinear problems since they involve tradeoffs between smaller, less "costly" time steps for explicit integration versus larger, but relatively more "costly" time steps for implicit integration. Reference to the term "costly" here is related to the degree of complexity and magnitude of subsidiary computations during each time step. Some of the distinctions of the two methods are outlined below.

Explicit integrator. The explicit formulation solves Eq. (23) directly as

$$M\Delta\ddot{u} = \Delta P - \Delta f + R \tag{24}$$

with Δf obtained from past information. For example, if $\Delta f = K_T \Delta u$, then using the central difference operator, $\Delta u = 2\Delta u_i - \Delta u_{i-1} + \Delta t^2 \Delta\ddot{u}_i$. Quantities without indices imply the $i+1^{th}$ increment. There is little distinction between the tangent stiffness and initial strain approaches for explicit integration since $\Delta f = K_T \Delta u$ for the tangent stiffness method and $\Delta f = K\Delta u + \Delta Q$ for the initial strain approach. In either case the end result is a residual internal load vector. Further, the implication is that the operations are performed on the element level rather than on the larger global system. Since, as stated above, the equations of motion require only the incremental vector of internal forces, the notion of a stiffness matrix can be discarded altogether (as suggested by Belytschko [73]), with Δf obtained directly from an integral involving stress and the matrix that maps displacement to strains. In either case calculations involve successive solutions to Eq. (24) with incremental alterations to the right-hand side. This becomes a simple procedure with a diagonal mass matrix since the operation involves simple division. With a consistent mass matrix an initial factorization can be performed so that subsequent solutions require only a forward and backward substitution of banded triangular matrices. In passing, we remark that Kreig and Key [72] indicate that there is an improvement in accuracy when the lumped mass approach is used with an explicit integrator because the errors in the discrete system caused by this combination tend to be counterbalancing. Because of the ease in obtaining solutions to Eq. (24), the computation time for an explicit method becomes strongly dependent on the element level stress/strain recovery and the formation of Δf. Computer costs are therefore directly tied to the number of elements in the discrete model and the number of time steps necessary in the analysis. This leads to the major drawback of explicit methods, namely that more refined models have an increased frequency spectrum, which for numerical stability require a smaller time step. Consequently, there is a complementary effect caused by a larger set of elements in combination with smaller time steps. Because of this situation a break-even point occurs when the economics of simpler calculations are overridden by the requirement of ever smaller time steps.

The most widely used explicit technique currently in use is the constant step central difference operator [63]. It has been our preference, however, to use a variable time step modified Adams predictor-corrector method [74] that is explicit in the predictor and implicit in the corrector solutions. The advantage of this method is that the time step is automatically chosen to reflect current system stiffness and dynamic response. Our experience has been that this method automatically chooses time steps near those required by the central difference method.

Use of an explicit integrator fits naturally into a nonlinear analysis since there are very few additional calculations required compared to a linear analysis. The smaller time steps are consistent with the initial premise that the assumptions of plasticity theory are not to be violated. However, as the frequency spectrum increases, stability requirements cause the critical time step to be reduced so that ultimately the method becomes uneconomical. We conclude this discussion with a direction for future research that leads to an explicit integrator capable of filtering out higher frequency response while maintaining the desired accuracy in the lower frequency regime.

<u>Implicit integrator.</u> The implicit formulation is based on difference operators that contain both the currently unknown acceleration and displacement. When an operator of this form is substituted into Eq. (23) this yields

$$\bar{K}\Delta u = \Delta P + Q_d + R \tag{25}$$

where $K = K_T + \frac{M}{\beta\Delta t^2}$, Q_d is a dynamic load vector that involves products of the mass matrix and vectors of known quantities such as displacements, velocities, and accelerations, and Δt and β are the time step and a parameter arising from the particular integrator used, respectively.

Unlike an explicit integrator, there is a distinction between the tangent stiffness and initial strain approaches when using an implicit integrator. This distinction is in the same sense as that existing for static problems. That is, the effect of plasticity can enter directly into the stiffness matrix and thereby the coefficient matrix, $\bar{K}$, or it can appear as an effective load vector. Equation (25) represents the tangent stiffness approach since the coefficient matrix explicitly contains the tangent stiffness matrix K_T. In this case the matrix $\bar{K}$ must be reassembled and a complete solution obtained in each time step. As the mesh size increases this becomes increasingly expensive and ultimately dominates the calculations.

Using the initial strain approach leads to

$$\tilde{K}\Delta u = \Delta P + Q_d + \Delta Q + R \tag{26}$$

where $\tilde{K} = K + \frac{M}{\beta \Delta t^2}$, K is the elastic stiffness matrix, and ΔQ is the plastic pseudoload vector. If a constant time step approach is used, the coefficient matrix remains constant so that subsequent solutions require only forward and backward substitutions of triangular matrices. This procedure is competitive with an explicit technique, since after the first step, computations involve only solutions of the factored coefficient matrix, the formation of the dynamic load vector Q_d, and the formation of ΔQ. It must be noted that the time step used in this procedure must be controlled by the linearization implicit in using estimated values of plastic strain increments, rather than an accuracy consideration defined entirely by the integrator.

An inner loop iterative procedure can be developed on the basis of Eqs. (25) or (26). Iterations are performed until the structure is in equilibrium to within some predetermined tolerance. This tolerance can be based on a measure of the change of the displacement increment [75] or on the work done by the residual load vector [71]. In either case, if the procedure does not converge within a prescribed number of iterations the time-step is reduced. Thus, the iterations can define a variable time-step approach in which the criterion for reducing the time step is based on the system nonlinearities. It is our opinion that accuracy checks should also be included based on the current system dynamics in the same manner as used in predictor-corrector methods. This has been suggested in [67] but to our knowledge has not been implemented and tested in a general purpose program.

There are currently a number of implicit operators that are frequently used for structural analysis. Among these are the Newmark-β family [76], Wilson -θ [77], Houbolt [78], and the more recently developed stiffly stable methods by Park [79]. No one method at this point seems to have been accepted as the "best" one for all problems.

Special Considerations

One of the distinguishing features of many practical problems associated with plastic analyses is that the nonlinearities can be contained in localized regions. Because of this, substructuring in a number of forms can be an important factor in reducing computational costs. The most straightforward approach is to use simply a Guyan [80] reduction technique to reduce the number of degrees of freedom in the entire model, particularly in the elastic region, and then to recover stresses and strains only in the limited region where plastic flow is postulated. Mixed methods [81, 82] are also used, where modal techniques are utilized in some well-defined elastic region with direct integration used in the plastic region. Other methods are currently being developed [83-86] for use in mixed media problems such as fluid structure interaction and hold promise for dynamic plastic analysis. Hughes [83] has demonstrated a mixed implicit-explicit method with a predictor-corrector explicit operator and a Newmark family implicit integrator. Within our context this method may be useful for elastic-plastic dynamic analysis with the implicit integrator used in the elastic region and the explicit used in the elastic-plastic region. Other techniques that allow different time steps in different regions [84, 85, 86] warrant investigations since simple explicit integration with time steps consistent with the path-dependence attributes of plasticity theory could be combined with larger time-step implicit integration in a larger elastic region.

Modal Methods

Modal superposition for linear elastic systems requires the equations of motion to be transformed into an uncoupled form in which only a portion of the eigenvalues and eigenvectors are retained. To reduce computational costs this transformation may be preceded by a condensation procedure that eliminates a prescribed set of degrees of freedom. One of two procedures is usually employed to eliminate the unwanted information; the first is the Guyan reduction scheme [80], and the second procedure is a static (zero mass) condensation method. Both procedures result in an approximate representation of the mass and stiffness characteristics of the discrete model. As in the case of substructuring in a static analysis, care must be taken to avoid eliminating regions where plasticity may develop. The effects of plasticity may be treated within the framework of the tangent stiffness or residual force method.

The use of modal superposition for nonlinear problems appears, at first glance, to violate the well-known fact that superposition principles are not applicable to nonlinear systems. However, nonlinear dynamic analysis by modal superposition requires some additional considerations. When used in conjunction with the tangent stiffness method the procedure requires that subsequent modes, developed beyond those associated with the elastic state, be obtained during regular intervals of the load-time history. Nickell [87] has discussed this procedure for the case of combined geometric and material nonlinearities. Although Nickell's formulation is sufficiently general for combined plasticity and large deflection, examples involving only geometric nonlinearities are considered in Ref. [87]. The subsequent modal spectrum for nonlinear states is determined by an iterative procedure, using the most recently determined spectrum as an initial estimate. A direct time integration scheme is then employed to solve the reduced set of uncoupled equations.

The use of a modal method in conjunction with the residual force approach does not appear to have been given much consideration. On the surface it appears particularly attractive since a single set of modes (based on the elastic behavior) could be used throughout analysis. Only the residual force due to plasticity would have to be transformed in each time step.

REVIEW OF AVAILABLE COMPUTER PROGRAMS

Developing a comprehensive finite element program remains a subjective undertaking since it invariably depends on the analysts designing the program, the computer hardware available, and the resources allocated for the project. Many of the basic criteria for both linear and nonlinear general purpose codes are similar. These include a comprehensive element library and efficient equation solver. A nonlinear program, in addition, must implement:

- An algorithm to linearize the path-dependent nonlinear analysis
- Constitutive relations to represent the experimentally observed material behavior

These features were discussed in the preceding sections. In addition, a program for nonlinear analysis must have:

- Added capability to trace an elastic-plastic boundary within individual elements
- Provision to store and update path-dependent field quantities such as displacement, stresses, strains
- Provision for user interaction through a restart procedure

It is also important to realize that the algorithms implemented in a nonlinear analysis are of the repetitive type so that unlike an elastic analysis, typical calculations must be carried out repeatedly. This is an important consideration because, while it is true that nonlinear analysis has reached a level of maturity such that any problem can be solved for a price, the cost for such an analysis can become prohibitive. Consequently, it is incumbent upon the designer of a nonlinear code to minimize the cost of an analysis so that solutions to meaningful problems are economically feasible.

This review has surveyed twelve programs for plastic analysis of structures. Since this paper is an update of the review in Ref. [1] we used the same tables to evaluate each program. Therefore, the original paper along with the associated tables were sent to each developer as a guide to evaluate their code. It is their response to this inquiry that is shown in the current review.

The following items are used to describe the individual programs that were reviewed:

1. Structural modeling capability
   a. Element library
2. Treatment of material nonlinearity
   a. Plasticity theory(ies)
   b. Material description
3. Solution technique
   a. Linearization scheme (initial strain, tangent, modulus, etc.)

Since the goal of this paper is to provide a critical review of the available programs, this section concludes with a table that evaluates each program on the basis of those features that we considered to be important.

Program Description

The table of element information originally presented in Ref. [88] is used here to describe the element libraries associated with each of the finite element programs. An explanation of the code used in this table follows.

In column B: Beams

Subcolumn a) Position of nodal point in cross section fixed

b) Arbitrary position of nodal point in cross section

In columns E and F; Plates and Shells

Subcolumn a) Kirchhoff: transverse shear neglected

b) Reissner: transverse shear included

In line 4: Model

K = Equilibrium model

V = Displacement model

H - Hybrid model or incompressible model

In line 5: Types of elements

L = Line shaped

D = Triangle

R = Rectangle
V = Arbitrary quadrilateral
T = Tetrahedron
P = Pentahedron
Q = Cube
H = Arbitrary hexagon
with elements L, D, R, V one may also specify:
r = Body of revolution
s = Sector of body of revolution
i.e.,: L_r = Shell of revolution
D_s = Sector with triangular meridional cross section

In lines 6 and 7: Element shape boundary
G = Rectilinear
K = Curvilinear or isoparametric
E = Plane
S = Shallow surface
B = Arbitrarily curved surface or isoparametric
for ring and sector types of elements these variables refer to the meridional cross section

In lines 8 and 9: Cross-sectional data
Material data

Properties:
Q = Area of cross section or thickness
T = Moment of inertia
I = Isotropic
O = Orthotropic
A = Arbitrary anisotropy
K = constant
V = variable
for example: QK, QV, IV, AK

In line 10: External loading
P = Concentrated load, L = Line load, F = Surface load
V = Volume load

In line 11: Initial strains
N = Not implemented
T = Isotropic thermal strains only
B = Arbitrary initial strains

A blank field indicates that the information is not applicable. An X indicates that the information was not obtained.

Program Name: ADINA
Technical Contract: Dr. K. J. Bathe
Mass. Institute of Technology
Cambridge Mass. 02139

Documentation: [89], [90]
Method of Analysis: FEM - displacement
State of Development: Fully operational
Element Information:

	A	B		C	D	E		F		G
ADINA	ROD	BEAM a)	b)	PLANE MEMBRANE	MEMBRANE IN SPACE	PLATE a) KIRCHHOFF	b) REISSNER	SHELL a) KIRCHHOFF	b) REISSNER	THREE-DIMENSIONAL CONTINUUM
1. NO. OF ELEMENTS AVAILABLE	1	1		1	1		1		1	1
2. NO. OF NODES PER ELEMENT	2–4	2		3–8	3–8		3–16		3–16	3–21
3. NO. OF FREEDOMS PER ELEMENT	6–12	12		6–16	9–24		9–48		15–80	9–63
4. MODEL	V	V		V	V		V		V	V
5. ELEMENT CONFIGURATION	L	L		VDR	VDR		DRV		DRV	TPQH
6. ELEMENT SHAPE	K	G		E	E		E		B	B
7. BOUNDARY				K	K		K		K	K
8. CROSS-SECTIONAL DATA				QK	QK		QK		QK	
9. MATERIAL DATA	I	I		IO	IO		I		I	IO
10. EXTERNAL LOADING	P,V	P,V		TVF	TVF		PV		TV	TVF
11. INITIAL STRAINS	T	T		T	T		T		T	T

Comments: ADINA is a computer program for general static and dynamic, linear and nonlinear analysis of structures. Capability includes inelastic (plasticity and creep) and large-displacement analysis as well as structural dynamics and wave propagation analysis. An associated heat transfer program is called ADINAT. An application users group has been formed [90].

Program Name: AGGIE I
Technical Contact: Dr. W. Haisler
Texas A & M University
College Station, Texas

Documentation: [91]
Method of Analysis: FEM - displacement
State of Development: Fully operational
Element Information:

AGGIE I	A	B		C	D	E		F		G
		BEAM				PLATE		SHELL		
	ROD	a)	b)	PLANE MEMBRANE	MEMBRANE IN SPACE	a) KIRCHHOFF	b) REISSNER	a) KIRCHHOFF	b) REISSNER	THREE-DIMENSIONAL CONTINUUM
1. NO. OF ELEMENTS AVAILABLE	1	1					1		1	1
2. NO. OF NODES PER ELEMENT	2	2-4					4-8		4-8	8-21
3. NO. OF FREEDOMS PER ELEMENT	6	12-24					24-48		24-48	24-63
4. MODEL	V	V					V		V	V
5. ELEMENT CONFIGURATION	L	L					V		V	H
6. ELEMENT SHAPE	G	K					EK		K	K
7. BOUNDARY									K	K
8. CROSS-SECTIONAL DATA	QK	QTV					QV		QV	QV
9. MATERIAL DATA	IK	IK					IK		IK	IK, OK, AK
10. EXTERNAL LOADING	P	PL					PLF		PLF	PLFV
11. INITIAL STRAINS	B	N					N		N	B

Comments: An extended version of this program and documentation should now be available. This version includes nonisothermal combined isotropic and kinematic plasticity, creep, and nonlinear viscoelastic models. This version also includes a shell and beam element not documented in Ref. [91].

Program Name: ANSYS
Technical Contact: Dr. John Swanson
Swanson Analysis Systems Inc.
P.O. Box 65
Houston, Pennsylvania 15342

Documentation: [92]
Method of Analysis: FEM - displacement
State of Development: Fully operational
Element Information:

	A	B		C	D	E		F		G
		BEAM				PLATE		SHELL		
ANSYS	ROD	a)	b)	PLANE MEMBRANE	MEMBRANE IN SPACE	a) KIRCHHOFF	b) REISSNER	a) KIRCHHOFF	b) REISSNER	THREE-DIMENSIONAL CONTINUUM
1. NO. OF ELEMENTS AVAILABLE	2	1		2	1	1		1		4
2. NO. OF NODES PER ELEMENT	2	2		3,4,5,6,7,8	3	3		3		4,6,8,20
3. NO. OF FREEDOMS PER ELEMENT	4,6	6		6,8,10,12,14,16	9	9		18		12,18,24,60
4. MODEL	V	V		V	V	V		V		V
5. ELEMENT CONFIGURATION	L	L		D,R,V, D_r, R_r, V_r	D	D		D		T,P,QH
6. ELEMENT SHAPE				E	E	E		E		
7. BOUNDARY				GK	G	G		G		
8. CROSS-SECTIONAL DATA	QK	QTK		QV	QV	QV		QV		
9. MATERIAL DATA	IK	IK		OK	OK	OK		OK		OK
10. EXTERNAL LOADING	P	PL		PF	PF	PF		P,F		P,F,V
11. INITIAL STRAINS	B	B		B	B	B		B		B

Comments: Program capabilities include many other elements than those listed above (i.e., special pipe and elbow elements for nonlinear piping analysis). In addition to a static and dynamic structural analysis capability (including elastic-plastic, creep, and swelling, small and large deflections), the program provides for heat transfer analysis (steady-state and transient; conduction, convection, and radiation).

Program Name: ASKA
Technical Contact: Dr. E. Schrem,
ASKA-Group
Pfaffenwaldring 27
Stuttgart-80, West Germany

Documentation: [93], [94], [95]
Method of Analysis: FEM - displacement
State of Development: Fully operational
Element Information:

ASKA	A	B		C	D	E		F		G
	ROD	BEAM a)	BEAM b)	PLANE MEMBRANE	MEMBRANE IN SPACE	PLATE a) KIRCHHOFF	PLATE b) REISSNER	SHELL a) KIRCHHOFF	SHELL b) REISSNER	THREE-DIMENSIONAL CONTINUUM
1. NO. OF ELEMENTS AVAILABLE	2		1		7	1		1		11
2. NO. OF NODES PER ELEMENT	2,3		2		3,6,4,8,9	3		3		3,4,6,8,9, 10,18,27
3. NO. OF FREEDOMS PER ELEMENT	6,9		12		9.12,18,24,27	18		18		6,8,12,16,18, 24,30,54,81
4. MODEL	V		V		V	V		V		V
5. ELEMENT CONFIGURATION	L		L		D,V	D		D		Dr,Vr,T,P,H
6. ELEMENT SHAPE					E	E		E		
7. BOUNDARY					K	G		G		G, K
8. CROSS-SECTIONAL DATA	QV		QTK		QV	QV		QV		
9. MATERIAL DATA	IK		IK		IK	IK		IK		IK
10. EXTERNAL LOADING	P,V				P,L	P,F,V		P,F,V		P,F,V
11. INITIAL STRAINS	B		B		B	B		B		B

Comments: An extensive well-known program for static and dynamic analysis. Program capabilities include many other elements than those listed above.

Program Name: ASAS
Technical Contact: Dr. K. C. Knowles
Atkins Research and Development
Woodcote Grove Ashley Road
Epsom Surray KT185BW, England

Documentation: [x]
Method of Analysis: FEM - displacement and equilibrium
State of Development: Fully operational

ASAS	A	B		C	D	E		F		G
	ROD	BEAM a)	BEAM b)	PLANE MEMBRANE	MEMBRANE IN SPACE	PLATE a) KIRCHHOFF	PLATE b) REISSNER	SHELL a) KIRCHHOFF	SHELL b) REISSNER	THREE-DIMENSIONAL CONTINUUM
1. NO. OF ELEMENTS AVAILABLE	3	3	1	3	7	1	1	2	4	6
2. NO. OF NODES PER ELEMENT	2,3,3	2,2,3	3	4,6,8	3,6,4,8, 4,6,8	3	8	2,3	6,8,6,8	6,8,15,20,32
3. NO. OF FREEDOMS PER ELEMENT	6,9,7	12,12, 17	18	12,9,12	9,18,12,24,12, 12,16	18	24	6,18	24,32,86,48	18,24,45,60,96
4. MODEL	V,V,K	V,V, V	V	K,K,V	V,V,V,V,V,K,K	V	V	V	V	V
5. ELEMENT CONFIGURATION	L	L	L	V	D,D,V,V,V,V,V	D	V		D,V,D,V	H
6. ELEMENT SHAPE				E	E,K D_r D_r V_r V_r	E	E		B	
7. BOUNDARY				G	GK	G	GK	G	K	G,G,K,K,K
8. CROSS-SECTIONAL DATA	QV	QTV	QTV	QV	QV	QK	QV	QV	QV	
9. MATERIAL DATA	I	I	I	AK	AK	AK	AK	AK	AK	AK
10. EXTERNAL LOADING	P,P, PL	PL	PL	PL	P,L,F	P,L,F	P,L,F	P,L,F,V	P,L,F,V	P,L,F,V
11. INITIAL STRAINS	T	T	T	T	T	T	T	T	T	T

Comments: The developers indicate that the inelastic capabilities of this program are contained in a separate version labeled ASASIH which at the moment is not available for general release.

Program Name: BERSAFE
Technical Contact: Dr. T. K. Hellen
Central Electricity Generating Board
Research Division
Berkeley Nuclear Laboratories
Berkeley Gloucestershire GL 139PB
U.K.

Documentation: [96]
Method of Analysis: FEM - displacement
State of Development: Fully operational
Element Information:

	A	B		C	D	E		F		G
		BEAM				PLATE		SHELL		
BERSAFE	ROD	a)	b)	PLANE MEMBRANE	MEMBRANE IN SPACE	a) KIRCHHOFF	b) REISSNER	a) KIRCHHOFF	b) REISSNER	THREE-DIMENSIONAL CONTINUUM
1. NO. OF ELEMENTS AVAILABLE	3	3	1	10				4	4	4
2. NO. OF NODES PER ELEMENT	2,2,2	2,2,3	2	3,4,6,8,12,3,4,6,8,12				3,3,6,8	6,8,10,12	8,15,20,32
3. NO. OF FREEDOMS PER ELEMENT	4,4,6	12, 12, 17	12	6,8,12,16,24,6,8,12, 16,24				12,54,24,32	30,40,50,60	24,45,60,96
4. MODEL	V	V	V	V				V	V	V
5. ELEMENT CONFIGURATION	L,L_r, L	L	L	D,V,D,V,V,D_r, V_r D_r V_r V_r				DDDV	DVDV	H,P,H,H
6. ELEMENT SHAPE		G,K, G	K	E				K	K	B
7. BOUNDARY				G				B	B	B
8. CROSS-SECTIONAL DATA	QK	QTK	QTK	QK				QK	QK	
9. MATERIAL DATA	IK	IK	IK	IK,OK				IK	IK	OK
10. EXTERNAL LOADING	P,L, F,V	P	P	P,L,F,V				P,F,V	P,F,V	P,L,F,V
11. INITIAL STRAINS	B			B						B

Comments: The developer has indicated that columns B and F (Beams and Shells) are thus far limited to elastic behavior. Additionally, special singularity elements for 2-D and 3-D nonlinear fracture analysis are available.

Program Name: EPACA
Technical Contact: Dr. Z. Zudans
Mechanical and Nuclear Engineering Dept.
Franklin Institute Research Laboratories
The Franklin Institute
Philadelphia, Pennsylvania 19103 U.S.A.

Documentation: [97]
Method of Analysis: FEM - displacement
State of Development: Operational
Element Information:

	A	B		C	D	E		F		G
EPACA	ROD	BEAM a)	b)	PLANE MEMBRANE	MEMBRANE IN SPACE	PLATE a) KIRCHHOFF	b) REISSNER	SHELL a) KIRCHHOFF	b) REISSNER	THREE-DIMENSIONAL CONTINUUM
1. NO. OF ELEMENTS AVAILABLE				2	6	2	2		4	
2. NO. OF NODES PER ELEMENT				3,4	3,4,6,8,10,12	3,4	3,4		6,8,10,12	
3. NO. OF FREEDOMS PER ELEMENT				6,8	9,12,18,24, 30,36	15,20	15,20		30,40,50,60	
4. MODEL				V	V	V	V		V	
5. ELEMENT CONFIGURATION				D,V	D,V,D,V,D,V	D,V	D,V		D,V,D,V	
6. ELEMENT SHAPE				E	E,E,K,K,K,K	E	E		K	
7. BOUNDARY				G	G	G	G		G	
8. CROSS-SECTIONAL DATA				QV	QV	QV	QV		QV	
9. MATERIAL DATA				IV	IV	IV	IV		IV	
10. EXTERNAL LOADING				P,L,F,V	P,L,F,V	P,L,F,V	P,L,F,V		P,L,F,V	
11. INITIAL STRAINS				B	B	B	B		B	

Comments: This is a program designed for elastic-plastic-creep analysis of thin or thick three-dimensional shells made up of curved or flat shell elements. The developer indicates that there has been no additional development since the last review. EPACA is available through the Argonne National Laboratory. Further technical information can be obtained from Dr. Shakif Iskander, Mail Stop 38, Bldg. K1007, P.O. Box P, Oak Ridge, Tenn. 37830

Program Name: MARC-CDC
Technical Contact: Dr. P. V. Marcal
Marc Analysis Research Corp.
260 Sheridan Avenue, Suite 200
Palo Alto, California 94306

Documentation: [98]
Method of Analysis: FEM - displacement
State of Development: Fully operational
Element Information:

	A	B		C	D	E		F		G
		BEAM				PLATE		SHELL		
MARC-CDC	ROD	a)	b)	PLANE MEMBRANE	MEMBRANE IN SPACE	a) KIRCHHOFF	b) REISSNER	a) KIRCHHOFF	b) REISSNER	THREE-DIMENSIONAL CONTINUUM
1. NO. OF ELEMENTS AVAILABLE	1	2		3	2	1		3		1
2. NO. OF NODES PER ELEMENT	2	2, 2		4, 3, 3	4, 6	6		2, 2, 3		8
3. NO. OF FREEDOMS PER ELEMENT	3	6, 12		8, 6, 6	12, 10	24		6, 8, 27		24
4. MODEL	V	V		V	V	V		V		V
5. ELEMENT CONFIGURATION	L	L		V, D, D_r	V	D		L_r, L_r, D		H
6. ELEMENT SHAPE		K		E	B, E	E		K		
7. BOUNDARY				G	G	G		G		G
8. CROSS-SECTIONAL DATA	QK	QTK		QK	QK	QK		QK, QV, QV		
9. MATERIAL DATA				AK	AK	AK		AK		AK
10. EXTERNAL LOADING	P, L	P, L		P, L	P, L, F	P, L, F		P, L, F		P, L, V
11. INITIAL STRAINS	B	B, B		B	B, B	B		B, B, B		B

Comments: This is a program designed, developed, and built specifically for nonlinear analysis (plasticity and large deflection). Elements, in addition to those listed above include many thin-walled open and closed section beams, and pipe bend (elbow) elements.

Program Name: NEPSAP
Technical Contact: Dr. S. Nagarajan
Dept. 81-12 Bldg. 154
Lockheed Missiles & Space Co.
P.O. Box 504
Sunnyvale, California 94088

Documentation: [99], [100], [101]
Method of Analysis: FEM - displacement
State of Development: Fully operational
Element Information:

NEPSAP	A	B		C	D	E		F		G
	ROD	BEAM a)	BEAM b)	PLANE MEMBRANE	MEMBRANE IN SPACE	PLATE a) KIRCHHOFF	PLATE b) REISSNER	SHELL a) KIRCHHOFF	SHELL b) REISSNER	THREE-DIMENSIONAL CONTINUUM
1. NO. OF ELEMENTS AVAILABLE	1		1	4	2	2 (2)	2	2(2)	3	2
2. NO. OF NODES PER ELEMENT	2		2	4,4,3-8,3-8	4, 3 TO 8	4,4	16,8	5,5	4,8 & 16 ISOPARAM	8, 8 TO 20
3. NO. OF FREEDOMS PER ELEMENT	6		12	8,8,6–16,6–16	12, 9 TO 24	24,24	48,40	24,24	48,40,12	24,24 TO 60
4. MODEL	V		V	V,H	V,H	V	V,HV	V	V,H V V	V,H
5. ELEMENT CONFIGURATION	L		L	V, V_r, V, V_r	V	V	H,V	V	H, V, L_r	H
6. ELEMENT SHAPE	G			E	E	E	B	S	B	E,B
7. BOUNDARY				G,G,K,K	G,K	G	K	G	K	G,K
8. CROSS-SECTIONAL DATA	QK		QTK	QK	QK	QV	QV	QV	QV	QV
9. MATERIAL DATA				AK	AK	AK	AK	AK	AK	AK
10. EXTERNAL LOADING	P,L		P,L	P,L	P,L	P,L,F	P,L,F	P,L,F	P,L,F	P,L,F,V
11. INITIAL STRAINS	B		B	B	B	B	B	B	B	B

Comments: This is a general purpose, three-dimensional program capable of treating large-displacement, thermo-elastic-plastic, and creep behavior of arbitrary structures. Nonlinear straight and curved pipe elements, gap and contact elements are also available. The developer also indicates the following points: for row (2) - additional pressure degrees of freedom for mean pressure in the case of incompressible elements; for columns F(a) and F(b) - one element for monocoque thin plate-shells another for multilayered anisotrophic thin plate-shells.

Program Name: PAFEC 75
Technical Contact: Dr. Richard D. Henshell
PAFEC Ltd.
PAFEC House
40 Broadgate, Beeston
Nottingham NG92FW England

Documentation: [102]
Method of Analysis: FEM - displacement and hybrid
State of Development: Fully operational
Element Information:

	A	B		C	D	E		F		G
		BEAM				PLATE		SHELL		
PAFEC 75	ROD	a)	b)	PLANE MEMBRANE	MEMBRANE IN SPACE	a) KIRCHHOFF	b) REISSNER	a) KIRCHHOFF	b) REISSNER	THREE-DIMENSIONAL CONTINUUM
1. NO. OF ELEMENTS AVAILABLE	1	3	1	SPECIAL CASE OF D	9	6	3	2	DEGENERATE CASE OF G	12
2. NO. OF NODES PER ELEMENT	2	2	3		3,4,6,8,9 12,17,6,8	3,3,4,6,8,12	6,8,12	6,8		6,8,9,12,15,18,20 24,28,32,21,16
3. NO. OF FREEDOMS PER ELEMENT	6	12	17		2 x NO. OF NODES	5 x NO. OF NODES	5 x NO. OF NODES	24,32		3 x NO. OF NODES
4. MODEL	V	V			V	V	V			V
5. ELEMENT CONFIGURATION	L	L	L		DV	DV	DV	DV		TPH
6. ELEMENT SHAPE	G	GK	K		E	E	E	B		B
7. BOUNDARY					K	G	K	K		K
8. CROSS-SECTIONAL DATA	QK	QTK	QT		QK	QK	QK	QK		QK
9. MATERIAL DATA	AK	AK			AK	AK	AK	AK		AK
10. EXTERNAL LOADING	PL	PL	PL		PLF	PLF	PLF	PLF		PLFV
11. INITIAL STRAINS	B	B	B		B	B	B	B		B

Comments: Since the last review [1] of the program, PAFEC 70+ has been superceded by PAFEC 75 and is marketed by PAFEC, Ltd.

Program Name: PLANS
Technical Contact: Dr. Allan Pifko
Applied Mechanics Group
Research Department
Grumman Aerospace Corp.
Bethpage, New York 11714

Documentation: [103], [104]
Method of Analysis: FEM - displacement
State of Development: Fully operational
Element Information:

	A	B		C	D	E		F		G
		BEAM				PLATE		SHELL		
PLANS	ROD	a)	b)	PLANE MEMBRANE	MEMBRANE IN SPACE	a) KIRCHHOFF	b) REISSNER	a) KIRCHHOFF	b) REISSNER	THREE-DIMENSIONAL CONTINUUM
1. NO. OF ELEMENTS AVAILABLE	1		1	2	2	1		2		2
2. NO. OF NODES PER ELEMENT	2–3		2	3–6,3	3–6,3	3		2,3		8–20,3
3. NO. OF FREEDOMS PER ELEMENT	6–9		12	6–12,15	9–18,18	36		12,36		24–60,9
4. MODEL	V		V	V	V	V		V		V
5. ELEMENT CONFIGURATION	L		L	D,D	D,D_r	D		L_r,D		H, D_r
6. ELEMENT SHAPE	G		G	E,E	E	E		K,B		B,E
7. BOUNDARY				G,G	G	G		G		K,G
8. CROSS-SECTIONAL DATA	QK		QTK	QK	QK	QK		QK		
9. MATERIAL DATA	IK		IK	OK	OK	OK		OK		OK
10. EXTERNAL LOADING	P		PL	PL	PL	PLF		PLF		PF
11. INITIAL STRAINS	B		B	B	B	B		B		B

Comments: The PLANS program is a group of finite element programs developed for nonlinear analysis of structures. They are based on an organizational philosophy in which classes of analysis are treated individually based on the problem class to be analyzed. On this basis, a number of programs have been developed for material nonlinear behavior alone, and for combined static or dynamic geometric and material nonlinear behavior. Portions of the program are available through COSMIC. The authors of this review are codevelopers of PLANS.

Program Name: WECAN
Technical Contact: Dr. A. W. Filstrup
Westinghouse Electric Corporation
Research and Development Center
1310 Beulah Road
Pittsburgh, Pennsylvania 15235

Documentation: [105], [106]
Method of Analysis: FEM - displacement
State of Development: Fully operational
Element Information:

	A	B		C	D	E		F		G
		BEAM				PLATE		SHELL		
WECAN	ROD	a)	b)	PLANE MEMBRANE	MEMBRANE IN SPACE	a) KIRCHHOFF	b) REISSNER	a) KIRCHHOFF	b) REISSNER	THREE-DIMENSIONAL CONTINUUM
1. NO. OF ELEMENTS AVAILABLE	2	8	1	2				1		2
2. NO. OF NODES PER ELEMENT	2,2	2–3	2	3–12				3–4		8–32
3. NO. OF FREEDOMS PER ELEMENT	4,6	6–12	12	6–24				18,24		24–96
4. MODEL	V	V	V	V				V		V
5. ELEMENT CONFIGURATION	L	L	L	D,V				D		P,H
6. ELEMENT SHAPE				E				E		K
7. BOUNDARY				G,K				G		B
8. CROSS-SECTIONAL DATA	QK	QTK	QTK	Q,K				QK		
9. MATERIAL DATA	IK	IK	IK	OK,IK				OK		IK
10. EXTERNAL LOADING	P	PFL	P	PL				PF		P,F,V,
11. INITIAL STRAINS	B	B	B	B				B		B

Comments: This is a general purpose program for static, linear, and nonlinear dynamic analysis. The developers indicate that cycle-dependent stress-strain behavior is included (as recommended in Ref. [45]). Furthermore, elbow elements are included to treat general piping analysis.

Analysis Information

The additional analytic features of the programs are presented in the following table.

Table 1 Analysis Features of Programs

Program	Plasticity Theory (1)	Material Property (2)	Linearization Technique (3)	Linear equation Solver (4)
ADINA	I, K	P, L	R, TM	S
AGGIE I	I, K, C	P, L, ML	TM	S, G
ANSYS	I, K	P, L, ML	R	W
ASAS	I, K, C	ML, RO	R, TM	W, PT
ASKA	I, K, C	P, L, ML, RO	R	PT
BERSAFE	I, K	P, L, ML, RO	R, TM	W
EPACA	I, K	P, L, RO	TM	G
MARC-CDC	I, K	P, L, ML, RO	TM	G
NEPSAP	I, K	P, L, ML	TM	S
PAFEC 75	I	P, L, ML	R	W, F, PT
PLANS	K	P, L, RO	R	S, PT
WECAN	I, K, C	P, L, ML	R	W

The code used in the above table is as follows:

In column (1): Plasticity Theory
- I = Isotropic hardening
- K = Kinematic hardening
- C = Combined Isotropic-Kinematic hardening

In column (2): Material Property
- P = Elastic-perfectly plastic
- L = Elastic-linear hardening
- ML = Elastic-multilinear segments
- RO = Ramberg-Osgood or any other power-law representation

In column (3): Linearization Technique
- R = Right-hand side (initial strain, or stress)
- TM = Tangent modulus

In column (4): Linear Equation Solver
- W = Wavefront
- F = Full matrix
- PT = Partitioning
- IT = Iterative
- G = Gaussian elimination
- S = Skyline
- B = Constant bandwidth

Comparison of Available Features

The following table is intended to serve as a means of evaluating the individual programs in terms of some select items chosen by this reviewer. By and large, the items listed are those discussed in the previous section. The ratings of each program are as supplied by each developer.

Table 2 Comparison and Rating of Available Features of Programs

Program	Element Library (1)	Material Treatment (2)	Ease of Use/ Documentation (3)	Special Features (4) a b c d e f g h
ADINA	3	3	3	1 1 1 0 1 1 1 1
AGGIE I	3	3	2	1 0 0 0 1 0 1 1
ANSYS	3	3	3	1 1 1 1 0 1 1 0
ASAS	3	3	2	1 1 1 1 1 0 1 0
ASKA	3	3	3	1 1 1 1 1 1 1 1
BERSAFE	3	3	3	1 0 1 1 1 0 1 1
EPACA	2	3	3	1 0 0 1 1 0 0 0
MARC-CDC	3	3	3	1 0 1 1 1 1 1 1
NEPSAP	3	3	3	1 0 1 1 1 1 1 1
PAFEC 75	3	2	3	1 0 1 1 1 1 1 1
PLANS	3	3	2	1 1 1 1 1 0 1 1
WECAN	3	3	3	1 1 1 1 0 0 1 0

The code used in the above table is as follows:

In column (1): Element library
1 = Limited to a special class of problems
2 = Moderately general
3 = General

In column (2): Material treatment
1 = Limited
2 = Moderately general
3 = General

In column (3): Ease of use/documentation

This rating is based on either of the above items and includes some user reaction

1 = Difficult/no documentation
2 = Moderate/limited documentation
3 = Easy/extensive documentation

In column (4): Special features

Subcolumn (a) Restart
(b) Substructuring
(c) Multipoint contraints (tying nodes)
(d) Pre- and postprocessors
(e) Equilibrium checks
(f) Assumption checks
(g) Selective I/O
(h) Taking advantage of linear range

The rating for the special features is based on the following code.

0 = Not available
1 = Available

A brief synopsis of items a-h follows:

a) Restart Capability

Since a nonlinear analysis is costly as well as path dependent, it is essential to be able to perform an analysis sequentially to intermediate loading levels. At each step the results can be examined and evaluated and a decision can be made whether or not to continue the analysis. This process enables user interaction and eliminates unnecessary or meaningless calculations.

b) Substructuring

For two- and particularly three-dimensional problems where plastic flow is judged (by the experience of the analyst) to be contained within a localized region, the use of a substructuring scheme can result in a significant reduction in cost. The cost associated with the additional computations of substructuring (or developing "superelements" to represent large regions of the structure) is offset by performing the bulk of the computations for only that portion of the structure that is of interest.

c) Multipoint Constraints

This capability enables a linear relationship to be written between dependent and independent degrees of freedom.

d) Pre- and Postprocessors

Satellite programs that can be used to automatically generate finite element meshes are, of course, equally significant for elastic and plastic analyses. Since plasticity is a path-dependent phenomenon the amount of information generated for a complete time history can be quite substantial. Thus, postprocessors that can digest the information determined from the program and graphically produce a desired set of results become a very desirable feature.

e) Equilibrium Checks

This refers to whether the equilibrium correction term of Eq. (17) is used in the governing equation.

f) Are assumptions being violated?

In many situations the effect of plasticity precipitates the development of large deformations, or strains. Subsequent results become meaningless if the treatment of such behavior is not accounted for. A further example is associated with developing increments of stress or strain that may be so large as to violate the assumptions of the flow theory of plasticity used in the analysis. These examples are but two of the many possible violations of assumptions that illustrate the need to include self-monitoring logic to check the validity of the underlying assumptions.

g) Selective I/O

Nonlinear analyses can produce a "mountain" of output. An analyst should be able to control the frequency of output, i.e., every n load steps,as well as the element and nodal information printed in each print step.

h) Is linear behavior being taken advantage of?

In situations involving complex loading paths, including reversed loading, the entire structure may be behaving as an elastic body during some period of the prescribed load history. This behavior eliminates the need to apply the load in small increments. Therefore, it is recommended that a provision be included to determine the limits of the elastic range for initial loading and subsequent reloadings.

CLOSING COMMENTS

The computational capability available for the plastic analysis of structures has experienced a tremendous growth during the past decade. Indeed, the level of structural analysis capability that has been achieved has at times outstripped our ability to describe accurately complex material behavior such as cyclic, time, and temperature dependent plasticity. Prior to the development of the programs now available, the designer or analyst confronted with a problem involving material nonlinearities was left with a choice of using his engineering judgment alone or in conjunction with potentially expensive laboratory tests. He now has the further option of performing numerical analysis to gain insight into the behavior of the structure.

The added generality of plastic analysis, however, places greater responsibilities on the analyst. Perhaps the greatest asset of programs for plastic analysis, namely, their ability to solve sophisticated problems, also represents a potential liability, i.e., they always produce numbers. How close these numbers are to the physical phenomena occurring in the structure depends on the accuracy of the mathematical model. Within current context this includes the finite element grid and element type, plasticity theory, input plastic material parameters, and the algorithm to solve the nonlinear equations. It was one of the goals of this review to present an overview of the theoretical basis of computational plasticity in order to facilitate a rational evaluation of the usage of general purpose programs for plastic analysis. Once an analysis is undertaken one must still exercise engineering judgment in order to determine if the results are meaningful. In short, the best way not to misuse a program is to understand its limitations and to always approach results with some skepticism.

This review has restricted its attention to program capability for the static, time, and temperature independent plastic analysis of structures. A natural extension of this type of capability is to include creep (time and temperature dependent materials). Since creep can be considered as time and temperature dependent plasticity, its implementation within the framework of a comprehensive structural analysis program is analogous to the implementation of plasticity alone. Indeed, many of the programs surveyed currently include creep behavior. Computational methods for creep alone or combined elastic-plastic-creep behavior are reviewed in Ref. [107], while a discussion of creep models can be found in Ref. [108].

The response to our survey has indicated that most of the programs make use of the pseudoload approach to account for material nonlinear behavior. The most widely used plasticity theories are isotropic hardening and kinematic hardening, with some program implementing combined isotropic-kinematic hardening behavior. To our knowledge, the higher-order theories that were discussed are not currently available in the programs surveyed. We expect that their implementation and testing in general purpose programs will represent the next increase in modeling capability.

Computational methods at this point are on a firm theoretical foundation. What remains is to consider reliability and cost. By reliability we mean internal error controls that check computational accuracy of the calculations by limiting step size and/or implementing interactive schemes to keep the errors to within some preset tolerances. These considerations also affect cost, since they should enable the program to maximize the step size based on the prescribed error tolerance. Research in this area is continuing so that it is expected that these very necessary features will become part of the available general purpose programs. Finally we refer the reader to two excellent recent papers. Noor [109] presents a comprehensive survey of computer programs for nonlinear analysis while Corum [110] discusses future needs for inelastic analysis in the design of high-temperature nuclear plant components.

ACKNOWLEDGMENTS

The authors wish to thank the respondents for their time and effort in providing the program information reported in this review.

REFERENCES

1 Armen, H., "Plastic Analysis," in Structural Mechanics Computer Programs, ed. W. Pilkey, K. Saczalski, and H. Schaeffer, University Press of Virginia, Charlottesville, 1974.

2 Armen, H., "Assumptions, Models, and Computational Methods for Plasticity," in Trends in Computerized Structural Analysis and Synthesis, ed. A. K. Noor and H. G. McComb, Jr., Pergamon Press, 1978.

3 White, G. N., Jr., and Drucker, D. C., "Effective Stress and Effective Strain in Relation to Stress Theories of Plasticity," J. Appl. Phys., Vol. 21, No. 10, 1950, pp. 1013-1021.

4 Drucker, D. C., "A More Fundamental Approach to Plastic Stress-Strain Relations," Proc. 1st U.S. National Cong. Appl. Mech., 1952, p. 487.

5 Bridgman, P. W., Studies in Large Plastic Flow and Fracture, McGraw Hill, New York, 1952.

6 Hu, L. W., "Development of a Triaxial Stress Testing Machine and Triaxial Stress Experiments," Proc. SESA, Vol. 16, No. 2, 1959, pp. 27-37.

7 Fung, P. K., Burns, D. J., and Lind, N. C., "Yield under High Hydrostatic Pressure," in Foundation of Plasticity, ed. A. Sawczuk Noordhoff, Leyden, 1972.

8 Lee, L. H. N., "Dynamic Plasticity," Nucl. Engng. Design, Vol. 27, 1974, pp. 386-397.

9 Hutchinson, J. W., "Plastic Buckling," in Advances in Applied Mechanics, ed. S. C. Yih, Vol. 14, Academic Press, New York, 1974, pp. 67-143.

10 Bijlaard, P. P., "Theory and Tests on the Plastic Stability of Plates and Shells," J. Aero. Sci, Vol. 9, 1949, pp. 529-541.

11 Isakson, G., Armen, H., and Pifko, A., "Discrete Element Methods for the Plastic Analysis of Structures," NASA CR-803, 1967.

12 Armen, H., Pifko, A., and Levine, H. S., "Finite Element Analysis of Structures in the Plastic Range," NASA CR-1649, 1971.

13 Hill, R., The Mathematical Theory of Plasticity, 1st Edn., Oxford University Press, 1950, pp. 24.

14 Hodge, P. G., Jr., "The Theory of Piecewise Linear Isotropic Plasticity," IUTAM Colloquium, Madrid, 1955.

15 Batdorf, S. B., and Budiansky, B., "A Mathematical Theory of Plasticity Based on the Concept of Slip," NASA TN 1871, 1949.

16 Hodge, P. G., Jr., "Piecewise Linear Plasticity," Proc. 9th Int. Cong. Appl. Mech, Vol. 8, 1957.

17 Stricklin, J. A., "Large Elastic, Plastic and Creep Deflections in Curved Beams and Axisymmetric Shells," AIAA J., Vol. 2, No. 9, 1964, p. 1613.

18 Hodge, P. G., Jr., and Berman, I., "Piecewise Linear Strain-hardening Plasticity," Constitutive Equations in Viscoplasticity - Computational and Engineering Aspects, ASME Special Publication AMD-Vol. 20, 1976, pp. 57-77.

19 Prager, W., "The Theory of Plasticity: A Survey of Recent Achievements," James Clayton lecture, Proc. Inst. Mech. Engrs., Vol. 169, 1955, pp. 41.

20 Prager, W., "A New Method of Analyzing Stress and Strains in Work-Hardening Solids," J. Appl. Mech., Vol. 23, 1956, pp. 493.

21 Ziegler, H., "A Modification of Prager's Hardening Rule," Quart. Appl. Math., Vol. 17, 1959, pp. 55.

22 Eisenberg, M. A. and Phillips, A., "On Nonlinear Kinematic Hardening," Acta Mech., Vol. 5, 1968, pp. 1-13.

23 Hodge, P. G., Jr., discussion of "A New Method of Analyzing Stress and Strains in Work-Hardening Solids," W. Prager (J. Appl. Mech., Vol. 23, 1956, pp. 493-496), J. Appl. Mech., Vol. 24, 1957, p. 482.

24 Duwez, P., "On the Plasticity of Crystals," Phys. Rev., Vol. 457, 1935, p. 494.

25 White, G. N., Jr., "Application of the Theory of Perfectly Plastic Solids to Stress Analysis of Strain Hardening Solids," Brown University Tech. Rep. 51, 1950.

26 Besseling, J. F., "A Theory of Plastic Flow for Anisotropic Hardening. Plastic Deformation of an Initially Isotropic Material," Nat. Aero. Res. Inst. Rep. S410, Amsterdam, 1953.

27 Mroz, Z., "On the Description of Anisotropic Work-Hardening," J. Mech. Phys. Solids, Vol. 15, 1967, pp. 163-175.

28 Mroz, Z., "An Attempt to Describe the Behavior of Metals under Cyclic Loads Using a More General Work-Hardening Model," Acta. Mech., Vol. 17, 1969, pp. 199-212.

29 Masing, G., Wiss Veröff. aus Siemans Konzern 3, 1927.

30 Eisenberg, M. A., and Phillips, A., "A Theory with Non-Coincident Yield and Loading Surfaces," Acta Mech., Vol. 11, 1971, pp. 247-260.

31 Dafalias, Y. F., and Popov, E. P., "A Model of Nonlinearly Hardening Materials for Complex Loading," Acta Mech., Vol. 21, 1975, pp. 173-192.

32 Krieg, R. D., "A Practical Two Surface Plasticity Theory," J. Appl. Mech., Vol. 31, 1975, pp. 641-644.

33 Jackson, L. R., Smith, K. F., and Lankford, W. T., "Plastic Flow in Anisotropic Sheet Metal," Metals Tech., T. p. 2440, 1948.

34 Dorn, J. E., "Stress-Strain Relations for Anisotropic Plastic Flow," J. Appl. Phys., Vol. 20, 1949, pp. 15-20.

35 Hu, L. W., "Studies on Plastic Flow of Anisotropic Metals," J. Appl. Mech., Vol. 12, 1956, p. 444.

36 Baltov, A., and Sawczuk, A., "A Rule of Anisotropic Hardening," Acta Mech., Vol. 1, 1965, pp. 81-92.

37 Tsai, S. W., and Wu, E. M., "A General Theory of Strength for Anisotropic Materials," J. Comp. Materials, Vol. 5, 1971, p. 58.

38 Malvern, L. E., "The Propagation of Longitudinal Waves of Plastic Deformation in a Bar of Material Exhibiting a Strain Rate Effect," J. Appl. Mech., Vol. 18, 1951, pp. 203-208.

39 Perzyna, P., "The Constitutive Equations for Rate Sensitive Plastic Materials," Quart. Appl. Math., Vol. 20, 1963, pp. 321-332.

40 Prager, W., "Non-Isothermal Plastic Deformation," K. Mederi, AK Wetensh.,Vol. 61, 1958, p. 176.

41 Ueda, Y., and Yamakawa, T., "Thermal Nonlinear Behavior of Structures," in Advances in Computational Methods in Structural Mechanics and Design, ed. J. T. Oden, R. W. Clough, and Y. Yamamoto, University Alabama in Huntsville Press, 1972.

42 Hibbitt, H. D., and Marcal, P. V., "A Numerical, Thermo-Mechanical Model for the Welding and Subsequent Loading of a Fabricated Structure," J. Comput. Structures, Vol. 3, 1973, pp. 1145-1174.

43 Valanis, K. C., "A Theory of Viscoplasticity Without A Yield Surface," Archiwum Mechaniki Stosowanej, Vol. 23, Warsaw, 1971, pp. 517-533.

44 Valanis, K. C., "Observed Plastic Behavior of Metals vis-à-vis the Endrochronic Theory of Plasticity," Foundation of Plasticity, ed. A. Sawczuk, Nordhoff, Leyden, 1972.

45 Corum, J. M., et al., "Interim Conditions for Detail Inelastic Analysis of High-Temperature Reactor System Components," ORNL-5014, 1974.

46 Morrow, J., "Cyclic Plastic Strain Energy and Fatigue of Metals," Internal Friction, Damping, and Cyclic Plasticity, ASTM STP 378, 1965, p. 45.

47 Winter, R., "Experiment on Cyclic Plastic Deformation of a Circular Plate with Work Hardening," Grumman Research Department Report, in preparation.

48 Nayak, C. C., and Zienkiewicz, O. C., "Elasto-Plastic Stress Analysis. A Generalization for Various Constitutive Relations Including Strain Softening," Int. J. Num. Meth. Engng., Vol. 5, 1972, pp. 113-135.

49 Zienkiewicz, O., Valliappan, S., and King, J., "Elasto-Plastic Solutions of Engineering Problems 'Initial Stress' Finite Element Approach," Int. J. Num. Meth. Engng., Vol. 1, No. 1, January-March 1969, pp. 75-100.

50 Tillerson, J. R., Stricklin, J. A., and Haisler, W. E., "Numerical Methods for the Solution of Nonlinear Problems in Structural Analysis," Numerical Solution of Nonlinear Structural Problems, ed. R. F. Hartung, ASME AMD-6 1973, p. 67.

51 Nayak, G. C., and Zienkiewicz, O. C., "Note on the "Alpha" - Constant Stiffness Method for the Analysis of Non-Linear Problems," Int. J. Num. Meth. Engng., Vol. 4, 1972, pp. 579-582.

52 Kalov, I., and Gluck, J. "Elasto-Plastic Finite Element Analysis," Int. J. Num. Methods Engng., Vol. 1, 1977, pp. 875-887.

53 Strang, G., "Numerical Computations in Nonlinear Mechanics," ASME Publication, 79-PVP-103, 1979.

54 Krieg, R. D., and Krieg, D. B, "Accuracies of Numerical Solution Methods for the Elastic-Perfectly Plastic Model," ASME J. Press. Ves. Tech., Vol. 99, 1977, pp. 510-515.

55 Schreyer, H. L., Kulak, R. F., and Kramer, J. M., "Accurate Numerical Solutions for Elastic-Plastic Models," ASME Preprint, 79-PVP-107, 1979.

56 Bushnell, D., "A Subincrementation Strategy for Solving Problems Involving Large Deflections, Plasticity and Creep," Constitutive Equations in Viscoplasticity Computational and Engineering Aspects, ASME Special Publications AMD-Vol. 20, 1976, pp. 171-199.

57 Vos, R. G., "Note on the Residual Force Method," Int. J. Num. Meth. Engng. Vol. 6, 1973, p. 446.

58 Levy, A., Pifko, A., and Armen, H., "Development and Application of the PLANS Computer Program for Analysis of Nuclear Reactor Structural Components," Grumman Research Dept. Rep. RE-542, 1977.

59 Alizadeh, A., and Will, C. T., "A Substructured Frontal Solver and Its Application to Localized Material Nonlinearity," in Trends in Computerized Structural Analysis and Synthesis, ed. A. Noor and H. M. McComb, Jr., Pergamon Press, 1978, p. 225.

60 Armen, H., and Levy, A., "Substructuring, Restart, and Variable Constraints in a Three-Dimensional Finite Element Program for Fracture Analysis," Grumman Research Dept. Rep. RE-553, 1978.

61 Waltz, J. E., Fulton, R. E., and Cyrus, M. J., "Accuracy and Convergence of Finite Element Approximations," Proc. 2nd Conf. Matrix Meth. Struct. Mech., ed. L. Berke et al., AFFDL-TR-68-150, 1968, p. 995.

62 Turcke, D. J., and NcNeice, G. M., "Guidelines for Selecting Finite Element Grids Based on Optimization Study," J. Comput. Structures, Vol. 4, 1974, pp. 499-519.

63 Belytschko, T., "Transient Analysis," in Structural Mechanics, Computer Programs, ed. W. Pilkey et al., University Press of Virginia Charlottesville, 1974, pp. 255-276.

64 Tillerson, J. R., "Selecting Solution Procedures for Nonlinear Structural Dynamics," The Shock and Vibration Digest, Vol. 7, No. 4, April 1975.

65 Weeks, G., "Temporal Operators for Nonlinear Structural Dynamics Problems," J. of Engr. Mech. Div., ASCE, October 1972, pp. 1087-1104.

66 Nickell, R. E., "Direct Integration Methods in Structural Dynamics," J. of Eng. Mech. Div., ASCE, Vol. 99, EM2, April 1973, pp. 303-17.

67 Tucker, J., and Chi, M., "State-of-the-Art Report on Numerical Integration Methods for Analysis of Stiff Structural Analysis Systems," Department of Transportation Report No. DOT-HS-7-10620, 1978.

68 Bathe, K. J., and Wilson, E. L., "Stability and Accuracy Analysis of Direct Integration Methods," Earthquake Engineering and Structural Dynamics, Vol. 1, 1973, pp. 283-291.

69 Park, K. C., "Evaluating Time Integration Methods for Nonlinear Dynamic Analysis," in Finite Element Analysis of Transient Nonlinear Structural Behavior, ed. T. Belytschko, J. R. Osias, and P. V. Marcal, Applied Mechanics Symposia Series, ASME, New York, 1975.

70 Hilber, H. M., Hughes, T. J. R., and Taylor, R. L., "Improved Numerical Dissipation for Time Integration Algorithms in Structural Dynamics," Earthquake Engineering and Structural Dynamics, Vol. 5, 1977, pp. 283-292.

71 Belytschko, T., and Schoeberle, D. F., "On the Unconditional Stability of an Implicit Algorithm for Nonlinear Structural Dynamics," J. Appl. Mech., Vol. 42, 1975, pp. 865-869.

72 Krieg, R. D., and Key, S. W., "Transient Shell Response by Numerical Time Integration," Int. J. Num. Methods in Eng., Vol. 17, 1973, pp. 273-286.

73 Belytschko, T., and Hsieh, B. J., "Nonlinear Transient Finite Element Analysis with Convected Coordinates," Int. J. of Num. Methods in Eng., Vol. 7, 1973, pp. 255-71.

74 Garnet, H., and Armen, H., "A Variable Time Step Method for Determining Plastic Stress Reflections from Boundaries," AIAA J., Vol. 13, No. 4, 1975, pp. 532-534.

75 Bathe, K. J., Ramm, E., and Wilson, E. L., "Finite Element Foundations for Large Deformation Dynamic Analysis," Int. J. Num. Methods Engng., Vol. 9, 1975, pp. 353-386.

76 Newmark, N., "A Method of Computation for Structural Dynamics," J. Eng. Mech. Div., Proc. of A.S.C.E., 1959, pp. 67-94.

77 Wilson, E. L., Farhoomand, L., and Bathe, K. J., "Nonlinear Dynamic Analysis of Complex Structures," Earthquake Eng. and Struct. Dyn., Vol. 1, 1973, pp. 241-252.

78 Houbolt, J. C., "A Recurrence Matrix Solution for the Dynamic Response of Elastic Aircraft," J. of Aero. Sciences, Vol. 17, 1950, pp. 540-550.

79 Park, K. C., "An Improved Stiffly Stable Method for Direct Integration of Nonlinear Structural Dynamic Equations," J. Appl. Mech., ASME, June 1975, pp. 464-570.

80 Guyan, R. J., "Reduction of Stiffness and Mass Matrices," AIAA J., Vol. 3, 1965, pp. 380-381.

81 Tong, P. and Rosettos, J. N., "Modular Finite Element Approach to Structural Crashworthiness Prediction," Computers and Structures, Vol. 7, 1977, pp. 109-116.

82 Morris, N., "The Use of Modal Superposition in Nonlinear Dynamics," Computers and Structures, Vol. 7, 1977, pp. 65-76.

83 Hughes, T. J. R., and Liu, W. K., "Implicit-Explicit Finite Elements in Transient Analysis: Stability Theory," ASME J. Appl. Mech., Vol. 45, June 1978, pp. 365-368.

84 Belytschko, T., and Mullen, R., "Mesh Partitions of Explicit-Implicit Time Integration," in Formulations and Computational Algorithms in Finite Element Analysis, U.S.-Germany Symp., ed. K. J. Bathe et al,. MIT Press, Cambridge, 1977, pp. 673-690.

85 Park, K. C., Felippa, C. A., and DeRuntz, J. A., "Stabilization of Staggered Solution Procedures for Fluid-Structure Interaction Analysis," in Computational Methods for Fluid-Structure Interaction Problems, ed. T. Belytschko et al., A.S.M.E. Applied Mechanics Symposia Series, AMD-Vol. 26, 1977, pp. 95-124.

86 Wright, J. P., "Mixed Time Integration Schemes," Trends in Computerized Structural Analysis and Synthesis, ed. A. K. Noor and H. A. McComb, Jr., Pergamon Press, 1978, p. 235.

87 Nickell, R. E., "Nonlinear Dynamics by Mode Superposition," presented at 15th AIAA Struct. Struct. Dynamics Mater. Conf. paper 74-341, 1974.

88 Buck, Schrem, E., and Stein, "Einige Allgemeine Programmsysteme für Finite Elemente," from Finite Elemente in Der Statik, Wilhelm Ernst and Sohne, 1973,

89 Bathe, K. J., "ADINA - A Finite Element Program for Automatic Dynamic Incremental Nonlinear Analysis," Report 82448-1, Acoustics and Vibration Laboratory, MIT, Department of Mechanical Engineering, Sept. 1975, revised May 1977.

90 Bathe, K. J., ed., "Applications Using ADINA - Proceedings of the ADINA Conference August 1977," Report 82448-6, Acoustics and Vibration Laboratory, MIT, Department of Mechanical Engineering, August 1977.

91 Haisler, W. "AGGIE I - A Finite Element Program for Nonlinear Structural Analysis," Technical Report 3275-77-1, Aerospace Engineering Dept., Texas A&M University, June 1977.

92 DeSalvo, G. J., and Swanson, J. A., "ANSYS Engineering Analysis Systems User's Manual," Swanson Analysis System, Inc., Houston, Pa., Aug. 1978.

93 Schrem, E., and Roy, J. R., "An Automated System for Kinetic Analysis," Instut für Statik und Dynamik der Luft- und Raumfahrtkonstructionen, University of Stuttgart, ISD Report No. 98, 1971.

94 Balmer, H., Doltsinis, J. St., and Koonig, M., "Elastoplastic and Creep Analysis with the ASKA Program System," Computer Methods in Applied Mechanics and Engineering, Vol. 3, 1974, pp. 87-104.

95 Balmer, H., and Doltsinis, J. St., "Extensions to the Elastoplastic Analysis with the ASKA Program System," Computer Methods in Applied Mechanics and Engineering, Vol. 13, 1978, pp. 363-407.

96 Hellen, T. K., and Protheroe, S. J., "The BERSAFE Finite Element System," Computer Aided Designs, Vol. 6, No. 1, Jan. 1974.

97 Zudans, Z., et al., "Theory and User's Manual for EPACA," Franklin Institute Report F-C-3038, June 1972.

98 "MARC-CDC Nonlinear Finite Element Analysis Program," User Information Manual, Vol. 1, Control Data Corp., 1979.

99 Nagarajan, S., "Introduction to NEPSAP - Nonlinear Elastic-Plastic Structural Analysis Program," Lockheed Missiles and Space Co. Report (to be published).

100 Nagarajan, S., "User's Manual for NEPSAP - Nonlinear Elastic-Plastic Structural Analysis Program," Lockheed Missiles and Space Co. Report, LMSC-D556019, Nov. 1978 Revision.

101 Sharifi, P., and Nagarajan, S., "Theoretical Manuals for NEPSAP," Lockheed Missiles and Space Co. Report, LMSC-D556041, Oct. 1976.

102 Henshell, R. D., "PAFEC 70+ Users Manual," Mechanical Engineering Department, Nottingham University, Nottingham, U.K., 1972.

103 Pifko, A., Levine, H., and Armen, H., Jr., "PLANS - A Finite Element Program for Nonlinear Analysis of Structures - Vol. I Theoretical Manual," Grumman Research Department Report RE-501; also NASA CR-2568, November 1975.

104 Pifko, A., Armen H., Levy A., and Levine H., "PLANS - A Finite Element Program for Nonlinear Analysis of Structures - Vol. II User's Manual," Grumman Research Department Report RM-633; also NASA CR-145244, May 1977.

105 "WECAN, Westinghouse Electric Computer Analysis, User's Manual," Advanced Systems Technology Division, Pittsburgh, Pa., 1976.

106 Chan, S. K., Fan, Y., Filstrup, A. W., and Gabrielse, S. T., "Verifying the Plastic Capabilities of a General Purpose Computer Code," in Pressure Vessels and Piping Computer Program Evaluation and Qualification, PVP-PB-024, ed. D. E. Dietrich, 1977.

107 Levy, S., and Pifko, A. B., "Computational Strategies for Problems Involving Plasticity and Creep," to appear in The International Journal for Numerical Methods in Engineering.

108 Nickell, R. E., "Thermal Stress and Creep," in Structural Mechanics Computer Programs, ed. W. Pilkey, K. Saczalski and H. Schaeffer, University Press of Virginia, Charlottesville, 1974, pp. 103-122.

109 Noor, A. K., "Survey of Computer Programs for Solution of Nonlinear Structural and Solid Mechanics Problems," Computers and Structures, Vol. 13, 1981, pp. 425-465.

110 Corum, J. M., "Future Needs for Inelastic Analysis in Design of High-Temperature Nuclear Plant Components," Computers and Structures, Vol. 13, 1981, pp. 231-240.

Fracture Mechanics

Albert Kobayashi

University of Washington

INTRODUCTION

With the increased use of linear elastic fracture mechanics (LEFM) in postmortem analysis of structural failures as well as in reliability assessments of future designs, the structural analysts have turned inevitably to numerical methods for computing stress intensity factors of complex two- and three-dimensional problems for which solutions do not exist in available handbooks [1,2,3]. Extensions of linear elastic fracture mechanics to ductile fracture and stable crack growth require detailed knowledge of the elastic-plastic state which could, in most cases, only be obtained by numerical analysis. Dynamic fracture, which is an emerging field of interest, also requires detailed knowledge of the elastic and elastic-plastic states surrounding the propagating crack tip and can only be analyzed by numerical procedures. These demands led Gallagher to conclude that, "the analysis of fracture mechanics problems has been one of the most active branches of numerical methods in structural mechanics in the 1970's." [4].

One of the earliest applications of numerical technique in fracture mechanics [5] was the elastic-plastic solution of an externally notched tension plate [5] which was obtained by the relaxation method prior to the era of modern high-speed computers. No specific fracture criterion was derived from these results or from subsequent papers which reported on the results of elastic-plastic finite difference and finite element analysis of cracked plates; therefore, little was added to the knowledge of ductile fracture in the sixties. With the emergence of efficient and accurate finite element codes in the late sixties and early seventies, however, this numerical technique was extensively used in LEFM to compute the opening and sliding mode stress intensity factors, K_I and K_{II}, in two-dimensional problems and on rare occasions, K_I, K_{II}, plus the tearing mode stress intensity factor, K_{III}, in three-dimensional problems. State-of-the-art reviews on the use of finite element techniques in fracture mechanics include, in addition to Ref. [4], the recent paper by Pian [6].

Other numerical techniques, such as boundary collocation [7], series expansion of a mapping function in a complex domain [8], and Laurent series [9] were also used to compute the mixed mode stress intensity factors for two-dimensional fracture problems, but these numerical techniques do not enjoy the popularity of the finite element method due to the varying degrees of inherent constraints involved with each of these two-dimensional codes. A cursory review of these and other numerical techniques up through 1974 is given in Ref. [10].

Concurrent with the explosive applications of elastic finite element analysis, papers on the use of elastic-plastic finite element analysis for studying the near-field states of stress and strain surrounding a stationary or slow-moving crack tip began to appear. The matured development in LEFM in this period provided the intellectual background for extracting possible ductile fracture parameters such as J-integral, crack opening displacement (COD), crack tip opening angle (CTOA), and tearing modulus. Reference [11] contains a collection of state-of-the-art papers on ductile fracture and stable crack growth. These papers rely heavily on results which were generated by the finite element method.

Despite the popularity and availability of three-dimensional finite element codes, the solution to a seemingly simple problem, such as K_I distribution along the crack front of a surface-flawed tension plate, requires an inordinate amount of computer time [12]. Substantial improvement in computational efficiency is effected by the use of enriched singular elements surrounding the crack front and by maintaining interelement compatibility between these singular elements with the adjacent regular elements. One such formulation was the hybrid finite element model which yielded the results of Ref. [12] with approximately one half of the degrees of freedom [13]. Other than in some isolated early efforts, the above requirement for large computer time has stymied efforts to analyze in detail the elastic-plastic state in a surface-flawed tension plate [14].

In searching for more efficient computational techniques, a hybrid procedure involving three-dimensional finite element analysis and elliptical crack solutions in the alternating technique [15] and another procedure involving the finite difference method and body force method of an embedded ellipse [16] have been developed. Although these procedures are still in the developmental stages and the crack profiles are limited to an ellipse or segment of an ellipse, the computational efficiencies of these procedures warrant future attention by practitioners in LEFM.

During the mid-1970s, a numerical procedure now commonly referred to as the boundary integral equation (BIE) method emerged with the prospect of developing into an efficient numerical procedure for solving three-dimensional problems in LEFM, since the procedure does not require substructuring of the elastic solid [17]. Although the BIE method is not as widely used as the three-dimensional finite element method, it is being developed by the several researchers for production computation of three-dimensional LEFM problems in real structures. Extension of the BIE method to fracture mechanics problems with mixed field equations, such as the elasto-plastic field surrounding a crack tip, is still in the exploratory stage. Also, no procedure which incorporates stress wave propagation into the BIE method has been proposed.

In the mid-70s, research in dynamic fracture emerged as a spinoff from the historical applications of finite difference codes to penetration mechanics [18]. The dynamic finite element method has also been used in solving elasto-dynamic problems associated with a propagating crack [19]. Admittedly, these efforts are limited in comparison to the vast applications of numerical techniques, but nevertheless they represent a new area of computational techniques in fracture mechanics.

In the following sections, a brief description of the computational techniques involved in extracting the static and dynamic stress intensity factors for LEFM and other fracture parameters, such as the J-integral and tearing modulus in ductile fracture and stable crack growth, will be discussed. A listing of some computer codes which incorporate the various algorithms necessary to generate these fracture parameters is found in tabular form at the end of this chapter. This listing was compiled from responses to questionnaires mailed by the author. In compiling this mailing list, he may have unintentionally omitted some proven and widely used computer codes in fracture mechanics. Also, some of the well-known computer codes are not available for public dissemination, and thus the codes in this chapter should be considered only as a partial listing of the known production or potential production codes in fracture mechanics.

CURRENT CAPABILITIES

Since many of the existing computer codes have been specifically designed to meet the immense demands for fracture mechanics solutions to hardware problems, most of these codes can be considered to be production programs. Nevertheless, the 42 systems which have been identified in this chapter fall into the following three categories:

1. Production Codes: Software which has been used successfully in fracture mechanics analysis
2. Potential Production Programs: Software which, because of some limitations, must undergo modification and verification for use in fracture mechanics analysis or for use on other computer systems
3. Restrictive Programs: Software, which due to severe limitations or restrictive scope, cannot easily be converted to production use

Summarized in Table 1 is information which, in very general terms, describes the capabilities of each of the codes which are available, the program source, a brief description of the code, the date the code became available, the computer for which the code was designed, and the language used. In Table 2 these codes are grouped in terms of the following analytical foundation and capabilities: two-dimensional elastic finite element method, two-dimensional elastic-plastic finite element method, three-dimensional elastic and elastic-plastic finite element method, two-dimensional elastic-dynamic finite element method, two- and three-dimensional boundary integral equation methods, alternating method, body force method, method of lines, and finite-difference method.

Indicated in Table 1 under "Description" is a brief statement as to the general category (defined above) in which the program falls. Although most of the respondents to the questionnaire did not specify the production capability of each code, many of these codes were assumed to be potential production programs, since they are generally available for distribution.

A notable absence in the "Description" section is the software for graphical display of the numerical results. Obviously, such software is not needed for fracture mechanics analysis of a stationary two-dimensional crack: Variations in stress intensity factor along a curved crack front in a three-dimensional problem, in J-integral value and COD of a stably growing crack, and in energy partitions and dynamic stress intensity factor of a propagating crack are numerical results which can be more easily evaluated through graphic visualization.

Also missing from the software is a procedure for predicting the path of crack growth under stable crack growth, fatigue crack growth, and the fast fracture path in two- and three-dimensional problems. This lack could be attributed to the lack of universally acceptable fracture criteria for crack extension under single or combined mode of crack tip deformation and could be left for future development once these criteria are established. Nevertheless, continuing efforts should be underway for the development of a suitable algorithm, such as the nodal grafting technique [20], which can expeditiously handle crack extension.

ANALYSIS CAPABILITIES

The difficulties that tend to deter engineers from using linear elastic fracture mechanics are not the lack of available analytical capabilities for solving such problems but are in their inexperience in the proper application of fracture mechanics as well as the immense computer time necessary to solve three-dimensional problems in LEFM. As a result, there exist few general purpose production codes which can be used for LEFM assessment of industrial designs. Also, there are no universally acceptable ductile fracture, stable crack growth, and dynamic fracture criteria, and no general purpose codes to analyze these modes of fracture are available at this time. Most of the codes described in this paper are therefore special purpose codes designed to analyze a limited class of problems.

Finite Element Codes

For problems in linear elastic fracture mechanics (LEFM), reasonably accurate K_I, K_{II}, and K_{III} values can be obtained through the use of special quadratic isoparametric elements with mid-side nodes at the quarter point [21]. By condensing two adjacent sides of a twenty-nodal brick element to form a segment of a crack front, the inverse square root singularity of LEFM and the rigid body motion are contained in this special three-dimensional finite element. Stress intensity factors can be extracted from the quarter-point nodal displacements by improved procedures proposed for two- and three-dimensional problems [22, 23]. The advantage of the condensed quarter-point isoparametric element is that it requires no special programming of a special crack-tip element if the quadratic isoparametric finite element is available in general purpose finite element code. Computer codes identified as FEFA for two-dimensional and as the well-known ADINA for three-dimensional finite element analyses of LEFM problems are based on this approach.

Another procedure for computing stress intensity factors with the use of standard finite element methods (FEM) is the method of virtual crack extension for determining energy release rates for crack extension in various directions. The codes FAST and SSAPZ and the code from Creusot-Loire essentially use this procedure to compute K_I and K_{II}. Although the procedure has been extensively used in analyzing two-dimensional problems in fracture mechanics under the term of strain energy release rate procedures for several years [24], its use in three-dimensional problems is limited [25]. BERSAFE appears to be the only code listed here with such a built-in three-dimensional virtual crack extension algorithm.

Unmodified standard elastic-plastic FEM codes have also been used to determine numerically fracture parameters which may govern ductile fracture. FAST, FEACG, TEPSA, ADINA, MARC, and TITUS all use regular elements around the crack tip for such elastic-plastic calculation while MARC and TITUS have additional algorithms to compute the J-integral [26]. A GE fracture package to ADINA also computes J in the presence of crack extension. For stable crack growth analysis, crack tip extension in FEACG is handled by releasing the crack tip nodal force, while the element stiffness is reduced to zero in TEPSA. On the other hand, the fully plastic crack analysis code of INFEM is based on incompressibility conditions [27-30].

For increased accuracy without sacrifice of computational efficiency, various codes have incorporated special crack tip elements with appropriate stress singularities of $r^{-\frac{1}{2}}$ for LEFM analysis. For the plastic yield zone surrounding the crack tip, often the HRR stress and strain singularities [31,32] of $r^{-1/(n+1)}$ and $r^{-n/(1+n)}$, respectively, are used for an incompressible strain-hardening material of the $\varepsilon/\varepsilon_o = (\sigma/\sigma_o)^n$ type. An $r^{-\frac{1}{2}}$ embedded singularity is contained in the finite elements surrounding the crack tip in APES, the NASTRAN program used by Lockheed-California, and in SKBP17, while NEUT-CRACK 1 contains HRR stress and strain singularities. Since the displacement fields of the enriched elements normally do not satisfy either interelement equilibrium or compatibility conditions, a penalty function technique [33] is used in NEUT-CRACK 1, and hybrid formulations [34,35] are used in SKB17 to minimize the errors involved. Extensive application of the assumed displacement hybrid finite element method has been made by Atluri, who developed possible production LEFM programs for 2-D isotropic and orthotropic materials [35,36], for bend plates [37], 2-D elastic-plastic analysis of a stationary crack [38,39,40] or of a stable crack growth [41,42,43], an LEFM program for 3-D cracks [44,45,46], and composite fracture [47] and 2-D dynamic fracture analysis [48].

Another procedure is to superpose a global singular stress field onto a standard finite element code. GLASS II uses a global element matrix with the appropriate stress singularity superposed on a local finite element mesh which accounts for the local geometric and boundary effects [49]. PCRACK, on the other hand, relies on the supposition of a known analytical solution, a finite element solution to satisfy the prescribed boundary condition of a complex geometry [50].

For dynamic crack propagation analysis, the two codes of EXPDYN and HCRACK are both based on standard FEM stress wave propagation codes with an explicit time integration scheme. Both codes compute the energy release rate through integration of the force velocity relation at the released crack tip node. The dynamic stress intensity factor is then computed by the use of Freund's relation [51].

Boundary Integral Equation

The two boundary integral equation codes listed are BIGIF and EITD, both of which compute three-dimensional (and two-dimensional) weight functions for given crack profiles [52]. The procedure is currently limited to static LEFM analysis and to the stress intensity factor that is obtained by extrapolating the numerically obtained COD to the regime closer to the crack tip for increased accuracy.

Finite Element Alternating Method

At the time of this writing the only available alternating method code is that which can be obtained from F. W. Smith, Colorado State University, although another code has been under development at FRAMATON [53]. The procedure, which relies on superposition of the two elastic solutions, is obviously limited to LEFM and to crack configurations consisting of the segment of an ellipse. The procedure, however, is extremely efficient for three-dimensional LEFM analyses, and its use results in an order of magnitude reduction in computer time for solving surface flaw problems [53].

Body Force Method

This relatively unknown procedure was developed by Nishitani et al. [54] based on Eshelby's elastic solution for an infinite region with an elastic inclusion [55]. The two-dimensional codes of CRHP, HOLCRK, MIXSIF SCONCB, SCONCT, SPDISK, and TCSIP, although they are special purpose codes, appear very competitive with FEM in terms of computational efficiency in determining the static stress intensity factors. The three-dimension code of TWELL I apparently is limited to interference studies of two semielliptical cracks in an infinite domain and requires a moderate running time. Further developments of three-dimensional codes based on the body force method are necessary before this method can be used in production calculation for three-dimensional fracture mechanics.

Method of Lines

Another unorthodox method in this listing is a numerical technique in which the field equations along a line are discretized and reduced to sets of ordinary differential equations [56]. In addition to the stress intensity factor for LEFM, the two-dimensional code of EPAX provides the J-integral in the presence of nonlinear strain hardening. The quoted computational efficiency is remarkable, but like other unusual numerical algorithms in fracture mechanics, further development is necessary before the code can be used for general purpose computation of ductile parameters.

Microdamage Model

The SRI code of TROTT is unusual in that crack growth is characterized by void nucleation, growth, and coalescence under stress wave loading in an otherwise standard finite difference code. This two-dimensional code [57, 58], again, like others in their development stages, requires further refinement before being declared a general purpose code. Nevertheless, such built-in damage criterion for crack growth shows promise in studying crack growth and failure under projectile penetration and in the presence of large-scale yielding. The obvious disadvantage is the large computation time required for solving simple problems, which places the SRI code out of reach in industrial research and developmental programs.

PROGRAM DETAILS

Axisymmetric / Planar Elastic Structures (APES)

Categories: Combined mode linear elastic fracture analysis; finite element, static

Title: Axisymmetric / Planar Elastic Structures (APES)

Author: L. Nash Gifford and Peter D. Hilton, Code 1720.4, David W. Taylor Naval Ship R & D Center, Bethseda, MD 20084

Maintenance: Same as above

Date: September 1979

Capability: Program can be used for Modes I and II stress intensity factors and complete stress analysis for up to 5 crack tips in plane stress, plane strain, or axisymmetric structures of arbitrary geometry; program is frequently used for nonfracture applications as well.

Method: APES employs standard 12-node isoparametric elements and a fracture mechanics enrichment of the 12-node element to treat the region around crack tips. The Modes I and II stress intensity factors are directly calculated for each crack tip as additional degrees of freedom and need not be inferred from the usual finite element output. Mesh refinement is not needed at crack tips. The use of high-order elements results in high accuracy and great economy in data preparation, since only a few elements are generally needed. Intermediate element node numbers and their coordinates may be automatically generated. (Elements may be treated as if they have only corner nodes; a frontal solution algorithm makes node numbering inconsequential.)

Limitation: Isotropic materials (up to five)
Programming Language: FORTRAN IV
Documentation: References [103] are listed at the end.
Input: Material properties, numbers, and coordinates of at least all corner nodes, element connectivity by at least corner nodes, point nodes, distributed loads, thermal loads, boundary conditions, graphic output options, and node numbers which correspond to crack tips comprise the input
Output: The output includes nodal displacements, nodal strains and stresses (global and principal) smoothed from the integration point values, stress intensity factors at crack tips, plot of deflected structure, and contour plots of selected stresses in selected areas (CALCOMP).
Software: Batch
Hardware: CDC 6400, 6600, 7600
Usage: The program can be used in design and analysis of cracked (or uncracked) structures. The program has been released to at least 20 organizations in government, industry, and universities.
Typical running time: A problem of 18 elements and 121 nodes required 46 seconds on a CDC 6400 computer. CALCOMP plotting of results, if requested, can take longer than the time required to do the analysis.
Availability: Aerospace Structures Information and Analysis Center (ASIAC)
AFFDL/FBR
Ohio 45433
(513) 255-6688
References: [59, 60, 61]

FEFA

Categories: Mixed mode crack propagation; finite element
Title: Finite Element Fracture Analysis
Author: V. E. Saouma, Department of Structural Engineering, Hollister Hall, Cornell University, Ithaca, NY 14853
Maintenance: Same as above
Date: June 1980
Capability: Determination of stress intensity factors, angle of crack propagation, mesh readjustment, new crack opening (for brittle material), and final histogram of load vs. crack configuration; plane or axisymmetric problems; dynamic memory allocation; graphic display on Tektronix terminal
Method: The basic finite element code is taken from Ref. [62]. Crack singularities are modeled by quarter-point isoparametric elements. Stress intensity factors are obtained from nodal displacements, and angle of crack propagation from any of three different mixed mode theories. Tensile stresses are checked with tensile strength for new crack opening. Finite element mesh is automatically modified to reflect the latest crack's configuration. Energy balance approach is used to determine load required to extend a crack by the given crack increment.
Limitation: 2D, linear elastic isotropic materials
Programming language: FORTRAN IV
Documentation: User manual
Input: Control information, nodal points, elements, material properties, loading; for crack propagation, specify crack increment size and maximum number of crack increments.
Output: Nodal displacements, Gauss point stresses, stress intensity factors, angles of crack extension, crack vs. load table
Software: Batch and interactive
Hardware: Currently operating on IBM 370/168
Usage: Program is being used for analysis of reinforced concrete structures.

Typical running time: A crack propagation analysis of 40 elements and 126 points required 5 seconds of CPU time.
Availability: Professor Anthony R. Ingraffea; Victor E. Sauoma, Department of Structural Engineering, Hollister Hall, Cornell University, Ithaca, New York 14835
Reference: [62]

Global-Local Analysis of Structural Systems (GLASS II) for Fracture Analysis

Categories: Fracture analysis; global-local finite elements
Title: Global-Local Analysis of Structural Systems (GLASS II)
Authors: L. G. Bradford, S. B. Dong, A. Tessler, R. A. Westmann, Mechanics and Structures Department, University of California, Los Angeles, CA 90024
Maintenance: Electric Power Research Institute (EPRI), Palo Alto, CA
Date: June 1979
Capability: The program yields stress intensity factors, displacement,and stress fields.
Method: The global-local finite element method of analysis is used to determine the stress intensity factors. The finite element code name is GLASS II. By supplying the singular stress field (in displacement form) as a global function (Ritz function) to Glass II, the displacement equations of equilibrium (representing conventional finite elements and the singular element for the crack tip or center crack) are solved.
Limitation: Elastic analysis
Programming Language: FORTRAN IV
Documentation: (1) Bradford, L. G., Dong, S. B., Tessler, A.,and Westmann R. A., "Glass II - Global-Local Finite Element Analysis of Structural Systems," NP-1089, Research Project 299-1, EPRI, June 1979. (2) Bradford, L. G., Dong, S. B., Nicol, D. A. C.,and Westmann, R. A., "Application of Global-Local Finite Element Method to Fracture Mechanics," NP-1089, Research Project 299-1, EPRI, September 1979
Input: The input includes control information, material properties, nodal and element data, load and displacement boundary conditions, and subprogram(s) supplying global function(s) in FORTRAN IV following prescribed format.
Output: The output includes stress intensity factors, displacement field, and stress field.
Software operation: Batch
Hardware: IBM 360 or 370 series machine
Usage: The program is used to calculate stress intensity factors. GLASS II is also used for other applications such as half-space programs, inclusions, diffraction and scattering due to steady-state incident waves.
Typical running time: Running time depends on the problem being solved and the machine being used; the program is generally very efficient and has a low core requirement because of the analytical technique it utilizes.
Availability: Dr. H. T. Tang, Project Manager, Nuclear Power Div., Electric Power Research Institute, 3412 Hillview Avenue, Palo Alto, CA 94304

Special Crack Tip Finite Element Library

Categories: Singularity element
Title: Special Crack Tip Finite Element Library

Authors: The Lockheed-California Company, Burbank, California 91250. Contact: S. T. Chiu, Department 76-23, Building 63G, Plant A-1
Maintenance: Same as above
Date: September 1979
Capability: The element library contains four singular crack tip elements, providing direct output on stress intensity factors for two-dimensional linear elastic crack problems.
Method: The elements have been developed based on the Westergaard stress functions. The singular term as well as higher-order terms are included in the stress functions. The stress-free crack surface boundary conditions are enforced. However, element boundary displacement compatability is not maintained. The four elements in the library differ in number of element nodes, element configurations, and symmetry considerations. A detailed discussion of the elements can be found in Robins (see Documentation). The elements are used at the Lockheed-California Company together with a general purposes finite element analysis program, the NASTRAN-Calac System. The stress intensity factor, which is the coefficient of the singular stress term multiplied by a constant, is calculated using the displacement solution and the stress-to-displacement transformation matrix.
Limitation: The element configuration is specific for each crack-tip element and is rectangular. The elements are limited to a two-dimensional linear elastic fracture problem.
Programming Language: FORTRAN IV
Documentation: Robins, J., Integrated Theory of Finite Element Methods, Chapter 11, Wiley, 1973; user manuals are limited to company internal reports.
Input: Element configuration, material properties, nodal numbers and NASTRAN specific data are needed.
Output: Stress intensity factor
Software Operation: Batch, the NASTRAN-Calac System
Hardware: IBM 370/3033
Usage: Analysis of damaged aircraft structure
Typical running time: An analysis of 47 elements, 131 degrees of freedom requires approximately 17 CPU seconds.
Availability: The basic formulation for element development is available in Robins.

Finite Element Analysis of Stress Intensity Factors for Cracks at a Bi-Material Interface (SKBP 17)

Categories: Crack finite element
Title: Crack Finite Element
Authors: K. Y. Lin, and J. W. Mai, Department of Aeronautics and Astronautics, MIT, Cambridge, Mass. 02139. Dr. Lin is presently at Boeing, Seattle.
Maintenance: Aeroelastic and Structures Research Lab., Bldg. 41, MIT, Cambridge, Mass. 02139
Date: August 1979
Capability: Computes stress intensity factors K_1 and K_2 for a crack at a bi-material interface.
Method: Hybrid 23-8 (π_{mc2}); boundary displacement interpolation linear from node to node; thirty-two stress parameter β model, complex variable elasticity solution near the tip of a sharp crack lying along an interface between two materials; mode I and mode II stress intensity factors may be computed from β_1 and β_{17} (see Ref. [63]).

Limitation: Square element shape; crack parallel to X axis; isotropic material only; rotation transformation to skewed coordinates not allowed; crack surface must be stress-free; programmed in double precision; compressible material, $\nu \leq 0.45$; analysis is two-dimensional.
Programming Language: FORTRAN IV
Documentation: FEABL/EGL user's guide [64]
Input: Element geometry, crack geometry, and material properties
Output: Element stiffness and stress matrices; using the stress matrix and the displacement solution, K_1 and K_2 can be computed.
Software Operation: User's choice
Hardware: Machine independent
Availability: Professor E. A. Witmer, ASRL, Bldg. 41, MIT, Cambridge, Mass. 02139
References: [63,64]

Modified Version of Solid SAP for Two-Dimensional Linear-Elastic Fracture Analysis (SSAP2)

Categories: Finite element, linear-elastic fracture mechanics (LEFM)
Title: Modified version of SOLID SAP for two-dimensional, linear-elastic fracture analysis (SSAP2)
Authors: H. M. Hilber and H. Kordisch, Institut für Werkstoffmechanik, Freiburg, West Germany
Maintenance: Same as above
Date: September 1979
Capability: The current version of the program is specially written for the finite element analysis of LEFM problems. The element library includes isoparametric, quadrilateral elements with bilinear and quadratic displacement functions. In addition to displacements and stresses, the program computes the strain energy. A RESTART-option for efficient analysis of sequences of similar structures is available.
Method: The basic data structure used in this program is that of SOLID SAP [65] with the following modifications and improvements:
- Limitation on two-dimensional analysis for increased efficiency
- Only planar and axisymmetrical isoparametric elements with bilinear and quadratic displacements functions (Q4, Q8)
- Computation of the strain energy and support reactions
- RESTART-option facilitating the use of the strain-energy-release-rate method ($G = dU/dA$)
- Options allowing for initial stresses, variable pressure and temperature loads
- Some options for mesh # generation

Limitation: Two-dimensional static and linear-elastic analysis
Language: FORTRAN IV (double precision)
Documentation: Reference [65] and a short user-manual for the modifications
Input: The usual mesh data, including geometry and boundary conditions, temperature-dependent material properties, loading information
Output: Nodal displacements, support reactions, stresses and energies for the elements, total strain energy
Software Operation: Batch
Hardware: UNIVAC 1100/80 (minimum requirements for core storage: 50K)
Usage: The program is used for conventional FE-analysis and especially for LEFM analysis at the IWM in Freiburg.
Typical Running Time: For an example, 327 nodes, 100 elements, 606 degrees of freedom, to 21 seconds of CPU time

Availability: FhG Institut für Werkstoffmechanik, Rosastr. 9, 7800 Freiburg, West Germany
Reference: [65]

Two-Dimensional Fracture Analysis

Categories: Two-dimensional plane or axisymmetric, static, finite element
Title: Two-dimensional Fracture Analysis
Author: J. Heliot, Creusot-Loire, 15 Rue Pasquier, 75383, Paris Cedex 08, France
Date: 1972
Capability: The program can calculate stress intensity factors (S.I.F) resulting from any load and functions attached to the geometry for the calculation of S.I.F., as well as Bueckner's weight functions, or a polynomial influence function for stresses approximated by a polynomial. The calculation is performed with a series of crack lengths (for example, 30), and the S.I.F or the weight or influence functions for any crack length are calculated in one computer run. Mixed mode problems can be treated.
Method: The finite element method is used, and is part of the more general code TITUS. Pure mode weight functions are calculated by the crack closure method, as described in Refs. [66] and [67]. The mixed mode problems are solved by extrapolation of displacements.
Limitation: Linear elasticity
Programming language: FORTRAN IV
Documentation: User manual in French
Input: Most input cards are those of the finite element code TITUS.
Output: S.I.F., polynomial influence functions, weight function for any crack length, and their approximations through polynomials.
Software: Operation, batch
Hardware: Currently available on CDC 7600
Usage: 2D L.E.F.M. analysis
Typical running time: 50 sec. CPU for a mesh of 400 nodes
Availability: See author
References: [66,67]

Two-Dimensional Elastic Fracture Analysis (HDCRK 2)

Categories: Hybrid crack element, two-dimensional, elastic isotropic and orthotropic
Title: Two Dimensional Elastic Fracture Analysis (HDCRK 2)
Authors: S. N. Atluri, M. Nakagaki, Center for the Advancement of Computational Mechanics, School of Civil Engineering, Georgia Institute of Technology, Atlanta, Georgia 30332
Maintenance: Same as above
Date: December 1974
Capability: Program directly yields stress intensity factors K_I and K_{II} for cracks in 2D problems with linear elastic isotropic or orthotropic materials.
Method: The program uses special crack-tip elements which are developed using the hybrid-displacement finite element method. Analytic asymptotic solutions for singular stresses and strains near a crack-tip in a general orthotropic material are embedded in these elements. Compatability of displacements and reciprocity of tractions, between these hybrid crack-elements and the surrounding isoparametric nonsingular

elements, are maintained through a Lagrange multiplier technique, and hence the name "hybrid-displacement finite element method." This method enables the direct computation of K_1 and K_{II}, which are retained as unknowns in the global finite element equations along with nodal displacements.

Limitation: Program can treat arbitrary crack shapes in plane elastic domains. Material properties are limited to linear elastic orthotropic (or isotropic) materials.

Programming Language: FORTRAN IV

Documentation: No user manual is available. All the details are available in Ref. [35, 36].

Input: Control information, material properties, nodal points, elements, boundary conditions

Output: K_I, K_{II}, nodal displacements, stresses

Software: Batch

Hardware: Currently operating on CDC Cyber 74

Usage: Program is being used for routine calculation of K_I and K_{II} for arbitrarily shaped two-dimensional domains.

Typical running time: Because of the special feature of hybrid crack elements, a maximum of only 200 degrees of freedom have been used in all the problems dealt with so far. Typical running time is 25 secs of CPU time.

Availability: S. N. Atluri at the address given above under "Authors"

References: [35, 36]

Bending of Plates with Through Cracks (HSPBTC)

Categories: Hybrid stress crack element, plate bending, through cracks, mixed mode intensities K_I, K_{II}, K_{III}

Authors: S. N. Atluri and H. C. Ree, Center for the Advancement of Computational Mechanics, School of Civil Engineering, Georgia Institute of Technology, Atlanta, Georgia 30332

Maintenance: Same as above

Date: 1978

Capability: Program directly yields K_I, K_{II}, K_{III} for through-thickness cracks in plates under general bending loads.

Method: Program deals with a higher-order (Reissner-Goldenwiser) plate theory in calculating the stress-intensity factors K_I, K_{II}, K_{III} which depend on the thickness of the plate. A hybrid stress finite element method is used in developing special crack-tip elements based on the Reissner-Goldenwiser plate theory.

Limitation: Limited to elastic plate analysis

Programming Language: FORTRAN IV

Documentation: No user manual. All the pertinent details are given in Ref. [37].

Input: Control information, material properties, nodal points, elements, and boundary conditions

Output: Mixed mode factors K_I, K_{II}, K_{III}

Software: Batch

Hardware: Currently operating on CDC Cyber 74

Usage: Being used at Georgia Tech

Typical running time:

Availability: S. N. Atluri at the above address

Reference: [37]

Two-Dimensional Elastic Plastic Fracture Analysis (HDCR2P)

Categories: Elastic-plastic fracture; hybrid finite element, HRR singularities; finite deformation; J; COD
Title: Two-Dimensional Elastic-Plastic Fracture Analysis (HDCR2P)
Authors: S. N. Atluri, M. Nakagaki, and W. H. Chen, Center for the Advancement of Compututational Mechanics, School of Civil Engineering, Georgia Institute of Technology, Atlanta, Georgia 30332
Maintenance: Same as above
Date: September 1976
Capability: Program calculates parameters, such as J and COD, for cracks in strain-hardening elastic-plastic materials in 2-D situations.
Method: Program deals with the finite element method for estimating J and COD for arbitrary strain-hardening materials in general situations of large-scale yielding. A finite deformation analysis is used to account for crack-tip blunting. Kinematic hardening is used. Material as well as geometric nonlinearities are treated by a tangent stiffness method. The well-known HRR singularities are embedded in sector-shaped special crack-tip elements which are developed by a hybrid displacement finite element procedure. The definition of J as appropriate for finite deformations is employed.
Limitation: Limited to two-dimensional problems, plane stress and plane strain
Programming Language: FORTRAN IV
Documentation: No user manual; all the pertinent details are given in Refs. [38, 39, 40]
Input: Control information, elastic-plastic material properties; nodal points, elements, and boundary conditions
Output: J. nodal displacements, COD
Software: Batch
Hardware: Currently operating on CDC Cyber 74
Usage: Program extensively used in basic research on elastic-plastic fracture at Georgia Tech.
Availability: S. N. Atluri at the above address
References: [38, 39, 40]

Two-Dimensional Elastic-Plastic Crack Growth (HDCG2P)

Categories: Ductile fracture; stable crack growth; fatigue crack growth; moving singularities; J; elastic-plastic release rate; process zone
Title: Two-Dimensional Elastic-Plastic Crack Growth (HDCG2P)
Authors: S.N. Atluri and M. Nakagaki, Center for the Advancement of Computational Mechanics, School of Civil Engineering, Georgia Institute of Technology, Atlanta, GA 30332
Maintenance: Same as above
Date: March 1979
Capability: Program calculates elastic-plastic energy release per unit crack growth, CTOA in elastic-plastic stable crack growth and fatigue crack growth situations.
Method: This program is developed to study phenomena of quasi-static stable crack growth; and crack-closure effects in fatigue crack growth. Crack growth is simulated by translation in steps, of a core of sector elements, with embedded singularities of H-R-R type by an arbitrary amount in each step, in the desired direction. A finite deformation analysis based on the incremental updated Langrangian formulation of the hybrid-displacement finite element method is used.

Limitation: Limited to two-dimensional problems: plane stress and plane strain
Documentation: No user manual; all the pertinent details are given in Refs. [41, 42, 43].
Input: Control information; elastic-plastic material properties; nodal points; elements; and boundary conditions
Output: Crack-tip energy release rate, process zone energy release rate in stable crack growth under rising load; in fatigue crack growth analysis under general spectrum (high-to-low, low-to-high, single overload) etc., the program gives crack-closure and opening stresses in each cycle.
Software: Batch
Hardware: Currently operating on CDC Cyber 74
Usage: Extensively used in basic research on elastic-plastic fracture at Georgia Tech.
Availability: S. N. Atluri at the above given address
References: [41,42,43]

Fully Plastic Crack Analysis (INFEM)

Categories: Fully plastic crack analysis; finite element
Title: Incompressible Plane Strain and Axisymmetric Finite Element Analysis, INFEM
Author: A. Needleman, Division of Engineering, Brown University; C. F. Shih and V. Kumar, Corporate Research and Development, General Electric Co.
Maintenance: Same as above
Date: October 1977
Capability: Program can analyze plane strain and axisymmetric fully plastic boundary value problems, including crack structural configurations. Program can also analyze power law creeping materials, including finite deformations.
Method: The program deals with the constraint of incompressibility by direct elimination of nodal degrees of freedom. The basic element is a quadrilateral composed of 4 constant strain triangles. The method is described in [1]. The nonlinear equations for the nodal displacements are solved by a linear or modified Newton-Raphson procedure, described in the Appendix of Ref. [2]. Examples of fracture mechanics applications of the method are given in Refs. [3,4,5].
Limitation: Incompressibility itself and the method of eliminating nodal degrees of freedom place certain constraints on admissible boundary conditions and meshes, which are discussed in [1-5].
Programming Language: FORTRAN IV
Documentation: No user manual, except for Refs. [1,5] and a sheet describing input and dimensioning, available at this time.
Input: Control information, material properties (assumed uniform in the current version), nodal points, prescribed point loads, and prescribed displacements. Additionally, a main program which sets dimensions must be supplied.
Output: Nodal displacements, finite element strain and stress deviators, and/or finite element stresses and hydrostatic stresses. Also, the J-integral is evaluated along various contours and by crack tip element.
Software: Batch/time sharing
Hardware: Currently operating on CDC 7600 and IBM 370
Usage: Program is being used to generate fully plastic crack solutions for

a variety of test specimens and structural configurations. These solutions are being cataloged in a particular format to develop a Plastic Fracture Handbook which, in conjunction with the existing elastic fracture handbooks, would provide an engineering approach to elastic-plastic fracture methodology and design. These are detailed in [4,5].
Typical running time: A grid of 12 x 24 quadrilateral elements required about 4 seconds per iteration on a CDC 7600. Three to eight iterations are required for convergence.
Availability: A. Needleman, Division of Engineering, Brown University, Providence, Rhode Island; C. F. Shih and V. Kumar, Corporate Research and Development, General Electric Co.
References: [27-38, 60]

FAST

Categories: Static two-dimensional fracture analysis, elastic-plastic, crack growth finite element
Title: FAST
Author: Dr. Harry Armen, Applied Mechanics Laboratory, Grumman Aerospace Corp., Bethpage, NY; currently with Hoffman Maritime Consultants, Glen Head, NY
Maintenance: Dr. Allan Pifko, Applied Mechanics Laboratory, Research Department, Grumman Aerospace Corporation, Bethpage, NY 11714
Date: 1973
Capability: Program yields static stress intensity factors using energy release rates, also calculates crack closure and crack opening loads associated with cyclic loading.
Method: The basic finite element method is used with added capability for calculating energy release rates by allowing an infinitesimal extension of a prescribed crack under constant loading conditions. Continuous crack propagation is modeled by one of two alternative schemes, the first of which involves an efficient modification of stiffness coefficients to constrain or release nodes to model crack closure and opening respectively. This procedure is applied only to those situations in which the crack lies along an axis of symmetry. The second procedure has the capability of modeling cracks propagating along an arbitrary direction by using variable stiffness springs between adjacent nodes.
Limitation: Elastic-plastic and elastic-cyclic-plastic response of planar structures in plane stress; membrane triangular, quadriliteral and axial force finite elements available
Programming Language: FORTRAN IV
Documentation: User's Manual - Method of analysis outlined in Refs. [69-71].
Input: Standard finite element information; additional input specifying crack closure/opening nodes
Output: Finite element stresses, strains and nodal displacements, stress intensity factor, energy release rate, crack opening and closure stresses
Software: Batch
Hardware: CDC 6000 series and IBM 370
Usage: Program is being used for crack propagation studies.
Typical running time: Not available
Availability: Dr. Allan Pifko, Applied Mechanics Laboratory, Research Department, M.S. A08-35, Grumman Aerospace Corporation, Bethpage, NY 11714
References: [69,70,71]

Finite Element Analysis of Crack Growth (FEACG)

Categories: Fracture mechanics; finite element; crack growth; plasticity
Title: Finite Element Analysis of Crack Growth, FEACG
Author: J. D. Lee, H. Liebowitz, School of Engineering and Applied Science, The George Washington University, Washington, D.C.
Maintenance: Same as above
Date: December 1977
Capability: The program analyzes the crack growth process from the onset of slow crack growth to that of fast fracture and also gives the yield stress field, displacement field, and the elastic and plastic strain energies at any intermediate stage.
Method: The finite element method employed in this program is based on the incremental theory of plasticity. The incremental stress-strain relations for loading and unloading situations are generated automatically by using the information obtained from a simple tension test of a given material. Continuous crack tip movement from one node to its adjacent node is treated by releasing the crack tip nodal force and setting that node free to move. This program has an iteration procedure built in to match the predicted and computed stresses of each element. It also records the maximum effective stress that each element has ever experienced, and that measurement is used to compute the ever increasing plastic energy. The applied loading can be either uniaxial or biaxial.
Limitation: This program is two-dimensional and static.
Programming Language: FORTRAN IV
Documentation: No user manual is available at this time.
Input: This program takes one of the following as input:
(1) An experimental record relating applied loading and crack size for the entire process of crack growth;
(2) Two parameters specifying the linear relation between plastic energy and crack size.
Output: According to the input, this program gives either (1) a relation (thus far, a linear relation is obtained for materials 2024-T3 and 7075-T6) between plastic energy and crack size, or (2) a computer-generated crack growth resistance curve relating applied loading and crack size, in addition to stress field, displacement field, strain energy, and crack tip position, etc.
Software: Batch
Hardware: Currently operating on IBM 370
Usage: Program is being used for crack growth studies for center-cracked specimens under uniaxial or biaxial loading at the George Washington University.
Typical running time: An analysis of a 518-element, 300-node center-cracked specimen takes 420 seconds of CPU time for each crack tip movement.
Availability: Prof. James D. Lee or Dean Harold Liebowitz, School of Engineering and Applied Science, The George Washington University, Washington, D. C. 20052

Two-Dimensional Linear and Nonlinear Crack Analyses (NEUT-CRACK 1)

Categories: Linear and nonlinear fracture; finite element
Title: Two-Dimensional Linear and Nonlinear Crack Analyses (NEUT-CRACK 1)
Authors: G. Yagawa, T. Aizawa, Department of Nuclear Engineering, University of Tokyo, Bunkyo-ku, Tokyo, Japan
Maintenance: Same as above

Date: September 1979
Capability: This program yields the J-integral and the crack opening displacement, etc., in a cracked plate of elastic as well as fully plastic materials.
Method: The 8-node isoparametric elements are used in this program. In the elastic as well as fully plastic cases, the superposition method is employed together with the penalty functional technique in order to take account of the HRR singularity in the solution. The stress-strain relation is represented by the power law, i.e., $\varepsilon = \kappa\sigma^n$ with κ and n being the material constants.
Limitation: Though NEUT-CRACK 1 is being modified to analyze the axisymmetric crack problems and also to handle the high nonlinearity (n>10), the nonlinear fracture parameters with n<10 can be obtained with enough accuracies at present.
Programming Language: FORTRAN IV
Documentation: No user's manual
Input: Control information, material properties, nodal points, elements, traction, and displacement boundary conditions. For a plate of simple geometry, an automesh generator is available.
Output: Finite element stresses, strains and nodal displacements, stress intensity for linear material or J-Integral value for nonlinear one. When the Fourier expansions are employed to represent HRR singularity, the approximate characteristic distributions are provided.
Software: Both TSS and batch
Hardware: Currently operating on both HITAC 8700/8800 and Prime 550
Usage: Program is being used at University of Tokyo to obtain the J-integral, the crack opening displacement, etc., in a cracked plate of elastic, as well as the power law materials.
Typical running time: A nonlinear fracture analysis of a 36-element, 133-node plate under plain strain requires 16 seconds of CPU time per step of Newton-Raphson iteration.
Availability: Associate Professor G. Yagawa, Department of Nuclear Engineering, University of Tokyo, Bunkyo-ku, Tokyo, Japan

Thermal Elasto-Plastic Stress Analysis (TEPSA)

Categories: Slow crack growth; finite element
Title: Thermal Elasto-Plastic Stress Analysis (TEPSA)
Author: T. R. Hsu, Y. J. Kim, Department of Mechanical Engineering, University of Manitoba, Winnepeg, Manitoba, Canada R3T 2N2
Maintenance: Same as above
Date: August 1979
Capability: The program predicts the slow crack growth rate and direction in a 3D axisymmetric or 2D planar elasto-plastic stress field induced by any combination of thermal and mechanical loads.
Method: TEPSA code is constructed on the basis of the incremental variable stiffness thermoelasto-plasticity theory. The stress/strain fields in the structure with the presence of cracks are first evaluated. The effective strain, $\bar{\varepsilon}$, in the elements near the crack tip is extrapolated toward the crack front. For an element with $\bar{\varepsilon}$ of the portion of the element volume exceeding $\bar{\varepsilon}_{rup}$, an assigned effective rupture strain, the stiffness of that element is to be reduced proportionally and a new crack front is created within that element.

When the entire element's $\bar{\varepsilon}$ exceeds the $\bar{\varepsilon}_{rup}$, the element stiffness simultaneously becomes zero, or the crack front has now propagated through one element. The elements behind the crack front are to be treated as gaslike elements. The value of $\bar{\varepsilon}_{rup}$ can be determined by TEPSA evaluation on K_{IC} of the material or on the experimentally determined "crack growth resistance (R) curve."

Limitation: Limited to 3D axisymmetric or 2D planar structures

Programming Language: FORTRAN IV

Documentation: User's manual available from the senior author at a cost

Input: Control information, properties of up to 5 different materials at up to 6 different temperatures, nodal coordinates and loads/displacements element descriptions, pressure and thermal boundary conditions, pressure and thermal loading histories, equivalent rupture strains at up to 6 temperatures, output options

Output: Temperature and displacements at nodes, stresses/strains in elements, instantaneous position of crack fronts

Software: Batch or through TSO

Hardware: IBM, CEC and AMDAHL 470/V7

Usage: Program is being used for the prediction of slow crack growth in thin-wall tubes subject to combined monotonic or cyclic thermomechanical loads.

Typical running time: About 10 sec per step of loads for a typical model with 300 elements

Availability: Negotiable through the senior author

Three-Dimensional Fracture Analysis for Plates with Through Cracks (PCRACK)

Categories: Stress intensity factor; finite element

Title: Three-Dimensional Fracture Analysis for Plates with Through Cracks PCRACK

Author: Y. Yamamoto, Dept. of Naval Architecture, Univ. of Tokyo, Tokyo 113, Y. Sumi, Dept. of Naval Architecture & Ocean Engineering, Yokohama National University, Yokohama 240

Maintenance: Y. Sumi, Dept. of Naval Architecture & Ocean Engineering, Yokohama National University

Date: March 1976

Capability: The program is used with SAP and yields three-dimensional distributions of stress intensity factors along through cracks.

Method: This method is developed on the basis of the concept of superposition of analytical and finite element solutions. The present program generated analytical solutions around a through crack, and the finite element analysis is performed with the use of SAP program. The final results can be determined by combining the analytical and finite element solutions.

Limitation: This program can be applied only for linear elastic solids.

Programming Language: FORTRAN IV

Documentation: No user manual except for Refs. [72,73] is available at this time.

Input: Control information, number of layers, thickness of layers, nodal points on plate surfaces

Output: Stress intensity factor, stress distributions

Software: Batch

Hardware: Currently operating on HITAC 8700/8800

Usage: The program is used at Yokohama National University.

Typical running time: A three-dimensional analysis of a 400-element, 594-node compact tension specimen required 412 seconds of CPU time.

Availability: Professor Y. Sumi, Department of Naval Architecture and Ocean Engineering, Yokohama National University, Hodogaya-ku, Yokohama 240 Japan

References: [72,73]

Automatic Dynamic Incremental Nonlinear Analysis (ADINA)

Categories: Linear and nonlinear, static and dynamic 3-D finite element analysis
Title: Automatic Dynamic Incremental Nonlinear Analysis, ADINA
Author: K. J. Bathe, Massachusetts Institute of Technology, Department of Mechanical Engineering
Maintenance: Same as above
Date: September 1975
Capability: In addition to the standard initial and boundary conditions, the code can handle initial stress, strain or velocities, contact loading, and elastic foundation [74-77]. Anisotropic, multilayered, and temperature-dependent material properties can be prescribed. A companion heat transfer program is available [78,79].
Method: In nonlinear analysis, the finite element system response is evaluated using an incremental solution of the equations of equilibrium with an accelerated modified Newton-Raphson iteration or the BFGS method [80]. In static analysis, all linear degrees of freedom can be condensed out prior to the step-by-step solution (using substructuring). In dynamic analysis mode superposition, implicit time integration with equilibrium iteration (the Newmark or Wilson methods) or explicit time integration (central difference method) can be employed. In all nonlinear analyses before the incremental solution is carried out, the constant structure matrices, namely the linear effective stiffness matrix, the linear stiffness, mass, and damping matrices, whichever are applicable, and the load vectors, are assembled and stored on low-speed storage. During the step-by-step solution the linear effective stiffness matrix is then updated only for the nonlinearities in the system.
Programming Language: FORTRAN IV
Documentation: See references
Availability: Professor K. J. Bathe, Department of Mechanical Engineering, Massachusetts Institute of Technology, Cambridge, Massachusetts, 02139
References: [74-82]

Elastic-Plastic Fracture Analysis (GEFRACT)

Categories: General nonlinear static and dynamic finite element program
Title: General Electric Fracture Version of ADINA, GEFRACT
Author: H. G. deLorenzi, M. D. German, and C. F. Shih
Maintenance: Same
Date: Last revised 1978
Capability: Modifications made by GE will calculate K, J-integral, and energy release rate for monotonic loading for deformation theory and flow theory formulations.
Method: The crack is propagated through the finite elements by the node shifting and node release technique. Stress intensity factor can be calculated from nodal displacement. J-integral is calculated for up to 10 paths around the crack tip (2D only); energy release rate is calculated by postprocessing program for 2D and 3D problems. Crack tip elements are the isoparametric 8-noded and 20-noded elements made singular with quarter point nodes or collapsed nodes.
Limitations: Crack propagation in 2D version; in 3D version, the J-integral is calculated by an energy release rate procedure.
Programming Language: FORTRAN IV
Documentation: Refs. [83-86]

Input: Control information, different material properties, nodal points, elements, loading boundary conditions and (time-dependent) J-resistance curve must be described for crack propagation analyses.
Output: Stresses, strains, displacements, J-integral, strain energy, crack position for propagation analysis, and energy release rate (from post-processing program), crack opening displacement, crack opening angle
Software: Batch
Hardware: ADINA runs on CDC and IBM computers, but fracture modifications are only in the version for the CDC 176.
Usage: Program is being used for elastic-plastic fracture analyses (including crack propagation) at GE CRD.
Typical running time: 2D elastic-plastic analysis with 600 nodes and 150 8-noded elements is 150 CPU seconds. 3D elastic-plastic analysis with 1600 nodes and 300 20-noded elements takes about 1800 CPU seconds on CDC 176.
Availability: ADINA is available from Prof. K. J. Bathe, M.I.T.; the Fracture modification has a limited availability from GE CRD.
Reference: [83-86]

Berkeley Structural Analysis by Finite Elements (BERSAFE)

Categories: General purpose finite element package with emphasis on fracture mechanics facilities
Title: BERSAFE
Author: Dr. T. K. Hellen, Berkeley Nuclear Laboratories, Berkeley, Glos., England
Maintenance: As above
Date: 1972, 1974, 1978 for various levels
Capability: General range of facilities for evaluating stress intensity factors in two- and three-dimensional structures; methods applicable for both LEFM and PYFM; ability to predict which direction cracks will tend to grow
Method: Static finite element analysis for elasticity, plasticity, and creep; restarts in plasticity and creep enable general alterations to data, e.g., different values or types of load, and geometry changes. In this way (via tangent stiffness) large deformation analysis is possible, crack tips may be followed through meshes using different criteria, and different types of energy can be accumulated. Postprocessor programs exist for, among other things, evaluating fracture parameters of interest. The corresponding dynamics (linear) is available in the parallel system BERDYNE.
Limitation: Small displacement, small strain
Programming Language: FORTRAN IV
Documentation: There is extensive user documentation which includes theory and exmaples.
Input: General finite element input with additional data to be describe up to 20 virtual crack extensions in different directions plus material
Output: Finite element stresses, displacements, strains, reactions, energy change for various virtual crack extensions plus area changes, G,K,J,J*, and total strain energy
Software: Batch with interactive mesh generations and mesh modifications for changing crack length and orientation of growth from previous mesh
Hardware: IBM 360/370 series, ICL System 4, Burroughs, Univac, Prime

Usage: Very wide range of applications in industry plus extensive use for assessment of defects in generating equipment
Typical running time: VCE for 3D structure with a curved crack front, 175 20 node isoparametrics and 1020 nodes, semibandwidth 384, 19 crack front extensions for 15 nodes around crack front; total IBM time minutes
Availability: Central Electricity Generating Board, BERSAFE Advisory Group, Berkeley Nuclear Laboratories, Berkeley, Gloucestershire, England

General Purpose **Finite** Element Analysis Program (MARC)

Categories: Nonlinear static, dynamic, heat transfer, J-integral, finite element
Title: General Purpose Finite Element Program (MARC)
Author: P. V. Marcal, President, MARC Analysis Research Corporation, 260 Sheridan Avenue, Suite 200, Palo Alto, CA 94306
Maintenance: Same as above
Date: MARC, Release H.4, March 1979
Capability: For fracture mechanics problems, the program yields the J-integral for several paths in two- and three-dimensional problems.
Method: The program uses the differential stiffness technique to determine the change in strain energy from which the J-integral can be found. The change in strain energy is based on prescribed nodal movements during any analysis. Several values may be obtained simultaneously for use in three-dimensional analysis or for multipath comparisons. For elastic-plastic analysis the plastic strains are included in the definition of the strain energy. Therefore, the J-integral is evaluated for the equivalent nonlinear elastic material.
Limitation: J-integral evaluation for isothermal conditions only
Programming Language: FORTRAN IV
Documentation: MARC General Purpose Finite Element Program, User Manual Volumes A-E, edited and distributed by author's corporation
Input: Lists of nodal points and distance by which they will be moved
Output: Element stresses, strains, nodal displacements, changes in strain energy
Software: Batch
Hardware: CDC, IBM, and UNIVAC mainframes, Prime minicomputers
Usage: General nonlinear structural mechanics applications in industry and research
Typical running time: Machine, configuration, and problem dependent
Availability: Major data centers and MARC Analysis Research Corporation
References: [87,88]

TITUS

Categories: 3D thermo-mechanical nonlinear dynamic, finite element
Title: TITUS
Author: FRAMATOME, Service CALCUL, B. P. 13, 71380 St. Marcel, France
Maintenance: Same as above
Date: June 1974
Capability: Stress, strain, displacement, support reaction, computation J- and M-integrals, strain energy, damage function for crack analysis
Method: TITUS is a basic dynamic nonlinear finite element code with a special algorithm added for crack extension computation. A damage criterion (void coalescence) is being used (Ref. [5]) to compute crack propa-

gation by automatically releasing nodal forces from one element node to its adjacent nodes.
Limitation: Crack extension computation is currently limited to static two-dimensional or axisymmetric solids.
Programming Language: FORTRAN IV
Documentation: User manual and sample problems manual available
Input: Free format input oriented language, automatic mesh generation processors
Output: Element stresses, strains, nodal displacements, support reactions; strain energy, damage function, J and M-integrals; graphic representations in principal stress space; batch and interactive graphic output processors
Software: SCOPE 2 on CDC 7600 (Batch), SCOPE 3.4 or NOS BE on CDC 6000 series (batch and interactive)
Usage: TITUS program is being used widely throughout France and Europe. The application field ranges from simple linear static to large 3D elasto-plastic problems. This program is being used for almost all the calculations done for the stress report of the three primary components of PWR manufactured by FRAMATOME.
Typical running time: A crack extension computation of a 269-element, 843-node specimen required 89 seconds of CPU time (CDC 7600) for one load step.
Availability: Franlab Informatique, 232 avenue Napoleon Bonaparte, 92500 Rueil Malmaison, France; Cisi, 35 boulevard Brune, 75680 Paris Cedex 14, France; CDC, Cybernet Service Network (Europe)
References: [89-95]

Three-Dimensional Linear Fracture Analysis (HDCRK 3)

Categories: 3D Hybrid Crack Element; Mixed Mode Intensities K_I, K_{II}, K_{III}; Surface Flaws
Title: Three-Dimensional Linear Fracture Analysis (HDCRK 3)
Authors: S. N. Atluri and K. Kathiresan, Center for the Advancement of Computational Mechanics, School of Civil Engineering, Georgia Institute of Technology, Atlanta, GA 30332
Maintenance: See above
Date: September 1975
Capability: Program directly yields combined mode stress-intensity factors K_I, K_{II}, K_{III} at various points along the front of an arbitrarily shaped three-dimensional embedded or surface flaws. Crack can also lie at the interface of two different materials.
Method: The program uses special three-dimensional 20-noded hybrid crack-elements near the crack front. Analytical asymptotic solutions for a 3D crack under mixed mode (K_I, K_{II}, K_{III}) conditions are embedded in these special elements. Compatability of displacements and reciprocity of tractions, between these special hybrid elements and the surrounding non-singular 20-noded isoparametric brick elements, are enforced through a Lagrange multiplier method, and hence the name hybrid displacement finite element method. The method leads to a direct computation of K_I, K_{II}, K_{III} at various points along the crack front, along with the nodal displacements from the global finite element equations.
Limitations: The program can handle arbitrary-shaped 3D surface and embedded flaws in arbitrary 3D configurations. The crack may also lie at the interface of two different materials. However, the program is limited to linear elastic material behavior.
Programming Language: FORTRAN IV

Documentation: No user manual; all the pertinent details are given in Refs. [44,45,46].
Input: Control information, material properties, and number of elements in each of the three directions. The program uses an automatic mesh generator, taking into account the special nature of hybrid crack elements.
Output: K_I, K_{II}, K_{III} at several points along the crack front; nodal displacements, and stresses
Software: Batch
Hardware: Currently operating on CDC Cyber 74
Usage: Program is used to compute K-factors for surface flaws in plates, shells, pressure vessel nozzle corners, corner flaws near holes, etc.
Typical running time: A complicated surface flaw analysis using 4000 degrees of freedom required 1700 sec of CPU time.
Availability: S. N. Atluri at the above address.
References: [44,45,46]

Three-Dimensional Composite Fracture Analysis (NISATC)

Categories: Composite fracture mechanics; assumed stress finite element
Title: Three-Dimensional Composite Fracture Analysis (NISATC)
Authors: S. N. Atluri and T. Nishioka, Center for the Advancement of Computational Mechanics, School of Civil Engineering, Georgia Institute of Technology, Atlanta, Georgia 30332
Maintenance: Same as above
Date: June 1979
Capability: Program yields the three-dimensional stress intensity factors along the crack front in angle-ply laminates. The conditions of stress equilibrium and interlayer traction reciprocity in the element are satisfied a priori; and the individual cross-sectional rotations of each layer are allowed.
Limitation: This program is limited to linearly elastic (anisotropic and isotropic) static problems.
Programming Language: FORTRAN IV
Documentation: No user manual is available. The basic formulation of this program is presented in Ref. [47].
Input: Specimen geometries, and material properties, orientation and thickness of laminates; information for the automatic mesh generation is required.
Output: Three components of stress intensity factors along the crack front, stresses, strains, and displacement.
Software: Batch
Hardware: Currently operating on CDC Cyber 74
Usage: Program is being used for the studies of three-dimensional composite fracture mechanics at Georgia Tech.
Typical running time: An analysis of through crack in an angle-ply laminate using 77 elements, 804 nodes required 2000 sec of CPU time.
Availability: S. N. Atluri at the above address.
Reference: [47]

Dynamic Fracture Analysis (NISATD)

Categories: Dynamic fracture mechanics; moving singular finite element
Title: Dynamic Fracture Analysis

Authors: S. N. Atluri and T. Nashioka, Center for the Advancement of Computational Mechanics, School of Civil Engineering, Georgia Institute of Technology, Atlanta, GA 30332

Maintenance: Same as above

Date: July 1979

Capability: The dynamic stress intensity factor of each time step can be calculated directly. The various stress contours (fringe patterns) can be produced. The program also computes total dissipated fracture energy, kinetic energy,and strain energy.

Method: A moving singular-element procedure is used for the dynamic analysis of fast crack-propagation problem in arbitrary-shaped finite bodies. In the moving singular element, analytical asymptotic solutions for a propagation crack are used as basis functions for displacements. The singular element may move along with the crack tip by an arbitrary amount in each time increment of the numerical time integration scheme. The moving singular element, within which the crack tip has a fixed location, retains its shape at all times, but the mesh of regular (isoparametric) finite elements, surrounding the moving singular element, deforms accordingly. An energy-consistent variational method is used as a basis for the above "moving singular element" procedure.

Limitation: Although the method is applicable for large-deformation elastic and inelastic dynamic problems, the program is developed for linearly elastic two-dimensional solids.

Programming Language: FORTRAN IV

Documentation: No user manual is available. The basic formulation of this program is presented in Ref. [48].

Input: Specimen geometries, material properties, information for automatic mesh generation are required. Dynamic fracture toughness versus crack velocity relation must be prescribed for the propagation phase and crack tip position versus time for the generation phase of fracture simulation analysis. In addition, the displacement, velocities, and acceleration of the previous step at which computation was stopped are required for a successive start-up.

Output: Dynamic stress intensity factors, stresses, strains, displacement, velocities, accelerations, fracture energy, strain energy,and kinetic energy

Software: Batch

Hardware: Currently operational on CDC Cyber 74

Usage: Program is being used for dynamic fracture studies, both in the generation and propagation phase at Georgia Institute of Technology.

Typical running time: A dynamic fracture analysis of a 59-element, 209-node center-cracked square plate specimen required 25 sec of CPU time for a typical time step.

Availability: S. N. Atluri at the above address.

Reference: [48]

Explicit Time Integration of Crack Propagation Problems (EXPDYN1) (EXPDYN2)

Categories: Dynamic crack propagation and arrest; finite element

Title: Explicit Time Integration of Crack Propagation Problems, EXPDYN1, EXPDYN2

Author: F. Nilsson, B. Brickstad, Dept. of Strength of Materials and Solid Mechanics, Royal Institute of Technology, S-100 44, Stockholm, Sweden

Maintenance: Same

Date: May 1979

Capability: 1) Generation mode: given the crack growth history in a 2D-plane problem and boundary conditions, EXPDYN1 yields the dynamic energy release rate and the stress intensity factor; 2) Propagation mode: given a material relation between critical energy-release rate and tip velocity, EXPDYN2 calculates the crack growth history.
Method: A specially developed FEM code is used. Crack growth from one node to its adjacent node is modeled by a gradually decreasing nodal force. The energy-release rate is calculated by integration of the force-velocity history for the currently relaxing node. In version EXPDYN2 an iterative procedure based on the Illinois algorithm is used for determination of the crack velocity. Explicit time integration is employed for solution of equations of motion. The initial state must be calculated separately in the current version.
Limitation: The program is limited to purely linear elastic behavior, in the current version only mode I growth. Only quadrilateral elements are available; in the current version all must have the same size in order to save storage and computer time. This limitation can be easily modified.
Programming Language: FORTRAN IV
Documentation: No user manual
Input: Elastic properties, nodal points, boundary conditions (time constant or variable), initial conditions (displacement and velocities), crack tip versus time in EXPDYN1, critical energy release rate versus velocity in EXPDYN2
Output: EXPDYN1: the energy-release rate averaged over each element along the crack path; EXPDYN2: the times when the tip passes the nodal points along the crack path
Software: Batch
Hardware: Currently operating on IBM 370/165
Usage: Program is used for crack propagation and arrest studies of the Royal Institute of Technology.
Typical running time: $T \approx 1.45 \cdot 10^{-4} \cdot F \cdot N$, where T = number of CPU-seconds, F = number of degrees of freedom and N = number of timesteps used.
Availability: Dr. F. Nilsson, Department of Strength of Materials, Royal Institute of Technology, S-100 44, Stockholm, Sweden

Two-Dimensional Dynamic Fracture Analysis (HCRACK)

Categories: Dynamic fracture; finite element
Title: Two-Dimensional Dynamic Fracture Analysis, HCRACK
Authors: A. S. Kobayashi, A. F. Emery, Department of Mechanical Engineering, University of Washington, Seattle, WA 98195
Maintenance: Same as above
Date: June 1979
Capability: Program yields the dynamic stress intensity factor, total dissipated fracture energy, kinetic energy, strain energy, and stress energy in a fracturing elastic plate.
Method: The basic dynamic finite element code used in this program is HONDO[1] with added algorithms for dynamic crack extension and computation of fracture parameters. Continuous crack tip movement from one finite element node to its adjacent node is modeled by a linearly decreasing crack tip nodal force with an iteration procedure to match each prescribed and computed nodal force released at the crack tip in this explicit dynamic finite element code. The dynamic stress intensity factor is computed from the dissipated energy at the released crack tip node. The latter is added into the running total of the fracture ener-

gy. In addition, a startup static finite element algorithm is attached for handling boundary value problems with initially prescribed displacements. The program can be used in either propagation or generation modes of dynamic fracture analysis.
Limitation: Although HONDO is designed to handle large-deformation elastic and inelastic transient dynamic response of axisymmetric solids, the added fracture mechanic package is limited to linearly elastic two-dimensional solids. Variable elastic properties can be prescribed, but this option has not been tested yet.
Programming Language: FORTRAN IV
Documentation: No user manual, except for Ref. [96],is available at this time.
Input: Control information, numbers of different material properties, nodal points,elements, pressure boundary conditions, and pressure-time histories are required for HONDO. In addition, the initial prescribed displacements are required for start-up finite element code. The dynamic fracture toughness versus crack velocity relation must be prescribed for the propagation mode and crack tip position versus time for the generation mode of dynamic fracture analyses.
Output: Finite element stresses, strains,and nodal displacements, dynamic stress intensity factor, fracture energy, strain energy,and crack position for propagation analysis
Software: Batch
Hardware: Currently operating on CDC 6400
Usage: Program is being used for dynamic fracture studies, both in the generation and propagation modes at the University of Washington
Typical running time: A dynamic fracture analysis of a 243-element, 280-node modified compact-tension specimen required 650 seconds of CPU time.
Availability: Professor Albert S. Kobayashi, Department of Mechanical Engineering, University of Washington, Seattle, WA 98195
Reference: [96]

Two-Dimensional Elastic Fracture Analysis (BEFAP)

Categories: Linear elastic fracture; boundary element
Title: Two-dimensional Elastic Fracture Analysis (BEFAP)
Author: George E. Blandford, Department of Civil Engineering, University of Kentucky, Lexington, KY 40506
Maintenance: Same as above
Date: January 1980
Capability: The program gives the computed stress intensity factors, the boundary displacements and tractions, and the domain stresses at user-specified points.
Method: The program uses a multidomain boundary element discretization to represent the boundary and crack surfaces. Isoparametric linear and/or quadratic boundary elements are used for the discretization. The quadratic boundary elements are transformed into traction singular quarter-point and transition elements at the crack tips. A complete description of the theory is contained in Ref. [97].
Limitation: Limited to linearly elastic fracture problems. Body force and thermal loading capabilities are currently being investigated for implementation into the program.
Programming Language: FORTRAN IV
Documentation: Internal program documentation and a user's manual, which is in preparation
Input: Control information, node point data, element data, nonzero pre-

scribed boundary values, crack tip node and element data, and user selected stress computation points

Output: All input data (including the generated node and element data), the element boundary displacements and tractions, the computed stress intensity factors, and the stresses at user-selected points

Software: The program can be run in batch or in the CMS interactive environment of the IBM 370.

Hardware: Currently operating on IBM 370, but there is no machine dependence with the program

Usage: The program is being used to perform two-dimensional analyses for linear elastic fracture problems.

Typical running time: For a two-subdomain breakup with 46 nodes and 23 quadratic elements in each subdomain, there are 19 sec of CPU time.

Availability: George E. Blandford, Department of Civil Engineering, University of Kentucky, Lexington, KY 40506

Reference: [97]

Fracture Mechanics Code for Structures (BIGIF)

Categories: Fracture mechanics, fatigue, subcritical crack growth

Title: BIGIF: Fracture Mechanics Code for Structures

Author: P. M. Besuner, J. L. Grover, Failure Analysis Assoc., Palo Alto, CA 94304

Maintenance: Same as above

Date: 1978; Current revision June 1980

Capability: The program performs a variety of fracture mechanics based on subcritical crack growth and stress intensity factor computations.

Method: For both two-dimensional and three-dimensional solutions in the BIGIF library, the program uses the "weight function" or "influence function" method due to Bueckner, Rice, Besuner,and others. Most of the influence functions are generated with the boundary integral equation method; hence, the acronym Boundary Integral Generated Influence Functions. All solutions account for the redistribution of stress as the crack grows through the structure,and some solutions model crack shape under several concurrent load transients.

Limitation: Linear elasticity (although a contained plasticity capability is contemplated for November 1980 release); crack locus elastic stress solution for the uncracked structure must be estimated from another independent source.

Programming Language: FORTRAN IV

Documentation: Full documentation published by Electric Power Research Inst.

Input: Control parameters, crack growth and roughness material properties, uncracked stress solutions, and frequencies of cyclic load transients, crack size and shape parameters

Output: Crack size and shape as functions of time, stress intensity solution for growing crack; Pointer Plots are provided.

Software: Batch

Hardware: The program operates on IBM 360- 370-series, CDC 6600, UNIVAC 1108,and other systems.

Usage: The program is being widely used by several corporations and individuals in the electric power and aerospace industries.

Typical running time: Less than 20 seconds on IBM 370/168 for 90+% of complete two- or three-dimensional model fatigue solutions

Availability: Authors or the EPRI Computer Center, Tech. Development Corp., 155 Moffet Park Dr. #C, Sunnyvale, CA (408) 734-5500

Three-Dimensional Thermoelastic Analysis
(E.I.T.D.)

Categories: Linear thermoelasticity; linear elastic fracture mechanics (LEFM): boundary integral equations

Title: Three Dimensional Thermoelastic Analysis

Authors: J. O. Watson, presently at Imperial College, London; Melle A. Chandouet, Department de Mecanique des Solides, CETIM, 52, avenue Felix Louat, 60304 Senlis, France; for three-dimensional influence functions for stress intensity factors (see below): J. Heliot, Creusot-Loire, 15, Rue Pasquier, 75383 Paris Cedex 08, France

Maintenance: Department of Solid Mechanics, CETIM

Date: 1975

Capability: Program yields displacement and stress field in linear elasticity strain energy; postprocessor developed for LEFM.

Method: Thermal, elastostatic, and thermoelastic equations are transformed into boundary integral equations, thus reducing a three-dimensional problem to a two-dimensional one. The body is divided into subregions. The surface of each subregion is meshed by quadrilateral and triangular elements. On each element, temperature, flux, displacement, and traction are supposed to vary linearly or quadratically. Its main advantages with respect to the classical methods are:

accurate results, since the functions used to approximate the boundary condition satisfy a priori the governing equations (the singularities are then taken into account);

considerable savings on computing time and input - output operations since only the surface of the domain has to be meshed.

Limitation: Linear isotropic elasticity, steady state thermal field (transient analysis is being developed at the present time)

Programming Language: FORTRAN IV

Documentation: A user manual (in French) is available at this time.

Input: Semiautomatic meshing on the surfaces; definition of subregions, material properties; loadings: pressure, traction on elements or lines, nodal forces, thermal loadings; boundary conditions: prescribed displacements, cyclic symmetry, elastic bearings or foundations, sliding between subregions

Output: Displacement and stress field on the surface and at any given point inside the body; strain energy; stress intensity factors by extrapolation of displacements; polynomial influence functions for three-dimensional problems

Software operation: Remote batch

Hardware: Currently operating on CDC 7600

Usage: Fracture mechanics analysis; linear thermoelastic analysis

Typical running time: (1) Thermoelastic analysis of cracked nozzle, 127 surface elements (meshing used for B.I.E. analysis is far coarser than the one used by FEM), 4 subregions, 1200 degrees of freedom; two load cases: 147 seconds CPU time. (2) Five polynomial influence functions for three-dimensional stress intensity factors, as defined in Ref. [101], 650 sec CPU time

Availability: Melle A. Chadouet, Departement de Mecanique des Solides, CETIM, 52 avenue Felix Louat, 60304 SENLIS, France

References: [98-101]

Finite Element-Alternating Method

Categories: Static fracture; three-dimensional; mode-one stress intensity factors
Title: Finite Element-Alternating Method
Authors: F. W. Smith, W. M. Browning, G. P. Ganong, T. E. Kullgren, Department of Mechanical Engineering, Colorado State University, Fort Collins, CO 80523
Maintenance: Same as above
Date: October 1979
Capability: Mode-one stress intensity factor along the border of a part-elliptical crack in a three-dimensional body and crack opening displacements
Method: Alternating between a finite element solution for an unflawed body and an analytic solution for a flat elliptical crack in an infinite solid satisfies boundary conditions and converges within four iterations. Results compare well with experiments. A series of four computer programs comprise the method:

1. MESH20 generates a three-dimensional finite element mesh of 20 node isoparametric elements.
2. SSAP3A forms the finite body stiffness matrix.
3. LDU2 uses Cholesky decomposition on the stiffness matrix.
4. SAPELL performs the alternation method/ for differing crack shapes/ sizes in the same body geometry; the previous three programs need not be rerun.

Limitation: While this method has the potential for solving problems with cracks in arbitrary bodies, its use has been restricted to cracks at fastener holes in plates and circumferential and longitudinal cracks in pipes. Crack shapes that are close to circular cause numerical errors.
Programming Language: FORTRAN IV
Documentation: No published user's manual
Input: Finite element mesh arrangement, finite body material properties, crack shape and location, unflawed crack plane stress field
Output: Mode-one stress intensity factor at any location on the crack border: Stress function coefficients from each iteration are input to a short routine to calculate crack opening displacements
Software operation: Batch
Hardware: CDC 6400, CDC 6600
Usage: Air Force Materials Laboratory (fastener hole problems), Air Force Weapons Laboratory (circumferential pipe cracks), Colorado State University (program development)
Typical running time: For a 112-element body; CDC 6600 (run once for each body geometry): MESH20, 30 CPU (sec); SSAP3A, 80 CPU (sec); LDU, 240 CPU (sec); SAPELL, total for each crack in the same body: 150 CPU (sec)
Availability: Professor F. W. Smith, Department of Mechanical Engineering, Colorado State University, Fort Collins, CO 80523
Reference: [101]

Arbitrarily Distributed Cracks in Joined Half Planes of Different Materials (CRHP)

Categories: Stress intensity factor; body force method
Title: Arbitrarily Distributed Cracks in Joined Half Planes of Different Materials (CRHP)
Author: M. Isida, Faculty of Engineering, Kyushu University, Hakozaki, Fukuoka 812, Japan

Maintenance: Same as above
Date: September 1979
Capability: Program yields the static stress intensity factors at tips of arbitrarily distributed cracks in joined half planes of different materials. It includes, as special cases, arbitrary arrays of cracks in infinite and semi-infinite plates. Moreover, branched cracks and sharp notches are treated just by joining straight cracks without any modification of the program.
Method: The program is based on the body force method improved by using continuous density functions and stress resultant conditions instead of step functions and stress conditions in the original procedure.
Limitation: It depends on the allowable number of the unknowns. In mixed mode problems, about forty unknowns should be assigned to each crack. Therefore, five crack problems are treated by solving two hundred equations.
Programming Language: FORTRAN IV
Documentation: No user manual, except for Ref. [1], is available at this time.
Input: Moduli of rigidity and Poisson's ratios of the two materials, stress components applied at infinity, and coordinates of both tips of the distributed cracks
Output: Stress intensity factors at all the crack tips
Software operation: Batch
Hardware: Currently operating on FACOM M-190
Usage: Program is being used for fracture studies at the Kyushu University.
Typical running time: Analysis of two cracks required 40 seconds of CPU time.
Availability: Professor M. Isida, Faculty of Engineering, Kyushu University, Hakozaki, Fukuoka 812, Japan
Reference: [102]

Two-Dimensional Mixed Mode Stress Intensity Prediction in the Presence of a Crack and Arbitrarily Shaped Holes in an Infinite Plate (HOLCRK)

Categories: Static fracture, body force method
Title: Two-Dimensional Mixed Mode Stress Intensity Prediction in the Presence of a Crack and Arbitrarily Shaped Holes in an Infinite Plate, HOLCRK
Author: Y. Murakami, Department of Mechanical Engineering, Kyushu Institute of Technology, Tobata, Kitakyushu, 804 Japan
Maintenance: Same as above
Date: June 1976
Capability: Program yields stress intensity factors K_I and K_{II} for a crack which emanates from or exists in the vicinity of a hole of arbitrary shape
Method: The basis of the analysis is the body force method, but the stress function is used for a point force that is applied at a point of an infinite plate with a stress-free crack. Then the boundary condition at the crack surface is completely satisfied. Only the boundaries of holes are approximated by sets of lines. Thus, only the input data related to boundary points of holes are necessary. Resultant force conditions along boundaries are satisfied by distributing point forces along the boundaries. Integrating all contributions of the distributed point forces to crack tip singularity, the stress intensity factors are automatically calculated [1].
Limitation: Static analysis; load condition is limited to uniform stress at infinity $(\sigma_x, \sigma_y, \tau_{xy})_\infty$.

Documentation: No user manual is available at this time but requests for the analysis will be received.
Input: Nodal points of boundaries of holes; coordinates of nodal points; load condition at infinity ($\sigma_x, \sigma_y, \tau_{xy}$)
Output: Stress intensity factors K_I and K_{II}
Software: Batch
Hardware: Currently operating FACOM-M-190
Usage: The program is being used at the Kyushu Institute of Technology for the analysis of stress intensity factors for a crack which emanates from or exists in the vicinity of various holes.
Typical running time: Most problems that include one crack and one hole can be solved accurately in 60 seconds of CPU time.
Availability: Professor Y. Murakami, Department of Mechanical Engineering, Kyushu Institute of Technology, Tobata, Kitakyushu, 804 Japan
Reference: [104]

Two-Dimensional Mixed Mode Stress Intensity Prediction for Arbitrarily Shaped Plate (MIXSIF)

Categories: Static fracture; body force method
Title: Two-Dimensional Mixed Mode Stress Intensity Prediction for the Arbitrarily Shaped Plate, MIXSIF
Author: Y. Murakami, Department of Mechanical Engineering, Kyushu Institute of Technology, Tobata, Kitakyushu, 804 Japan
Maintenance: Same as above
Date: December 1978
Capability: The program yields stress intensity factors K_I and K_{II} for an inner or edge crack in a plate with an arbitrary shape.
Method: The basic method is the body force method, but the stress function for a point force applied at a point of an infinite plate with a stress-free crack is used. Then, the boundary condition at the crack surface is completely satisfied. The numerical procedure is similar to Ref. [1] but is revised to assure high accuracy with smaller numbers of boundary nodal points. The shape of the plate is arbitrary. The boundaries are approximated with sets of lines. The resultant force boundary conditions are satisfied. Accurate stress intensity factors can be obtained without extrapolation.
Limitation: The program is limited to static analysis. Only the stress boundary condition is designated at this time.
Programming Language: FORTRAN IV
Documentation: No user manual is available at this time but requests for calculations will be answered.
Input: Nodal points of plate boundaries; coordinates of nodal points; stress boundary conditions
Output: Stress intensity factors K_I and K_{II}; crack propagation angle on maximum tangential stress criterion
Software: Batch
Hardware: Currently operating on FACOM M-190
Usage: Program is being used in Kyushu Institute of Technology for the analysis of stress intensity factors K_I and K_{II} and the prediction of the crack propagation path in various plates and boundary conditions.
Typical running time: The case of 12 boundary points required 20 seconds of CPU time. Most of two-dimensional crack problems can be solved accurately in 60 seconds of CPU time.
Availability: Professor Y. Murakami, Department of Mechanical Engineering, Kyushu Institute of Technology, Tobata, Kitakhyshu, 804 Japan
Reference: [105]

A Method of Classical Bending Analysis of the Arbitrarily Shaped Plate with an Elliptical Hole or Notch (SCONCB)

Categories: Static fracture; body force method

Title: A Method of Classical Bending Analysis of the Arbitrarily Shaped Plate with an Elliptical Hole or Notch (SCONCB)

Author: Y. Murakami, Department of Mechanical Engineering, Kyushu Institute of Technology, Tobata, Kitakyushu, 804 Japan, and S. Araki (undergraduate student)

Maintenance: Same as above

Date: March 1978

Capability: The program yields bending and twisting moments (M_x, M_y, M_{xy}) at any point of a plate including an elliptical hole or notch. The shape of the plate is arbitrary.

Method: The basic method is the body force method, but the displacement function is used for a concentrated moment applied at a point of an infinite plate with a moment-free elliptical hole. Then the boundary condition at the elliptical hole is completely satisfied. Other boundaries are approximated by sets of lines. The resultant moment conditions are satisfied by distributing concentrated moments along boundaries. Details of the method are explained in Ref. [106].

Limitation: The program is limited to the Classical Bending Theory. Only moment boundary conditions are satisfied at this time.

Programming Language: FORTRAN IV

Documentation: No user manual is available at this time.

Input: Dimensions of the ellipse, longer and shorter radius a and b; nodal points of boundaries; coordinates of nodal points; load conditions; coordinates at points where the values of moments are wanted.

Output: Moment values at the points designated

Software: Batch

Hardware: Currently operating on FACOM M-190

Usage: The program is being used for the analysis of moment concentration and moment distribution of plates with various shapes.

Typical running time: Most problems can be solved accurately enough in 60 seconds of CPU time.

Availability: Professor Y. Murakami, Department of Mechanical Engineering, Kyushu Institute of Technology, Tobata, Kitakyushu, 804 Japan

Reference: [106]

Stress Concentration Analysis for the Arbitrarily Shaped Plate (SCONCT)

Categories: Static fracture; body force method

Title: Two-Dimensional Stress Concentration Analysis for the Arbitrarily Shaped Plate with an Elliptical Hole or Notch, (SCONCT)

Author: Y. Murakami, Department of Mechanical Engineering, Kyushu Institute of Technology, Tobata, Kitakyushu, 804 Japan

Maintenance: Same as above

Date: February 1976

Capability: Program yields stress ($\sigma_x, \sigma_y, \tau_{xy}$) at any point of a plate including an elliptical hole or notch. The shape of the plate is arbitrary.

Method: The basis of the analysis is the body force method but the stress function for a point force applied at a point of an infinite plate with a stress-free elliptical hole is used. Then, the boundary conditions along the elliptical hole are completely satisfied. Other boundaries are approximated by sets of lines. The resultant force conditions are

satisfied by distributing point forces along boundaries. Details of the method are explained in Ref. [107].
Limitation: Static problem; only the stress boundary condition is allowed at this time.
Programming Language: FORTRAN IV
Documentation: No user manual is available at this time.
Input: Dimensions of ellipse, longer and shorter radius a and b; nodal points of boundaries of the plate; coordinates of nodal points; load conditions; coordinates at points where the values of stresses are wanted
Output: Stress values at the points designated
Software: Batch
Hardware: Currently operating on FACOM M-190
Usage: The program is being used for the analysis of stress concentration and stress distribution of the plates with various shapes.
Typical running time: Most problems can be solved accurately in 60 seconds of CPU time.
Availability: Professor Y. Murakami, Department of Mechanical Engineering, Kyushu Institute of Technology, Tobata, Kitakyushu, 804 Japan
Reference: [107]

Stress Intensity Analysis for a Spin Disk (SPDISK)

Categories: Static fracture; body force method
Title: Stress Intensity Analysis for a Spin Disk (SPDISK)
Authors: Y. Murakami, Department of Mechanical Engineering, Kyushu Institute of Technology, Tobata, Kitakyushu, 804 Japan; H. Nisitani, Faculty of Engineering, Kyushu University, Fukuoka, 812 Japan
Maintenance: Y. Murakami, Kyushu Institute of Technology
Date: April 1974
Capability: The program yields the stress intensity factor K_I for various combinations of dimensions of hollow spin disks with two symmetrical cracks which emanate from an inner hole.
Method: The basis of the analysis is the body force method, but the stress function is used for a point force applied at a point of an infinite plate with a stress-free circular hole. Then the boundary conditions at the surface of an inner hole are completely satisfied. The boundary conditions along the outer boundary and the crack surface are satisfied by distributing the body force. Details of the method are explained in Ref. [108].
Limitation: Static analysis; the sizes of two cracks are the same at this time.
Programming Language: FORTRAN IV
Documentation: No user manual is available at this time.
Input: Control information related to a circular plate or cylinder; crack length; inner and outer radius; division number related to outer boundary and crack part
Output: Stress intensity correction factors in various expressions
Software: Batch
Hardware: Currently operating on FACOM M-190
Usage: The program is being used at the Kyushu Institute of Tehcnology for the analysis of stress intensity factors for a spin disk with cracks. The program is being improved for the analysis of more general cases.
Typical running time: Most of the problems can be solved accurately in 60 seconds of CPU time.
Availability: Professor Y. Murakami, Department of Mechanical Engineering, Kyushu Institute of Technology, Tobata, Kitakyushu, 804 Japan

Reference: [108]

Two-Dimensional Crack Problems in a Semi-Infinite Plate (TCPSIP)

Categories: Static fracture, body force method
Title: Two-Dimensional Crack Problems in a Semi-Infinite Plate, TCPSIP
Author: H. Nisitani, Faculty of Engineering, Kyushu University, Rukuoka, 812 Japan
Date: October 1971
Capability: Program yields K_I values of a semi-infinite plate with various types of cracks: for example, two inclined edge cracks having different size and angle, a bent-edge crack, and an elliptic-arc notch with a crack, etc. The other examples are found in Ref. [109-112]. The K_I value of the infinite plate obtained by the symmetry operation of a semi-infinite plate is also calculated.
Method: The body force method [112] is used. The values of K_I are obtained from the density of the body force distributed at the prospective crack site. By increasing the number of divisions, the solution becomes exact. The final results are determined by extrapolation.
Limitation: Not specified
Programming Language: FORTRAN IV
Documentation: No user manual is available at this time.
Input: Shape of notches or cracks; numbers of divisions; some other geometrical factors
Output: Body force densities at each division; stress intensity or concentration factor
Software Operation: Batch
Hardware: Currently operating on FACOM M-190
Usage: Program is being used at Kyushu University for the analysis of fatigue problems.
Typical running time: The calculation of K_I of a semielliptical notch with a crack required 20 seconds of CPU time in the case where the numbers of divisions of the notch and crack were 80 and 20, respectively.
Availability: Professor H. Nisitani, Faculty of Engineering, Kyushu University, Fukuoka, 812 Japan
Reference: [109-112]

Three-Dimensional Interference Analysis of Two Semielliptical Cracks of the Same Size (TWELLI)

Categories: Static fracture; body force method
Title: Three-Dimensional Interference Analysis of Two Semielliptical Cracks of the Same Size (TWELLI)
Authors: H. Nisitani, Faculty of Engineering, Kyushu University, Fukuoka, 812 Japan; Y. Murakami, Department of Mechanical Engineering, Kyushu Institute of Technology, Tobata, Kitakyushu, 804 Japan
Maintenance: Same as above
Date: August 1979
Capability: Program yields stress intensity factors along the crack front of two semielliptical cracks.
Method: The body force method is used. The numerical procedure used is the same as in Ref. [113]. The domain to become an elliptical crack is divided into fan-shaped areas designated by input data. Dividing is done automatically in the program. The stress intensity factors are computed from the density of body force distributed at prospective crack sites. By increasing the number of divided areas, the solution becomes exact.

The final results are obtained by extrapolation. The stress intensity factors K_I along the crack front are calculated for various configurations of two semielliptical cracks, i.e., the shape of the semielliptical crack and the mutual distance between two semielliptical cracks.

Limitation: Static analysis; Poisson's ratio must be kept equal to zero.

Programming Language: FORTRAN IV

Documentation: No user manual is available at this time.

Input: Shape of the ellipse, i.e., two radii a and b; number of divisions; mutual distance between two semiellipses

Output: Body force densities at each divided area; stress intensity factors along a semielliptical crack front

Software: Batch

Hardware: Currently operating on FACOM-M-190

Usage: Program is being used at Kyushu University and Kyushu Institute of Technology for the analysis of interference effect between two semielliptical cracks of the same size.

Typical running time: The case of 16 divided areas required 52 seconds of CPU time. But the case of 64 divided areas required 830 seconds of CPU time.

Availability: Professor H. Nisitani, Faculty of Engineering, Kyushu University; Professor Y. Murakami, Dept. of Mechanical Engineering, Kyushu Institute of Technology

Reference: [113]

Axisymmetric Elasto-Plastic Fracture Analysis (EPAX)

Categories: Elasto-plastic fracture; method of lines

Title: Axisymmetric Elasto-Plastic Fracture Analysis (EPAX)

Authors: L. S. Fu, S. N. Malik, Department of Engineering Mechanics, The Ohio State University, Columbus, OH 43210

Maintenance: Same as above

Date: December 1977

Capability: The program yields the stresses and displacements at nodes, the stress intensity factor (for elastic loading), the crack-opening displacement, the J-integral, the plastic zone growth and the load and load-point displacement curve for an elastic/plastic, nonlinear, work hardening, axially loaded, and finite cylinders with either internal or external planar cracks perpendicular to the axis of loading.

Method: The method of lines is used to discretize the region and to reduce the governing equations in elasto-plasticity to sets of ordinary differential equations. An iterative scheme is devised to determine the increments of the displacements and the stresses at nodes [114]. A start-up elasticity solution algorithm is attached for handling boundary value problems with appropriately prescribed boundary values before the first yielding is detected. The computational procedure used for elasticity solutions follows that of Irobe [115] and Gyekenyesi and Mendelson [116]. The growth of the plastic zone is determined by scanning nodes where the yield condition is satisfied. The crack tip location is determined by the two-term expansion procedure through which the stress intensity factor is computed. The crack-opening displacement and the load and load-point displacement plot are direct computational results from displacements at nodes. The J-integral values are computed from chosen paths.

Limitation: The formulation is based on small strain and axial symmetry. Although the prediction of stable crack growth can be obtained with the criterion for growth prescribed, this has not yet been done.

Programming Language: FORTRAN IV
Documentation: No user manual is available at this time.
Input: Control information, numbers of different material properties, geometric dimensions, nodal points, lines, pressure, and displacement boundary conditions are required for the elasticity solution. In addition, the load increment steps for the elasto-plasticity solution must be prescribed.
Output: The stresses, displacements, and first normal derivatives of displacements at nodes, the stress intensity factor for elastic loading, crack-opening displacement, the J-integral, and the growth of plastic zone size
Software Operation: Batch
Hardware: Currently operating on IBM 370/168 and AMDAHL 470 time-sharing systems
Usage: The program is being used at the Ohio State University for elasto-plastic crack analysis with possible extension to include stable crack growth.
Typical running time: For any given crack length with thirteen lines in both the radial and the z-directions, a typical computer run requires 180 seconds of CPU time.
Availability: Professor L. S. Fu, Department of Engineering Mechanics, The Ohio State University, Columbus, OH 43210
References: [114-116]

Creep Crack Growth Analysis (CCGDAM)

Categories: Creep crack growth, damage function in creep rupture
Title: Creep Crack Growth Analysis (CCGDAM)
Author: L. S. Fu, Department of Engineering Mechanics, The Ohio State University, Columbus, OH 43210
Maintenance: Same as above
Date: October 1978
Capability: The program yields incubation time, crack growth rate,and time to failure.
Method: The phenomenological theory of brittle creep rupture [1] is used to describe crack growth rates in a cracked body under steady state creep conditions. Through the use of Norton's creep law and the double cantilever model, the rate of change of the damage function is governed by an integro-differential equation. A step-by-step procedure is devised to give the damage function at discrete points as the time changes [2]. The material is taken to be perfect at initial time and it is assumed that compressive stresses make no contribution to the damage. The coordinate is moved to a new origin after each step of crack growth. The program can be used to study creep crack growth for a variety of technical alloys.
Limitations: Although other geometries and creep laws can be incorporated, this program is written for the double cantilever beam models and Norton's law, respectively.
Programming Language: FORTRAN IV
Documentation: User's manual and computer program are available.
Input: Control information, numbers of different material properties including those from tension, creep and creep rupture tests, numbers of geometric dimensions, crack growth steps (before crack speed changes), time steps, and sustained load are required. That the material is disintegrated when the damage function reaches zero magnitude is the criterion for growth.
Output: Damage function, damage rate, stress intensity factor, crack tip

strain rate, incubation time, creep crack growth rate, time to failure
Software: Batch
Hardware: Currently operating on IBM 370/168
Usage: The program is being used for creep crack growth studies at the Ohio State University.
Typical running time: For Δx=0.002 and Δt=0.005, a typical run on the IBM 370/168 is 50 seconds of CPU time.
Availability: Professor L. S. Fu, Department of Engineering Mechanics, The Ohio State University, Columbus, OH 43210
References: [117,118]

Two-Dimensional Wave Propagation (TROTT)

Categories: Finite difference, wave propagation
Title: Two-Dimensional Wave Propagation (TROTT)
Author: L. Seaman, SRI International, Menlo Park, CA 94025
Maintenance: Same
Date: 1978
Capability: Two-dimensional (planar or axisymmetric) wave propagation caused by impact, explosion, or imposed velocity boundary conditions; with a crack in the field, crack growth occurs by the nucleation, growth, and coalescence of microdamage in cells in the vicinity of the crack tip. J can be computed during the growth process.
Method: Finite difference, artificial viscosity code based on von Neumann and Richtmyer method
Limitation: The program is limited to two-dimensional solids. The layout of cells is currently limited to K-J lines and quadrilateral or triangular cells.
Programming Language: FORTRAN IV
Documentation: "TROTT Computer Program for Two-Dimensional Stress Wave Propagation," Final Report to Ballistic Research Laboratory, Aberdeen, Maryland, by L. Seaman, SRI International, August 1978.
Input: Control and printing information, material layout into grid, material properties including special nucleation and growth damage, parameters
Output: Stresses, velocities, and microdamage levels at cells, plus J at each time step
Software Operation: Batch
Hardware: CDC 6400 and CDC 7600
Usage: Primarily used in large-deformation projectile penetration simulations and in detonation-caused phenomena.
Typical running time: 20 min. to 3 hours on 6400
Availability: L. Seaman, SRI International, Menlo Park, CA 94025

PROJECTED REQUIREMENTS

The well-known requirement for static LEFM is the accurate determination of K_I, K_{II}, K_{III} at moderate computer costs. While most two-dimensional codes are easily available or can be developed with moderate efforts, most of the known three-dimensional codes are not generally available outside of the developer's organization. The limited three-dimensional codes in the public domain normally require inordinate computer time to generate numerical solutions of questionable accuracy. While one obvious solution is the development of faster and larger computers to execute the large and time-consuming three-dimensional codes, perhaps a greater effort should be expended in developing efficient solution procedures which can be executed on the present computers.

Another requirement in LEFM is the development of efficient algorithms to handle crack extension under stable crack growth or dynamic crack propagation. While the current codes are generally limited to two-dimensional problems, and are mostly for crack extension in the plane of the original crack surface, a numerical algorithm which can handle crack extension in an arbitrary direction is needed not only in two-dimensional but also in three-dimensional analysis. The latter is virtually an untouched field at this time.

As for computer codes for ductile fracture analysis, the same requirements mentioned above are valid with the replacement of stress intensity factors with ductile fracture parameters, such as the J-integral values, COD, and crack tip opening displacement (CTOA). An obvious need is to account for the Baushinger's effect in the unloaded region trailing the extending crack tip. Large deformations and large strains which exist in the vicinity of the crack tip and which result in crack tip blunting must be incorporated in the numerical analysis for meaningful results in the presence of large scale yielding. Again, three-dimensional analysis of the elastic-plastic state surrounding a crack tip subjected to mixed mode loading is nonexistent.

With the extension of fracture mechanics to structural components subjected to high-temperature environments, the time-dependent deformation process must be incorporated into the analysis. Since this creep process introduces another variable into the already overburdened elastic-plastic, large-deformation, and variable material property computer codes, and increases the computer cost by another order, its general use in hardware design appears prohibitive at this time. Again, the need for efficient and innovative numerical algorithms is noted.

ACKNOWLEDGMENT

The author gratefully acknowledges the efforts of the respondents to his questionnaires without which this paper would not have been a reality.

REFERENCES

1. Tada, H., Paris, P., and Irwin, G., "The Stress Analysis of Cracks Handbook," Del Research Corporation, 1973.

2. Sih, G. C., "Handbook of Stress Intensity Factors," Institute of Fracture and Solid Mechanics, Lehigh University, 1973.

3. Rooke, D. P., amd Cartwright, D. J., "Compendium of Stress Intensity Factors," Her Majesty's Stationary Office, 1976.

4. Gallagher, R. C., "A Review of Finite Element Techniques in Fracture Mechanics," Numerical Methods in Fracture Mechanics, ed. A. R. Luxmoore and D. R. J. Owen, University College of Swansea, January 1978, pp. 1-25.

5. Jacobs, J. A., "Relaxation Methods Applied to Problems of Plastic Flaw I, Notched Bar Under Tension," Philosophical Magazine, Vol. 41, 1950, pp. 349-361.

6. Pian, T. H. H., "Crack Element," Proceedings of the World Congress on Finite Element Methods in Structural Mechanics, Vol. 1, Bournemouth, England, 1975, pp. F.1-39.

7. Gross, B., Srawley, J. E., and Brown, W. F., "Stress Intensity Factors for a Single-Edge-Notch Tension Specimen by Boundary Collocation of Stress Function," NASA TN D-2395, August 1964.

8. Bowie, O. L., "Rectangular Tensile Sheet with Symmetric Edge Cracks," Journal of Applied Mechanics, Transaction of ASME, Vol. 31, 1964, pp. 726-728.

9. Isida, M., "On the Tension of a Strip with a Central Elliptical Hole," Transaction of the Japan Society of Mechanical Engineers, Vol. 21, No. 107, 1955, pp. 507-518.

10. Kobayashi, A. S., "Numerical Analysis in Fracture Mechanics," Experimental Techniques in Fracture Mechanics, 2, ed. A. S. Kobayashi, Society for Experimental Stress Analysis, 1975, pp. 166-199.

11. Elastic-Plastic Fracture, ed. J. P. Landes, J. A. Begley, and G. A. Clarke, ASTM STP 668, 1979.

12. Raju, I. S., and Newman, J. C., "Analyses of Surface Cracks in Finite Plates Under Tension or Bending Loads," NASA TP -1578, December 1979.

13. Atluri, S. N., Nakagaki, M., Kathiresan, K., Rhee, H. C., and Chen, W. H., "Hybrid Finite Element Models for Linear and Nonlinear Fracture Analyses," Numerical Methods in Fracture Mechanics, ed. A. R. Luxmoore and D. R. J. Owen, University College of Swansea, January 1978, pp. 52-66.

14. Marcal, P. V., "Three-Dimensional Finite Element Analysis for Fracture Mechanics," The Surface Crack: Physical Problems and Computational Solutions, ed. J. L. Swedlow, ASME, 1972, pp. 187-202.

15. Smith. F. W., and Kullgren, T. E., "Theoretical and Experimental Analysis of Surface Cracks Emanating from Fastener Holes," Air Force Flight Dynamic Laboratory AFFDL-TR-76-104, February 1977.

16. Nishitani, H., and Murakami, Y., "Stress Intensity Factors of an Elliptical Crack or a Semi-Elliptical Crack Subjected to Tension," International Journal of Fracture, Vol. 10, No. 3, 1974, pp. 353-368.

17. Cruse, T. A., "Application of the Boundary-Integral Equation Method to Three-Dimensional Stress Analysis," Computers and Structures, Vol. 3, 1973, pp. 509-527.

18. Chen, Y. M., and Wilkins, M. L., "Fracture Analysis with a Three-Dimensional, Time-Dependent Computer Program," International Journal of Fracture, Vol. 12, 1976, pp. 607-617.

19. Kobayashi, A. S., Emery, A. F., and Mall, S., "Dynamic-Finite-Element and Dynamic-Photoelastic Analyses of Two Fracturing Homalite-100 Plates," Experimental Mechanics, Vol. 16, No. 9, September 1976, pp. 321-328.

20. Ingraffea, A. R., "Nodal Grafting for Crack Propagation Studies," International Journal of Numerical Methods in Engineering, Vol. 11, 1977, pp. 1185-1187.

21. Barsoum, R. S., "On the Use of Isoparametric Finite Elements in Linear Fracture Mechanics," International Journal of Numerical Methods in Engineering, Vol. 10, 1976, pp. 25-37.

22. Shih, C. F., de Lorenzi, H. G., and German, M. D., "Crack Extension Modeling with Singular Quadratic Isoparametric Elements," International Journal of Fracture, Vol. 12, 1976, pp. 647-651

23. Ingraffea, A. R., and Cornelia, M., "Stress Intensity Factor Computation in Three-Dimensions with Quarter-Point Elements," to be published.

24. Watwood, V. B., "Finite Element Method for Prediction of Crack Behavior," Nuclear Engineering and Design, Vol. 11, No. 2, March 1970, pp. 323-332.

25. Hellen, T. K., and Blackburn, W. S., "The Calculation of Stress Intensity Factors in Two- and Three-Dimensions Using Finite Elements," Computational Fracture Mechanics, ed. E. F. Rybicki and S. E. Bengley, ASME.

26. Rice, J. R., "A Path Independent Integral and the Approximate Analysis of Strain Concentrating by Notches and Cracks," Journal of Applied Mechanics, Transaction of ASME, Series E, Vol. 35, 1968, pp. 379-386.

27. Needleman, A., and Shih, C. F., "Finite Element Method for Plane Strain Deformations of Incompressible Solids," in Computer Methods in Applied Mechanics and Engineering, 1978, pp. 223-240.

28. Shih, C. F., "J-Integral Estimates for Strain Hardening Materials in Antiplane Shear Using Fully Plastic Solutions," in Mechanics of Crack Growth, ASTM Special Technical Publication 590, 1976, pp. 3-22.

29. Hutchinson, J. W., Needleman, A., and Shih, C. F., "Fully Plastic

Crack Problems in Bending and Tension," Fracture Mechanics, ed. N. Perrone et al., University Press of Virginia, Charlottesville, VA, 1978, pp. 515-528.

30. Kumar, V., and Shih, C. F., "Fully Plastic Crack Solutions, Estimation Scheme, and Stability Analyses for Compact Specimen," presented at the ASTM Symposium on Fracture Mechanics, St. Louis, MO, May 1979.

31. Hutchinson, J. W., "Singularity Behavior at the End of a Tensile Crack in a Hardening Material," Journal of Mechanics and Physics of Solids, Vol. 16, 1968, pp. 13-31.

32. Rice, J. R., and Rosengren, G. F., "Plane Strain Deformation Near a Crack Tip in a Power Hardening Material," Journal of Mechanics and Physics of Solids, Vol. 16, 1968, pp. 1-12.

33. Yagawa, G., Nishioka, T., Ando, Y., and Ogawa, N., "The Finite Element Calculation of Stress Intensity Factors Using Superposition," Computational Fracture Mechanics, ed. E. F. Rybicki and S. Benzley, ASME, 1978, pp. 31-34.

34. Lin, K. Y., Tong, P., and Orringer, O., "Effect of Shape and Size on Hybrid Crack Containing Elements," Computational Fracture Mechanics, ed. E. F. Rybicki and S. Benzley, ASME, 1975, p. 1-20.

35. Atluri, S., Kobayashi, A. S., and Nakagaki, M., "An Assumed Displacement Hybrid Finite Element Model for Linear Fracture Mechanics," International Journal of Fracture Mechanics, Vol. 11, 1975, pp. 257-271.

36. Atluri, S. N., Kobayashi, A. S. and Nakagaki, M., "Fracture Mechanics Application of a Hybrid Displacement Finite Element Model," AIAA Journal, Vol. 13, No. 6, 1975, pp. 734-739.

37. Rhee, H. C., Atluri, S. N., Moriya, T. and Pian, T. H. H., "Hybrid Finite Element Procedures for Analyzing Through Flaws in Plates in Bending," Paper M-2/4, Trans. 4th SMIRT, San Francisco, August 1977, Vol. M.

38. Atluri, S. N., and Nakagaki, M., "J-Integral Estimates for Strain-Hardening Materials in Ductile Fracture Problems," AIAA Journal, Vol. 15, No. 7, 1977, pp. 842-851

39. Atluri, S. N., Nakagaki, M. and Chen, W. H., "Fracture Analysis Under Large-Scale Plastic Yielding: A Finite Deformation, Embedded Singularity, Elasto-Plastic Incremental Finite Element Solution," in Flaw Growth and Fracture, ASTM STP 631, 1977, pp. 42-61.

40. Atluri, S. N., Nakagaki, M. and Chen, W. H., "Fracture Initiation in Plane Ductile Fracture Problems: An Elastic-Plastic Finite Element Incremental Analysis,"in Pressure Vessel Technology Part II. Materials and Fabridation, ASME, New York, 1977, pp. 579-593.

41. Nakagaki, M., Chen, W. H., and Atluri, S. N., "A Finite Element Analysis of Stable Crack Growth" in Elastic-Plastic Fracture, ed. J. Landes and J. Begley, ASTM STP, 668, 1979, pp. 195-213.

42. Nakagaki, M., and Atluri, S. N., "Elastic-Plastic Finite Element Analyses of Fatigue Crack Growth in Mode I and II Conditions," NASA CR-158987, 83 pages.

43. Atluri, S. N., Nishioka, T., and Nakagaki, M., "Numerical Modeling of Nonlinear and Dynamic Crack Propagation in Finite Bodies, by Moving Singular Elements," in Nonlinear and Dynamic Fracture Mechanics, ed. N. Perrone and S. Atluri, ASME AMD, Vol. 35, 1979, pp. 37-67.

44. Atluri, S. N., Kathiresan, K. and Kobayashi, A, S., "Three-Dimensional Linear Fracture Mechanics Analysis by a Displacement-Hybrid Finite Element Model," Paper No. L-7/3, Trans. 3rd SMIRT, CEES, CESA, Luxembourg, Brussels, Vol. L.

45. Atluri, S. N., and Kathiresan, K., "Stress Analysis of Typical Flaws in Aerospace Structural Components Using 3-D Hybrid Displacement Finite Element Method," AIAA Paper 78-513, 19th AIAA/ASME/SDM Conference, Bethesda, MD, April 1978, pp. 340-351.

46. Atluri, S. N., and Kathiresan, K., "3 D Analysis of Surface Flaws in Thick-Walled Reactor Vessels Using Displacement Hybrid Finite Element Method," Nuclear Engineering and Design, Vol. 51, No. 2, 1979, pp. 163-176.

47. Nishioka, T., and Atluri, S. N., "Fracture-Stress Analysis of Through-Cracks in Angle-Ply Laminates: An Efficient Assumed-Stress Finite Element Approach - Part I," AIAA, 20th Structures, Structural Dynamics and Materials Conference, St. Louis, MO, April 4-6, 1979.

48. Atluri, S. N., Nishioka, T., and Nakagaki, M., "Numerical Modeling of Dynamic and Nonlinear Crack Propagation in Finite Bodies, by Moving Singular-Elements," ASME AMD,Vol. 35, 1979, pp. 37-66.

49. Bradford, L. G., Dong, S. B., Nicol, D. A. C.,and Westman, R. A., "Applications of Global-Local Finite Element Analysis," Transaction of the 4th International Conference on Structural Mechanics in Reactor Technology, Vol. M, CECA, CEE AND CEEA, Luxembourg, 1977, M2/2.

50. Yamamoto, Y., and Tokuda, H., "Determination of Stress Intensity Factors in Cracked Plates by Finite Element Method," International Journal of Numerical Methods in Engineering, Vol. 6, 1973, pp. 427-439.

51. Freund, L. B., "Crack Propagation in an Elastic Solid Subjected to General Loading-II Non-Uniform Rate of Extension," Journal of Mechanics and Physics of Solids, Vol. 20, 1972, pp. 141-152.

52. Bueckener, H. F., "Field Singularities and Related Integral Representation," Methods of Analysis of Solutions of Crack Problems, ed. G. C. Sih, Vol. I, Noordhoff International, 1973.

53. Barrachin, B., Bhandari, S., Kobayashi, A. S., Picou, J. L., and Sarthe, M. H., "Stress-Intensity-Factors for Complex Cracked Structures Under Arbitrary Loading," to be published in the Proceedings of the Fourth International Conference on Pressure Vessel Technology, May 19-23, 1980, London.

54. Nishitani, H., and Murakami, Y., "Interaction of Elastic-Plastic Cracks Subjected to a Uniform Tensile Stress in an Infinite or Semi-Infinite Plate," Proceedings of International Conference on Mechanical Behavior of Materials, Vol. 1, Society of Material Science Japan, 1972, pp. 346-356.

55. Eshelby, J. D., "The Determination of the Elastic Field of an Ellipsoidal Inclusion and Related Problems," Proceedings of the Royal Society, London, Series A, 1957, pp. 376-396.

56. Fu, L. S., and Malik, S. M., "The Methods of Lines Applied to Crack Problems Including Plasticity Effects," Computers and Structures, Vol. 10, 1979, pp. 447-456.

57. Seaman, L., Curran, D. R., and Shockey, D. A., "Computational Models for Ductile and Brittle Fracture," Journal of Applied Physics, Vol. 47, No. 11, 1976, pp. 4814-4826.

58. Shockey, D. A., Seaman, L., and Curran, D. R., "Microfailure Models and Their Application to Nonlinear Dynamic Fracture," Nonlinear and Dynamic Fracture Mechanics, ed. N. Perrone and S. N. Atluri, ASME AMD-Vol. 35, pp. 79-104.

59. Gifford, L. N., "APES - Second Generation Two-Dimensional Fracture Mechanics and Stress Analysis by Finite Elements," David W. Taylor Naval Ship R & D Center Report 4799, Dec. 1975 (ADA 025217).

60. Gifford, L. N., and Hilton, P. D., "Stress Intensity Factors by Enriched Finite Elements," Engineering Fracture Mechanics, Vol. 10, No. 3, 1978, pp. 485-496.

61. Gifford, L. N., "APES - Finite Element Fracture Mechanics Analysis: Revised Documentations," David Taylor Naval Ship R & D Center Report 79/023, March 1979 (ADA066246).

62. Hinton and Owen, Finite Element Programming, Academic Press, 1977.

63. Lin, K. W., and Mar, J. W., "Finite Element Analysis of Stress Intensity Factors for Cracks at a Bi-Material Interface," Int. J. Fracture, Vol. 12, No. 4, August 1976, pp. 521-531.

64. Orringer, O., French, S. E., and Weinrich, M., "User's Guide for the Finite Element Analysis Library and the Element Generator Library", Aeroplastic and Structures Research Laboratory Report, ASRL TR 1024, MIT, January 1978.

65. Wilson, E. L., "SOLID SAP, A Static Analysis Program for Three-dimensional Solid Structures," Report UC SESM 71-19, University of California, Berkeley, 1972.

66. Labbens, R., Pellissier-Tanon, A., Heliot, J., "Practical Method for Calculating S Intensity Factors Through Weight Functions," ASTM-STP 590-1976, pp. 368-384.

67. Heliot, J., Vagner, J., "Use of the Weight Function Concept and the Crack Closing Method for Calculating Stress Intensity Factors in Plane or Axisymmetric Problems," Fracture 1977, Vol. II, ICF-4, Waterloo, Canada, June 19-24, 1977.

68. Shih, C. F., and Kumar, V., "Estimation Technique for the Prediction of Elastic-Plastic Fracture of Structural Components of Nuclear Systems," First Semiannual Report to EPRI, Contract No. RP1237-1, General Electric Co., Schenectady, NY, June 1, 1979.

69. Newman, J., Jr., and Armen, H., Jr., "Elastic-Plastic Analysis of a Propagation Crack Under Cyclic Loading," AIAA Journal, Vol. 13, August 1974, pp. 1017-1023.

70. Armen, H., Salame, E., Pifko, A., and Levine, H., "Non-Linear Crack Analysis with Finite Elements," Numerical Solution of Nonlinear Structural Problems; ed. R. F. Hartung, ASME AMD, Vol. 6, 1973.

71. Armen, H., Jr., "Application of a Substructuring Technique to the Problem of Crack Extension and Closure," Grumman Research Department Report RE-480, July 1974, also NASA CR-132458.

72. Yamamoto, Y.,and Sumi, Y., "Stress Intensity Factors for Three-Dimensional Cracks," Int. J. Fracture, Vol. 14, 1978, pp. 17-38.

73. Yamamoto, Y., and Sumi, Y., "Finite Element Analysis for Stress Intensity Factors," in Computing Methods in Applied Sciences and Engineering, 1977, 1, Lecture Notes in Mathematics 704, Springer-Verlag, 1979, pp. 154-168.

74. Bathe, K. J., "ADINA - A Finite Element Program for Automatic Dynamic Incremental Nonlinear Analysis," 82448-1, Acoustics and Vibration Laboratory, M.I.T., Department of Mechanical Engineering, September 1975, rev. December 1978.

75. Bathe, K. J., "Static and Dynamic Geometric and Material Nonlinear Analysis Using ADINA," 82448-2, Acoustics and Vibration Laboratory, M.I.T., Department of Mechanical Engineering, May 1976, rev. May 1977.

76. Bathe, K. J., ed. , "Applications Using ADINA - Proceedings of the ADINA Conference August 1977," 82448-6, Acoustics and Vibration Laboratory, M.I.T., Department of Mechanical Engineering, August 1977.

77. Bathe, K. J., ed. , "Nonlinear Finite Element Analysis and ADINA-Proceedings of the ADINA Conference August 1979," 82448-9, Acoustics and Vibration Laboratory, M.I.T., Department of Mechanical Engineering, August 1979.

78. Bathe, K. J., "ADINAT - A Finite Element Program for Automatic Dynamic Incremental Nonlinear Analysis of Temperatures," 82448-5, Acoustics and Vibration Laboratory, M.I.T., Department of Mechanical Engineering, May 1977, rev. December 1978.

79. Bathe, K. J., and Cimento, A., "Some Practical Procedures for the Solution of Nonlinear Finite Element Equations," J. Comp. Meth. in Appl. Mech. and Eng., in press.

80. Dingwell, I. W., "ADINAP - Piping Analysis Program," A. D. Little, Acorn Park, Cambridge, Mass.

81. Bathe, K. J., "On the Current State of Finite Element Methods and our ADINA Endeavors," in Proceedings of the ADINA Conference August 1979, (ref. [4] above).

82. Bathe, K. J., ADINA Information Letter, January 4, 1978.

83. Bathe, K. J., "ADINA: A Finite Element Program for Automatic Dynamic Incremental Nonlinear Analysis," M.I.T. Report No. 82448-1.

84. DeLorenzi, H. G., "J-Integral and Crack Growth Calculations with the Finite Element Program ADINA," General Electric Report SRD-78-124, August 1978.

85. DeLorenzi, H. G., and Shih, C. F., "Application of ADINA to Elastic-Plastic Fracture Problems," in Proceedings, ADINA User's Conference, Report No. 82448-6, Cambridge, MA, 1977.

86. Shih, C. F., Andrews, W. R., deLorenzi, H. G., German, M. D., et al., "Methodology for Plastic Fracture," Final Report to EPRI (under preparation), Contract No. RP601-2, General Electric Co., Schenectady, NY.

87. Parks, D. M., "A Stiffness Derivative Finite Element Technique for Determination of Elastic Crack Tip Stress Intensity Factors," International Journal of Fractures, Vol. 10, No. 4, December 1974, pp. 487-502.

88. Barsoum, R. S., "On the Use of Isoparametric Finite Elements in Linear Fracture Mechanics," International Journal Num. Methods in Engineering, Vol. 10, 1976, pp. 25-37.

89. Launay, P., Charpenet, G., and Vouillon C., Nuclear Engineering and Design, 1968.

90. Charpenet, G., Vouillon C., PTRC - Bridge Program Reviews, 1971.

91. Launay, P., Charpenet, G., Vouillon, C., SMIRT 1971.

92. Hasselin, G., Heliot, J., Vouillon, C., SMIRT 1973.

93. D'Escatha, Y., Devaux, J. C., ASTM Symposium on Elastic Plastic Fracture, Atlanta, Georgia, U.S.A., November 1977.

94. D'Escatha, Y., Devaux, J. C., Lederman, P., Mudry, F., "Fracture Resistance of Reactor Components," Berlin, 1979.

95. Key, S. W., "HONDO. A Finite Element Computer Program for the Large Deformation Response of Axisymmetric Solids," Sandia Laboratory Report SLA-74-0039, April 1974.

96. Blandford, G. E., Ingraffea, A. R., and Liggett, J. A., "SIF Computations Using the BEM," in preparation.

97. Lachat, J. C., "Further Developments of the Boundary Integral Technique for Elasto Statics," Thesis, Southampton, February 1975.

98. Watson, J. W., and Lachat, J. C., "Integral Equations Illustrated by Examples," Computed Method in Applied Mechanics and Engineering, Vol. 10, No. 3, 1977.

99. Chaudouet, A., Loubignac, G., "Analysis of Bodies of Incompressible Materials under Thermal Loading by the Boundary Integral Equation Method," International Conference on Numerical Method in Thermal Problems, University College of Swansea, July 1979.

100. Heliot, J., Labbens, R. C., and Pellissier-Tanon, A., "Semi-Elliptical Cracks in a Cylinder Subjected to Stress Gradients," ASMT-STP 677, 1979.

101. Smith, F. W., and Kullgren, T. E., "Theoretical and Experimental Analysis of Surface Cracks Emanating from Fastener Holes," Air Force Flight Dynamics Laboratory Report AFFDL-TR-76-104, February 1977.

102. Isida, M., "A New Procedure of the Body Force Method with Applications to Fracture Mechanics," Proc. First Intern. Conf. Numer. Meth. Frac. Mech., Swansea, January 1978, pp. 81-94.

103. Murakami, Y.,"A Method of Analysis of Stress Intensity Factors for a Crack Which Emanates from or Exists in the Vicinity of an Arbitrarily Shaped Hole," Trans. Japan Soc. Mech. Engrs., Vol. 44, No. 378, 1978, pp. 423-432.

104. Murakami, Y., "Application of the Body Force Method to the Calculation of Stress Intensity Factors for a Crack in the Arbitrarily Shaped Plate," Engineering Fracture Mechanics, Vol. 10, 1978, pp. 497-513.

105. Murakami, Y., Araki, S., "A Method of Classical Bending Analysis of the Arbitrarily-Shaped Plate with an Elliptical Hole or Notch," Trans.

Japan Soc. Mech. Engrs., Vol. 45, No. 397, 1979, pp. 998-1006.

106. Murakami, Y., "A Method of Plane Stress Analysis of Stress Concentration for the Arbitrarily Shaped Plate with an Elliptical Hole or Notch," Trans. Japan Soc. Mech. Engrs., Vol. 43, No. 372, 1977, pp. 2837-2844.

107. Murakami, Y., Nisitani, H., "Stress Intensity Factors for a Spin Disk with Two Symmetrical Cracks Which Emanate from the Inner Hole," Trans. Japan Soc. Mech. Engrs., Vol. 41, No. 348, 1975, pp. 2255-2264.

108. Nisitani, H., "Solutions of Notch Problems by Body Force Method," Mechanics of Fracture 5, edited by G. C. Sih, Nordhoff International Publishing, Leiden, 1978, p. 1.

109. Nisitani, H., "Interference Effects among Cracks or Notches in Two-Dimensional Problems," Proc. Inter. Conf. Frac. Mech. Tech.,Vol. II, 1977, 1127.

110. Nisitani, H., "A Method for Calculating Stress Concentrations and Its Application," Strength and Structure of Solid Materials, Nordhoff International Publishing, Leiden, 1977, p. 53.

111. Nisitani, H., "The Two-Dimensional Stress Problems Solved Using an Electric Digital Computer," Bull. Japan Soc. Mech. Engng., 11-43, 1968, p. 14.

112. Nisitani, H., and Murakami, Y., "Stress Intensity Factors of an Elliptical Crack or a Semi-Elliptical Crack Subject to Tension," International Journ. Frac. Mech., Vol. 10, No. 3, 1974, pp. 353-368.

113. Fu, L. S., and Malik, S. M., "The Method of Lines Applied to Crack Problems Including Plasticity Effect," Computers and Structures, Vol. 10, 1979, pp. 447-456.

114. Irobe, M., "Method of Numerical Analysis for Three Dimensional Elastic Problems," Proceedings 16th Japan National Congress for Applied Mechanic, Central Scientific Publications, 1968, pp. 1-7.

115. Gyekenyesi, J. P., and Mendelson, A., "Three Dimensional Elastic Stress and Displacement Analysis of Finite Geometry Solids Containing Cracks," Internation Journal of Fracture, Vol. 11, 1975, pp. 409-429.

116. Odquist, F. K. G., "Mathematical Theories of Creep and Creep Rupture," Clarendon Press, Oxford, 1966.

117. Fu, L. S., "A Model of Quasi-Static Crack Growth in a DCB at Elevated Temperature," paper No. L 5/8, 5th. Int. Conf. on SMIRT, Berlin, West Germany, 1979.

Table 1 Program Data

NAME	SOURCE	DESCRIPTION	DATE AVAIL.	COMPUTER	LANGUAGE
APES	David W. Taylor Naval Ship R & D Center	Combined mode static stress intensity factors and stress analysis for 2-D and axisymmetric structures. Highly user-oriented. Production program.	3/79	CDC 6400 CDC 6600	FORTRAN IV
FEFA	Cornell University	Mixed mode crack propagation analysis by the finite element method. Production program.	6/80	IBM 370/168	FORTRAN IV
GLASS II	UCLA	Using global-local finite element, stress intensity factors for elasto-static loading are determined. Potential production program.	6/79	IBM 360	FORTRAN IV
Special Crack Tip Element Library	The Lockheed-California Company, Burbank, CA	Four crack tip elements developed using singular stress functions. Elements are used through a general purpose finite element analysis program, the NASTRAN-Calac System. Production program.	Note	IBM 370	FORTRAN IV

Note: The basic formulation for element development is available in Reference 1; see Program Details, Documentation

Table 1 Program Data (cont.)

NAME	SOURCE	DESCRIPTION	DATE AVAIL.	COMPUTER	LANGUAGE
SKBP17	Massachusetts Institute of Technology	Computers stress intensity factors K_1 and K_2 for a crack at a bi-material interface. Production program.	8/76	IBM 370	FORTRAN IV
SSAP2	IWM, Freiburg Western-Germany	Modified version of "Solid Sap" for 2D linear-elastic fracture analysis. Production program.	9/79	Univac 1100/80	FORTRAN IV
————	Creusot-Loire	2D LEFM Analysis	1972	Univac 1108 CDC 7600	FORTRAN IV
HDCRK2	Georgia Institute of Technology	Program directly calculates K_I and K_{II} for cracks in 2D problems with linear elastic isotropic and orthotropic materials. Potential production program	12/74	CDC Cyber 74	FORTRAN IV
HSPBTC	Georgia Institute of Technology	Program directly yields K_I, K_{II}, and K_{III} for through-thickness cracks in plates under general bending loads. Potential production program	1/78	CDC Cyber 74	FORTRAN IV

Table 1 Program Data (cont.)

NAME	SOURCE	DESCRIPTION	DATE AVAIL.	COMPUTER	LANGUAGE
HDCR2P	Georgia Institute of Technology	Program calculates parameters such as J, COD, for cracks in strain-hardening elastic-plastic materials in 2D situations.	9/76	CDC Cyber 74	FORTRAN IV
HDCG2P	Georgia Institute of Technology	Program calculates elastic-plastic energy release per unit crack growth, CTOA in elastic-plastic stable crack growth and fatigue growth situations. Potential production program	3/79	CDC Cyber 74	FORTRAN IV
INFEM	Brown University General Electric Co.	Performs two-dimensional fully plastic analyses of test specimens and cracked structural configurations. Potential production program	6/79	IBM 360, CDC 7600	FORTRAN IV
FAST	Grumman Aerospace Corp.	Fracture analysis of planar structures including plasticity and the effect of crack growth. Potential production program	1973	IBM 370	FORTRAN IV
FEACG	The George Washington University	Performs a two-dimensional finite element analysis of stable crack growth until fast fracture occurs. Potential production program	12/77	IBM 370	FORTRAN IV

Table 1 Program Data (cont.)

NAME	SOURCE	DESCRIPTION	DATE AVAIL.	COMPUTER	LANGUAGE
NEUT-CRACK 1	University of Tokyo	Performs linear and nonlinear crack analyses of two-dimensional problems. Potential production program	9/79	HITAC 8700/8800 and PRIME 550	FORTRAN IV
TEPSA	University of Manitoba	Predicts slow crack growth in a 3D axisymmetric or 2D planar structure subject to combined monotonic or cyclic thermomechanical loads during elasto-plastic deformation. Potential production program	8/79	AMDAHL/V7	G or H level
PCRACK	Yokohama National Univ.	Performs a three-dimensional analysis of through crack in a plate in stretch or bending. Potential production program	3/76	HITAC 8700/8800	FORTRAN IV
ADINA	Massachusetts Institute of Technology	General linear and nonlinear, static and dynamic 2D and 3D analysis. Production program.	1975	CDC, IBM and UNIVAC	FORTRAN IV

Table 1 Program Data (Cont.)

NAME	SOURCE	DESCRIPTION	DATE AVAIL.	COMPUTER	LANGUAGE
GEFRACT	M. I. T. (Crack Modification by GE CRD)	General purpose nonlinear analysis code. Performs fracture analysis in 2D and 3D. Crack propagation in 2D only.		CDC 176 CDC 7600 CRAY	FORTRAN IV
BERSAFE	CEGB, Berkeley Nuclear Laboratories, Berkeley, Gloucestershire, England	General finite element package with extensive features for fracture mechanics analysis. For 2D and 3D structures for linear elastic and post yield fracture. Production program.	1972	IBM 370 IBM 360 ICL System UNIVAC 1108 Burroughs.	FORTRAN IV
MARC	MARC Analysis Research Corporation, Palo Alto, CA	General purpose finite element program. Production code used for sophisticated nonlinear problems. Production program.	3/79	CDC, IBM, UNIVAC, Prime	FORTRAN IV
TITUS	FRAMATOME Service CALCUL B.P. 13 71380 Saint Marcel FRANCE	3D thermo-mechanical nonlinear dynamic finite element code with special algorithm added to perform crack extension computation. Production program.	6/74	CDC 7600 CDC 6600 series	FORTRAN IV

Table 1 Program Data (Cont.)

NAME	SOURCE	DESCRIPTION	DATE AVAIL.	COMPUTER	LANGUAGE
HDCRK3	Georgia Institute of Technology	Program directly calculates K_I, K_{II} and K_{III} at various points along the front of an arbitrarily shaped 3D embedded or surface flaws.	9/75	CDC Cyber 74	FORTRAN IV
NISATC	Georgia Institute of Technology	Program yields the three-dimensional stress intensity factors along the crack front in angle-ply laminates. The conditions of stress equilibrium and interlayer traction reciprocity in the element are satisfied a priori.	6/79	CDC Cyber 74	FORTRAN IV
NISATD	Georgia Institute of Technology	The dynamic stress intensity factor of each time step can be calculated directly. The various stress contours (fringe patterns) can be produced. The program also computes total dissipated fracture energy, kinetic energy, and strain energy.	7/79	CDC Cyber 74	FORTRAN IV

Table 1 Program Data (cont.)

NAME	SOURCE	DESCRIPTION	DATE AVAIL.	COMPUTER	LANGUAGE
EXPDYN 1,2	Dept. of Strenth of Materials and Solid Mechanics, Royal Institute of Technology, Stockholm, Sweden	Performs dynamic fracture analysis of 2D elastic problem in the generation or propagation mode. Potential production program.	7/79	IBM 370/ 165	FORTRAN IV
HCRACK	University of Washington	Performs a dynamic fracture analysis of two-dimensional problems in the generation or propagation mode. Potential production program.	6/79	CDC 6400	FORTRAN IV
BEFAP	Cornell University University of Kentucky	Performs a linear elastic analysis of two-dimensional crack problems. Production program.	9/79 1/80	IBM 370 IBM 370	FORTRAN IV FORTRAN IV
BIGIF	Fracture Analysis Association	Computes fracture mechanics based subcritical crack growth lines and stress intensity factors for two- and three-dimensional linear elastic idealizations. Production program	1978 Current Revision June 1980.	Several systems including: IBM 360, 370 CDC 6600 UNIVAC 1108	Yes, FORTRAN IV

Table 1 Program Data (cont.)

NAME	SOURCE	DESCRIPTION	DATE AVAIL.	COMPUTER	LANGUAGE
EITD	CETIM	Three-dimensional thermo-elastostatics; analysis by boundary integral equations. Production program	1975	CDC 7600	FORTRAN IV
MESH20 SSAP3A LDU2 SAPELL	Colorado State University	K_I along the border of a part-elliptical crack in a 3D body under general loading. Alternates between two solutions. Production program.	10/79	CDC 6400	FORTRAN IV
CRHP	Kyushu University	Calculate the stress intensity factors at tips of arbitrarily distributed cracks in joined half planes of different materials. Potential production program.	9/79	FACOM M-190	FORTRAN IV
HOLCRK	Kyushu Institute of Technology	Performs a stress intensity analysis in the presence of a crack and arbitrarily shaped holes in an infinite plate. Potential production program.	6/76	FACOM M-190	FORTRAN IV

Table 1 Program Data (cont.)

NAME	SOURCE	DESCRIPTION	DATE AVAIL.	COMPUTER	LANGUAGE
MIXSIF	Kyushu Institute of Technology	Performs a mixed mode stress intensity analysis of the arbitrarily shaped plate with an inner or edge crack. Potential production program.	12/78	FACOM M-190	FORTRAN IV
SCONCB	Kyushu Institute of Technology	Performs a moment concentration analysis of the arbitrarily shaped plate with an elliptical hole or notch by classical bending theory. Potential production program.	3/78	FACOM M-190	FORTRAN IV
SCONCT	Kyushu Institute of Technology	Performs a stress concentration analysis of the arbitrarily shaped plate with an elliptical hole or notch. Potential production program.	2/76	FACOM M-190	FORTRAN IV
SPDISK	Kyushu Institute of Technology	Performs a stress intensity analysis of a spin disk with a hole and two symmetrical cracks. Potential production program.	4/74	FACOM M-190	FORTRAN IV
TWELLI	Kyushu University and Kyushu Institute of Technology	Stress intensity analysis for two semielliptical cracks of the same size. Restrictive.	8/79	FACOM M-190	FORTRAN IV

Table 1 Program Data (cont.)

NAME	SOURCE	DESCRIPTION	DATE AVAIL.	COMPUTER	LANGUAGE
TCPSIP	Kyushu University	Stress intensity analysis of edge cracks or a notch with a crack in a semi-infinite plate. Potential production program.	10/71	FACOM M-190	FORTRAN IV
CCGDAM	Ohio State University	Performs creep crack growth analysis and yields incubation time, growth rate, and time to failure. Limited to Northon's law and DCB model. Restrictive program.	10/78	IBM 370/168	FORTRAN IV
EPAX	Ohio State University	Performs elasto-plastic crack analysis in axisymmetric problems. Restrictive program.	12/77	IBM 370/168	FORTRAN IV
TROTT	SRI International	Two-dimensional (planar or axisymmetric) wave propagation caused by impact, explosion, or velocity boundary. Fracture occurs by nucleation, growth, and coalescence of microdamage. Restrictive program.	8/78	CDC 6400 or CDC 7600	FORTRAN IV

Table 2 Analysis Capability

NAME	DIMENSION					METHOD	ELEMENTS				LOAD TYPES			GENERAL CAPABILITY				
	NUMBER OF NODAL POINTS	NUMBER OF ELEMENTS	NUMBER OF MATERIALS	NUMBER OF PRESSURE BAL.	NUMBER OF POINTS IN PRESSURE TIME HISTORY		STRAIGHT	CURVED	MASS	BODY FORCE	PRESSURE POINTS	DISPLACEMENT PRESCRIBED	THERMAL STRESSES	ELASTIC	ELASTIC-PLASTIC	DYNAMIC	VISCOELASTIC	THERMAL STRESSES
APES	400 to 1400	50 to 200	5	Any Number	N/A	Static finite element	X	X			X	X	X	X				X
FEFA	Limited by core storage capacity					Crack propagation; finite element	X	X		X	X	X	X	X				
GLASS II	No significant limit				N/A	Global-local finite elements	X		X	X	X	X	X	X		X Natural modes only		X

Table 2 Analysis Capability (cont.)

NAME	DIMENSION					METHOD	ELEMENTS				LOAD TYPES			GENERAL CAPABILITY				
	NUMBER OF NODAL POINTS	NUMBER OF ELEMENTS	NUMBER OF MATERIALS	NUMBER OF PRESSURE BAL.	NUMBER OF POINTS IN PRESSURE TIME HISTORY		STRAIGHT	CURVED	MASS	BODY FORCE	PRESSURE POINTS	DISPLACEMENT PRESCRIBED	THERMAL STRESSES	ELASTIC	ELASTIC-PLASTIC	DYNAMIC	VISCOELASTIC	THERMAL STRESSES
Special Crack Tip Element Library	DIMENSION N/A					Two-dimensional linear elastic problem	X					X		X				
SKBP17	17	1	2	-	-	Hybrid stress finite element	X				X	X		X				
SSAP2	Depending on the available storage capacity For example: 50K					Finite element displacement-method	X	X		X	X		X	X				X

Table 2 Analysis Capability (cont.)

NAME	DIMENSION					METHOD	ELEMENTS				LOAD TYPES			GENERAL CAPABILITY				
	NUMBER OF NODAL POINTS	NUMBER OF ELEMENTS	NUMBER OF MATERIALS	NUMBER OF PRESSURE BAL.	NUMBER OF POINTS IN PRESSURE TIME HISTORY		STRAIGHT	CURVED	MASS	BODY FORCE	PRESSURE POINTS	DISPLACEMENT PRESCRIBED	THERMAL STRESSES	ELASTIC	ELASTIC-PLASTIC	DYNAMIC	VISCOELASTIC	THERMAL STRESSES
FAST	900	600	20	N/A	-	Static finite element	X				X	X	X	X	X			X
FEACG	300	518	1			Finite element analysis based on incremental theory of plasticity	X				X	X		X	X			
NEUT-CRACK 1						Nonlinear finite element	X				X	X		X	X			
TEPSA	999	999	5	N/A	limit	Quasi-thermomechanical coupled finite element elasto-plastic stress analysis	X		X	X	X	X	X	X	X			X

Table 2 Analysis Capability (cont.)

NAME	DIMENSION					METHOD	ELEMENTS				LOAD TYPES			GENERAL CAPABILITY				
	NUMBER OF NODAL POINTS	NUMBER OF ELEMENTS	NUMBER OF MATERIALS	NUMBER OF PRESSURE BAL.	NUMBER OF POINTS IN PRESSURE TIME HISTORY		STRAIGHT	CURVED	MASS	BODY FORCE	PRESSURE POINTS	DISPLACEMENT PRESCRIBED	THERMAL STRESSES	ELASTIC	ELASTIC-PLASTIC	DYNAMIC	VISCOELASTIC	THERMAL STRESSES
PCRACK	1+6x	+45x	—	—	—	Method of superposition of analytical and finite element solutions.	X				X	X		X				
ADINA	Only limited by size of computer					Static and dynamic geometric and material nonlinear finite element analysis	X	X	X	X	X	X	X	X	X	X	X	X
BERSAFE* Phase II (elastic)	3000	4000	50			Static finite element	X	X		X	X	X	X	X				X
BERSAFE Phase III (plasticity + creep)	800	1000	3			Static finite element	X	X		X	X	X	X	X	X	*		X
MARC	Only hardware limits					Differential stiffness for evaluating change in strain energy	X	X	X	X	X	X	X	X	X	X	X	X

*A comprehensive linear dynamics facility has been developed in a parallel system to BERSAFE known as BERDYNE.

Table 2 Analysis Capability (cont.)

NAME	DIMENSION					METHOD	ELEMENTS				LOAD TYPES			GENERAL CAPABILITY				
	NUMBER OF NODAL POINTS	NUMBER OF ELEMENTS	NUMBER OF MATERIALS	NUMBER OF PRESSURE BAL.	NUMBER OF POINTS IN PRESSURE TIME HISTORY		STRAIGHT	CURVED	MASS	BODY FORCE	PRESSURE POINTS	DISPLACEMENT PRESCRIBED	THERMAL STRESSES	ELASTIC	ELASTIC-PLASTIC	DYNAMIC	VISCOELASTIC	THERMAL STRESSES
TITUS	No limitation					Nonlinear finite element with crack extension algorithm	X	X	X	X	X	X	X	X	X	X	X	X
EXPDYN 1,2			2			Explicit time integration finite element	X		X		X	X		X		X		
Limited by HONDA which is:																		
HCRACK	1+12x	+18x	+32x	+5x	+2x	Dynamic finite element	X		X		X	X		X	X	X		
*BFAP	50	30	1	-	-	Boundary element method	X	X			X	X		X				
BIGIF	Dimension not applicable					Weight or influence function	Not applicable											

*These limits are for each subdomain and may be increased by the user.

Table 2 Analysis Capability (cont.)

NAME	DIMENSION					METHOD	ELEMENTS				LOAD TYPES			GENERAL CAPABILITY				
	NUMBER OF NODAL POINTS	NUMBER OF ELEMENTS	NUMBER OF MATERIALS	NUMBER OF PRESSURE BAL.	NUMBER OF POINTS IN PRESSURE TIME HISTORY		STRAIGHT	CURVED	MASS	BODY FORCE	PRESSURE POINTS	DISPLACEMENT PRESCRIBED	THERMAL STRESSES	ELASTIC	ELASTIC-PLASTIC	DYNAMIC	VISCOELASTIC	THERMAL STRESSES
EITD	1200	400	10	5		Three-dimensional static boundary integral equations		X		X	X	X	X	X				X
Limited by central memory which for the CDC 6400 was:																		
MESH20 SSAP3A LDU2 SAPELL	695	112	1	(untested more but capability exists)		Finite element-alternating method		X				X		X				
CRHP						Body force method												

Table 2 Analysis Capability (cont.)

NAME	DIMENSION					METHOD	ELEMENTS				LOAD TYPES			GENERAL CAPABILITY				
	NUMBER OF NODAL POINTS	NUMBER OF ELEMENTS	NUMBER OF MATERIALS	NUMBER OF PRESSURE BAL.	NUMBER OF POINTS IN PRESSURE TIME HISTORY		STRAIGHT	CURVED	MASS	BODY FORCE	PRESSURE POINTS	DISPLACEMENT PRESCRIBED	THERMAL STRESSES	ELASTIC	ELASTIC-PLASTIC	DYNAMIC	VISCOELASTIC	THERMAL STRESSES
HOLCRK			1			Body force method					X			X				
MIXSIF			1			Body force method					X			X				
SCONCB			1			Body force method					X			X				
SCONCT			1			Body force method					X			X				
SPDISK			1			Body force method					X			X				
TWELLI			1			Body force method								X				
TCSIP			1			Body force method								X				
CCPDAM						Numerical integro-differential equation	X				X						X	

Table 2 Analysis Capability (cont.)

NAME	DIMENSION					METHOD	ELEMENTS				LOAD TYPES			GENERAL CAPABILITY				
	NUMBER OF NODAL POINTS	NUMBER OF ELEMENTS	NUMBER OF MATERIALS	NUMBER OF PRESSURE BAL.	NUMBER OF POINTS IN PRESSURE TIME HISTORY		STRAIGHT	CURVED	MASS	BODY FORCE	PRESSURE POINTS	DISPLACEMENT PRESCRIBED	THERMAL STRESSES	ELASTIC	ELASTIC-PLASTIC	DYNAMIC	VISCOELASTIC	THERMAL STRESSES
EPAX	16x16 256	16				Method of lines	X				X	X			X			
TROTT	1200*	1200*	6*	-	-	Finite difference, explicit	X					X		X	X	X	X	X

Evaluation of NASTRAN

J. W. Jones

H. H. Fong

Swanson Service Corporation

INTRODUCTION

NASTRAN is a large, general purpose, finite element computer program used primarily for linear structural analysis. In its ten years of existence NASTRAN has achieved the distinction of being the program with the most users worldwide, most documentation, most user conferences, most cited, and probably the most expensive to develop [1-6].

This chapter summarizes a study made

1. to assess the current status (usage, documentation, trends) of public domain versions of NASTRAN
2. to evaluate its program architecture, and to compare it with some other general purpose codes
3. to survey its functional description, and to comment on its capabilities/limitations and such items as matrix operations, eigenvalue extraction schemes, element library, material properties, etc.
4. to perform advanced evaluation exercises on some selected structural elements, and to test their convergence, completeness, and efficiency.

The study focused attention on a user survey, review of documentation, program architecture, the functional description, selected verification exercises, and on advanced evaluation exercises that are designed to assess element quality and limitations.

There are literally thousands of NASTRAN users. For convenience in this study, we shall divide them into four categories.

1. Expert - This person knows NASTRAN inside and out. He is familiar with all the documentation, including the NASTRAN Programmer's Manual. He is adroit with the Direct Matrix Abstraction Program (DMAP). He has used NASTRAN in a variety of problems for probably close to ten years, and is recognized in his organization as <u>the</u> NASTRAN expert, the person to whom everyone comes for help.
2. Experienced - This person knows NASTRAN well, and has probably used the code for five to seven years. He is competent in finite

element theory and modeling, and most likely, has used several other codes. He knows how to plot models to his liking with minimum effort. He has used several of the NASTRAN rigid formats and DMAP, and knows the input/output well. This person is usually a senior engineer in a large company.

3. Common User - The common NASTRAN user has generally used the code for two to five years and is familiar with rudimentary finite element theory. He is likely to have used one rigid format (e.g., statics) almost exclusively, to analyze different designs of one product. This person finds the concept of DMAP very difficult.

4. Novice - The new NASTRAN user has zero to two years experience. He is becoming familiar with NASTRAN modeling, input, and output. He needs guidance in modeling techniques, works for the experienced or common user, and is apt to make mistakes in element connectivity and boundary conditions.

Most NASTRAN users fall into categories 2 and 3.

Unlike most current general purpose finite element computer programs developed by individuals, companies, and universities, NASTRAN was originally conceived by and developed under NASA's sponsorship in 1964-1969. After consulting with an ad hoc committee of finite element experts from the aerospace industry, NASA established a NASTRAN project management office which administered the software development contracts, released and updated periodically the voluminous documentation, established a systematic error reporting and correction procedure, and shaped the contents of the code. This responsibiity was shifted in 1979 to the Computer Software Management and Information Center (COSMIC) at the University of Georgia. NASA was therefore the "code developer" of NASTRAN. This short history on NASTRAN's development serves to explain why, unlike other competing codes, COSMIC/NASTRAN currently does not offer a "hot-line service" to answer promptly user questions on the telephone.

The future success and usefulness of NASTRAN (as well as any other structural analysis software) is intimately related to the current and future developments in computers. For some excellent recent reviews and projections on this subject, the reader is referred to Ref. [1] to [6]. These articles review computer developments in the past thirty years and project trends into the 1980s. Topics which are covered, most of which will have an effect on the future of NASTRAN, are: operating systems; high-level languages; time sharing; CAD/CAM; minicomputers; interactive terminals; new memory chips; virtual and bubble memories; disk files; distributed processing; and supercomputers ("number crunchers"). The computer industry is on the threshold of very large scale integration (VLSI) chip technology and bubble memories, both of which appeared on a commercial scale in 1979. The future impact of these developments on structural analysis software is difficult to predict. In view of the current proliferation of minicomputers on the structural analysis scene, brief comments on minicomputer versions of NASTRAN and also on pre- and postprocessors now commercially available for NASTRAN will be given in this chapter. Above all, however, the real worth of a code lies in its maintenance and support.

User Survey Results

This section summarizes the findings of a telephone survey of approximately 25 NASTRAN users, most of whom fall into Categories 2 and 3 and work at large aerospace companies. This survey was not a comprehensive picture of NASTRAN usage; rather, it was basically a regional consensus which reflected each user's own opinions and experiences. The aims of the survey were to obtain a quick feel of current NASTRAN usage, to obtain user comments and experiences, and to solicit suggestions for improvement.

The main problem with the survey was in finding current users of public-domain versions of NASTRAN. In fact, only a few users of the latest release (Level 17.5) of COSMIC/NASTRAN were found. Many users had learned NASTRAN using the COSMIC version but had switched to commercial versions (such as MSC/NASTRAN). In the past, many government agencies when awarding contracts had dictated that the vendor use NASTRAN for structural analysis, without specifying the particular public or commercial version. Therefore, the vendor could choose the version he preferred. The overwhelming reason for switching to commercial versions such as UAI/NASTRAN and MSC/NASTRAN was because of better user support for day-to-day problems. Other important reasons were significant cost improvements and more efficient solution algorithms. The following statements summarize some major findings of the survey. Several interesting comments are amplified later.

1. There still exists a large group of government and industry users who prefer the public-domain versions of NASTRAN, and who like to modifiy the code to suit their own needs.

2. The biggest single complaint of COSMIC/NASTRAN users is the lack of a hotline service for prompt support. (See comment at the end of this section.)

3. NASTRAN users generally think of the code favorably and consider their NASTRAN experience as a valuable asset in their career development.

4. Most users confine their analyses to rigid formats and perform linear elastic analysis. A few of the sophisticated users create their own DMAP sequences, but this appears to be quite rare.

5. Another big complaint is cost. NASTRAN is rated too costly for small and medium-sized jobs. Efficiency and run-time improvements are reported in several sources (for example, Ref. [7] and [8]) comparing MSC/NASTRAN and UAI/NASTRAN to COSMIC/NASTRAN, but the present study will not evaluate this aspect.

6. NASTRAN documentation is bulky and difficult to read and use.

7. There is a need for an internal mesh generation capability.

8. Many users wished NASTRAN had nonlinear material and geometry capabilities. (Its present nonlinear capability is limited and consequently will not be evaluated in this study).

Most users agreed that the executive system-functional modules approach in NASTRAN program architecture produces a very flexible and powerful program. They use a few rigid formats heavily and rarely have a need for creating DMAP sequences. Usually, DMAP alters are used for output variations. The program can be used for matrix manipulations, again a feature due to DMAP and the modular concept. This feature brought out another interesting observation. Years ago, computer core was expensive and the modules were created to limit the dependence on core size. Today, core is plentiful and cheap (and rapidly becoming cheaper), virtual memories are commonplace, and bubble memories are emerging. Most contemporary programs are manipulated by the machine operating system rather than an executive system internal to the program (such as NASTRAN). This NASTRAN program architecture prevents the user from communicating interactively with the program.

In the area of error and bug correction, the user's views depend largely on the size of his organization and whether there exists a competent in-house staff to correct bugs and implement new elements or modules. The small or medium-sized user finds it virtually impossible to get things corrected on his own on COSMIC/NASTRAN and will very likely opt for a commercial version. The larger user has the computing and manpower resources necessary for corrections and implementations, and may prefer COSMIC/NASTRAN for its flexibility. Apparently, the released versions of the program from COSMIC have not been thoroughly tested and verified, causing many reported system-type problems and errors. When a user discovers a bug, his only course of action (other than correcting it himself) is to report it to the current maintenance contractor. Then, the government decides on the priority of correcting various reported errors, and the maintenance contractor may not be able to correct the error until the next released level. Another problem is the development effort required for the different machine versions of a given NASTRAN release level. A level is usually developed on one machine, and the testing reliability and quality assurance may not be as high on another machine.

Users complained about possible errors in the capabilities dealing with: substructuring; cyclic symmetry; differential stiffness with thermal loading; axisymmetric analysis; piecewise linear analysis; eigenvalue extraction methods and their accuracy in computing rigid-body modes for large problems; and the QUAD2 element. Capabilities and options not presently in NASTRAN but desired by many users are: incompressible elements; composite materials; strain recovery; mesh generation; timing estimates; nonzero initial conditions for modal analysis; alternate time integration schemes; and nonlinear geometric and material analyses.

Commentary

A very interesting comment on NASTRAN maintenance was made by several users. COSMIC/NASTRAN was first released to the public in 1969, and has been updated through continuous government contracts. Each new updating contract is bid on by private companies. Then, the successful bidder's responsibility is to define, to initiate, to integrate, and to assure the quality of all work done on the program. Therefore, each new level released to the public is a direct reflection of the performance of the maintenance contractor and subcontractors. In the past, continuity and coordination of efforts on some occasions could have been better.

Currently, user support on COSMIC/NASTRAN is coordinated by Dr. Robert L. Brugh, NASTRAN Project Manager at COSMIC, University of Georgia at Athens, telephone (404) 542-3265. He is responsible for providing answers to users' questions or problems, and coordinates closely with Computer Sciences Corporation,the current COSMIC/NASTRAN maintenance contractor. COSMIC maintains and updates the NASTRAN Software Problem Report (SPR) log, which can be requested by any user. Several recent reports from COSMIC/NASTRAN users with specific questions and problems (and who decided to use this channel of communication with Dr. Brugh and COSMIC) have been favorable. COSMIC/NASTRAN users are therefore urged to contact COSMIC promptly when they discover system problems, element anomalies, and other bugs.

NASTRAN DOCUMENTATION

Some general comments are made here about NASTRAN documentation (References [9-13]). The first four manuals were designed for reference purposes. They are bulky and sometimes difficult to use. In general, the documentation in these four manuals is fairly complete though of uneven quality. Of the four user categories, the expert user is probably the only one to have examined all these thick volumes. It is often difficult to find information. Examples of this difficulty are given below:

MANUAL	"DIFFICULT-TO-FIND" INFORMATION (OR MISSING)
Theoretical	Number of nodes and degrees of freedom for each element.
Theoretical	User hints and limitations of each element.
Theoretical	Section 5.8 (80 pages long): adequate description of 15 membrane and bending 2-D surface elements but element names are missing in half of the subsections.
User's	Element summary table showing: classification, name, brief description, nodes, degrees of freedom, material options, and element developer and date.
User's	Time and cost estimates for different rigid formats and elements.
User's	Tables showing: geometry cards, heat transfer, fluid, mass, rigid and dummy elements; material properties; constraints and partitioning; loads (static, dynamic, heat transfer); problem control.
Programmer's	Number of overlay levels and system flow charts for the IBM, UNIVAC, and CDC computer systems.
Demonstration	Simple problems explaining input stream line-by-line to the novice user.

Most experienced and common users have undoubtedly read only those sections in the manuals necessary for their day-to-day use. The last two sections in the User's Manual are particularly helpful and commendable (since they do not usually appear in most other code manuals): the well-cataloged diagnostic messages and the dictionary of NASTRAN terms. An attempt to improve many of the above-mentioned difficulties and missing items in the four manuals of NASTRAN documentation is made in the NASTRAN User's Guide (Level 17.5).

The User's Guide is indispensable to all users of COSMIC/NASTRAN. It gives a concise overview of: the documentation; NASTRAN modeling; descriptions of the varius rigid formats; program architecture; input deck description; executive control, case control, and substructure control decks; printing and plotting features; NASTRAN implementation and input decks for the IBM 360/370 (OS), UNIVAC 1108/1110 (EXEC 8), CDC 6000/CYBER (NOS and NOS/BE) computer systems;

NASTRAN information sources; estimate of resource and time requirements DMAP; and application examples for all major types of analyses. This 618-page guide is an admirable attempt to place in one document most of the useful information a user will ever need. The following items are especially valuable: a table summarizing NASTRAN finite element names versus their characteristics (nodes, mass, load types allowed, heat transfer capability, etc.); a general discussion of general modeling restrictions in NASTRAN; a summary table of analysis options for dynamic rigid formats; a comprehensive summary table of modeling options versus each of the 20 rigid formats (15 displacement, 3 heat transfer, 2 aeroelasticity); many examples of executive and case control deck setups; a 13-page summary table of bulk data options (badly needed in front of the User's Manual); a clear explanation of the NASTRAN overlay system; practical guidelines to estimate cost, rigid format resource requirements, CPU time, and other hardware requirements; and finally, many detailed line-by-line input deck explanations of application examples illustrating the proper use of all major rigid-format analyses. Therefore, the User's Guide is strongly recommended as the first NASTRAN document to read for the novice user, and as a handy reference for the common, experienced, and expert users alike.

Other NASTRAN-related documentation which may be of interest:

1. NASTRAN User's Experiences and Colloquia (First through Ninth, 1971-1980, available from National Technical Information Service, Springfield, Virginia 22161)
2. NASTRAN Software Problem Report (SPR) Log (periodically updated and published by COSMIC)
3. NASTRAN Newsletter (free subscription, from COSMIC)
4. Documentation Error Reports (DER) (COSMIC)
5. NASTRAN - NASA Structural Analysis (1979) (COSMIC)
6. MSC/NASTRAN Basic Training Manual (Ref. [14])
7. MSC/NASTRAN Primer: Static and Normal Modes Analysis (Ref. [15])
8. A Brief Description of MSC/NASTRAN (Ref. [8]) (compares MSC/NASTRAN and Level 16 COSMIC/NASTRAN, as of April, 1978; This document is scheduled to be updated in Spring 1981 and will compare MSC/NASTRAN to Level 17.5 COSMIC/NASTRAN.)
9. MSC/NASTRAN Application Manual (Ref. [16])
10. MSC/NASTRAN Demonstration Manual
11. MSC/NASTRAN Handbook for Linear/Static Analysis (June 1980)

PROGRAM ARCHITECTURE

The key concept behind NASTRAN program architecture is modularity. When NASTRAN was originally designed, certain design criteria were stipulated (Ref. [7, 9, 11]), such as: simplicity of input, minimization of chances for human error and the need for human intervention during program execution; functional independence of solution modules; ease of program modification and extension; versatility and adaptability for various computer systems; restart capability, etc. The resulting NASTRAN program architecture is shown in Fig. 1, which illustrates the major functional subdivisions and their interrelationships.

The two major components are the Executive System and the Functional Modules. The Executive System is the heart of the system. It executes the program in two phases: the preface (where a basic setup is performed) and the execution of the DMAP program in which the

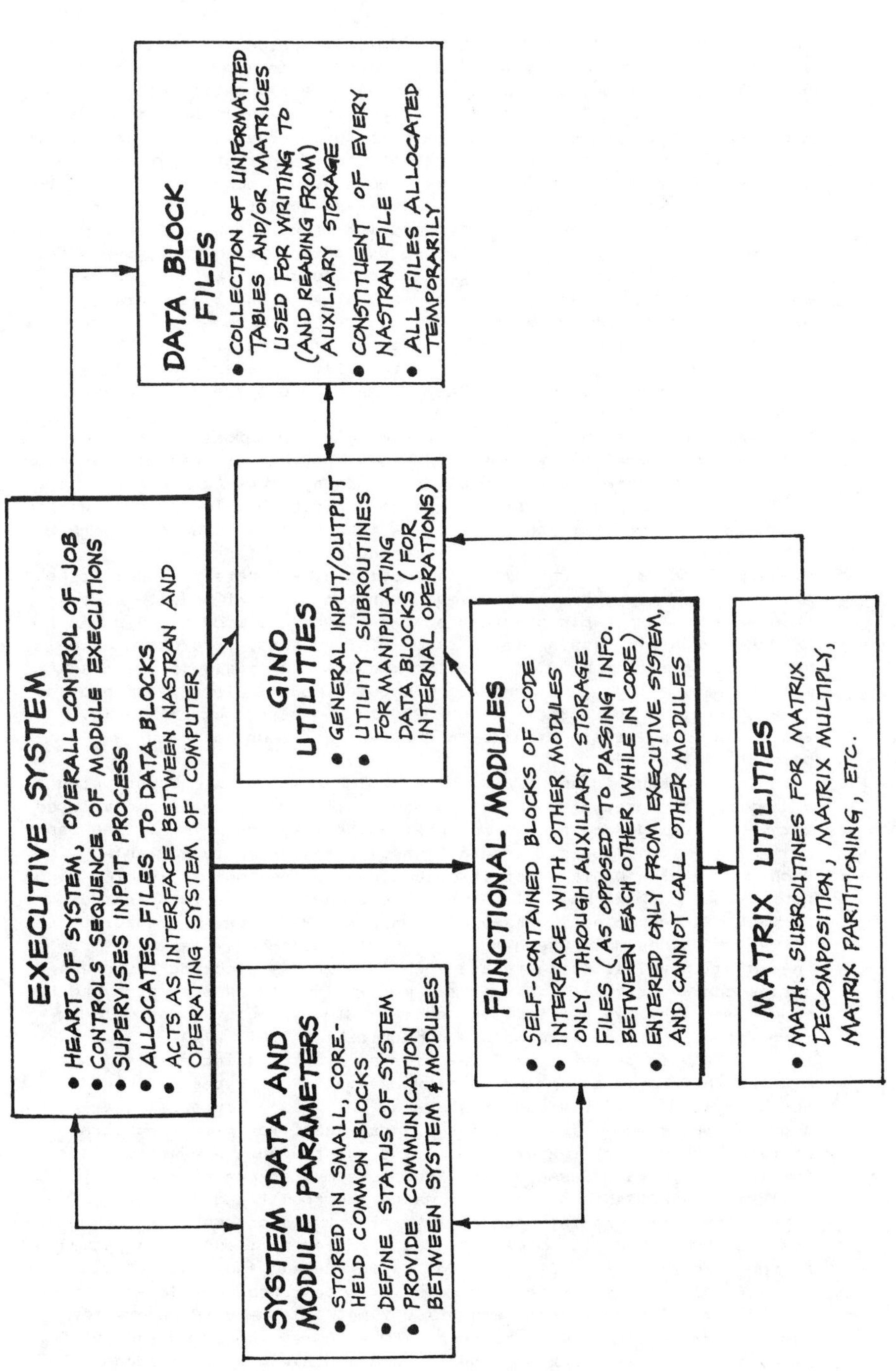

Fig. 1 NASTRAN program architecture and functional subdivisions

modules are controlled. The preface does extensive preprocessing and sorting of bulk data (this function of NASTRAN is superior to most general purpose codes), generates initial file allocation tables, and initializes the problem. The Executive System establishes, protects, and communicates values of parameters for each module. It allocates system files to all data blocks generated during program execution; a file is "allocated" to a data block, and a data block is "assigned" to a file. It also maintains a full restart capability for restoring program execution after either a scheduled or unscheduled interruption. The general philsophy in programming Executive System routines is that reliability and efficiency are paramount concerns. Few changes were anticipated in the Executive System as NASTRAN grew. Therefore, a few general rules were imposed on the Executive System code, resulting in a sophisticated, but difficult to modify, system (Ref. [13]). The Executive System is dependent on a particular computer and its operating system. It comprises approximately 10 percent of the total code.

The Functional Modules are self-contained subprograms which may not call, or be called by other modules. They may be entered only from the Executive System. Each module has: data blocks (an important type is a matrix); subroutines (which can communicate with each other within a module); parameters; and drivers. A change in one module affects no others, as long as the interface with the Executive System is preserved. No module can directly specify or allocate physical files. A module can vary in size from less than ten lines of code to many thousands of executable statements. Four types of modules exist in NASTRAN, each with its specific range of functions: preface modules; executive operation modules; utility modules; and analysis-oriented modules (Ref. [13]). Communication between modules is performed using data block file and parameters (stored in the blank common block). Functional modules are machine-independent and comprise about 90 percent of the code.

Input/output is supported through GINO (Generalized Input/Output), a comprehensive set of machine-dependent utility subroutines developed for manipulating data blocks in internal NASTRAN operations. The basic unit of I/O is a "logical record," whose word length is variable. Each column of a NASTRAN matrix data block is one logical record. Two subroutines convert special NASTRAN input card formats to standard FORTRAN data words easily handled by all NASTRAN input processors. All NASTRAN routines must use GINO. They are consequently isolated from the actual physical hardware and such concerns as blocking factors and device characteristics. Since main memory is used as a scratch pad (no module may leave values in main memory), GINO-formulated data blocks form the bulk of the intermodule communication (Ref. [7]).

NASTRAN is primarily a file-oriented system, using mass storage devices for nearly all major data transfers. Four types of input/output systems are provided in NASTRAN (Ref. [13]): external user-supplied interfaces; internal data blocks (used for temporary data storage); checkpoint/restart files; and substructure operating files (storing all data necessary for a complete multistage substructuring analysis). NASTRAN has a sophisticated checkpoint and restart capability, offering the user four general types of restarts: unmodified restart; pseudo-modified restart; modified restart; and rigid formal switch. Refer to Ref. [9, 10, and 13] for details on restarting.

NASTRAN is not a core program. It is designed to allocate core dynamically so that at execution time, all the core memory that can be made available will be used. "Open core" memory management means a contiguous block of randomly addressable working storage

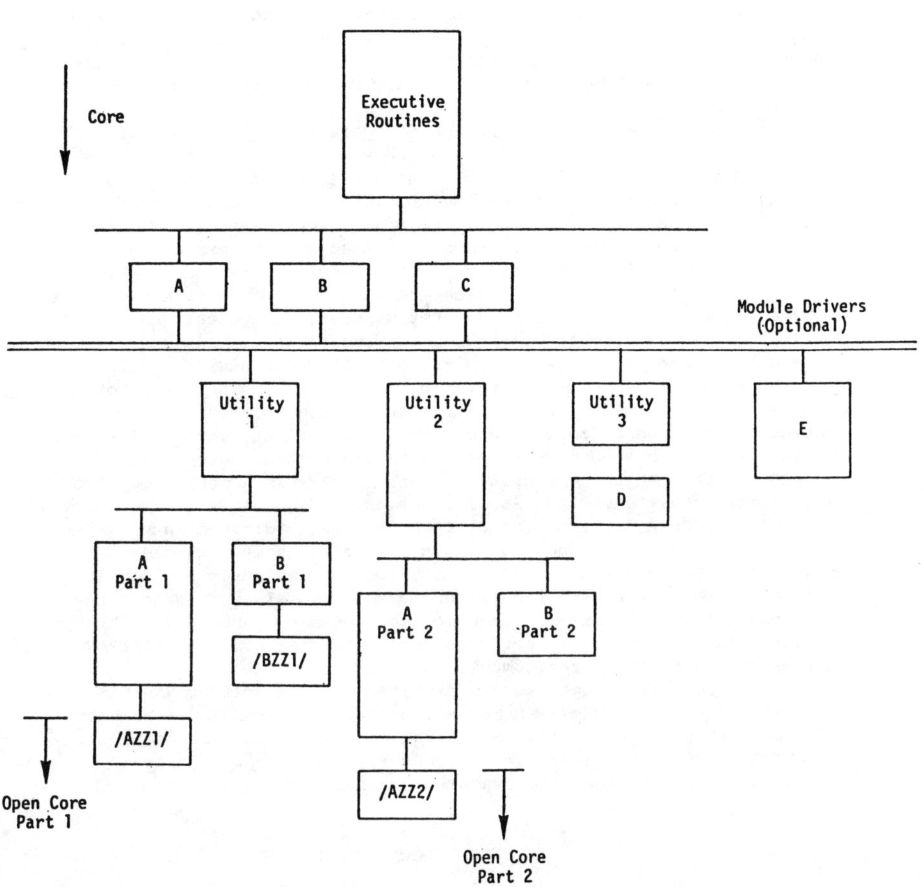

Fig. 2 Illustration of NASTRAN overlay system

defined by a labeled common block, whose length is a variable determined by the NASTRAN executive subroutine KORSZ. Main memory is treated as a large single-dimensional scratch array by all modules. The length is communicated dynamically to the module by the Executive System. Fixed-dimension statements for arrays are not allowed in any module, as all user input is open-ended (Ref. [14]). Spill logic is provided to transfer data to scratch files if complete core allocation is impossible. NASTRAN was not originally designed to operate under a time-sharing system.

Each module in NASTRAN is assigned separate overlay segments independent of the other modules. During execution, only the module code and the required utility subroutine are loaded into core. Furthermore, a common block assigned by the module is loaded below the current code for use in an "open-core" storage space. Open core exists from this point to the maximum core space requested for the execution. All matrix and table data required for a given module operation are brought into open core for temporary storage. Results are moved from open core to data block files for access by other modules. A typical NASTRAN overlay tree is illustrated in Fig. 2. Examples of modules are shown; these are divided into separate parts, consisting of a small "driver" routine which calls the major sections of code located near the bottom of core. This scheme allows the large and complex matrix utility routines to be used by more than one module in a link, yet still allows the largest possible open core space for each module (Ref. [11]).

COSMIC/NASTRAN and the open core concept are implemented on three major computer systems: IBM 360/370 series; UNIVAC 1108/1110 series; and CDC 6600/CYBER series. The NASTRAN program is divided into a series of logical pieces called "links." Each link is a complete program or load module and contains its own overlay structure and its own root segment (the set of subprograms which is always resident in main memory for that link). Communication between links occurs through computer files. Table 1 illustrates some characteristics of NASTRAN implementation on the three computer systems.

Table 2 compares some program architecture features of NASTRAN with four general purpose codes: MARC, ADINA, AGGIE, and ANSYS. The only code among these five to offer a general matrix manipulation capability is NASTRAN. Two recent articles which survey and compare general purpose code capabilities and features are Ref. [17] and [18].

FUNCTIONAL DESCRIPTION

Highlights of some NASTRAN functional descriptions, to give the reader an overview of the versatility and capabilities of the code are given here.

Rigid Formats

A total of 20 rigid formats exist in Level 17.5 of COSMIC/NASTRAN. A rigid format is an established sequence of DMAP instructions stored in the Executive System to perform some standardized analyses, such as:

- -Static analysis - conventional linear static analysis; with inertia relief (inertia effects of unconstrained rigid body accelerations); with differential stiffness (nonlinear effects of large deflections)
- -Normal mode analysis (linear elastic models)
- -Buckling analysis

Table 1 NASTRAN Implementation on Three Major Computer Systems

	IMB 360/370 Series	UNIVAC 1108/1110 Series (Exec 8 OS)	CDC CYBER/6000 Series (NOS)
Word size	32 bits	36 bits	60 bits (single precision
Character capacity	8 bits/character 4 characters/ word	6 bits/character 6 characters/ word	6 bits/character 10 characters/word
Number of links	16	15	15
Overlay	Open core, labeled common block	Open core, segment loader, common block	Segmentation loader, segments loaded dynamically
Input/ Output	GINO consists of 3 decks: -GINO -NASTIO -OPEN	3 categories of I/O routines: -Identify and obtain logical files GNFIAT -Perform actual I/O (GINO, IO1108) -SGINO: generate plot tape	4 ways: -Card input, printed/ punched output, binary output -All other I/O uses GINO -SGINO: Plot output -SOFIO: substructuring I/O

-Piecewise linear (material plasticity) analysis
-Direct complex eigenvalue analysis
-Direct frequency and random response
-Direct transient analysis
-Modal complex eigenvalue analysis
-Modal frequency and random response
-Modal transient analysis
-Normal modes with differential stiffnes
-Static analysis using cyclic symmetry
-Normal modes with differential stiffness
-Static analysis using cyclic symmetry
-Normal modes analysis using cyclic symmetry
-Heat transfer analysis - linear or nonlinear steady-state; transient
-Aeroelasticity analysis - modal aerodynamic flutter analysis; modal aeroelastic response due to applied loads and gusts

Rigid formats are identified with an integer number and an analysis approach. There are three approaches: fifteen rigid formats in displacement (APProach DISP); three in heat transfer (APProach HEAT); and two in aerodynamic (APP roach AERO). Page 4.12-3 of Ref. [13] contains an excellent table which summarizes the various modeling

Table 2 Comparison of Program Architecture of Five General Purpose Codes

FEATURE	NASTRAN (Refs. 7,9,11)	MARC (Ref. 15)	ADINA (Refs. 16,35)	AGGIE I (Ref.19)	ANSYS (Ref.20)
1. Root Segment in Overlay Structure	IBM:NASTRAN UNIVAC: MAIN1→ MAIN15 CDC:NAST01→ NAST15	CONTRO	AAMAIN	MAIN (plus 9 other subroutines in control phase)	None
2. Data Input	GINO (machine-dependent subroutine)	OAREAD (first level overlay)	ADINI	NONSPI (most important of 20 subroutines in input block)	1 subroutine processes element and nodal info.
3. No. of overlay levels	3 to 7 (depends on system)	5 (mostly 3)	4 (same as number of execution phases)	4	3 to 6 (depends on system)
4. Solver option					
In-core	No	Yes (subroutine)	No	Yes (OPTSOL)	Yes
Out-of-core	Yes	Yes (random access; sequential)	Yes (COLSOL)	Yes (OPTBLK)	Yes
5. Dynamic Storage Allocation	Yes, labeled common block	Yes, labeled common block	Yes, blank common block with variable length	Yes, labeled common block	Extended core capability, random access files
6. Matrix storage scheme	PACK/UNPACK by columns (PAKUNPK)	by columns	"Skyline" scheme (by columns)	"Skyline" scheme (by columns)	Wave-front scheme
7. Interactive Mesh Generation	No	Yes	No	No	Yes
8. General matrix operations capability	Yes (DMAP)	No	No	No	No

options offered versus rigid format number. These rigid formats provide the typical user with a tremendous range of analysis options, using pre-established module call sequences (the usual case for all but the expert user). If he chooses, the expert/experienced user can modify the rigid formats by DMAP alters for a particular problem.

Table 3 shows the DMAP sequency for a typical rigid format, in this case the flow sequence of the 30 major functional modules for linear statics analysis. Note that the modules have been classified into preprocessing, analysis, and postprocessing modules. This is the only rigid format with a fully stressed design optimization capability, and the optimization loop is shown. SSG3 is the key analysis module here since it solves for the independent displacements. The rigid format for normal modes analysis has a very similar DMAP sequence to that of linear statics. The key analysis module for normal modes analysis is named READ (real eigenvalue analysis -displacement), consisting of 52 subroutines.

Direct Matrix Abstraction Program (DMAP)

DMAP is one of the most powerful matrix manipulation tools offered in any code. It is the programming language of NASTRAN. DMAP is simply a language of macro instructions which enables the user to sequence any combination of matrix operations. A DMAP instruction has the form:

```
(Module Name)  (Input Data Blocks)/(Output Data Blocks)/(Parameter List)$
```

where the slash is used as a delimiter between data blocks and the dollar sign is used to terminate the DMAP instruction.

A short DMAP example is explained below (Ref. [7]):

To compute [C] = [A] + [B]
[D] = [A] [C]

The DMAP sequence is:

```
BEGIN $   START DMAP
ADD A,B/C/$   ADDS A TO B
MATPRN C//$   PRINT C
MPYAD A,C,/D/$   COMPUTE D
MATPRN D//$   PRINT D
END $   TERMINATE
```

This simple DMAP example provides an illustration of the use of DMAP which is easy to understand even for the relatively inexperienced novice and common users of NASTRAN. In addition to matrix arithmetic,DMAP in NASTRAN can be used for tasks categorized as executive, utility, and structural (e.g., assemble tables, calculate element data).

A rigid format sequence may be modified by the user using the ALTER capability. A library of useful predefined DMAP alter sequences exists, and these sequences are called RFALTERS. The user must merge RFALTERS into the Executive Control Deck by using a machine-dependent operating system utility for merging files.

Table 3 DMAP Sequence for Rigid Format 1 - Linear Statics

Group	Module Name	FUNCTION
Pre-processing Modules	GP1	Coordinate system, grid point locations, relate internal to external grid points
	GP2	Element connection table
	PLOT	Undeformed structure plots
	GP3	Static loads, grid point temperatures
	TA1	Element tables for use in matrix assembly and stress recovery
	OPTPR1	Phase 1 property optimization, initialization check
Analysis Modules (OPTIMIZATION LOOP)	EMG	Element stiffness and mass matrices, for later assembly
	EMA	Element matrix assembler assembles stiffness matrix, grid-point table singularity
	GPWG	Weight and balance information
	SMA3	Adds general elements to stiffness matrix
DMAP Loop	GP4	Displacement sets, MPC equations, enforced displacement vector
	GPSP	Determines if possible grid point singularities remain
	MCE1	Positions MPC equations
	MCE2	Partitions stiffness matrix
	SCE1	Partitions out SPCs
	SMP1	Partitions constrained stiffness matrix
	RBMG1	Partitions out free-body supports
	RBMG2	Decomposes constrained stiffness matrix
	RBMG3	Rigid body transformation and check matrices, error ratio
	SSG1	Generates static load vectors
	SSG2	Applies constraints to static load vectors, calculates determinate reactions
	SSG3	Solves for independent displacements
	SDR1	Recovers dependent displacements and SPC forces
	GDFDR	Calculates grid point force balance element strain energy as requested
	SDR2	Calculates element forces and stresses
Post-processing Modules	SDR3	Prepares requested output sorted by grid point number of element number
	XYTRAN	Prepares input for X-Y plots
	XYPLOT	Prepares X-Y plots of displacements, stresses, forces, SPC forces vs. subcase
	OPTPR2	Performs Phase 2 property optimization
	PLOT	Deformed structure and contour plots

Structural Elements

Table 4 gives a summary of the structural elements available in Level 17.5 of COSMIC/NASTRAN. Of the 33 elements listed. 4 are higher-order elements (TRIM6. TRPLT1. TRSHL. TORDRG) and 4 are isoparametric elements (QDMEM1. IHEX1. IHEX2. IHEX3). Nineteen elements have heat transfer capability. [For simplicity, not included in Table 4, are fluid such as the viscous damper. scalar spring and mass. concentrated mass. general element. and dummy element.] By today's standards. the element library in NASTRAN is rated only fair. Many of the elements are 10 to 15 years old and have existed in NASTRAN since its inception. One glaring weakness is the absence of a quadrilateral solid-of-revolution element for plane strain, plane stress, or axisymmetric analyses. The trapezoidal ring element TRAPRG, which requires two sides of the element to be parallel, is simply too restrictive and not versatile enough. A major portion of this study was spent performing advanced evaluation exercises on selected NASTRAN elements. The elements selected for advanced evaluation are noted in Table 4. Page 3.2-2 of Ref. [13] contains a detailed summary table of NASTRAN finite element characteristics (e.g., thermal loads. lumped or consistent mass, differential stiffness, plasticity, heat transfer). A library of more than 60 different finite element formulations is offered in COSMIC/NASTRAN Level 17.5.

Constitutive Library

As already indicated in Table 4, NASTRAN allows three basic types of material properties: isotropic; orthotropic (for TORDRG and solid-of-revolution elements only); and anisotropic (2-D flat surface elements only). In addition to these elastic properties, NASTRAN material data cards are also used to define mass density, thermal expansion coefficients, and stress limits. Each material is given a unique identification number which may be referenced by any number of property cards. Material data cards are identified in the Bulk Data Deck as follows:

- Temperature-independent material properties (MATi)
  - MAT1 elastic isotropic
  - MAT2 anisotropic, 2-D flat surface elements only
  - MAT3 elastic orthotropic, TORDRG and solid-of-revolution elements only
  - MAT4 heat transfer analysis, isotropic properties
  - MAT5 heat transfer analysis, anisotropic properties
- Temperature-dependent material properties
  - MATTi temperature dependence in conjunction with MATi
  - TABLEMi tabular functions of temperature-dependent properties
- Stress-dependent material properties
  - MATSi stress dependence in conjunction with MATi

Table 4 Structural Elements Summary

Category	Name	Element Description	Nodes	DOF's at ea. Node	Material Property*	Remarks
Linear (1-D)	ROD	Tension, torsion only	2	2	I	
	CONROD	Tension, torsion only, with property	2	2	I	Undocumented in theoretical manual
	TUBE	Tension, torsion only	2	2	I	
	BAR	Tension, torsion, bending, and shear	2	6	I	MSC/NASTRAN also has BEAM & BEND elements
Surfaces (2-D)	SHEAR	In-plane shear panel, quadrilateral	4	1	I	No thermal expansion
	TWIST+	Twist panel	4	1	I	Not in MSC/NASTRAN
	TRMEM+	Triangular membrane (no bending)	3	2	I,A	Constant strain triangle
	TRIM6	Linear strain membrane triangle	6	2	I,A	Argyris (1965), Cowper et al. (1968), Zienkiewicz (1971)
	QDMEM+	Quadrilateral membrane (no bending)	4	2	I,A	4 overlapping TRMEM's
	QDMEM1+	Isoparametric form of QDMEM	4	2	I,A	Taig-Irons (1966)
	QDMEM2+	Quadrilateral membrane, 1 center node	4	2	I,A	4 non-overlapping constant strain TRMEM's
	TRPLT+	Bending, transverse shear	3	3	I,A	Clough triangle, centroid node
	TRPLT1+	Nonconforming, quintic polynomial for transverse displacement	6	3	I,A	Narayanaswami (1974) Cowper et al. (1968)
	QDPLT+	Quadrilateral bending, transverse shear	4	3	I,A	4 basic TRPLT's
	TRBSC+	Basic unit for all elements except TRPLT1, triangular bending	3	3	I,A	Clough-Tocher (1965), not in MSC/NASTRAN
	TRIA1+	Triangular membrane plus bending, also transverse shear	3	5	I,A	Sandwich plate
	TRIA2	Triangular membrane plus bending, solid cross section	3	5	I,A	MSC/NASTRAN also has TRIA3 and TRIA6
	QUAD1+	Quadrilateral membrane and bending	4	5	I,A	Similar to TRIA1, QDMEM + QDPLT
	QUAD2+	Quadrilateral like TRIA2	4	5	I,A	MSC/NASTRAN has isoparametric QUAD4 and QUAD8; UAI/NASTRAN has isoparametric QUAD3

Table 4 Structural Elements Summary (cont.)

Category	Name	Element Description	Nodes	DOF's at ea. Node	Material Property[*]	Remarks
Shells	TRSHL[+]	Higher-order thin shell element, quadratic membrane displacements, quintic normal displacement, nonconforming	6	5	I	Sum of TRIM6 and TRPLT1, Narayanaswami (1974), Novozhilov shallow shell theory
	CONEAX[a]	Conical shell element, with transverse shear capability, axisymmetric	2	5	I	Cannot combine with other elements; problems with thermal loads (?)
	TORDRG[+]	Toroidal shell element and shell cap, cubic membrane displacement, quintic flexural displacement	2	2	I,0	Mallett-Jordan (1969) MAGIC code
Solids of Revolution	TRIARG[a]	Triangular ring, axisymmetric loading	3	3	I,0	Mallet-Jordan's MAGIC (1969) and MAGIC II (1971) codes, based on Clough-Rashid (1965) and Wilson (1965) papers
	TRAPRG[a]	Trapezoidal ring, axisymmetric loadings	4	3	I,0	
	TRIAAX[+]	Triangular ring, nonaxisymmetric loading	3	3	I,0	
	TRAPAX[+]	Trapezoidal ring, nonaxisymmetric loading	4	3	I,0	MSC/NASTRAN has linear strain triangular ring TRIAX6
Solids (3-D)	TETRA	Constant-strain tetrahedron	4	3	I	
	WEDGE[+]	Constant-strain wedge	6	3	I	MSC/NASTRAN offers PENTA (6-15 nodes) and HEXA (8-20 nodes)
	HEXA1[+]	Constant-strain brick, 5 tetrahedra	8	3	I	
	HEXA2[+]	Constant-strain brick, 10 overlapping tetrahedra	8	3	I	
	IHEX1[+]	8-node isoparametric solid, linear displacement variation	8	3	I	Suitable for problems with large shear stresses
	IHEX2[+]	20-node isoparametric solid, quadratic displacement variation	20	3	I	IHEXi elements based on theoretical work by: Irons & Zienkiewicz (1966-1968), Clough (1969), Zienkiewicz, Taylor, Too (1971), Pawsey-Clough (1971)
	IHEX3[+]	32-node isoparametric solid, cubic displacement variation	32	3	I	

* I = isotropic, 0 = orthotropic, A = anisotropic
\+ Not in library of Version 60 of MSC/NASTRAN
a Not recommended for use in Version 60 of MSC/NASTRAN (May 1980)

Constraints and Partitioning

NASTRAN offers the user a variety of options to constrain and reduce his problem. These constraints are used to specify fixed boundary conditions, to eliminate matrix singularities, to define rigid elements, and to support free body motion. The most important of these are multiple point constraints (MPC's), single point constraints (SPC's), OMIT, and ASET. A multipoint constraint is a linear relationship between two or more displacement degrees of freedom. Closely related to MPC's are the rigid elements (RIGDR, RIGD1-3) in NASTRAN, which are very stiff connections. These can be used to model levers, pulleys, gear trains, and rigid links to remove matrix ill-conditioning. SPC's are vectors of enforced displacements, any or all of whose elements may be zero. SPC's commonly represent structural boundary conditions of zero displacement and slope, or enforced deformations at nodes.

For matrix reduction the user can select either the OMIT card or the ASET card, but not both. OMIT specifies degrees of freedom to be reduced out of the analysis set, while ASET specifies independent degrees of freedom to be retained. Since they represent complementary sets, the user should specify the smaller of the two. The specified degrees of freedom for elimination by reduction are restricted to only nonconstrained coordinates. Another bulk data card, SUPORT, may also be used to specify the degrees of freedom which will remove rigid body motion. SUPORT is used to supply temporary, nonredundant constraints on free body motion. It is required for inertial relief analysis (Rigid Format 2), and recommended for use in modal analysis of free bodies.

Errors in constraint data are not automatically corrected by NASTRAN. Conflicting constraint data, when detected, are treated as fatal errors (Ref. [13]). Grid point singularity tests are performed to detect null columns in the stiffness matrix resulting from deficient constraints or element connectivities.

Matrix Operations

A unique feature of NASTRAN is the user's option to manipulate matrices using DMAP. Therefore, theoretically, he can solve any numerical analysis problem which can be expressed in matrix form. Elements of matrices can be specified by the DMI card. The user can build a DMAP sequence using any combination of 43 matrix handling subroutines. Design philosophy of the modules is strictly based on handling large matrices. All matrices are stored on peripheral devices (tapes, disks, and/or drums) by columns, and are packed in nonzero strings. Matrix sparsity and bandedness are emphasized and utilized. The user may select single or double precision control by the executive control card PREC; this is the only method offered in NASTRAN to combat round-off error accumulation. This matrix handling feature in NASTRAN is elaborate, sophisticated, and powerful. (The only other general purpose code which offers a similar matrix operations capability is SPAR.)

Eigenvalue Extraction and Time Integration

Table 5 compares the eigenvalue extraction methods and direct time

Table 5 Comparison of Eigenvalue Extraction and Time Integration Methods in Ten U.S. General Purpose Codes

	CODE	EIGENVALUE EXTRACTION METHODS	TIME INTEGRATION SCHEMES
1	NASTRAN (Ref. 7,11)	1. Tridiagonal (Givens) 2. Inverse Power with Shifts 3. Determinant Method 4. Tridiagonal Reduction Method - or Fast Eigenvalue Extraction Routine (FEER)	Newmark Beta ($\beta = \frac{1}{3}$) method .For heat transfer transient analysis: user's choice $0<\beta<1$
2	MARC (Ref. 15)	Inverse power sweep	1. Central difference 2. Newmark Beta ($\beta = \frac{1}{4}$) 3. Houbolt method
3	ADINA (Ref. 17,35)	1. Determinant Search Method (with Sturm sequence) 2. Subspace iteration	1. Central difference 2. Wilson $\Theta = 1.4$ 3. Newmark Beta
4	AGGIE I (Ref. 19)	1. Determinant Search 2. Subspace Iteration	1. Newmark Beta 2. Wilson $\Theta = 1.4$
5	ANSYS (Ref. 20)	Jacobi	Houbolt
6	STARDYNE (Ref. 23)	1. Householder-QR Method (tridiagonalization) 2. Inverse iteration (same as NASTRAN's inverse power with shifts) 3. Lanczos modal extraction method (same as NASTRAN's FEER method)	None (planned for implementation, but undocumented)
7	SAP6 (Ref. 24)	1. Determinant Search 2. Subspace Iteration	Wilson $\Theta = 1.4$
8	EAC/EASE2 (Ref. 25)	1. Determinant Search 2. Subspace Iteration	1. Newmark Beta 2. Wilson Θ
9	SDRC/SUPERB (Ref. 26)	1. Determinant Tracking (with Sturm sequence property) 2. Jacobi (with Guyan reduction)	None (NASTRAN & ANSYS interface packages offered)
10	MSC/NASTRAN (Ref. 41)	1. Modified Givens (MGIV) 2. Inverse 3. Givens	Newmark Beta Method Analytical solution of equation (Quasi-closed form) (also has component mode synthesis and superelement dynamic capability and generalized dynamic reduction

integration scheme of NASTRAN with nine other U.S. general purpose codes. This comparison reveals that while NASTRAN offers more eigenvalue extraction routines (4) than any other code, its one time integration scheme is less than an average of two schemes offered by the other codes. The most recent method of eigenvalue extraction, subspace iteration (Ref. [13]), is implemented in only three codes: ADINA; SAP6; and EASE2.

For direct time integration, the Newmark Beta, Wilson, and Houbolt methods have gradually emerged as the most popular among U.S. code developers. Newmark Beta and Wilson are "implicit" methods, where a matrix system is solved, one or more times per step, to advance the solution. Both algorithms are unconditionally stable, but recent research has indicated that the Wilson algorithm introduces damping into the solution, is sensitive to time step size, and may require more steps to obtain the same accuracy as the Newmark method. The Houbolt method is a third-order backward difference scheme which is unconditionally stable for all time step sizes. However, it introduces damping into the solution, in addition to having a tendency to remove higher modes from the system. The central difference scheme offered in ADINA and MARC is an "explicit" method, in which the solution may be advanced without storing a matrix or solving a system of equations. It requires very small time steps, but can be cheaper in cost per time step. For nonlinear dynamic problems, the most sophisticated codes are ADINA, MARC, and a new code called ABAQUS being developed by Hibbitt and Karlsson, Inc.

Table 6 is a detailed comparison of the four NASTRAN eigenvalue extraction methods. The method desired for a particular solution is selected by the user on the EIGR card. The two tridiagonalization methods (Givens and FEER) are categorized as "transformation" methods (obtaining all the eigenvalues at once) and can be used only for real matrices. The newer FEER method is a tridiagonalization procedure based on the Rayleigh-Ritz method. It combines the best features of the inverse power and Givens methods. The other two methods (inverse power and determinant) are "tracking" schemes and can also be applied to complex matrices. Proper selection of the extraction method depends on the number of eigenvalues desired, matrix character, problem size, and accuracy demanded; Table 5 offers some hints in this choice. This subject is discussed in more detail in Ref. [19] and Chapter 13 of Ref. [13].

Plotting Capabilities

The user can specify undeformed or deformed structure plots at the end of the Case Control Deck. The structure plot request packet begisn with the card OUTPUT (PLOT). The plotting capabilities in NASTRAN are excellent, comprehensive, and well-documented (Ref [9, 10, and 13]) with many sample plot card setups. The following types of plots may be selected:

- Undeformed geometry plots for all rigid formats
- Static deformations, and stress/displacement contours
- Modal deformation (eigenvectors or mode shapes)
- Transient response or frequency response vectors or deformed shape for specified times or frequencies
- X-Y graphs of transient/frequency response

Table 6 Comparison of NASTRAN Eigenvalue Extraction Methods

	Tridiagonal Method (Givens)	Inverse Power with Shifts	Determinant Method	Tridiagonal Reduction Method (FEER)
1. Type of method	Transformation	Tracking	Tracking	Transformation
2. Most general form of matrix	[A-pI]	$[Mp^2+Bp+K]$	[A(p)]	$[Mp^2+K]$
3. Restrictions on matrix character	A real, symmetric, constant; nonsingular mass matrix	M,B,K constant	None	M,K real, symmetric, constant; M may be singular
4. Obtains eigenvalues in order	All at once, in the order of highest to lowest frequency	Nearest to shift point (highly accurate roots regardless of order of appearance in frequency)	Usually nearest to starting point	Vibration: nearest to shift point Buckling: lowest eigenvalue first
5. Takes advantage of bandwidth	No	Yes	Yes	Yes (and of sparsity)
6. No. of calculations, order of (n = no. of equations b = semi-bandwidth E = no. of eigenvalues extracted)	$O(n^3)$ Tridiagonalize first using Givens; then eigenvalues & eigenvectors using Q-R (Francis, Ortega & Kaiser)	$O(nb^2E)$ (linearly proportional to number of extracted eigenvalues	$O(nb^2E)$	$O(n(b + E)^2)$ Single initial shift, one matrix decomposition
7. Handles closely spaced eigenvalues?	No explicit mention; but can handle double eigenvalues	Known to converge slowly, but corrected by shift strategy	Yes, provides for shift from starting point	No explicit mention

Table 6 Comparison of NASTRAN Eigenvalue Extraction Methods

	Tridiagonal Method (Givens)	Inverse Power with Shifts	Determinant Method	Tridiagonal Reduction Method (FEER)
8. Efficiency and limitations	Least efficient, most effort expended before extracting first eigenvalue; can't use for buckling and complex roots; good for large bandwidth problems needing all the modes	Most efficient when only a few eigenvalues are required. These 2 methods are better for problems with a narrow bandwidth, with <u>inverse power method slightly more efficient overall</u>. Problems with a very narrow bandwidth (e.g. beam) favors determinant method. Lengthy computer runs required to obtain a large number of modes. User must estimate frequencies and number of modes in region.		Major efficiency improvement over tridiagonal method. Computation effort is proportional to number of extracted eigenvalues. Probably most efficient for getting several modes of a real eigenvalue problem. Sparse and banded matrices desirable
9. Adequacy of documentation	Adequate, but needs simple example. Good description of flow diagram and algorithms	Good. Fair flow charts but coding description missing.	Fair. Muller's quadratic method and Wilkinson's convergence criterion explained	Good, but too long and difficult to understand
10. Special comments	Efficient only when matrix size is small enough (250) to be held in core. Produces numerical round-off errors for low-frequency modes at or near zero frequency. (MSC/NASTRAN has a modified givens method)	Good method, expecially for bifurcation buckling loads and modes. Effectiveness sensitive to problem size. Static model requires little modification for a normal modes solution.	Insensitive to form of $[A(p)]$. Can use for hydroelastic and aeroelastic problems. Much slower than inverse power method. Now eliminated in Version 60 of MSC/NASTRAN (May 1980).	Very efficient core requirements. Useful compromise between the Givens and inverse power methods.

-V-f and V-g graphs for flutter analysis
-Topological displays of matrices showing nonzero element locations when the SEEMAT utility module is requested

NASTRAN plotting is compatible with most plotter hardware, such as Stromberg-Carlson and CALCOMP. The user has a choice of three types of projections: orthographic; perspective; and stereoscopic (microfilm plotters only). Plot labeling and scaling are user-controlled or automatically provided. NASTRAN plotting does not have hidden-line capability, which exists in codes such as MARC and ANSYS. Currently, no iteractive preprocessing and postprocessing capabilities exist or are planned, and NASTRAN runs, as well as plots, are used in the batch mode. Cost estimates for plotting are missing from the documentation; plotting costs can be considerable.

Restart Capability

NASTRAN contains a sophisticated restart capability. Restarts are effective for: (1) continuing problem execution having an unscheduled interruption caused by a data error; (2) requesting additional information for a problem already completed; (3) running additional load cases in static analysis; and (4) extracting real eigenvalue for additional frequency ranges in normal modes analysis. Restarts are ineffective when the problem is small, or when changes are made in the element properties or grid point information. A CHKPNT YES card in the Executive Control Deck will save information on a new problem tape NPTP, subsequently renamed an old problem tape OPTP in a future run. One disadvantage of using restarts is the necessity of maintaining checkpoint files.

Nonlinear Capabilities

The nonlinear capabilities in NASTRAN are limited. A rough guess is that less than 5 percent of all NASTRAN users have ever attempted the nonlinear usage. Two types of static nonlinearities are offered: differential stiffness and material plasticity. The geometric stiffness effects treated by Rigid Formats 4 and 5 provide the user with a second-order approximation to the nonlinear effects of large deflection. Rigid Format 6 offers a piecewise linear analysis capability (material plasticity). Only isotropic materials are allowed, and the capability is restricted to certain elements: ROD, TUBE, BAR, and plate elements (based on 2-D plasticity theory by J. L. Swedlow). The material properties are assumed to be stress dependent. The stiffness matrix is assumed to be constant over each load increment. After each increment, a new stiffness matrix is generated based on the current state of stress in each element. All static load options are allowed, except temperature and enforced element deformations.

For transient analysis, the module TRD provides for four types of nonlinear elements, mainly for control systems simulation. Nonlinear effects are treated as an additional applied load vector, whose elements are functions of either displacements or velocities. One additional nonlinear capability is nonlinear steady-state heat transfer analysis, which allows for temperature-dependent conductivities for the elements, nonlinear radiation exchange, and a limited use of multipoint constraints. Nonlinaer elements such as gaps and friction elements do not exist in COSMIC/NASTRAN. The NASTRAN nonlinear capabilities offered are primitive when compared to those of current nonlinear codes such as ADINA, AGGIE, ABAQUS, ANSYS, and MARC.

Special NASTRAN Features

NASTRAN contains certain special or unique features not commonly found in most general purpose codes. These are briefly surveyed in Table 7. In general, the most likely users of these features are the expert/ experienced ones. The common and novice users will probably find most of these features too difficult to use. These features represent a considerable investment of time and money and are no doubt valuable to certain small pockets of the user community. However, their overall effectiveness and extent of usage are difficult to assess and were not evaluated in the study.

Substructuring

The automated multistage substructuring system (Ref. [9, 13, 20]) in NASTRAN, developed by Universal Analytics, Inc., is very powerful yet flexible and user-oriented. It incorporates an automated multistage modal synthesis procedure (Ref. [24]) for the dynamic analysis of very large models and a multistage component mode synthesis method (Ref. [22]). Table 8 compares the NASTRAN automated multistage substructuring capability versus that offered by ANSYS. Both codes have highly developed substructuring capabilities which have been used widely. Similarities and differences are seen in the design philosophy of the two codes, and both advantages and disadvantages are noted. Substructuring is suggested only for the expert/experienced users. A learning curve is invariably necessary. However, for certain classes of problems, substructuring offers tremendous benefits and savings.

VERIFICATION EXERCISES

In the course of reviewing the copious NASTRAN documentation, the authors were very impressed with the complexity of the problems solved using NASTRAN. However, it is often difficult to determine the accuracy of such complex solutions as there are often no theoretical solutions available. Experimental results are limited and it is difficult to obtain the idealized loading and boundary conditions assumed in analysis. Therefore, a limited number of structural verification problems were run. The problems selected could be easily verified against "textbook" solutions. These examples are included in this section.

A number of interesting observations can be made based upon these results. Example 1 indicates that the accuracy of the code is in good agreement with the closed form solution for this problem. Example 2 illustrates the effect that MPC's can have on the solution for certain elements. Example 3 was chosen to exercise the various options available in NASTRAN for eigenvalue extraction. All were in good agreement when a consistent mass matrix was used.

The solutions to these problems using the ANSYS general purpose computer program are available from the open literature Ref. [30] and are included for comparison.

Table 7 Special NASTRAN Features

FEATURE	DESCRIPTION
1. Static analysis with inertia relief	.Treats structural models not fully constrained. .Computes inertia effects of unconstrained rigid body accelerations
2. Manual single-stage substructure analysis	.Phase I analyze each substructure, establish master degrees of freedom .Phase II analyze "pseudo-structure" .Phase III back substitute for substructure displacements and stresses .Can be used for all rigid formats except piecewise linear analysis
3. Fully stressed design optimization (Rigid Format 1 - Linear Statics) (Ref. 11 Sec. 26)	.Very simple design algorithm to resize elements .For each design iteration, change each element's cross-sectional properties to get a limit stress somewhere within element .Procedure works reasonably well for statically determinate structures, acceptable for slightly indeterminate, and poor for indeterminate structure with high redundancy
4. Cyclic Symmetry (Ref. 7,11,40)	.Linear problems only; static and normal modes analyses .Uses finite Fourier transformation .Symmetric with respect to axis: rotational, dihedral symmetry .Model 1 segment; use uncoupled, transformed equations
5. Component Mode Synthesis (Ref. 29)	.Design tool - evaluate critical component modes in total response .Divide structure into separate components, reduce order of component matrices, combine them using compatibility at common boundary points
6. Automated multi-stage substructure analysis (Ref. 11,27,28)	.3 phases like item 2, substructure operating file (SOF) created .User can repeatedly combine and reduce structures .Linear static and dynamic analyses .Sequence control now automated using Substructure Case Control deck
7. Representation of part of a structure by its vibration modes	.Use modal information from other analyses or vibration test data .3 cases: all connection coordinates free, restrained, or mixed .Restrictions: linearity, conservation of energy, reciprocity
8. Representation of control systems	.Linear and nonlinear control systems simulated .Properties of control system treated in quadratic format like in dynamics: $Mp^2 + Bp + K$
9. Structure/fluid interaction (Hydroelastic analysis)	.Compressible fluids in axisymmetric tanks .Compressible fluids in rotationally symmetrical cavities with slots
10. Acoustic cavity analysis	.For each element, pressure field assumed to vary linearly over the cross section and sinusoidally around the axis in circumferential direction. .Slot portion of cavities limited to certain shapes
11. Aeroelastic analysis	.Can be used in conjunction with structural analysis .2 rigid formats: modal flutter analysis (by 3 methods); modal transient and frequency response analysis of aeroelastic models
12. Special elements	.General element GENEL .Dummy elements CDUMi .Rigid elements RIGDi .Aeroelastic elements AEROi .Acoustic elements AXIFi .Hydroelastic elements FLUIDi

Table 8 Comparison of NASTRAN Automated Multistage Substructuring vs. ANSYS Superelement Capability

	NASTRAN	ANSYS
A. Major phases	Phase 1. Analyze each substructure to produce a description of its properties at boundary degrees-of-freedom "u_a." Restrictions: .Statics, normal modes only .No piecewise linear analysis .All points on boundaries to be joined must be included .Internal gridpoint identification must be in same order Initial generation of individual basic matrices. Several runs performed, one for each substructure.	Substructure Generation Pass: Creates reduced stiffness mass, and/or damping matrices, and load vectors of superelements, master degrees of freedom (MDOF's) selected. Restrictions: .Linear elements .Constant material properties .No convection B.C.'s in load vector
	Phase 2. Analyze "pseudostructure," assembly and solution, recovery: .1 or more executions .Any number of substructure reductions and/or combinations .Can be stopped at any stage, restarted .Obtain u_a vector	Superelement Use Pass: Superelement STIF 50 used like any other ANSYS element; solved at MDOF's; degree-of-freedom directions are fixed to the element
	Phase 3. Analyze each substructure using u_a, complete data recovery for displacements and stresses in each individual basic substructure	Superelement Stress Pass: Use MDOF's into each superelement to recover a full set of displacements (or temperatures) and stresses (or heat flows)
B. Reduction Technique	Static: Guyan reduction Modal synthesis: Modal reduction	"Dynamic matrix condensation" technique (or Guyan reduction)

Table 8 Comparison of NASTRAN Automated Multistage Substructuring vs. ANSYS Superelement Capability (cont.)

	NASTRAN	ANSYS
C. User Control	Automated: substructure control deck required	User keeps track of tape numbers in each pass
D. Advantages	1. Automated data base management system: substructure operating file, which can be edited	1. Separates linear from nonlinear portions
	2. Data transfer possible among IBM, UNIVAC, and CDC computers at any stage of analysis	2. Separates "fixed design" portion from portion undergoing design change
	3. Model only 1 of two or more identical substructures, superelement tree	3. Transferable matrices for different analysis types within ANSYS
	4. Dry run for data deck; STEP option	4. Capability for "reflected superelements", symmetry, hierarchy
	5. Symmetry, repeatability, and hierarchy possible	5. Automated selection of master degrees of freedom (Rev. 3 Update 67, 1979)
	6. Automatically generated DMAP alters	
	7. No restrictions on grid point and element numbering	
E. Disadvantages	1. No heat transfer, nonlinear, or transient response	1. New learning curve and terminology
	2. Difficult for novice; learning curve	2. MDOF's can limit problem size
	3. Reduced computer-to-computer mobility	3. More file handling and more runs required

Example 1. Bending of a Tapered Plate

Type: State analysis, plate elements

Reference: Harris, C. O., Introduction to Stress Analysis. The MacMillan Co., New York, 1959, Page 114, Problem 61.

Problem: A tapered cantilever plate with a rectangular cross section is subjected to a load P at its tip. Find the maximum deflection δ and the stress σ_x in the plate.

Given: $E = 30 \times 10^6$ psi, L = 20 in., b = 3 in., d = 0.5 in., P = 10 lb.

Results:

	δ (in.)	σ_x (psi)
Theory	−0.0426666	1600.
ANSYS (STIF 6) (Ref. [23], Problem 34)	−0.0426668	1600.
NASTRAN (TRIA2)	−0.0426672	1625.

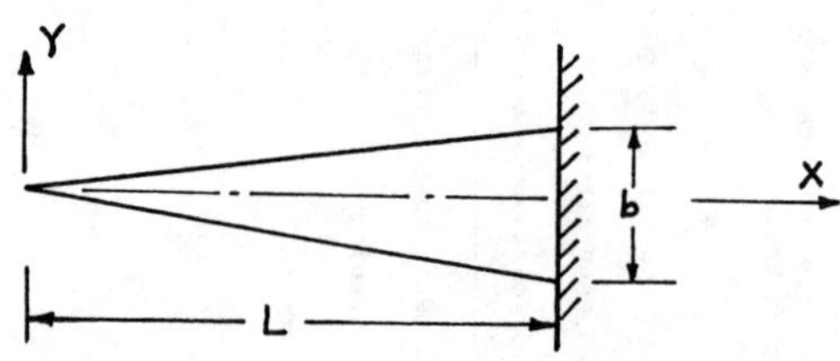

Problem Sketch

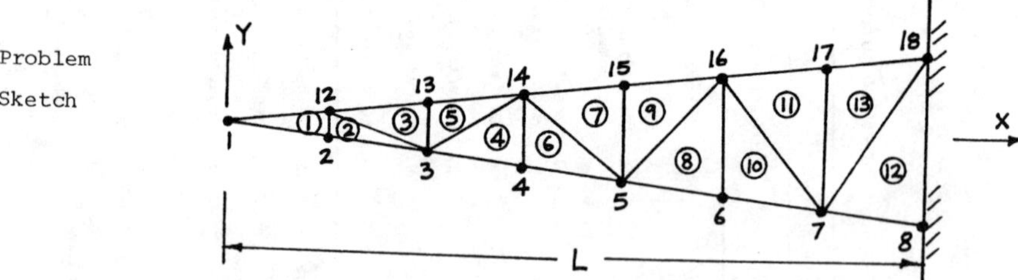

Finite Element Model

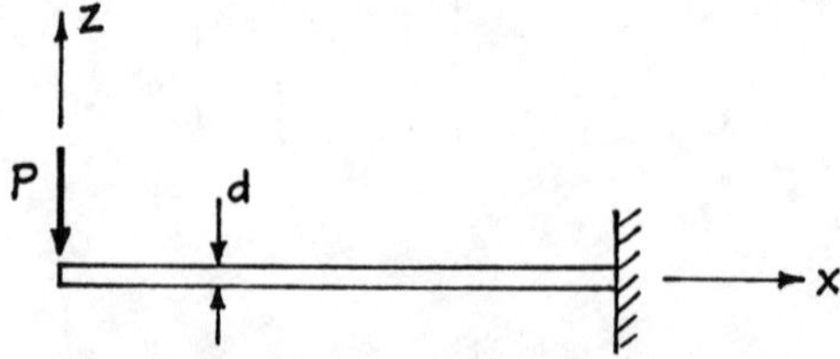

Example 2. Elongation of a Solid Bar

Type: State analysis, solid elements

Reference: Harris, C. O., Introduction to Stress Analysis, The MacMillan Co., New York, 1959, page 237, Problem 4.

Problem: A tapered bar with a square cross section, made of an aluminum alloy for which E is 10,400,000 psi, is suspended from a ceiling. An axial load Q is applied to the end of the bar. Determine the maximum axial deflection δ in the bar and the axial stress σ_y at midlength.

Given: L = 10 in., d = 2 in., Q = 10,000 lb

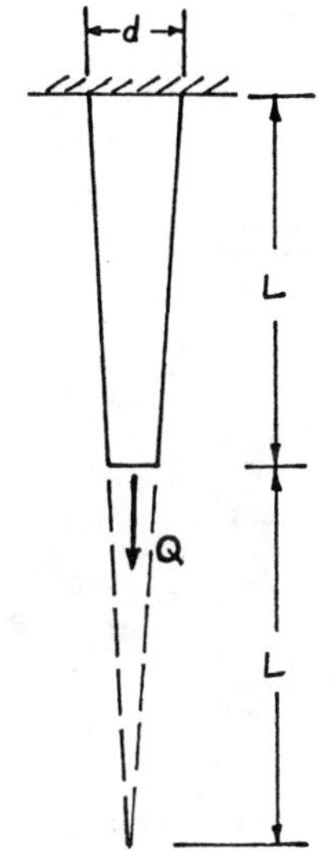

Problem Sketch

Finite Element Model

Results:

	δ (in.)	σ_y (psi)	No. of Cards
Theory	0.00480769	4444.	-
ANSYS (Ref. [23], Problem 37) (STIF 5) Difference	0.00478878 0.39%	4441. 0.067%	33
NASTRAN: HEXA1 with MPC's Difference	0.00479047 0.36%	4441. 0.067%	91
Without MPC's to enforce symmetry:			
1. HEXAL (Nodes 28,68)	0.006179	4441.	67
(Nodes 6,48)	0.007493		
Difference	30.0%/56.4%	.067%	
2. IHEX1	0.00479047	4441.	67

Example 3: Natural Frequencies of a Cantilever Beam

Type: Normal mode analysis (eigenvalue extraction), beam elements

Reference: Thomson, W. T., <u>Vibration Theory and Applications</u>, Prentice-Hall, Inc., Englewood Cliffs, N.J., 1965, pages 275 and 357.

Problem: Determine the first three natural frequencies f_i of a uniform beam clamped at one end and free at the other end.

Given: $E = 30 \times 10^6$ psi, $I = 1.3333$ in^4, $A = 4$ in^2, $h = 2$ in.
$L = 80$ in., $w = 1.124$ lb/in.

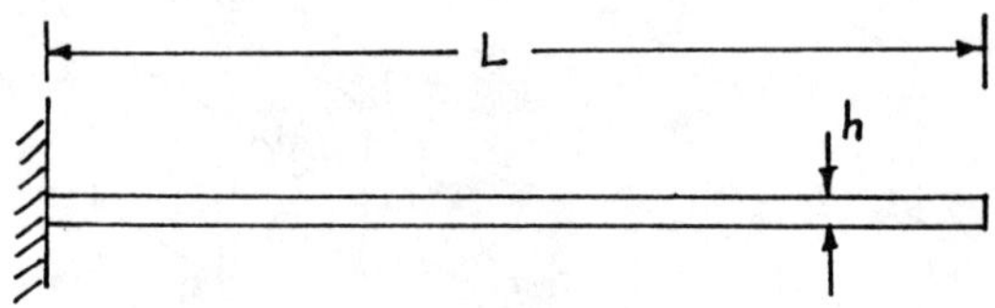

PROBLEM SKETCH

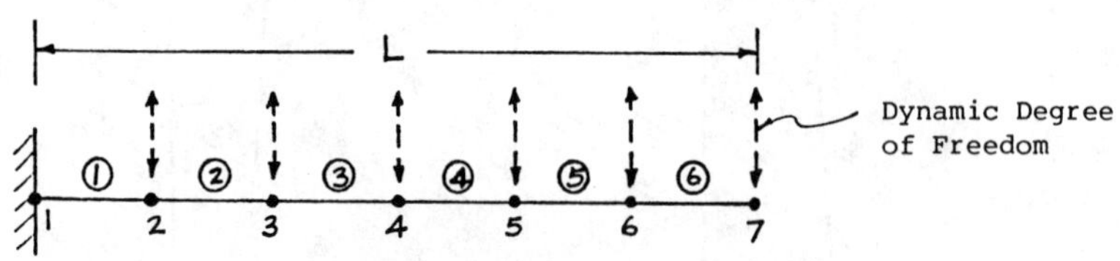

Finite Element Model
(Uses 6 lateral dynamic degrees of freedom)

Results:

	f_1(Hz)	f_2(Hz)	f_3(H
Theory	10.247	64.221	179.82
ANSYS (Ref. 23, Problem 51)	10.247	64.197	180.14
(STIF 3) Difference	None	0.037%	0.178%
NASTRAN (BAR)			
1. Lumped mass model	10.105	61.437	167.542
2. Inverse power method-consistent mass	10.203	64.145	179.905
3. Determinant method	10.233	64.148	179.905
4. Givens method	10.233	64.148	179.905
5. Unsymmetrical inverse power	10.233	64.148	179.905
6. Unsymmetrical determinant	10.233	64.148	179.905

ADVANCED EVALUATION

The advanced evaluation consisted of doing a comprehensive literature survey on a selected group of NASTRAN finite elements and performing a series of computer runs aimed at assessing element quality, convergence, completeness, and efficiency. As much as possible, the framework of this evaluation is based on comparisons with other well-known benchmark tests and on recent publications on simple element evaluation tests and criteria **[24–28]**. The intent of this section is to document in one place what is currently known about the quality of some representative COSMIC/NASTRAN structural elements, namely

QDPLT, TRSHL, TRIM6, TRPLT1, CONEAX, TRAPRG, TRAPAX, HEXA1, HEXA2, IHEX1 and IHEX2.

After these element evaluation results are described, we will also briefly discuss current minicomputer versions of NASTRAN, commercially available pre- and postprocessors for NASTRAN, and a study that was conducted on trends of run cost and CPU time versus mesh sizes.

Advanced Evaluation Tests

To aid in the overall assessment of any finite element, Robinson has suggested several evaluation tests and the following assessment points **[24]** before "the element is turned loose in the commercial arena":

1. Element shape.
2. Basic assumption (stress, displacement, or mixed).
3. Number of nodes.
4. Degrees of freedom, types of freedom, and number of freedoms per node.
5. Are the freedoms conventional and understandable?
6. Does the element pass the standard and recognized tests?
7. How general is the element in its application?
8. Are the assumed stress or displacement functions simple?
9. Is the derivation of the element matrices simple, straightforward, and understandable, and are the matrices given in explicit form?
10. What element matrices are available?
11. Is the element a synthesized element; that is, is it built up of a number of elements?
12. Are the element matrices easy to code?
13. Is the element theory and coding well documented together with check examples?
14. Does the element contain any false zero energy modes (false zero stress or strain states) other than those corresponding to rigid body modes?
15. Is the element mixable with other elements within a particular program?
16. Can the element be easily incorporated into a particular program?
17. Has the element been fully checked out? How often and in what problems has it been used? The debugging of an element is very difficult and is made even more difficult by element complexity.
18. Is the originator of the element available for consultation if problems arise? In many cases, the software developers are unaware of the detailed theory behind their elements.
19. What are the element material properties?

20. Does the element help to reduce the effort to prepare the model, to obtain computer results, to interpret the results?

21. For a given model, do the results change if the element specifying nodes are written in a different order?

Table 9 is our assessment of how COSMIC/NASTRAN rates in these categories for the selected group of elements. This assessment is, in many cases, quite subjective and is based largely on the documentation (primarily the Theoretical Manual). Results show that in general, according to Robinson's criteria, COSMIC/NASTRAN rates a "fair" ranking in its documentation for any particular element.

Robinson also recommended these basic evaluation tests: [22, 27]

1. Single element test
2. Convergence test
3. Element completeness test
4. Patch test
5. False zero energy mode test

The "single element test" consists of taking a single element in rectangular form, considering it as a structure and then investigating its behavior under various loading and constraint conditions for various geometries. This test is very helpful in understanding the load-carrying capabilities of the element and shows its sensitivity to aspect ratio. (This test is relatively simple to apply only for triangular or quadrilateral membrane and plate bending elements.)

The "convergence test" consists of studying the behavior of some parameter or parameters for various numbers of elements in a model for a particular problem. As the number of elements in a model is increased, and the mesh becomes more refined, the results should approach the true solution.

The "element completeness tests" consist of showing that the element displacement/stress assumptions contain the constant strain/stress modes and the zero strain/stress (rigid body) modes. These are essential requirements for any finite element. If each element in a model passes these tests, and the model is a compatible/equilibrium one, the results will converge monotonically.

The "patch test" consists of applying a constant strain/stress state to an assemblage of elements and showing that all the elements contain the same constant strains/stresses. This test is for "nonconforming" or "noncompatible" and "nonequilibrium" models and should be passed if the results are to converge (though not necessarily monotonically). The patch test is a completeness condition for an assemblage of elements as against an individual element. The primary purpose of this test is to provide an estimate of the error which will be incurred. It is noted that increasing the number of elements in the "patch" will probably reduce the error if the element performs well in the convergence test.

The "false zero energy mode test" consists of showing that an element does not contain zero strain/stress fields other than those associated with rigid body modes. Elements can contain false zero states which are due to the basic strain/stress assumptions and the subsequent choice of nodal degrees of freedom.

In addition to these tests, results on the "element efficiency test" will often be included. This test will, in general, be different for each type of element and shows a measure of element performance and coding efficiency for that problem. Some well-known benchmark cases used by many researchers include:

Table 9 Advanced Evaluation of NASTRAN Structural Elements - Points of Assessment

QUESTION	QDPLT	TRSHL	CONEAX	TRAPRG	HEXA 1 HEXA 2	IHEX1	IHEX2
1. Element shape	Quadrilateral	Triangular	Conical Shell	Trapezoidal Ring	Brick, constant strain, 5 or 10 tetrahedra	Brick	Brick
2. Basic assumption	← DISPLACEMENT FORMULATION →				(constant strain).	(isoparametric)	(isoparametric)
3. No. of nodes	4	6	2	4	8	8	20
4. Degrees of freedom at each node	1 transverse displacement 2 rotations	3 translations 2 rotations	3 translations 2 rotations	3 translations	3 translations	3 translations	3 translations
5. Freedoms understandable and conventional?	Yes	Yes (No transverse shear flexibility)	Unique, incl. transverse shear flexibility	Yes	Yes	Yes	Yes
6. Does element pass standard and recognized tests?		See Advanced Evaluation Discussions For Each Element					
7. How general is element in its application?	General	General, thin, shallow shell element	Axisymmetric but loads and deflections do not have to be	Must have 2 parallel sides, restrictive use. No input option for pressure on an element face.	General, but requires too many elements for accuracy	General; good for problems with high shear stresses	General; good for plate bending type deformations

Table 9 (Cont.)

	QDPLT	TRSHL	CONEAX	TRAPRG	HEXA1 HEXA2	IHEX1	IHEX2
8. Assumed displacement functions simple?	Yes, x^2y term omitted	No; quadratic polynomial for membrane, quintic for w	Yes	Yes, harmonic expansion in circumferential direction	Yes	Linear displacement variation	Quadratic displacement variation
9. Element matrices simple, understandable, given explicitly?	Yes	Not given	No, could be better	Not given explicitly	No	No	No
10. Element matrices available?	Yes	No	Yes, to an extent	No	No	No	No
11. Built-up element?	Yes, 4 basic TRPLTs	Yes, constituents are TRIM6 and TRPLT1	No	No	Yes, 5 or 10 overlapping tetrahedra	No	No
12. Element matrices easy to code?	Yes	No	No	No	Yes	No	No
13. Element theory well-documented? Check examples?	Yes	Fair, no examples	Yes, but no examples	Fair; is modified Wilson element	No; poor documentation, no examples	Poor, no examples	Poor, no examples
14. Any false zero energy modes?	←		UNDOCUMENTED				→
15. Element mixable with others in code?	Yes	Yes	No	No	Yes	Yes, except with special stand-alone elements	Yes, except with special stand-alone elements

Table 9 (Cont.)

QUESTION	QDPLT	TRSHL	CONEAX	TRAPRG	HEXA1 HEXA2	IHEX1	IHEX 2
16. Element easily incorporated into code?	Yes	Yes	Yes	Yes	Yes	Yes, coding of numerical integration important	Yes, coding of numerical integration important
17. Element fully debugged?	Yes, except for a twist load	No	Yes, but thermal load capability reported to be in error	Yes	Yes, but poor in bending problems	Yes	Yes
18. Element originator available for consultation?	No	Yes, but Narayanaswami now at MSC	No	No	No	No	No
19. Element material properties	Isotropic, anisotropic	Isotropic only	Isotropic only	Isotropic, orthotropic	Isotropic only	Isotropic only	Isotropic only
20. Element helps to reduce model preparation effort, obtain & interpret results?	Yes	Yes, higher order, but results questionable	Yes, good performance even with a few elements	Yes, except for trapezoidal restriction and no pressure input option	No, too many elements required for satisfactory accuracy	Yes, 8-node element easy to use	No, 20-node element requires more cumbersome input
21. Results change if node ordering different?	Not evaluated in this study	Not evaluated in this study	No	Not evaluated in this study	HEXA1: Yes HEXA2: No	Not evaluated in this study	Not evaluated in this study

1. Plate-bending element. Simply supported, or clamped, square plate loaded centrally by a concentrated load.
2. Plate/shell element. Scordelis-Lo cylindrical shell problem loaded by its own weight.
3. Conical shell element. Cantilevered cylindrical shell loaded at its own free end by a line load around the circumference.
4. Solid of revolution element. Thick-walled cylinder loaded by internal pressure.
5. 3-D solid elements. Slender cantilever beam problem, a pressurized thick-walled cylinder problem, and a study of element eigenvalues and eigenvectors.

At the end of each element evaluation, an assessment will be made of that element's quality and efficiency.

The QDPLT Element

QDPLT was selected for advanced evaluation because it is one of the more complex plate-bending elements in the NASTRAN library. Also, there is less documentation in the Theoretical Manual for this element than for most other shell elements. In the course of this investigation, it was determined that deficiencies had been previously observed in QDPLT [27]. QDPLT consists of four nonconforming TRPLTs, models bending behavior only, and does not have membrane-bending coupling.

Single Element Test

The single element test for a plate-bending element consisted of evaluating the displacement and rotation for eight cases (giving various combinations of constraints and loads) for a range of element aspect ratios:

1. Cases 1, 2, 3, and 4: Displacement in the z-direction (U_z) and rotation about the y-axis at node 3 (Θ_y).
2. Cases 5, 6, 7, and 8: Displacement in the z-direction (Uz) and rotation about the x-axis at node 3 (Θ_x).

The single element test results are plotted in Figs. 3 to 10, where they are compared with the standard beam solutions.

For our evaluation of QDPLT, the following material properties were used:

1. Young's Modulus $E = 10^7$ psi
2. Shear Modulus $G = \dfrac{E}{2(1+\nu)} = 3.8462 \times 10^6$ psi
3. Poisson's Ratio $\nu = 0.3$

For example, the theoretical values are presented on the following three pages. The critical single element tests for QDPLT are Cases 6 and 8 (Figs. 8 and 10). In both cases where the performance was poor, a twisting moment was applied to the element with one edge fully clamped. This activates differential (bilinear) bending. It is interesting to note that when the rotational restraint was not applied (Cases 5 and 7) with the loading otherwise identical, the element performed well.

Other 4-node plate-bending elements, such as Lockheed/NASTRAN's LORA and MSC/NASTRAN's QUAD4 correlated reasonably well with theory up to aspect ratios of 12. [33] Except for load cases 6 and 8, QDPLT performed well in the single element tests.

CASE	BOUNDARY CONDITIONS AT SUPPORTED EDGE	THEORETICAL RESULTS AT FREE END
1	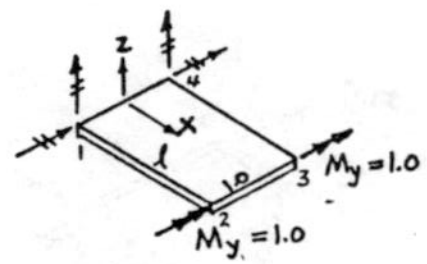 $(\Theta_y)_1 = (\Theta_y)_4 = 0$ $(U_z)_1 = (U_z)_4 = 0$	$\Theta_y = \frac{M_y \ell}{EI} = 2.40 \times 10^{-3} \cdot \ell$ $U = \frac{M_y \ell^2}{2EI} = 1.20 \times 10^{-3} \cdot \ell^2$
2	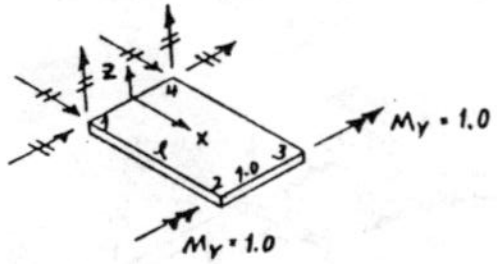 $(\Theta_y)_1 = (\Theta_y)_4 = 0$ $(\Theta_x)_1 = (\Theta_x)_4 = 0$ $(U_z)_1 = (U_z)_4 = 0$	$\Theta_y = \frac{M_y \ell (1-\nu^2)}{EI} = 2.18 \times 10^{-3} \cdot \ell$ $U_z = \frac{M_y \ell^2 (1-\nu^2)}{2EI} = 1.09 \times 10^{-3} \cdot \ell^2$
3	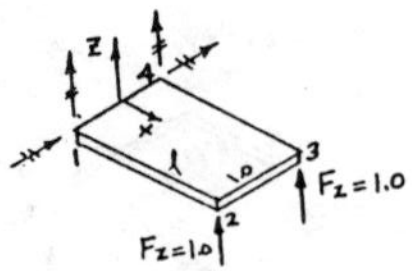 $(\Theta_y)_1 = (\Theta_y)_4 = 0$ $(U_z)_1 = (U_z)_4 = 0$	$\Theta_y = \frac{F_z \ell^2}{2EI} = 1.20 \times 10^{-3} \cdot \ell^2$ $U_z = \frac{F_z \ell^3}{3EI} = .800 \times 10^{-3} \cdot \ell^3$

CASE	BOUNDARY CONDITIONS AT SUPPORTED EDGE	THEORETICAL RESULTS AT FREE END
4	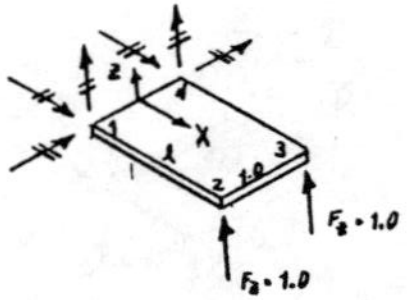 $(\theta_y)_1 = (\theta_y)_4 = 0$ $(\theta_x)_1 = (\theta_x)_4 = 0$ $(U_x)_1 = (U_x)_4 = 0$	$\theta_y = \frac{F_z \ell^2 (1-\nu^2)}{2EI} = 1.09 \times 10^{-3} \cdot \ell^2$ $U_z = \frac{F_z \ell^3 (1-\nu^2)}{3EI} = .780 \times 10^{-3} \cdot \ell^3$
5	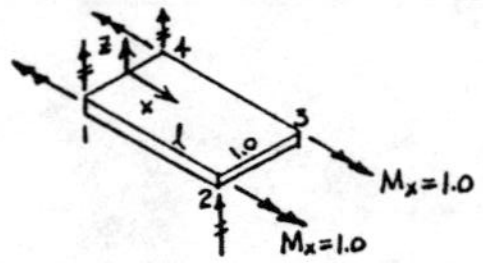 $(U_z)_1 = (U_z)_2 = (U_z)_4 = 0$	$\theta_y = \frac{T\Delta y}{GJ} = .780 \times 10^{-3}$ $\theta_x = \frac{M_x \ell}{GJ} = .780 \times 10^{-3} \cdot \ell$ $U_z = \frac{M_x \ell \Delta y}{GJ} = .780 \times 10^{-3} \cdot \ell$
6	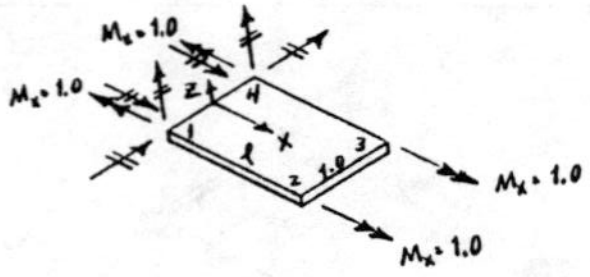 $(\theta_y)_1 = (\theta_y)_4 = 0$ $(\theta_x)_1 = (\theta_x)_4 = 0$ $(U_z)_1 = (U_z)_4 = 0$	$\theta_y = \frac{T\Delta y(1-\nu^2)}{GJ} = .710 \times 10^{-3}$ $\theta_x = \frac{M_x \ell (1-\nu^2)}{GJ} = 1.42 \times 10^{-3} \cdot \ell$ $U_z = \frac{M_x \ell \Delta y (1-\nu^2)}{2GJ} = .710 \times 10^{-3} \cdot \ell$

CASE	BOUNDARY CONDITIONS AT SUPPORTED EDGE	THEORETICAL RESULTS AT FREE END
7	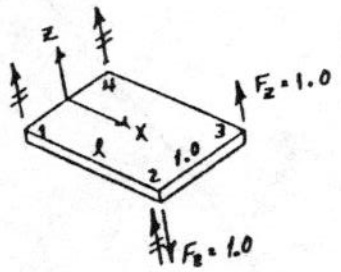 $(U_z)_1 = (U_z)_2 = (U_z)_4 = 0$	$\Theta_y = \frac{T\Delta y}{GJ} = .780 \times 10^{-3}$ $\Theta_x = \frac{M_x \ell}{GJ} = .780 \times 10^{-3} \cdot \ell$ $U_z = \frac{M_x \ell \Delta x}{GJ} = .780 \times 10^{-3} \cdot \ell$
8	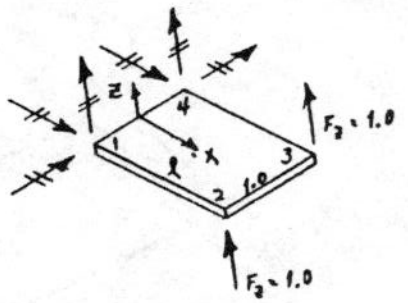 $(\Theta_y)_1 = (\Theta_y)_4 = 0$ $(\Theta_x)_1 = (\Theta_x)_4 = 0$ $(U_z)_1 = (U_z)_4 = 0$	$\Theta_y = \frac{T\Delta y(1-\nu^2)}{2GJ} = .355 \times 10^{-3}$ $\Theta_x = \frac{M_x \ell (1-\nu^2)}{GJ} = .710 \times 10^{-3} \cdot \ell$ $U_z = \frac{M_x \ell \Delta y(1-\nu^2)}{2GJ} = .355 \times 10^{-3} \cdot \ell$

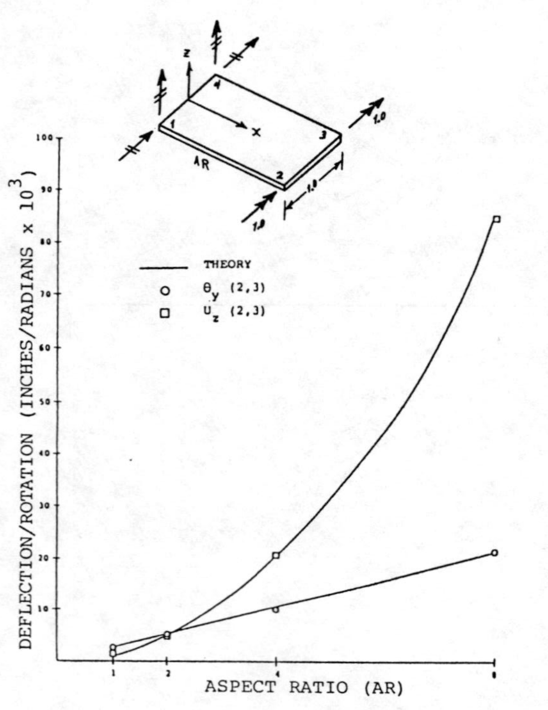

Fig. 3 Single element test for QDPLT - Case 1

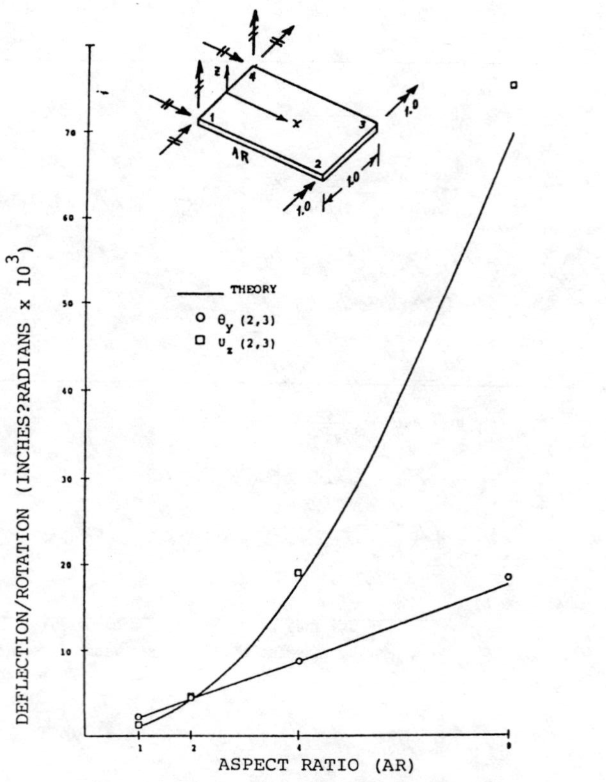

Fig. 4 Single element test for QDPLT - Case 2

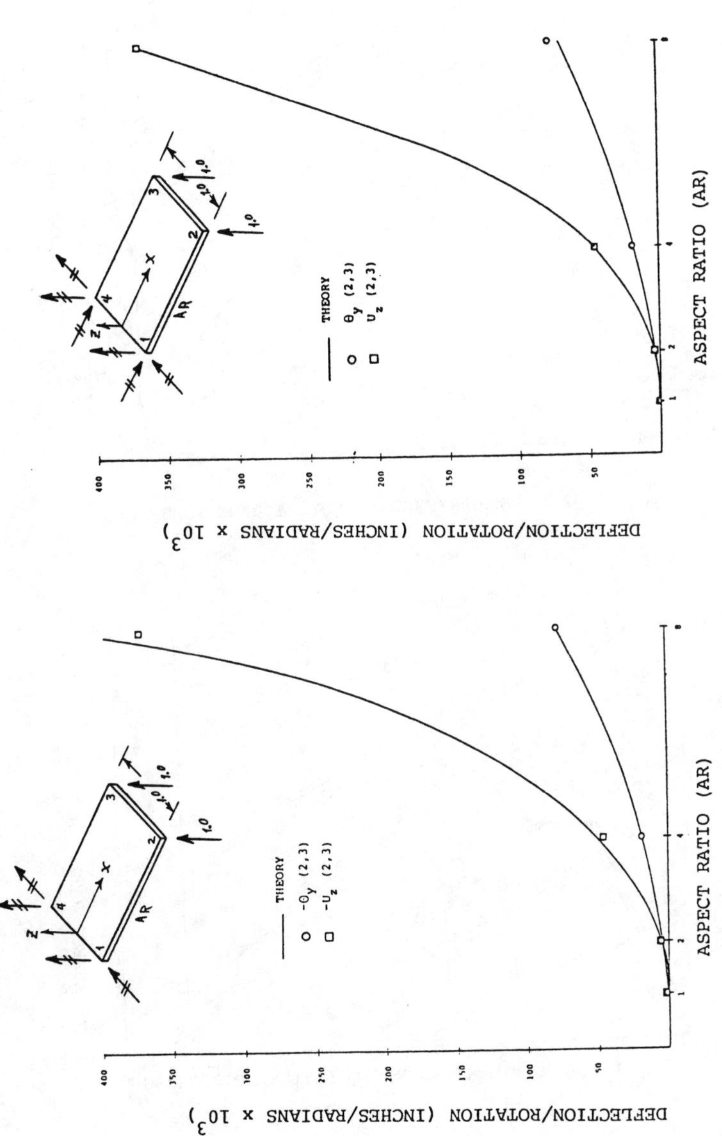

Fig. 5 Single element test for QDPLT - Case 3

Fig. 6 Single element test for QDPLT - Case 4

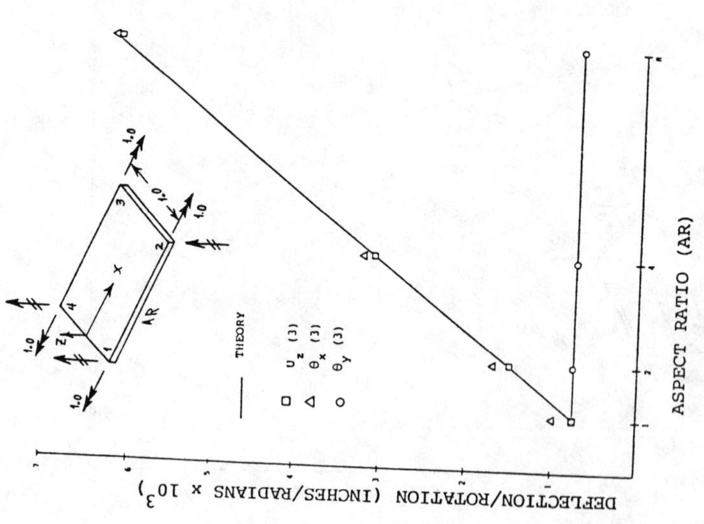

Fig. 7 Single element test for QDPLT - Case 5

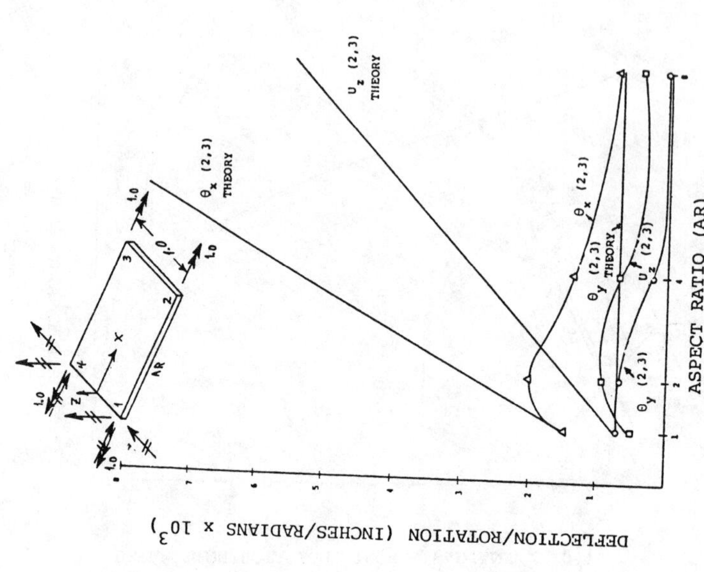

Fig. 8 Single element test for QDPLT - Case 6

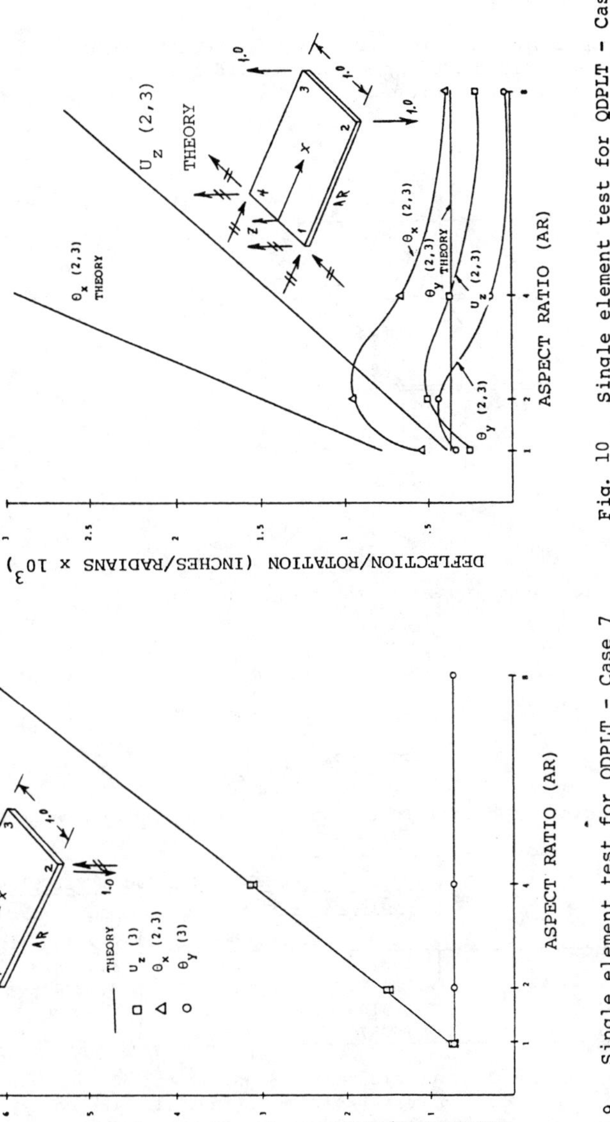

Fig. 9 Single element test for QDPLT - Case 7

Fig. 10 Single element test for QDPLT - Case 8

Convergence Test

A simple convergence test often used for-plate bending elements is a square plate centrally loaded by a concentrated load P, with simply-supported and clamped boundary conditions:

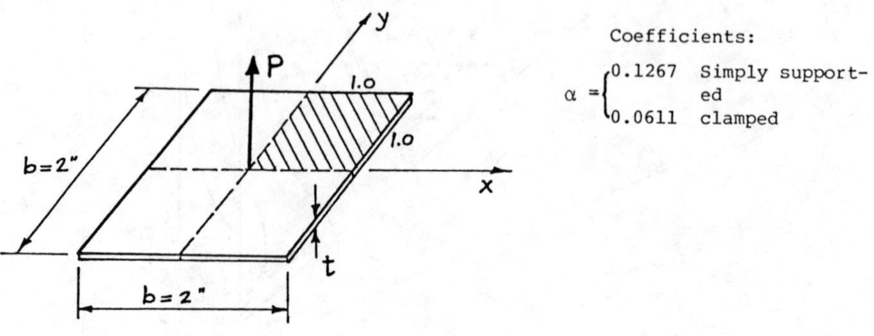

Theoretical deflections at the center are[36] :

$$\delta = \frac{\alpha P b^2}{E t^3}$$

$$\delta = \begin{cases} 2.0272 \times 10^{-4} \text{ in.} & \text{simply supported} \\ 9.976 \times 10^{-5} \text{ in.} & \text{clamped} \end{cases}$$

Assume: $b = 2$ in.
$P = 4$ lb
$t = 0.1$ in.
$E = 10^7$ psi
$\nu = 0.3$

We evaluated QDPLT for four mesh sizes using this convergence test:

NO. OF ELEMENTS FOR 1/4 OF PLATE	COMPUTED CENTRAL DEFLECTION (in.)			
	SIMPLY SUPPORTED		CLAMPED	
	$\delta \times 10^4$ (in.)	% Error	$\delta \times 10^5$ (in.)	% Error
1	2.198274	8.43	5.475623	-42.3
4	2.134809	5.31	9.989985	0.140
9	2.109106	4.04	10.33296	3.57
16	2.100579	3.61	10.41435	4.39

These QDPLT results are plotted in Figs. 11 and 12 and show the same convergence trends as in Ref. [24]. Jnfortunately, the modeling error discussion (Sec. 15.2) in Ref. [7] does not contain QDPLT results. It is interesting to note that the convergency trend is not monotonic and, in fact, appears to diverge slightly for the clamped case as the number of elements is increased, with four elements yielding very accurate results.

Patch Test

The patch test, first proposed by B. Irons in 1972, requires a nonconforming element to produce constant stresses/strains when these elements are

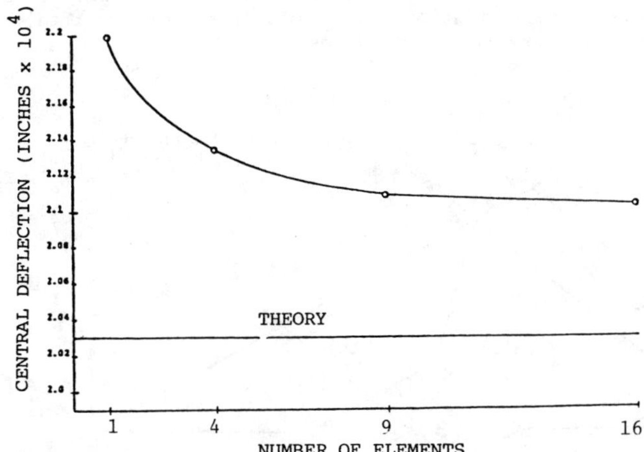

Fig. 11 Convergence test for QDPLT. Simply supported square plate (AR=1) with central point load

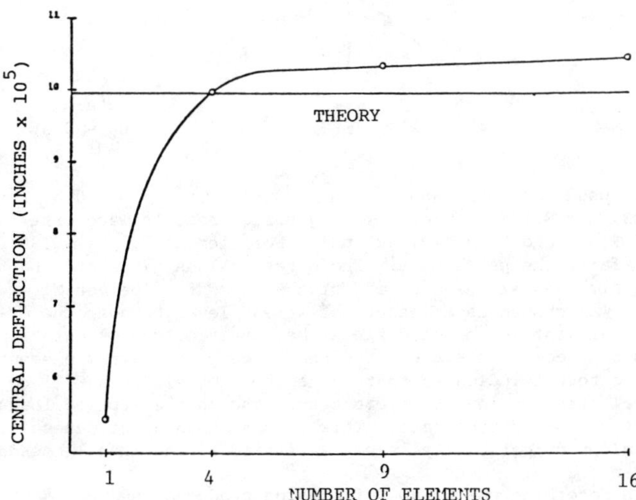

Fig. 12 Convergence test for QDPLT. Clamped square plate (AR=1) with central point load

formed together in a model which has at least one internal node. It thus measures completeness for an assemblage of elements. For a quadrilateral plate-bending element such as QDPLT, one possible patch test is this "picture frame" model subjected to the loads shown [24].

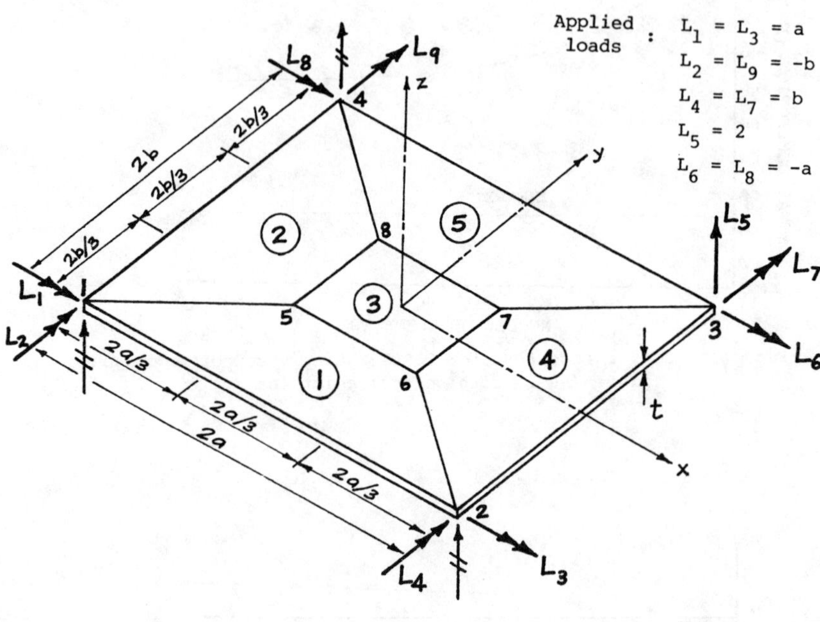

Note:
$u_z = 0$ at
nodes 1, 2, 4

Such a model was used for QDPLT and it was assumed that a = b = 0.5, E = 10^7 psi, ν = 0.3, t = 0.1 in. The following stress results were obtained. For elements 1, 2, 4, and 5, σ = 1,421 psi. For element 3, σ = 1,138 psi. QDPLT therefore fails the patch test. The stress values given are the Von Mises effective stresses at the centroid of the element. The Von Mises effective stress was chosen as a measure of stress level because the orientation of the element i-j nodes defines the stress output orientation and therefore stress components are not directly comparable from element to element. This result indicates that an assembly of elements will not produce identical stresses in each element even though the applied loads should produce a uniform stress rate. This is not an unexpected result, however, since slope compatibility is not satisfied at the mutual boundaries of the elements.

In order to determine which type of loading produced the most severe disparity, the combined loading was divided into individual load components as shown in Fig . 13. As can be seen, the loading consists of edge moments, M_x and M_y, and an out-of-plane force at one corner. The two moment load cases should produce a constant curvature, R_x or R_y, resulting in a uniform stress distribution on each surface of the plate. The third loading condition produces a twisting load on the plate and should result in a constant state of stress in all elements. The results indicate that

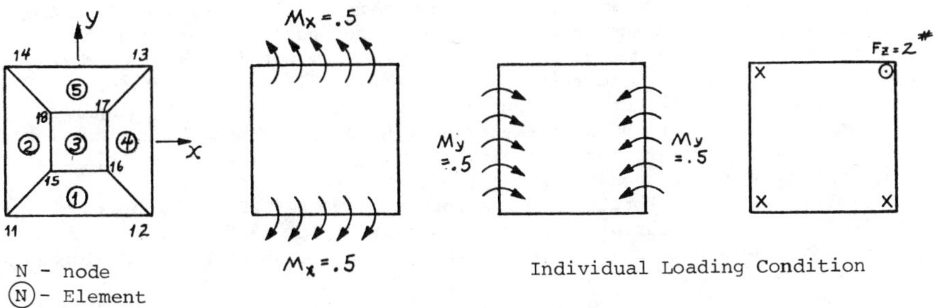

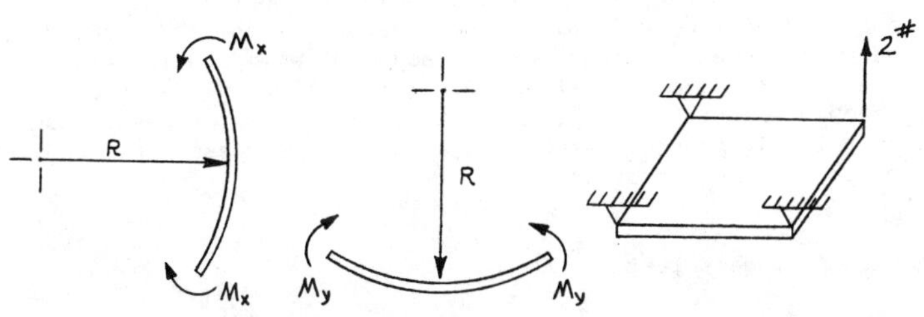

Constant Stress Shapes

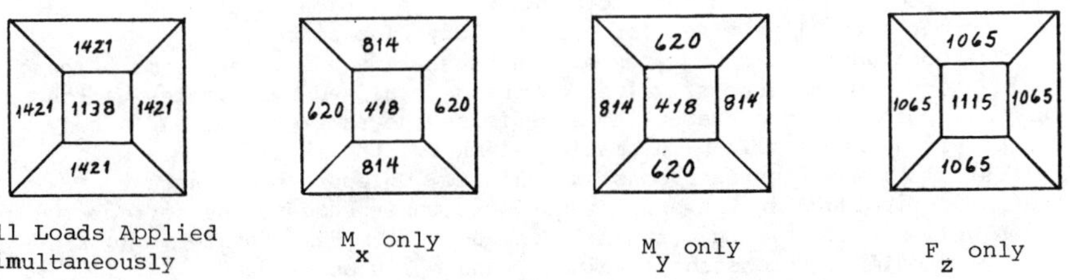

Von Mises Effective Stress at Centroid

Fig. 13 QDPLT patch test results for individual loading conditions

the moment loads produce the largest range of stress values in the elements.

A detailed examination of the displacement solution revealed that the slopes were discontinuous across the element boundaries, therefore the constant curvatures were not correctly predicted. It was interesting to note that the concentrated load at the corner resulted in a fairly uniform stress field, even though this appears to be the most severe loading condition due to the warping of the element. However, the single element test, Fig. 9, does indicate that the element will perform well under this loading as long as moment constraints are not applied (as in Case 8, Fig. 10). Possibly, the reason for the poor performance of the QDPLT element in modeling the constant curvature is related to its poor performance in Cases 6 and 8 of the single element tests, where slope constraints were enforced at the support.

The poor performance of QDPLT in the patch test illustrates the need for the analyst to be aware of the limitations of QDPLT or any other plate-bending elements that are being used in a structural analysis. The results should be checked thoroughly, especially in areas where large stress or strain gradients occur. Also, the fineness of the mesh should be such that the difference in stress between adjacent elements is relatively small. Areas of the mesh that exhibit large stress differences between elements should either be reanalyzed with a finer mesh or results should be assigned a fairly generous error range when the stresses are used to assess the adequacy of the structure.

Element Completeness Test

The completeness requirement for an element is satisfied if the rigid body displacements and constant strain states are represented. A rigid body displacement is the most elementary deformation that an element may undergo. This condition states that combinations of values of the generalized coordinates q_i that cause all points on the element to experience the same displacement should exist. One such combination should occur for each of the rigid body translations and rotations. In a typical displacement model, the constant term q_1 provides for a rigid body displacement.

The constant strain requirement can be stated in similar terms. There should exist combinations of values of the generalized coordinates q_i that cause all points on the element to experience the same strain. As a body is subdivided into smaller and smaller elements, the strains in each infinitesimal element approach constant values. Unless these constant strains are included in the shape function, convergence to the correct solution will not occur. In a typical displacement model, the terms (q_2x) and q_3y) provide for constant strains ε_x and ε_y in an element.

QDPLT is a quadrilateral bending element which is composed of four overlapping basic bending triangles. Upon close examination of the theoretical development of this element in Ref. [7] it was concluded that the terms for both rigid body displacements and constant strain states are included in the displacement model.

False Zero Energy Mode Test

If the number of element independent deformation variables plus the number of rigid body modes is less than the number of nodal degrees of freedom in the local system, an element may contain false zero energy modes [24, 27]. Zero energy modes are always associated with rigid body modes since these give zero elastic energy and zero stress or strain fields. Even when the number of independent deformation variables plus rigid body modes is equal to the number of nodal degrees of freedom, false modes can exist.

False zero energy modes can be found by numerical techniques directly using the element matrices, an iterative static method of gradually increasing the number of support freedoms [24], or a modal procedure whereby the eigenvalues are computed for an unsupported structure [27], as suggested by Wilson, Taylor, and Doherty (1969). Although a single element may contain false zero energy modes, in many cases experience has shown that these modes do not propagate when combined with other elements to form a structural model, therefore causing no problems. To perform this test rigorously for QDPLT would have meant setting up either a static method of iteratively searching for false modes by gradually increasing the number of support freedoms for a variety of supports and loading cases or an exhaustive eigenvalue interpretation procedure similar to what was done for the NASTRAN solid elements. Because of the relative lack of importance of this test and extensive work previously reported to characterize QDPLT performance in the single element test, convergence test, and patch test, it was decided to forgo the false zero energy mode test on QDPLT.

Conclusions

Advanced evaluation tests on the QDPLT bending element show it rated fair in performance. In summary it may be said that QDPLT performed well in the single element test in six out of eight cases of various loading/support combinations (the exceptions being the twist load cases 6 and 8); converged satisfactorily in the two convergence tests of a simply supported and clamped square plate under a concentrated center load; and failed the patch test. Its overall performance is inferior to other currently available 4-noded plate elements, such as MSC/NASTRAN's QUAD4, Lockheed-California NASTRAN's LORA stress-based plate-bending element, and T. H. H. Pian's stress-based element with nine independent force variables [26].

The TRSHL Element

TRSHL is a triangular shallow shell element implemented into Level 16.0 of COSMIC/NASTRAN in 1976. When TRSHL was originally selected for advanced evaluation, it seemed a logical choice because it is a higher-order shell element recently incorporated into the COSMIC/NASTRAN element library. A description of TRSHL documentation, theory, status, and efficiency follows. Most or all of this background information is unavailable to the average NASTRAN user, and it is included to illustrate the implementation history and current status of a typical element in the NASTRAN library.

Background

TRSHL was developed and implemented into COSMIC/NASTRAN by Dr. R. Narayanaswami in 1974-1976 [29, 30], while he was at Old Dominion University, Norfolk, Virginia. The element models curved thin shell behavior by approximating the membrane behavior using the linear strain TRIM6 element, the bending behavior using the quintic transverse displacement TRPLT1 element, and membrane-bending coupling using Novozhilov shallow-shell theory. This 6-noded element has 30 degrees of freedom; at each node there are five degrees of freedom consisting of three translations and two rotations. The element is designed for use with the statics, normal modes, and buckling rigid formats of NASTRAN.

In our early investigations, two interesting things were discovered about TRSHL. First, the documentation of TRSHL in the NASTRAN manuals was poorly written, short, and incomplete. Narayanaswami's two Old Dominion University reports cited in the NASTRAN Theoretical Manual were unavailable through the usual NASA or NTIS publication sources, even though the research was funded by NASA/Langley. (Ref. [29] was obtained by writing directly to Old Dominion University.) Second, although TRSHL still exists in the COSMIC/NASTRAN Level 17.5 element library, its use appears to be limited and has been abandoned in both the latest versions of NASTRAN offered by the MacNeal-Schwendler Corporation (MSC) and Universal Analytics, Inc. (UAI)

The history of the development and implementation of the TRSHL element illustrates one of the weaknesses of the piecemeal development of a large general purpose program such as NASTRAN. The use of a number of different subcontractors to provide finite elements or solution algorithms often leads to a situation where the developer is not available to completely debug the program modification in its final form. Furthermore, the completeness and accuracy of the documentation often vary significantly. Additionally, the developer is usually not available to provide user support for this part of the program. This latter criticism is often cited (for example [18]) as an important evaluation point in comparing computer programs.

Universal Analytics, Inc., was contacted to inquire why TRSHL is not included in UAI/NASTRAN anymore. In response, Mr. M. J. Morgan of UAI informed us that UAI found TRSHL did have a poor performance and reputation, and UAI had decided instead to implement its own QUAD3 and QUAD8 elements for shell analysis. He referred us to Dr. A. B. Potvin of Exxon Production Research Company (Houston, Texas) for more TRSHL evaluation results. Dr. Potvin told us that he discovered several minor coding errors in the TRSHL implementation into Level 16.0 of COSMIC/NASTRAN, and after correcting these himself, he found its performance and convergence to be relatively poor in the Scordelis-Lo problem [31]. Potvin's TRSHL data are included in Fig. 14.

Based upon these inquiries, the following conclusions have been drawn concerning TRSHL. The documentation in NASTRAN is inadequate; its use is apparently quite limited; there is little technical support available from its developer; its performance is inferior (as can be seen from Fig. 14) to other currently available shell elements, and its coding implementation into COSMIC/NASTRAN was apparently not thoroughly tested.

Theory

The TRSHL element uses only displacements and rotations as nodal degrees of freedom (Fig. 15). The displacement functions for u, v, and w are chosen as follows:

$$u = q_1 + q_2x + q_3y + q_4x^2 + q_5xy + q_6y^2$$

$$v = q_7 + q_8x + q_9y + q_{10}y^2 + q_{11}xy + q_{12}y^2$$

$$\begin{aligned} w = {} & q_{13} + q_{14}x + q_{15}y + q_{16}x^2 + q_{17}xy + q_{18}y^2 + q_{19}x^3 \\ & + q_{20}x^2y + q_{21}xy^2 + q_{22}y^3 + q_{23}x^4 + q_{24}x^3y + q_{25}x^2y^2 + q_{26}xy^3 \\ & + q_{27}y^4 + q_{28}x^5 + q_{29}x^4y + q_{30}x^3y^2 + q_{31}x^2y^3 + q_{32}xy^4 \\ & + q_{33}y^5 \end{aligned}$$

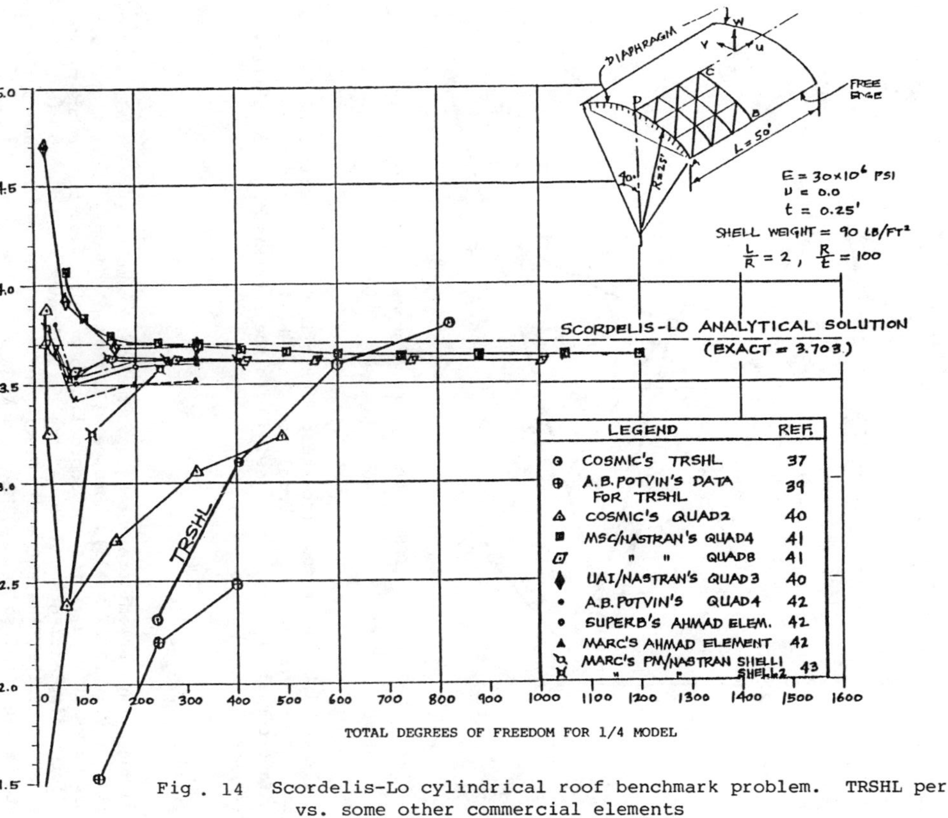

Fig. 14 Scordelis-Lo cylindrical roof benchmark problem. TRSHL performance vs. some other commercial elements

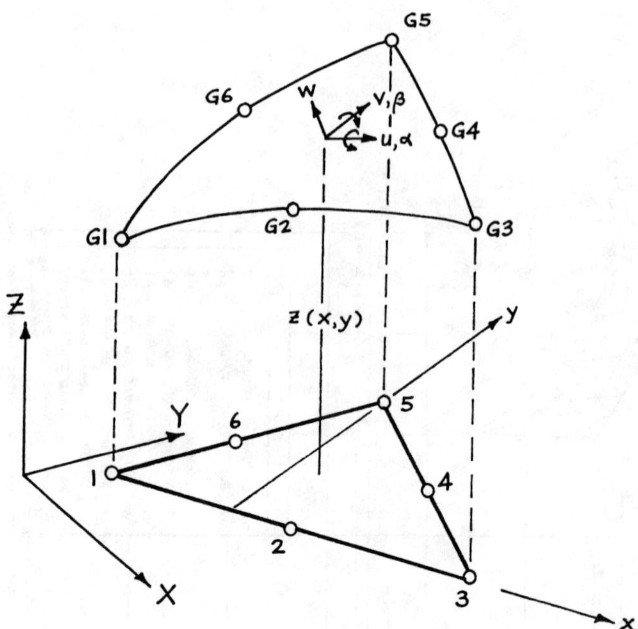

Fig. 15 TRSHL shell element geometry and coordinate systems

The element includes transverse shear flexibility in the stiffness formulation. Use of quadratic polynomials for the shell surface geometry implies constant curvatures, thereby agreeing with the approximations of shallow shell theory.

Evaluation Results

Although Narayanaswami presented two numerical examples (spherical cap, Scordelis-Lo cylindrical shell), here we will comment on only the latter. Table 10 shows TRSHL results for the Scordelis-Lo problem, and the trends of four predicted displacements and three stress resultants versus mesh size. Note that even for the fine 6x6 mesh, discrepancies are quite pronounced for four of the seven results, V_B, W_C, M_{yy_C}, and M_{xx_C}.

Narayanaswami [29] did not provide a complete explanation for the difference between the calculated values and the exact solution. If one examines only the free edge midpoint vertical displacement (Fig. 14), TRSHL fared somewhat better, though it is still inferior to Cowper et al. (1970) and many other available commercial shell elements. Potvin's independent check of TRSHL results [31] is also shown. It is noted that there is a considerable difference between Potvin's results and those reported by Narayanaswami. It is also interesting to note that although TRSHL is described in Ref. [7], it was omitted in a table which lists available COSMIC/NASTRAN finite elements in Ref. [13].

Table 10 TRSHL Results for Scordelis-Lo Cylindrical Shell Roof Problem

Finite Element Grids	$10u_A$ (in.)	w_B (in.)	$10v_B$ (in.)	$10w_C$ (in.)	$10^{-3}N_{xxB}$ (lb./in.)	$10^{-3}M_{yyC}$ (lb. in./in.)	$10^{-2}M_{xxC}$ (lb. in./in.)
1 x 1	-0.45168	-0.29100	-2.48424	-4.0700	2.4659	0.7685	2.8520
2 x 2	-0.7812	-1.2516	-4.77312	-2.1344	4.2801	-0.9395	-0.8896
3 x 3	-1.09590	-2.49876	-7.12872	-1.3606	5.4948	-2.0283	-1.1136
4 x 4	-1.2939	-3.4332	-8.57580	2.2224	6.0277	-2.3828	-1.7912
2 x 4	-0.9041	-2.2815	-6.15	0.888	5.1312	-1.415	-2.0196
3 x 6	-1.1244	-3.6227	-8.5968	3.1031	6.1862	-1.9414	-1.8912
4 x 8	-1.3845	-4.1526	-9.5295	3.9238	6.4839	-2.0459	-1.6724
5 x 5	-1.4160	-3.88152	-9.29000	2.8182	6.3279	-2.3538	-1.9770
6 x 6	-1.4733	-4.09176	-9.76992	3.0900	6.444	-2.3242	-2.0638
Exact (Scordelis-Lo)	-1.51325	-4.09916	-8.76147	5.2494	6.4124	-2.0562	-0.9272

Conclusions

Based on the results of this investigation, it is concluded that TRSHL element quality and efficiency rate considerably below those of currently available shell elements in competing software. A low (and declining) level of its use in the future is predicted, leading to its probable ultimate demise in the COSMIC/NASTRAN element library.

The TRIM6 and TRPLT1 Elements

Closely related to TRSHL are the linear strain triangular membrane element TRIM6 and the higher-order triangular bending element TRPLT1. This section gives a short summary of the element theory and efficiency for both elements. Evaluation results are already well documented in Refs. **[9 30]**. **TRIM6**, TRPLT1, and TRSHL were added to Level 16.0 of COSMIC/NASTRAN by Dr. Narayanaswami in December 1976.

Theory

The linear strain triangular membrane element TRIM6 is based on J. H. Argyris's derivation in 1965. The element has six nodes, three at the vertices and three at the midpoints of the sides. The element uses a quadratic displacement field.

$$u = q_1 + q_2x + q_3y + q_4x^2 + q_5xy + q_6y^2$$

$$v = q_7 + q_8x + q_9y + q_{10}x^2 + q_{11}xy + q_{12}y^2$$

The thickness of the element, as well as the temperature distribution within the element, can have bilinear variation. TRIM6 may be used for the statics and normal modes rigid formats but cannot be used for differential stiffness and piecewise linear analyses. Element stresses are computed at the three vertices and at the centroid.

TRPLT1 was developed by Narayanaswami in 1974 as a modification of Cowper et al. (1968). Like TRIM6 and TRSHL, TRPLT1 has six nodes, three at the vertices and three at the midpoints of the sides. A quintic displacement field is chosen for the transverse displacement w. The element is nonconforming, meaning it has no slope continuity for two adjacent elements with a common edge. Each node has three degrees of freedom, two rotations, and the transverse displacement w. Transverse shear flexibility is included in the stiffness formulation. The element thickness can have bilinear variations. TRPLT1 may be used in the statics and normal modes rigid formats. The element internal forces are recovered at the three vertices and at the centroids.

Evaluation Results

The performances of TRIM6 and TRPLT1 are already adequately described in Refs. [7] and [38]. A decision was made not to repeat these exercises and to report here only some representative test problems which demonstrate their efficiency and convergence characteristics.

1. Example 1 - Cantilevered beam using membrane elements.
   Figure 16 shows the excellent correlation of TRIM6 with theory and

its superiority over the QDMEM1 isoparametric membrane element and the conventional quadrilateral membrane element QDMEM. This example demonstrates the improved accuracy due to use of a quadratic displacement polynomial and appears in both Refs. [9, 30].

2. Example 2 - Rectangular plate bending using TRPLT1.

Figure 17 gives a typical TRPLT1 deflection convergence study for a rectangular plate, simply supported at the four edges and with a central concentrated load. Note that TRPLT1 converges monotonically from above the theoretical value, a behavior which is typical of nonconforming elements and which suggests a need for a patch test. This example was for a (b/a) ratio of 2.

Conclusions

A careful review of all the convergence efficiency and demonstration examples in Refs. [9] and [30] reveals that the TRIM6 and TRPLT1 elements performed quite well for a variety of conditions and load cases - including statics, thermal loads, vibration, and buckling problems.

The CONEAX Element

CONEAX is a conical shell element which can have either axisymmetric or asymmetric loading. This section briefly explains CONEAX theory and the advanced evaluation results using an edge-loaded cylinder to assess its accuracy.

Theory

The CONEAX element coordinate geometry and 5 degrees of freedom are shown below.

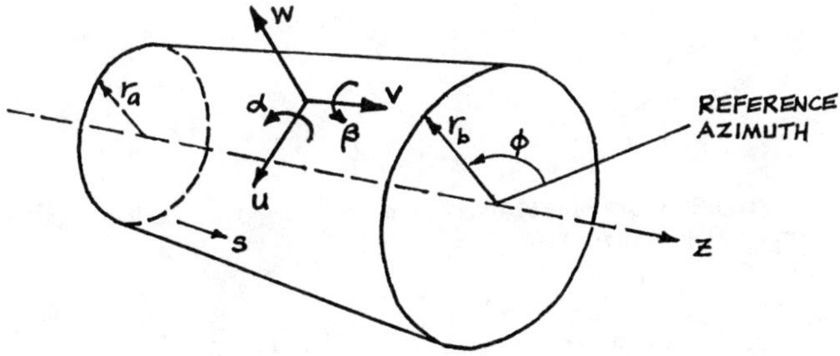

The displacements u and v are assumed to be linear functions of the meridional position s, while w is assumed to be a cubic. For each harmonic order q_n, the harmonic components of deflection are [9]:

$$u_n(s) = q_{1n} + q_{2n}s$$

$$v_n(s) = q_{3n} + q_{4n}s$$

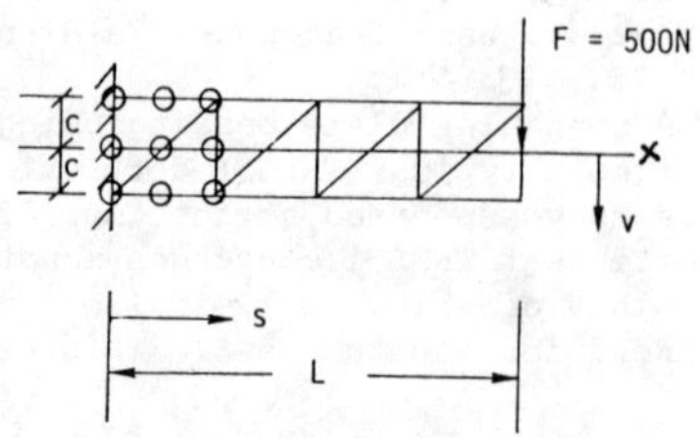

TRIM6 modeling scheme

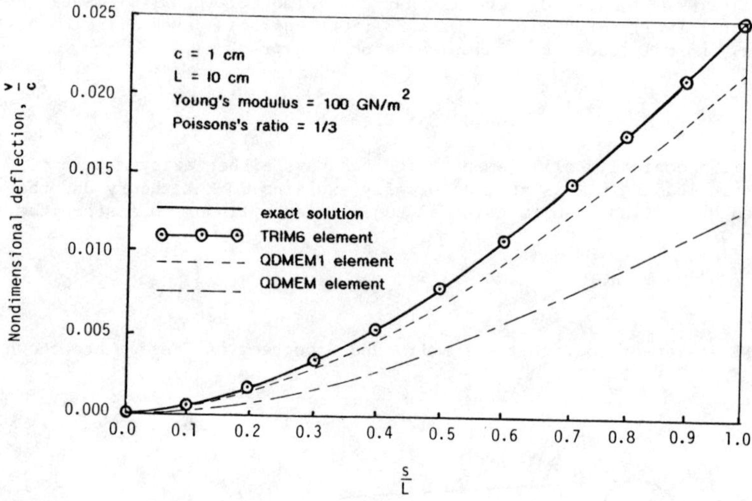

Fig. 16 Deflection of cantilever beam idealized by QDMEM, QDMEM1, and TRIM6 elements

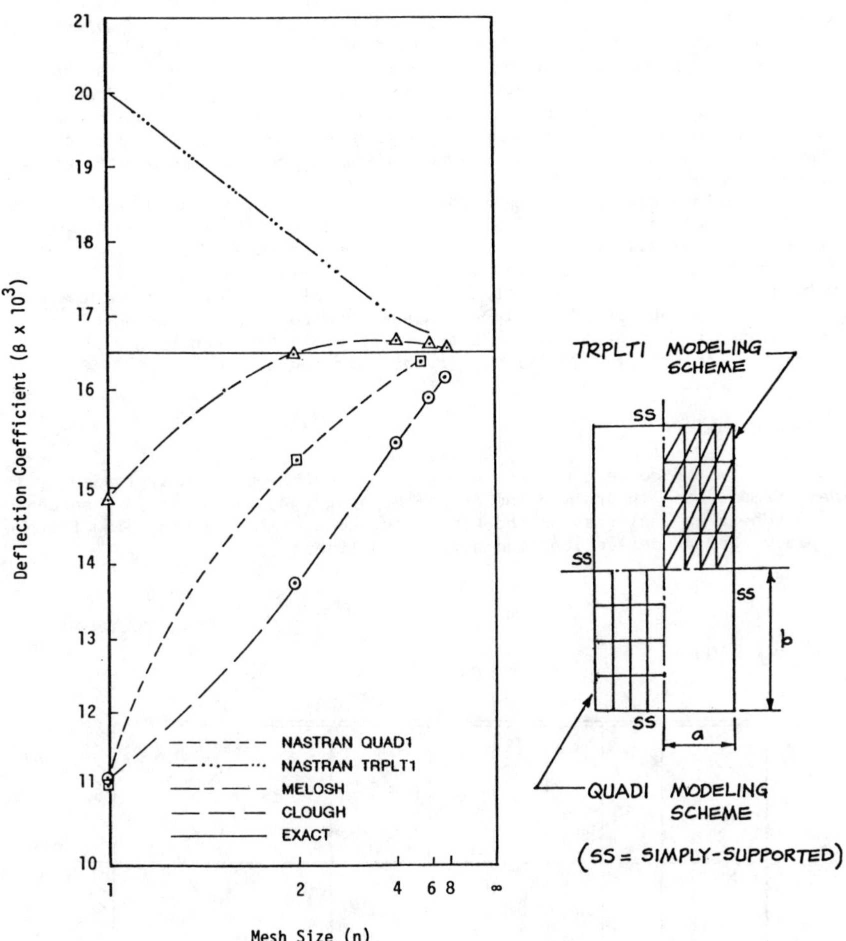

Fig . 17 Central deflection of rectangular plate

$$w_n(s) = q_{5n} + q_{6n}s + q_{7n}s^2 + q_{8n}s^3$$

Therefore, CONEAX is similar in derivation to the conical shell element of Grafton and Strome [32]. In a conical assemblage the structure modeled by this conical element is permitted to deform only approximately but is loaded in a manner consistent with those deformations. The philosophy is that many small elements, each deforming in a simple way, should provide a good approximation to the actual structure. In any region of the structure in which the character of the deformation varies rapidly, it is necessary to use a fairly large number of such elements. Clearly, this is the case in edge-bending calculations [33].

Properties of CONEAX are axisymmetric. However, the loads and deflections need not be axisymmetric; they are expanded in Fourier series with respect to the azimuth coordinate. An unusual feature of CONEAX is that it included transverse shear flexibility. The rotations α and β are independent motions because of the transverse shear flexibility. Rotation about the normal to the surface is not included, since such rotation can be adequately represented by the gradients of u and v. The element cannot be combined with other NASTRAN structural elements in the solution of problems.

Advanced Evaluation

To evaluate the convergence and accuracy of CONEAX, the radial-loaded cylinder example used in Grafton and Strome's paper [32] and by many subsequent researchers was selected as the benchmark. The example given below features rapidly varying deflections and stress resultants.

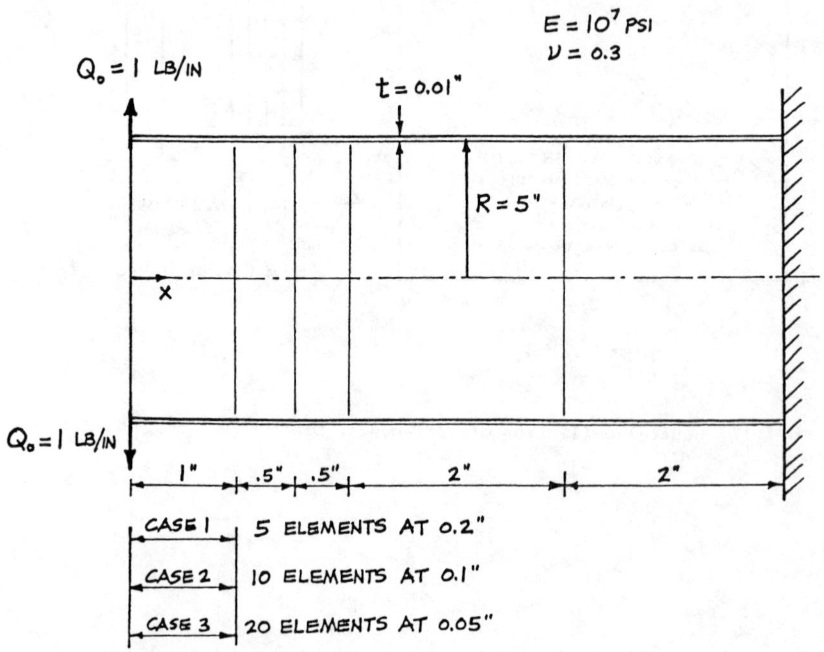

Theoretical predictions for the radial deflection and meridional moment can be obtained using Hetenyi [34] :

Radial deflection: $$w = \frac{Q_o}{2\beta^3 D} e^{-\beta x} \cos \beta x$$

Meridional moment: $$M = \frac{Q_o}{\beta} e^{-\beta x} \sin \beta x$$

where: (ν=.3)

$$\beta = \frac{1.285}{\sqrt{Rt}} = \frac{1.285}{\sqrt{5(.01)}} = 5.746694$$

$$D = \frac{Et^3}{12(1-\nu^2)} = \frac{10^7(.01)^3}{12(1-.3^2)} = 0.915751$$

Computed results using CONEAX were remarkably close to theoretical results, even for Case 1 (5 elements). All three models produced consistently better correlation with theory for radial deflection and meridional moment, as compared to Grafton and Strome [32]. Results are listed below and on the next page and are plotted in Figs. 18 and 19.

Radial Deflection:

x (in)	THEORY (10^{-3} in)	CONEAX RESULTS (10^{-3} in.) Case 3 (20 elements)	Case 2 (10 elements)	Case 1 (5 elements)
0.00	2.8769	2.8723	2.8623	2.8152
0.05	2.0699	2.066		
0.10	1.3919	1.356	1.3527	
0.15	0.79086	0.7888		
0.20	0.37291	0.3722	0.37259	0.3708
0.25	0.091453	0.09145		
0.30	-0.07831	-0.07775	-0.07555	
0.35	-0.16416	-0.16326		
0.40	-0.19215	-0.1911	-0.1892	-0.1811
0.45	-0.18410	-0.1831		
0.50	-0.15676	-0.1558	-0.1547	
0.55	-0.12195	-0.1212		
0.60	-0.08725	-0.0867	-0.0862	-0.0831
0.65	-0.05690	-0.0565		
0.70	-0.03278	-0.03261	-0.0325	

.Meridional Moment: ($\bar{x}$ is at element centroid)

	20 ELEMENTS			10 ELEMENTS			5 ELEMENTS		
	Case 3 (10^3 in-lbs)			Case 2 (10^3 in-lbs)			Case 1 (10^3 inches)		
Element	$\bar{x}$ (in.)	Theory	CONEAX	$\bar{x}$ (in.)	Theory	CONEAX	$\bar{x}$ (in.)	Theory	CONEAX
1	0.025	21.58	20.39						
				0.05	36.99	33.23			
2	0.075	47.24	46.36						
							0.10	53.24	43.04
3	0.125	55.83	55.23						
				0.15	55.78	54.04			
4	0.175	53.75	53.36						
5	0.225	45.92	45.71						
				0.25	40.99	40.52			
6	0.275	35.82	35.74						
							0.30	30.67	30.21
7	0.325	25.71	25.70						
				0.35	21.06	21.18			
8	0.375	16.82	10.86						
9	0.425	9.379	9.805						
				0.45	6.912	7.192			
10	0.475	4.545	4.619						
							0.50	2.606	3.565
11	0.525	1.058	1.129						
				0.55	-0.1408	0.0953			
12	0.575	-1.035	-0.9753						
13	0.625	-2.085	-2.039						
				0.65	-2.323	-2.185			
14	0.675	-2.418	-2.386						
							0.70	-2.403	-2.055
				0.75	-2.151	-2.097			

Other CONEAX Uses

In addition to handling axisymmetric loadings, CONEAX is versatile in its use and can be applied to a variety of other loading conditions:

1. Unsymmetric loading - using standard Fourier expansion techniques
2. Line loads - uniformly distributed or harmonic coefficients
3. Concentrated loads - at specified azimuth positions
4. Pressure loads - normal to surface
5. Gravity loads
6. Thermal loads
7. Enforced strains
8. Enforced displacements
9. Branched shells

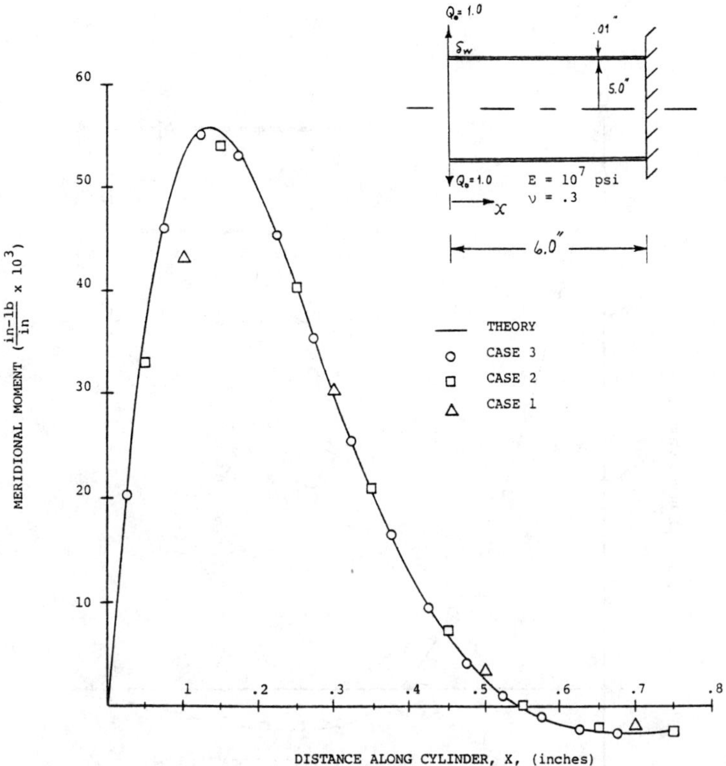

Fig . 18 Radial deflection - CONEAX vs. theory

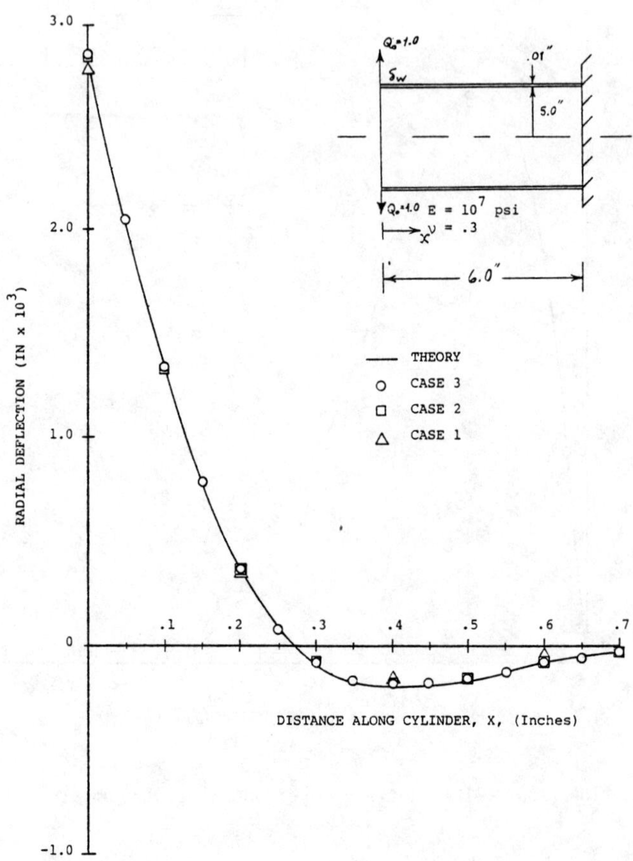

Fig. 19 Meridional moment - CONEAX vs. theory.

Conclusions

Our investigations indicate that CONEAX is a good conical shell element, with good convergence properties and exceptional versatility. Only the axisymmetric mechanical load capability was evaluated in this study. It has been reported [16] that the thermal loading capability that exists may contain errors and is not recommended for use.

The TRAPRG and TRAPAX Elements

TRAPRG is one of the four solid-of-revolution elements offered in COSMIC/ NASTRAN. It is a four-noded, axisymmetric, trapezoidal ring element with axisymmetric loading capability. The other three are TRIARG, which is the same as TRAPRG except it is triangular, TRAPAX, and TRIAAX, which are axisymmetric trapezoidal and triangular ring elements with nonaxisymmetric loading capabilitities. The benchmark problem selected to test TRAPRG and TRAPAX performance is a thick-walled cylinder under internal pressure. This has been used by many past researchers and is a good test to measure their capability to represent simple radial dilatation behavior.

Theory

According to the Theoretical Manual [9], the formulation of the theory behind TRAPRG is "mathematically consistent" with that in Mallet and Jordan's MAGIC (1969) and MAGIC II (1971) codes developed at the Air Force Flight Dynamics Laboratory. The two original finite element papers on the subject of structural analysis of axisymmetric solids were by Clough and Rashid (1965) and Wilson (1965). There was apparently [9] an extension of the Wilson formulation to include orthotropic material properties for TRAPRG in COSMIC/ NASTRAN. The TRAPRG theoretical derivations are quite standard for solid-of-revolution elements. The 31-page documentation in [9] is adequate in describing coordinate notations, displacement functions (Fourier harmonics in circumferential direction), derivation of the element stiffness matrix and mass matrix, treatment of orthotropic behavior, development of nonaxisymmetric load vectors (including thermal loads), prestrain, pressure and thermal load vectors, displacement, and stress recovery. The TRAPRG element and the other axisymmetric elements are therefore ten to fifteen years old. They represent fairly typical solid-of-revolution elements available in all general purpose codes and documented in every finite element text and have been incorporated in NASTRAN from the very beginning of the code.

The basic displacement assumption for TRIARG is shown below:

$$u = q_1 + q_2 r + q_3 z$$

(6 terms)

$$w = q_4 + q_5 r + q_6 z$$

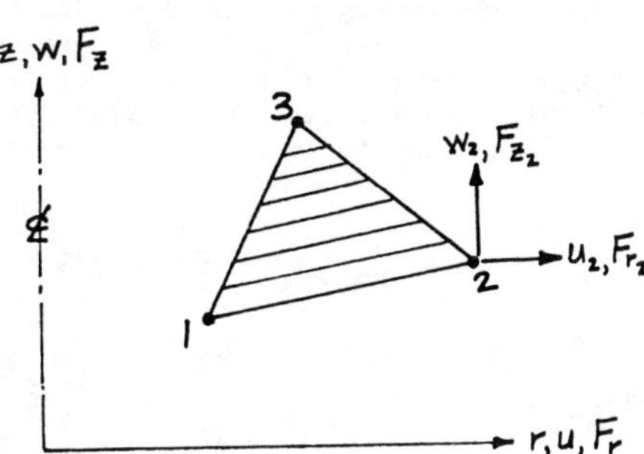

But the generalized harmonic displacements for TRAPRG are:

$$u_n = q_{1n} + q_{2n}r + q_{3n}z + q_{4n}rz$$

(8 terms)

$$w_n = q_{5n} + q_{6n}r + q_{7n}z + q_{8n}rz$$

Stresses for TRAPRG are "evaluated at the four nodal regions as well as at a fifth region which corresponds to a point that is obtained by averaging the coordinates of the four nodal points." (Currently, many other codes offer more accurate axisymmetric elements with mid-side nodes.)

Any point within a solid-of-revolution element can be located by specifying a radial coordinate (r), an axial coordinate (z), and a circumferential position (ϕ). In TRAPRG and TRIARG, the point "i" displacements u_{ri} and u_{zi} are constants with respect to ϕ. In TRAPAX and TRIAAX, the displacements u_{ri}, u_{zi}, and $u_{\phi i}$, as well as the forces F_{ri}, F_{zi}, and $F_{\phi i}$ at each point i are assumed to be sinusoidal functions of the circumferential location ϕ. Directly applied nonaxisymmetric loads, pressure loads, gravity loads, and thermal loads are applied to the TRAPAX and TRIAAX elements using the same method as in the conical shell element CONEAX.

Two shortcomings are noted in the documentation of solid-of-revolution elements in NASTRAN. First, there is no explanation or justification for the trapezoidal requirement; that is, two opposite sides of TRAPRG must be parallel. This strict trapezoidal requirement exists only in COSMIC/NASTRAN and is extremely restrictive on the analyst's choice of mesh to the point of inconvenience. Second, no mention is made of the relationship or similarity of the NASTRAN solid-of-revolution elements to those in the SAAS code. The SAAS II and III codes (and the asymmetric ASAAS code) also utilize the Wilson element, handle orthotropic behavior, and have been extensively used in the aerospace industry for ten years. Moreover, SAAS offers the user a choice of plane strain, plane stress, or axisymmetric analyses, a choice not found in NASTRAN. SAAS has an excellent reputation as a versatile and cheap code to run. It seems to the authors that before and during implementation of the NASTRAN solid-of-revolution elements, there should have been several test cases made to compare NASTRAN efficiency with SAAS III, and possibly to incorporate SAAS numerical algorithms and its powerful Laplacian mesh generation capability. The fact is that a user who has SAAS in-house will probably never use NASTRAN for axisymmetric analysis of solids.

Advanced Evaluation

The benchmark problem chosen to evaluate TRAPRG efficiency and convergence characteristics is a thick-walled cylinder (plane strain) under internal pressure. This problem was selected because its elasticity solution is well known, and it has been used by past researchers, including Clough and Rashid (1965) and Wilson (1965). The theoretical equations for radial and hoop stresses and for radial displacement are [35]:

$$\sigma_r = \frac{a^2 p}{b^2 - a^2} \quad (1 - \frac{b^2}{r^2})$$

$$\sigma_\Theta = \frac{a^2 p}{b^2 - a^2} \quad (1 + \frac{b^2}{r^2})$$

$$u_r = \frac{1}{E}\left[\frac{a^2 p_i}{b^2-a^2}\left(r+\frac{b^2}{r}\right)(1-\nu^2) - \frac{a^2 p_i}{b^2-a^2}\left(r-\frac{b^2}{r^2}\right)(\nu+\nu^2)\right]$$

These equations show that both stresses are maximum at the inner surface where r is minimum, σ_r is always a compressive stress and smaller than σ_Θ, and σ_Θ is a tensile stress which is maximum at the inner surface.

For assumed values in the test case of $E = 10^7$ psi, $\nu = 0.3$, a = 5 in., b = 10 in., p = 1000, the above expressions become:

	@ r = 5 in.	@ r = 10 in.
$\sigma_r = 333.3 - \frac{3.333 \times 10^4}{r^2}$	-1000 psi	0 psi
$\sigma_\Theta = 333.3 + \frac{3.333 \times 10^4}{r^2}$	1667 psi	666.7 psi
$u_r = (1.733\times10^{-5})r + \frac{(4.33\times10^{-3})}{r}$	9.53×10^{-4} in.	6.07×10^{-4} in.

Since there is no input option to apply pressure on the element face for TRAPRG in COSMIC/NASTRAN, we had to calculate and input equivalent nodal forces. TRAPRG was evaluated using three meshes, 2, 5, and 10 elements through the thickness. Results are compared with theory in Figs. 20 and 21. The correlation is good.

TRAPAX was also evaluated using the same three meshes, and the excellent pressurized thick-walled cylinder results are plotted in Figs. 22 and 23. Unlike TRAPRG, TRAPAX does have an input option for pressure directly applied to an element face. We were primarily interested in verifying the accuracy and correctness of coding of TRAPAX. The consistency of results between TRAPRG and TRAPAX verified this coding. Harmonic superposition used to handle nonaxisymmetric loads was not evaluated in this study, since this procedure is fairly standard in all the well-known codes. Another reason TRAPAX was not evaluated for nonaxisymmetric loadings was the difficulty of formulating a pathological test case for such loadings.

Conclusions

For the "uniform-dilatation" thick-walled cylinder benchmark, our evaluation results showed both TRAPRG and TRAPAX to perform well even for a crude 2-element model. The only drawbacks are the TRAPRG trapezoidal modeling restriction, lack of a direct pressure load input capability for TRAPRG, and the absence of one element in NASTRAN to handle plane strain, plane stress, or axisymmetric analyses.

The HEXA1, HEXA2, IHEX1, and IHEX2 Solid Elements

COSMIC/NASTRAN has four constant strain solid elements of various shapes (TETRA, WEDGE, HEXA1, HEXA2) and three isoparametric solid elements of 8, 20, and 32 nodes (IHEX1, IHEX2, IHEX3). A decision was made to evaluate only four of these and compare their accuracy and performance together in two

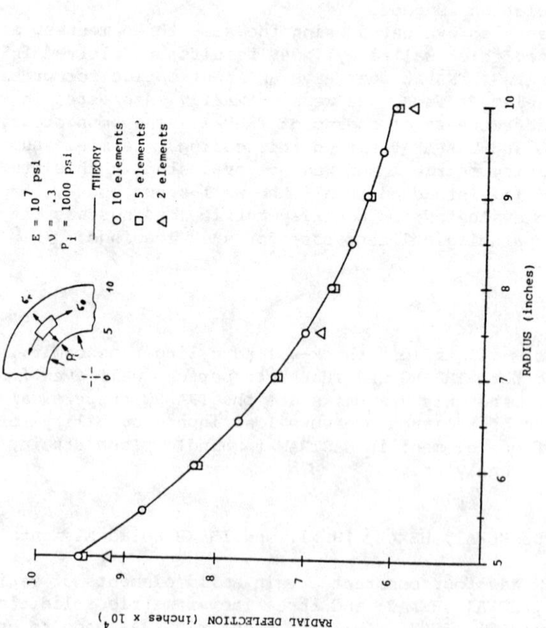

Fig. 20 Radial deflection of thick-walled cylinder - TRAPAX vs. theory

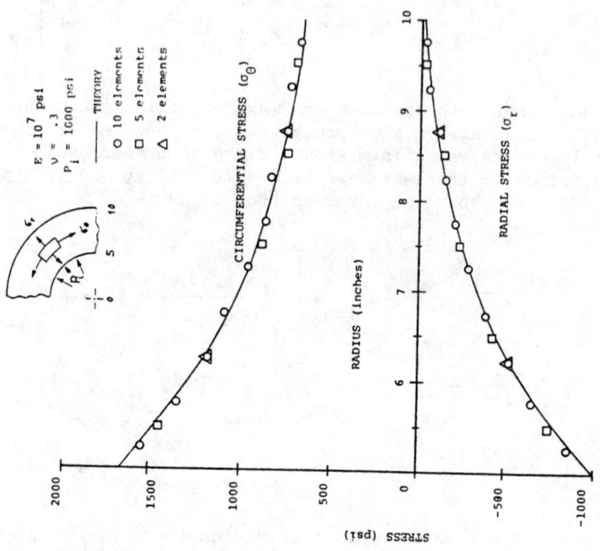

Fig. 21 Stresses in thick-walled cylinder - TRAPRG vs. theory

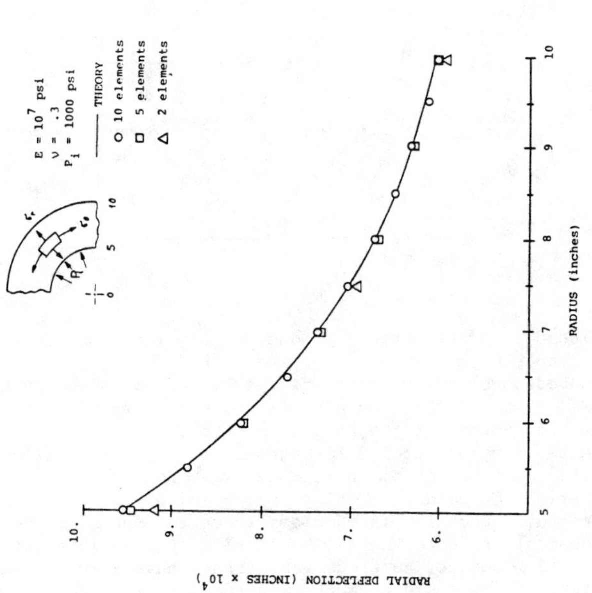

Fig . 22 Radial deflection of thick-walled cylinder - TRAPAX vs. theory

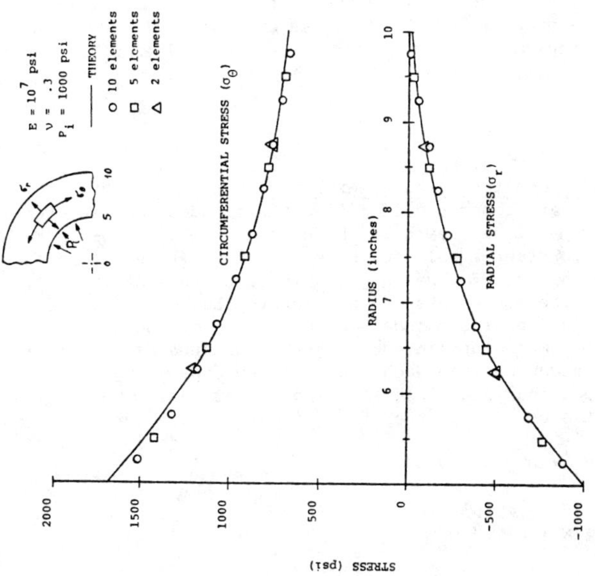

Fig . 23 Stresses in thick-walled cylinder - TRAPAX vs. theory

test problems, a slender cantilevered beam under four different loading conditions; and a pressurized thick-walled cylinder. In addition to these two static test problems, we also studied the eigenvalues of a one-inch cube, using the available eigenvalue extraction schemes.

Theory

HEXA1 and HEXA2 Constant Strain Hexahedral Elements. The HEXA1 and HEXA2 solid elements are comprised of five subtetrahedra and ten overlapping subtetrahedra respectively, each of which is merely a three-dimensional equivalent of the constant strain triangle. Each of the eight nodes in the hexahedron thus consists of three translational degrees of freedom, for a total of 24 DOF's. These elements are subject to the following restrictions: constant strain in each subtetrahedron; uniform and isotropic material properties; uniform temperature in each tetrahedral subelement; translational degrees of freedom only at each node; and no capability for differential stiffness, buckling, and piecewise linear analyses. The assumed displacement field at each node is therefore linear in each Cartesian coordinate:

$$u = q_1 + q_2 + q_3y + q_4z$$

$$v = q_5 + q_6x + q_7y + q_8z$$

$$w = q_9 + q_{10}x + q_{11}y + q_{12}z$$

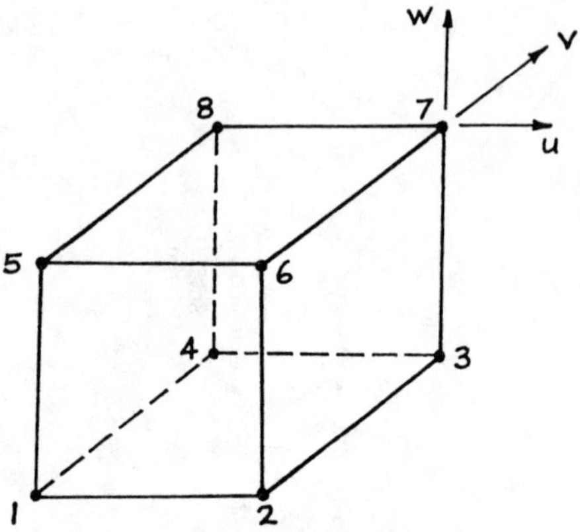

This assumed displacement field produces a constant (uniform) strain and stress in each element.

A hexahedron can be cut into five subtetrahedra in only two different ways. HEXA1 represents a single subdivision into five subtetrahedra, while HEXA2 uses the average of the results of the two types of subdivisions. HEXA2 results in symmetrical deformations when symmetrical loads are applied to a symmetrical hexahedron, while HEXA1 does not [9]. This subtle but important distinction renders HEXA1 to be definitely inferior to HEXA2 and the IHEXi elements, especially in problems where the out-of-plane deflections (or mode shapes) are important. The spurious deflections are discussed later.

In actual practice, numerous researchers have all concluded that far too many constant strain solid elements are required in a three-dimensional analysis to obtain acceptable results (see for instance, Refs.[36 to 38].) From a practical standpoint, these constant strain solid elements are obsolete by current standards, should be omitted in a modern general purpose finite element code, and have been rendered inferior by the isoparametric solid elements since the late sixties and the early seventies.

<u>IHEX1 and IHEX2 Isoparametric Hexahedral Elements</u>. The IHEXi isoparametric hexahedral solid elements are effective for analyzing a three-dimensional continuum. The material must have isotropic temperature-dependent material properties. "Isoparametric" means the element deformations are represented with the identical interpolating functions used to define the geometry. COSMIC/NASTRAN offers the user a choice of three isoparametric hexahedron solid elements, 8-node (IHEX1), 20-node (IHEX2), and 32-node (IHEX3). These correspond to assumed displacement variations of linear, quadratic, and cubic shapes.

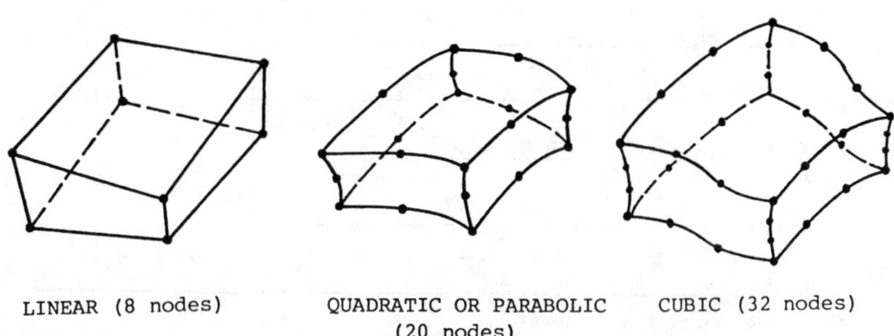

LINEAR (8 nodes) QUADRATIC OR PARABOLIC (20 nodes) CUBIC (32 nodes)

Clough [36] and subsequent researchers have evaluated various three-dimensional solid elements, concluding that the isoparametric elements are superior to other solid elements. The 8-node and 20-node isoparametric solid elements now appear in all general purpose finite element codes. Experience has shown that the 8-node linear element is recommended for problems with high shear deformations and stresses, while the 20-node quadratic element appears to work best in problems with plate or beam bending type deformations. Of these three elements, the 20-node quadratic isoparametric solid element apparently offers the best combination of accuracy, efficiency, and cost, and may well be the most often used solid element today.

The integrals in the isoparametric element stiffness, mass, and load matrices are evaluated by the use of numerical integration. Gaussian quadrature is used in NASTRAN, and the user has a choice of a 2 x 2 x 2 Gaussian integration scheme or a 3 x 3 x 3 integration scheme. For most problems, the 2 x 2 x 2 scheme seems to work best for the linear element (IHEX1), and a 3 x 3 x 3 scheme works best for the two higher-order elements. Only HEXA1, HEXA2, IHEX1, and IHEX2 were evaluated in the advanced evaluation.

Advanced Evaluation

The two test cases used to evaluate HEXA1, HEXA2, IHEX1, and IHEX2 were a slender cantilevered beam (with four loading conditions) and an internally pressurized thick-walled cylinder. The cantilevered beam problem is commonly used to test the ability of a solid element to represent bending behavior.

The thick-walled cylinder problem enables us to assess the behavior of the solid elements in an enforced radial dilatation mode. A third test problem, eigenvalue extraction of a unit cube, allows us to verify both NASTRAN solid element theory and eigenvalue extraction efficiency.

Cantilevered Beam. The four loading cases for the cantilevered beam are:

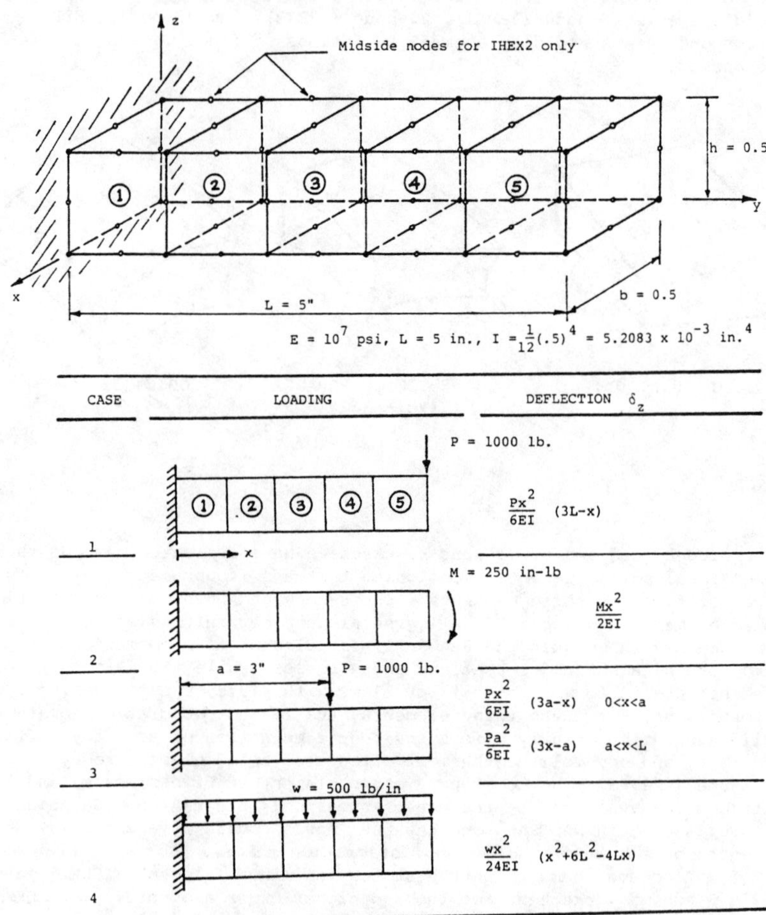

Theoretical and finite element deflections and stresses are plotted in Figs. 24 to 27. It is obvious from these plots that of the four solid elements evaluated in this bending example, the only element which performed reasonably well is IHEX2. IHEX2 consistently produced good correlation with theoretical deflections and stresses in all four load cases.

The next best solid element is IHEX1, but it gave deflections and stresses only 30 to 50 percent of those predicted by theory. HEXA1 and HEXA2 both correlated very poorly with theoretical deflections. This lackluster performance of IHEX1, HEXA1, and HEXA2 in a beam-bending test problem can probably be attributed to the fact that only one layer of elements was used through the thickness. This leads to the conclusion that, for these three solid elements, the analyst should use more than one element through the thickness in a beam-bending problem before he can hope for reasonably accurate answers. However, it is noted that for a similar problem, MSC/NASTRAN's 6- and 16-node PENTA and 8- and 20-node HEXA isoparametric solid elements as well as STARDYNE's 8-node isoparametric solid element all correlated fairly well with theoretical displacements even for a beam model with one layer through the thickness.

Results for HEXA1 in the cantilevered beam benchmark also indicated the existence of spurious modes in the lateral x-direction when the primary deflection occurs in the z-direction. These lateral sidesway modes for HEXA1 were attributed to its composition of five subtetrahedra and the basic unsymmetrical nature of this composition. The magnitude of this sidesway deflection was approximately 5 to 10 percent of the z-deflection.

The effects of modeling a cantilevered beam with more than one layer in depth and in width and slender versus short deep beams have already been discussed elsewhere by several researchers (e.g., Refs. [36, 38, 40]). These references cite the superiority of the 20-node isoparametric solid element in slender beam bending problems over 8-node isoparametric solid elements and constant strain as well as higher-order hexahedra. However, for short-deep cantilever beams where shear deformation is important, the 8-node isoparametric solid is better than the 20-node isoparametric solid and constant strain or higher-order hexahedra.

NASTRAN does not offer the analyst an option to improve solution accuracy by the use of "incompatible bending modes" [41]. These so-called bubble modes have often been used effectively in bending problems; they improve microscopic equilibrium within the element, though violating interelement compatibility. Such a device has been used very successfully to improve the general performance of the 8-node isoparametric solid element (for instance, the ANSYS STIFF 45 element).

For the NASTRAN user, therefore, the only solid element which should be used in bending problems is IHEX2, the 20-node isoparametric solid element. Use of a 20-node element implies a more complex and time-consuming input, leading to a higher probability of input error. IHEX3 (the 32-node isoparametric solid element) was not evaluated in this study but the same comments apply.

Thick-Walled Cylinder. This test problem is identical to that used for TRAPRG. The problem measures the ability of the solid elements to represent a dilatational type of deformation (in the radial direction only). The displacement results for the four solid elements are shown in Figs. 28 to 31 and the radial and hoop stress correlations with theory are shown in Figs. 32 to 35. In this problem, three mesh sizes were used; 2, 5, and 10 elements through the cylinder thickness. This time, the radial displacement correlations are usually 12 percent or better, and the stress correlations with theory were all remarkably good. Even though the thick-walled cylinder test problem is not as severe a test on the solid elements as a cantilevered beam, the outstanding performance of all four NASTRAN solid elements is still

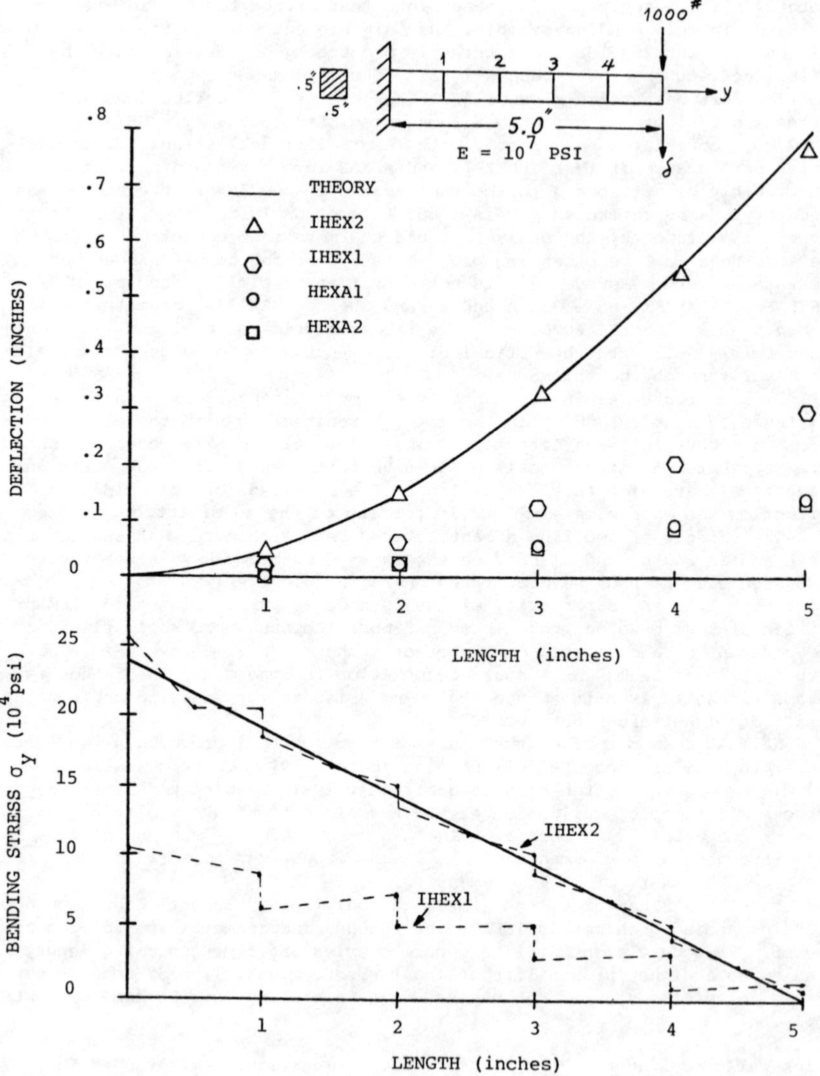

Fig. 24 Results of cantilevered beam test of solid elements - Case 1 end load

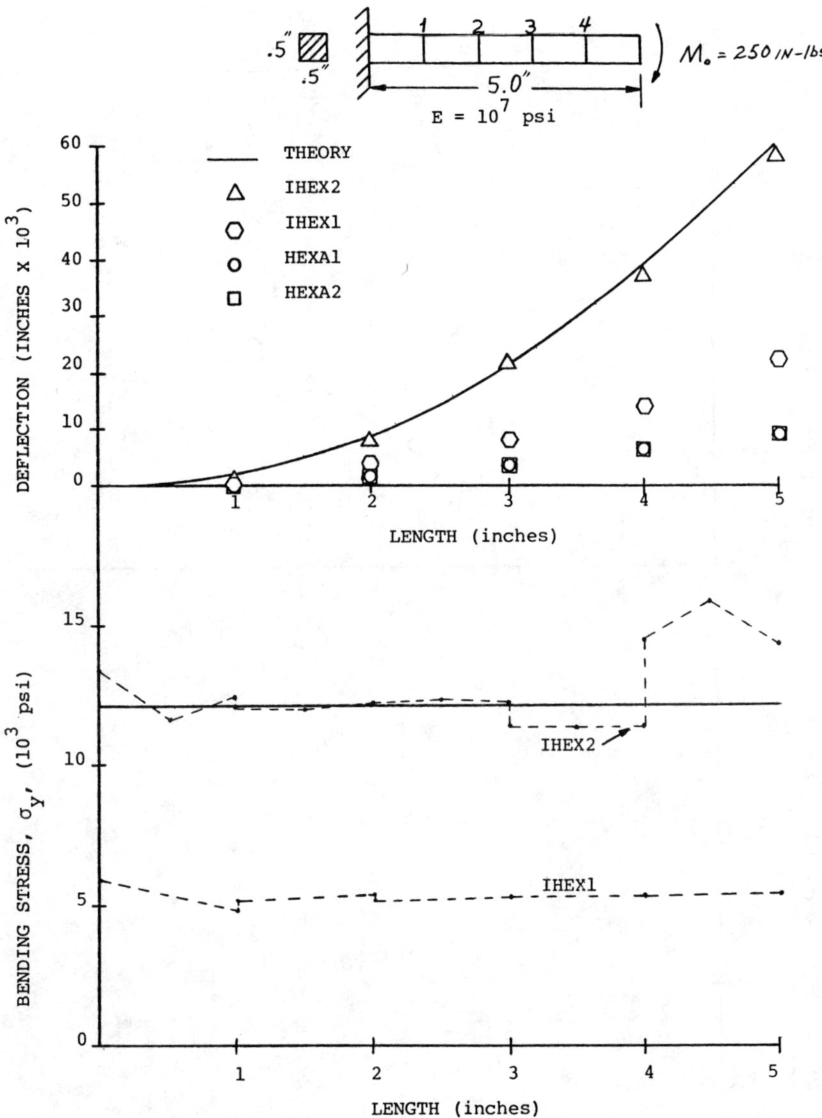

Fig. 25 Results of cantilevered beam test for solid elements - Case 2. End moment

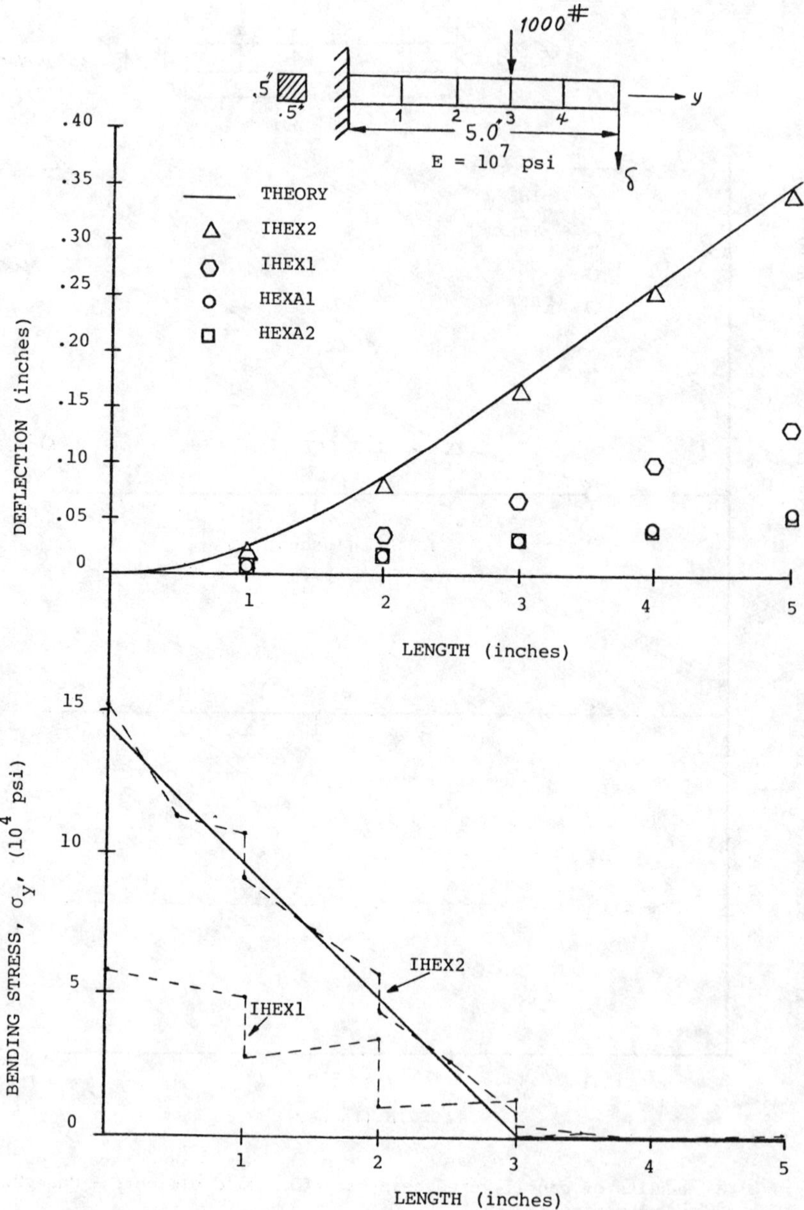

Fig. 26 Results of cantilevered beam test for solid elements - Case 3. Intermediate load

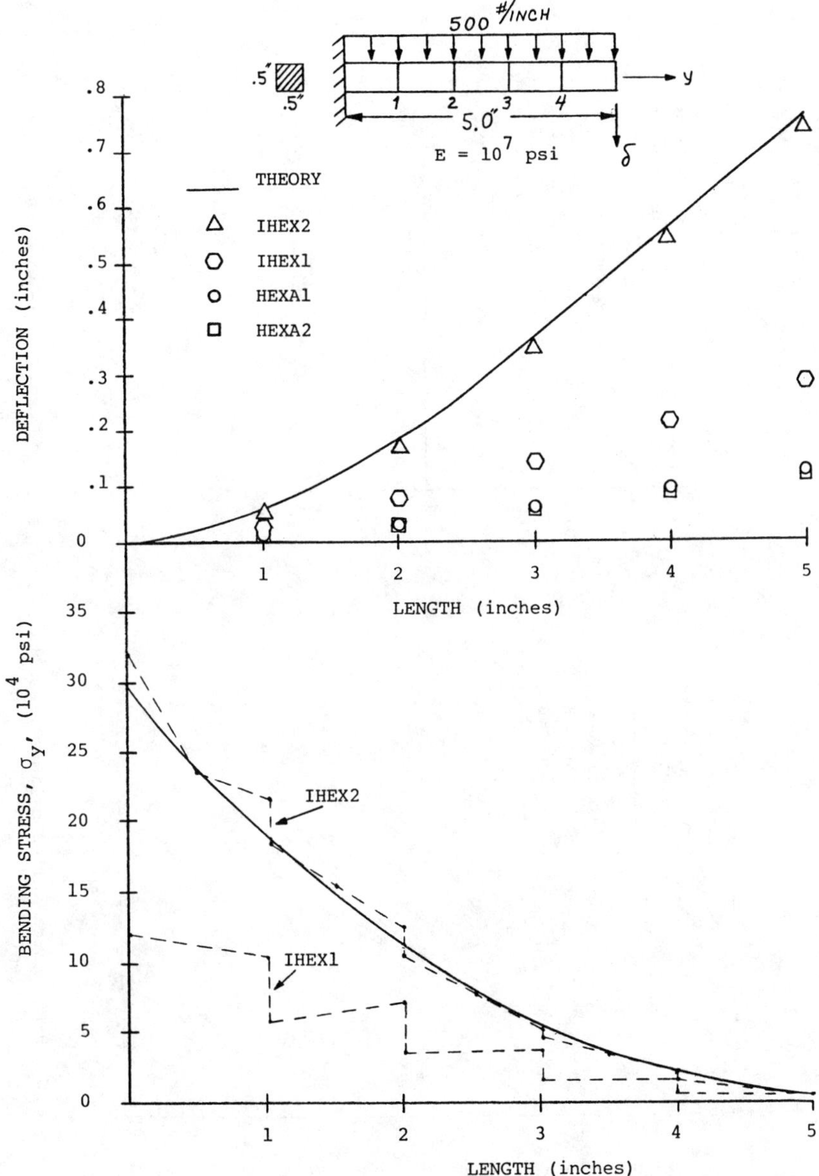

Fig. 27 Results of cantilevered beam test for solid elements - Case 4. Uniform load

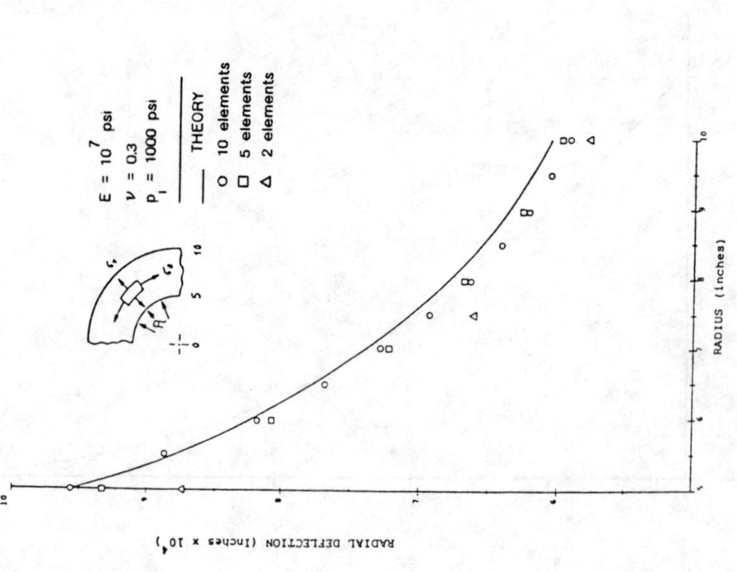

Fig. 28 HEXAl thick-walled cylinder results - deflections

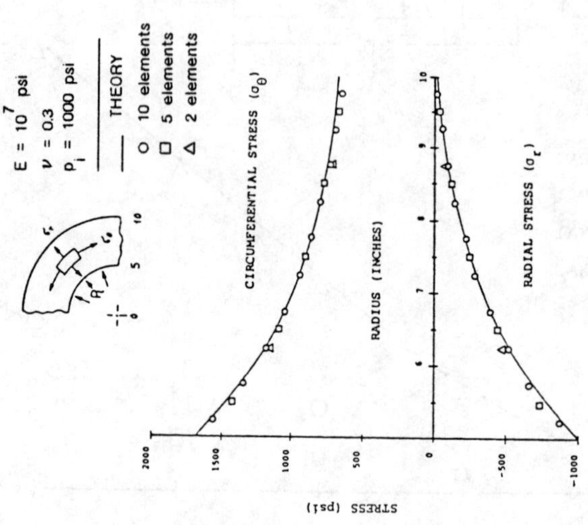

Fig. 29 HEXAl thick-walled cylinder results - stresses

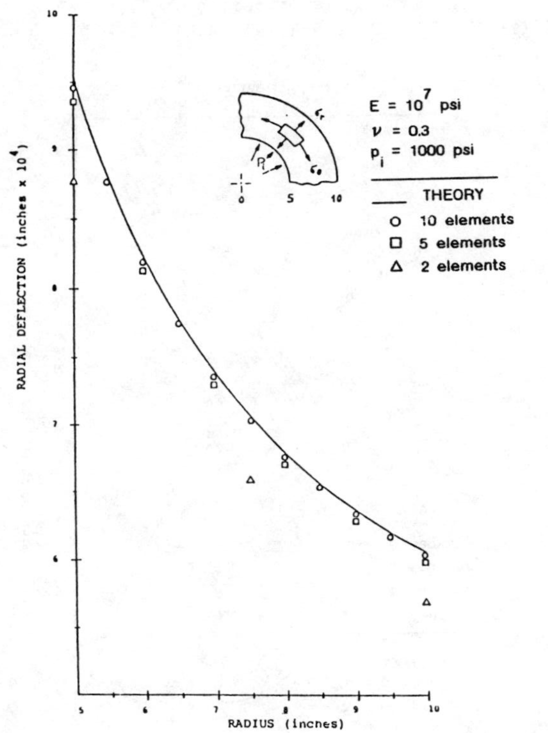

Fig. 30 HEXA2 thick-walled cylinder results - deflections

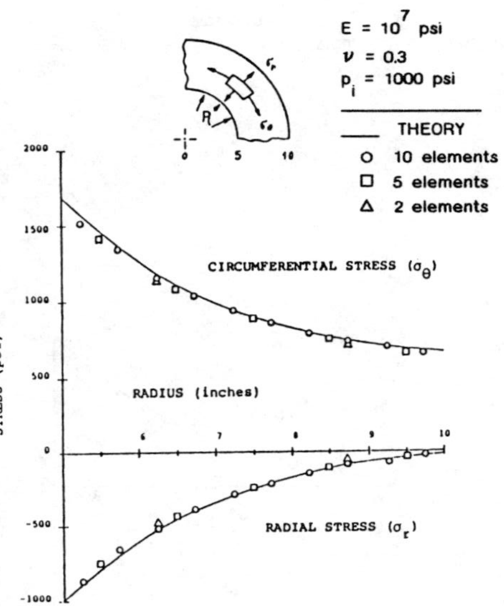

Fig. 31 HEXA2 thick-walled cylinder results - stresses

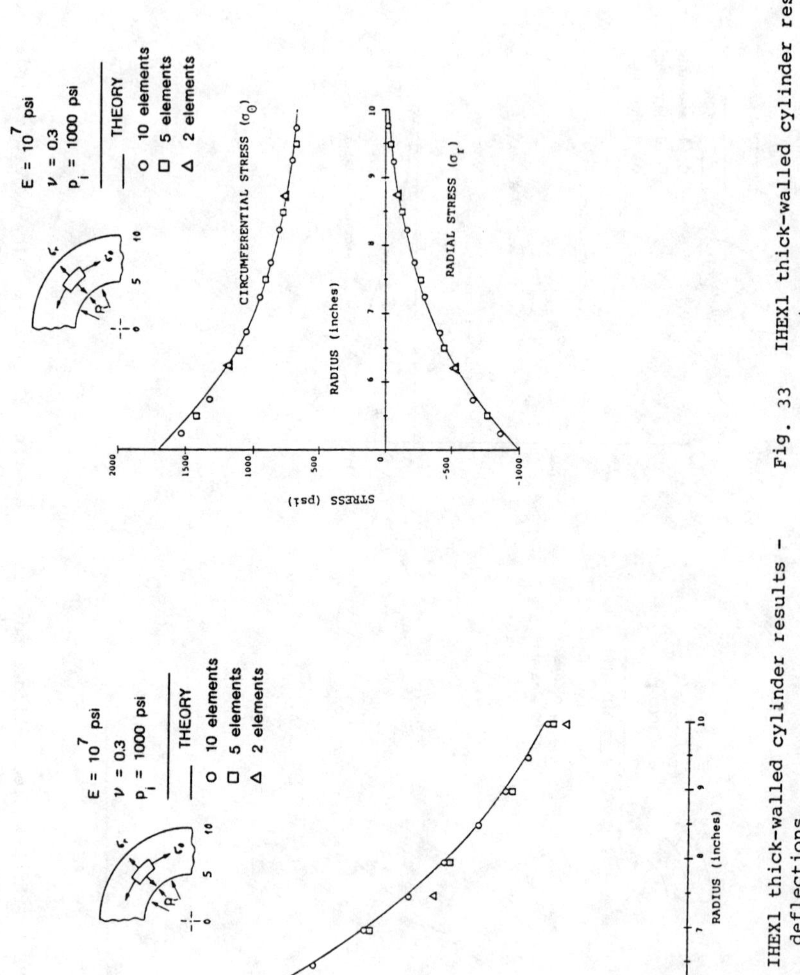

Fig. 32 IHEX1 thick-walled cylinder results - deflections

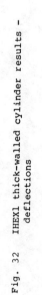

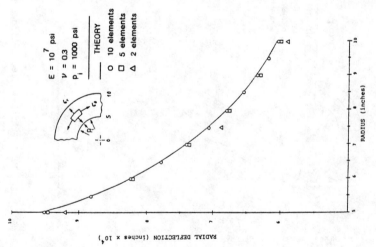

Fig. 33 IHEX1 thick-walled cylinder results - stresses

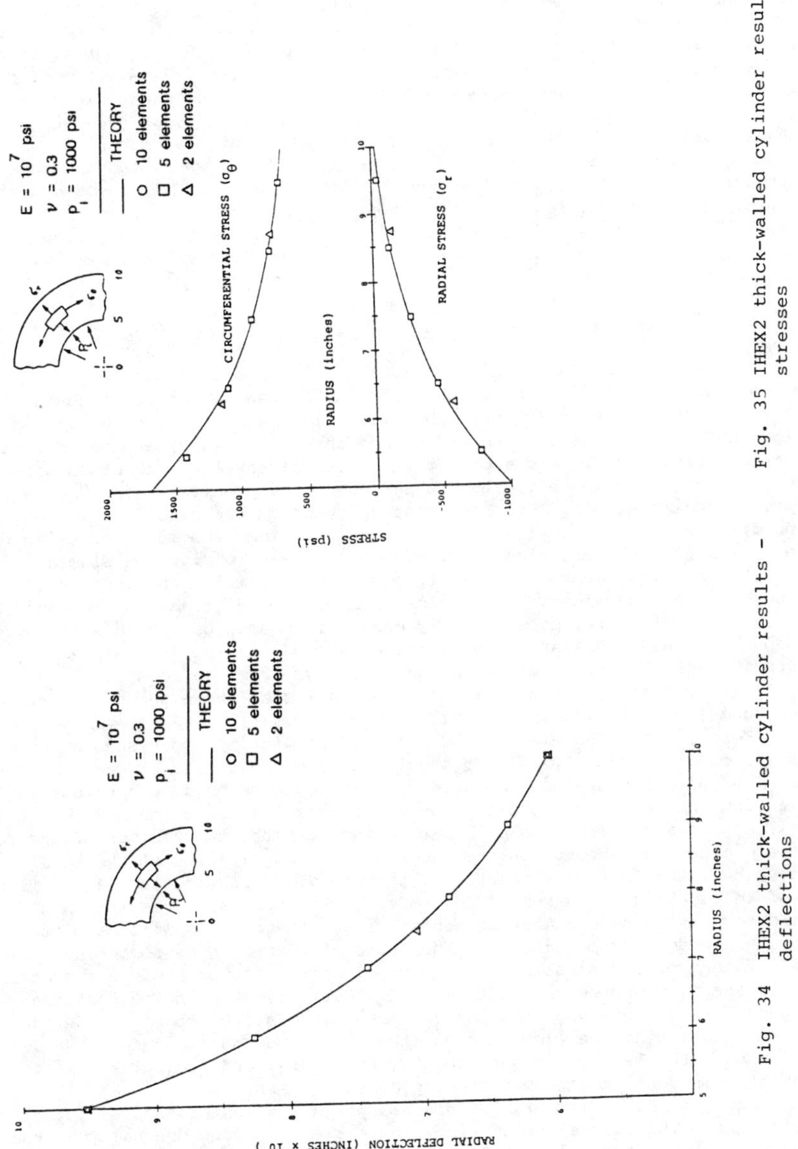

Fig. 34 IHEX2 thick-walled cylinder results - deflections

Fig. 35 IHEX2 thick-walled cylinder results - stresses

remarkable, even for the 2-element model.

Eigenvalue Extraction. The NASTRAN solid elements HEXA1, HEXA2, and IHEX1 were subjected to three different eigenvalue extraction methods in a third type of element test. An eigenvalue and vector solution has been used to study the convergence characteristics of an element [19], though it is believed that this procedure has previously been applied only to two-dimensional elements. It has been shown that, provided that the monotonic convergence conditions are satisfied, the finite element analysis overestimates the stiffness of the system, i.e., the calculated displacements are smaller (in some norm) than the exact displacements. Hence, when studying the effectiveness of an element, we need to investigate its stiffness characteristics, and an element that is less stiff will be more effective. One way of investigating the element stiffness characteristics is to represent the element stiffness matrix on the basis of its eigenvector, namely, solving the eigenvector problem:

$$([K] - \lambda I) \quad \phi = 0$$

The results of this test are important in several respects. First, the eigenvalue extraction methods available in NASTRAN may be compared to each other and to a known solution. The eigenvalues are expected to contain rigid body modes (three translations and three rotations) and several repeated roots, thus posing a good test of the eigenvalue extraction methods for both accuracy and efficiency. Second , the problem was solved as if it were a modal analysis. Two different approaches were used in this regard. The first method was to require the program to lump the mass according to the particular element algorithm. The second was to give the element a zero density and place lumped masses at each node. Finally, the mode shapes produced from the eigenvalue extraction should be distinct and recognizable, i.e., shear, flexure, dilatational, etc. Failure to produce distinct mode shapes indicates that spurious displacement modes exist in the element formulation. Several conclusions can be drawn from the results of these analyses (a complete description of the results of the eigenvalue tests can be found in Ref.[42]).

First, the HEXA1 element did not produce distinct mode shapes for any of the conditions analyzed. It should be noted that this element is composed of 5 tetrahedra and has already been shown to produce spurious deflection shapes. Additionally, the masses are lumped at the nodes on the following basis. The mass calculation involves the calculation of the total mass of each tetrahedron in the element and assigning 1/4 of the total mass to each of the four node points. This method of distributing mass will not produce eight equal masses at the nodes. This procedure results in a dependency on the node numbering scheme; i.e., the results will be different for this element depending upon the order of element node numbering, which is, of course, undesirable. Thus, the element does not produce symmetrically shaped eigenvectors as it should. Further, it is noted that the eigenvalues changed when the masses were lumped at the nodes by the analyst rather than using the element algorithm. This was not true for HEXA2, which uses the same basic subelement (tetrahedra) and indicates that there may be some error in the programming of the element.

For the HEXA2 element, the eigenvalues are almost identical for all cases run. This was expected since the masses are lumped equally at the nodes (because of the 10 overlapping tetrahedra) and the symmetry of the resulting displacement functions within the element. It is noted also that the frequencies are lower than for the HEXA1 element, which indicates that HEXA2 is less stiff and thus should produce better results.

For IHEX1, the eight-node isoparametric hexahedron, it was found that recognizable mode shapes were not evident until the lumped mass case was run. Even though the documentation stated that a lumped mass formulation is used as a default option in the program, the Programmer's Manual indicates that no provision is made for the computation of a lumped mass matrix for the isoparametric hexahedron elements. Thus, when the eigenvalue problem for this element is solved using the modal analysis rigid format and using a nonzero material density, the mass is calculated according to the shape function for the element. Therefore, in order to compare the element stiffness to the HEXA1 elements, the lumped mass cases must be used. On this basis, it was determined that the eigenvalues are lower for IHEX1 than either of the HEXA1 elements, indicating that the element is less stiff. It was also noted that the mode shapes were not produced in the same order as for the HEXA2 elements.

Conclusions

Our evaluation results indicate that the overall quality, performance, and efficiency of the COSMIC/NASTRAN solid elements are fair - but one must be very careful in selecting the appropriate element and mesh for a particular application.

	NASTRAN SOLID ELEMENT			
BENCHMARK PROBLEM	HEXA1	HEXA2	IHEX1	IHEX2
1. Cantilevered Beam (5 elements, 1 layer)	Poor	Poor	Poor	Good
2. Thick-walled Cylinder (2,5,10 elements)	Good	Good	Good	Good
3. Unit-cube Eigenvalues (1 element, consistent or lumped mass)	Poor	Fair	Good	(Not evaluated)

In the eigenvalue extraction benchmark, it was found that the Givens or tridiagonal method was better than the inverse power method with shifts, and both were superior to the determinant method for this problem. (The FEER method was not used in this evaluation, but is expected to be equal to or better than the Givens method.)

The fairly good performance of the constant-strain HEXA2 element in this study corroborates with the conclusions reached in a recent Air Force Aero Propulsion Laboratory/NASA Lewis joint study on a three-dimensional stress analysis of a thermally cycled double-edge wedge geometry specimen similar to those used in aircraft gas turbine engines [39]. Drake et al. found excellent correlation for both displacements and stresses between a 354-element NASTRAN HEXA2 model and a 64-element model using a Garrett/AiResearch-developed code called ISO3DQ which used 12-node isoparametric solid elements.

Minicomputer Versions of NASTRAN

Minicomputers offer many advantages to the user and have increasingly gained popularity among structural analysis code users and developers. Among these advantages are vastly lower cost per problem (sometimes by an order of magnitude or more); practical decentralization and greater flexibility; suitability for interactive graphics; economical time-sharing by many users (up to as many as 63 simultaneous users); shorter and predictable turnaround time; local control over computing resource allocation; and for the first time, a chance for the software developer to request operating system characteristics on minicomputers to be tailored to his needs. Typically, minicomputers cost about a quarter of a million dollars, contain virtual memories, and offer 32-bit architecture. Users of minicomputers usually rave about the reduced cost, versatility, turnaround, and efficiency.

Many U.S. minicomputer manufacturers compete for the market. The leader is Digital Equipment Corporation (DEC), with approximately 40% of the market[4]. Other well-known mini manufacturers include Hewlett-Packard, Data General, Honeywell Information Systems, Prime, Modcomp, and Perkin-Elmer. The 1979 revenues to U.S. minicomputer makers were estimated to be $4.7 billion, and in 1980 135,000 minis were expected to be shipped. Codes already on minis include SAP6 and SAP7, SDRC/SUPERB and SUPERTAB, Westinghouse/WECAN, ANSYS, PDA/PATRAN, MARC/PM NASTRAN and MENTAT, and of course, versions of NASTRAN.

As far as is known, four minicomputer versions of NASTRAN currently exist.

Name	Code Developer	Mini	Mini Manufacturer
MSC/NASTRAN	MacNeal-Schwendler Corp. Los Angeles, CA	DEC VAX-11/ 780	Digital Equipment Marlboro, Mass.
UAI/NASTRAN	Universal Analytics, Inc. Playa Del Rey, CA	Perkin-Elmer 3240	Perkin-Elmer Corp. Oceanport, N.J.
PM/NASTRAN	MARC Analysis Research Corp. Palo Alto, CA	Prime 450, 550, 650, 750	Prime Computer Inc. Wellesley Hills, Mass.
COSMIC/NASTRAN	NASA Goddard Greenbelt, Maryland	VAX 11/ 780	Digital Equipment Marlboro, Mass.

The minicomputer version of MSC/NASTRAN is most commonly available on the DEC VAX-11/780, and thus VAX/NASTRAN is by far the most popular minicomputer version of NASTRAN around. DEC is also the leader in implementing structural analysis and design codes on minis. Its latest "Engineering Systems Software Referral Catalog"(5th edition, 1980) features no less than forty structural analysis and design packages available on various DEC minicomputers. UAI/NASTRAN and PM/NASTRAN are relative newcomers to the field. UAI/NASTRAN is being offered on the Perkin-Elmer 3240, the latest in the Series 3200, which reputedly performed faster than the DEC VAX-11/780 in 44 out of 58 benchmark tests. PM/NASTRAN is offered by MARC Analysis on Prime minicomputers, and its Version 80 features four new elements, HEXA3 and HEXA4 (8-node constant strain and 20-node linear strain isoparametric solid elements), and SHELL1 and SHELL2 (8-node linear strain and 12-node quadratic strain doubly-curved isoparametric shell elements). A minicomputer version of COSMIC/NASTRAN is currently available. This version of the program was developed by NASA Goddard and, according to Dr. Brugh at COSMIC, has the same capabilities as the standard mainframe version. It is an all-Fortran version of NASTRAN and is currently running on the VAX 11/780. It is available on a lease basis from COSMIC.

Preprocessors and Postprocessors for NASTRAN

One weakness of COSMIC/NASTRAN is its lack of a built-in interactive mesh generation capability. In the past five years, many software packages have been developed commercially to facilitate preprocessing and postprocessing for NASTRAN. These usually offer the user a capability to generate and modify the model in a time-sharing mode and an instantaneous check of model connectivity on a cathode-ray-tube terminal screen. In addition, several U.S. government agencies and aerospace companies - such as the Naval Ship Research and Development Center, NASA Goddard Space Flight Center, and Rockwell International Corporation - have developed pre- and postprocessing packages (available from COSMIC) to aid the NASTRAN user in his model generation and results interpretation.

Only some of the more popular commercial NASTRAN pre- and postprocessing packages will be discussed here. These codes are typically available in minicomputer versions, and most are also available through the leading service bureaus. Table 11 shows some well-known commercial NASTRAN pre- and post processors, their developers, marketing partner, and availability on service bureaus. The acknowledged leader in the field is SDRC/SUPERTAB, the first interactive preprocessing code to emerge. For finite element modeling and NASTRAN preprocessing, SUPERTAB has the most users and benefits from a marketing associative effort with Tektronix, the leader among CRT terminal manufacturers. FASTDRAW3 is offered by McAUTO and supports finite element modeling for NASTRAN and other codes. GIFTS was developed at the University of Arizona under Professor H. A. Kamel; its popularity appears to have declined recently. A versatile preprocessor which is rapidly gaining in popularity is PDA/PATRAN, a powerful second-generation finite element modeling package which offers color interactive graphics. MENTAT and GRAFAX are less well-known packages which are beginning to build a user base. FEMGEN is a popular European finite element code which reportedly can also generate NASTRAN models. In the European market, it competes with ASKA, ASAS, SESAM69, BERSAFE, FINEL, SAMCEF, TPS10, and PAFEC75 [17]. Preprocessors and minicomputers are here to stay. The NASTRAN user should take advantage of them because the future will bring more powerful packages, increased availability of minis and graphics terminals, and reduced costs in model generation and postprocessing.

Program Efficiency Study

One of the stated objectives of this project was to evaluate the program efficiency. This is a formidable task for a general purpose program such as NASTRAN because of the complex nature of the program. For example, the mainframe version that is utilized (i.e., CDC, IBM, etc.) will certainly affect the results of such a study. In each version there are numerous differences, such as overlay structure, use of double precision arithmetic, type of loader, availability of central memory, etc., that can affect running time and efficiency. Even if the study is restricted to a particular machine, the program efficiency is an elusive commodity to assess. Not only is there a wide variety of rigid format solution procedures to be evaluated, but within the rigid formats there are often several options that may affect the efficiency, i.e., selection of eigenvalue extraction method. The use of DMAP and ALTER features will also have an effect (usually adverse) on the efficiency of NASTRAN. However, there are some general observations that can be made concerning program efficiency, some of which were learned during the course of

Table 11 Commercial NASTRAN pre- and postprocessor software packages

NAME	DEVELOPER	MARKETED IN CONJUNCTION WITH	AVAILABILITY ON SERVICE BUREAUS
SUPERTAB	Structural Dynamics Research Corp. Cincinnati, Ohio	Tektronix, Beaverton, Oregon Digital Equipment Corp. Marlboro, Massachusetts	Control Data Corp. CYBERNET and others
FASTDRAW 3	McDonnell Douglas Automation Co., St. Louis, Missouri	McDonnell Douglas Automation Company	McAuto
PATRAN-G (Version 1.2)	PDA Engineering Santa Ana, California	.Digital Equipment Corporation, Marlboro, Massachusetts (VAX-11/780) .Atkins (United Kingdom) .Rikei (Japan)	.United Computing Services .Martin-Marietta Data Systems, Inc. .University Computing Company
GIFTS5	University of Arizona, Tucson	Information Systems Design, Inc. Santa Clara, California	ISD
MENTAT	MARC Analysis Research Corp. Palo Alto, California	Prime Computer Inc., Wellesley Hills, Massachusetts	None. Currently used at MARC code installations
GRAFAX	A. O. Smith Corp. Milwaukee, Wisconsin		TELENET
FEMGEN	FEGS LTD. Cambridge, England	Jordan, Apostal, Ritter, Assoc. Davisville, Rhode Island	Primarily on European service bureaus

this project and others obtained in the course of discussions with users.

It is generally accepted that NASTRAN was designed to solve large problems. Indeed, some of the problems that have been solved using NASTRAN probably could not have been solved using any other computer program. Clearly, program efficiency is not an influencing factor in such cases. The automated substructuring capability in NASTRAN may be particularly efficient for large problems in which parts of the geometry are repeated. This capability, which was recently added, is probably the most convenient substructuring method that is currently available and requires a minimum of file handling by the user. Also, it is easy to use and can result in large savings in computer cost and engineering time.

It is generally felt that NASTRAN solves medium to large shell and beam structures as well or better than most general purpose programs. This is probably one of the strongest virtues of the code. Also, it is generally concluded that the rigid format solutions in NASTRAN have been well written and work efficiently. However, use of the ALTER or DMAP features can greatly increase running times. As a particular example, one user reported that NASTRAN was being used for seismic analysis of piping systems. DMAP was used to calculate modal participation factors and to perform the modal superposition. Running times appear to be almost an order of magnitude greater than would be expected using programs that are normally used in such analyses.

In order to obtain a quantitative measure of the efficiency of the program for one particular case, a series of runs were made in which a static analysis was performed of a flat plate with a central point load. (These runs were actually an extension of the convergence test described earlier for QDPLT). The results of these runs are shown in Figure 36. The computer used was a CDC Cyber 175. The costs were obtained from the day file from each run and were computed using an internal algorithm that is used by the commercial data center (United Computing Systems) where the runs were made.

The largest problem run was just over 2000 degrees of freedom, which could be classified as a "moderate" size problem. The results of this study indicated that both the cost and CPU time increased approximately linearly with the number of degrees of freedom over the problem size range studied. A linear increase in cost versus problem size implies that the code will be relatively more efficient for larger problems. For a more complete discussion on estimates of run time and costs, see Section 14 of Ref. [13].

CONCLUSIONS AND RECOMMENDATIONS

The results of this evaluation study of COSMIC/NASTRAN reveal that the code can be given an overall fair rating in its element library, capabilities, and efficiency. Documentation is rated good, and in our opinion NASTRAN has the most complete documentation of any general purpose program. There are some areas where the documentation could be improved, but, in general, it is quite good. The strengths of NASTRAN are the DMAP capability, versatility of analysis capabilities as offered in the 20 rigid formats, eigenvalue extraction options, plotting, restarting; and automated multistage substructuring analysis. Its weaknesses are lack of a higher-order 2-D solid-of-revolution element to handle plane strain, plane stress, or axisymmetric cases, user support and lack of a "hot-line" service, difficult-to-read documentation, lack of an adequate nonlinear analysis capability, a program architecture which is unsuitable for interactive use, and a time-consuming and ineffective error correction procedure. In the following subsections, an assessment of the program features and conclusions/recommendations will be covered separately.

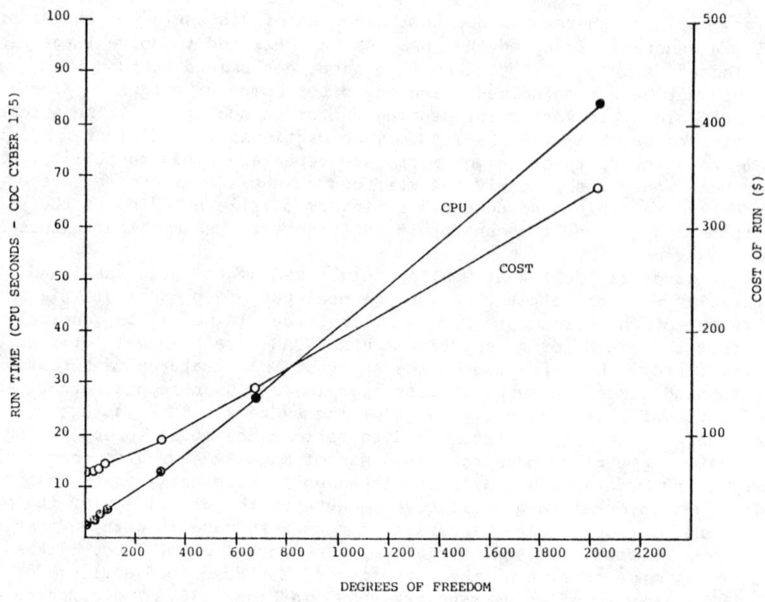

Fig. 36 Effect of problem size on completion time and cost

Program Assessment

1. Element Library

Element	Performance Rating	Comments
QDPLT	Fair	Twist moment with one edge clamped caused problems; passed convergence tests; failed patch test. Inferior to many other available plate-bending elements.
TRSHL	Poor	Convergence performance in Scordelis-Lo cylindrical roof benchmark inferior to other commercial shell elements.
TRIM6	Good	Performed well in cantilevered beam benchmark in comparison to QDMEM and QDMEM1 elements.
TRPLT1	Good	Compared well in simply supported rectangular plate-bending benchmark with QUAD1, Melosh, and Clough elements.
CONEAX	Good	Thermal loading capability is suspect. Otherwise, overall performance and versatility are good.

Element	Performance Rating	Comments
TRAPRG	Fair	Good performance in thick-walled cylinder benchmark but **restrictive** in use due to trapezoidal element requirement. Needs plane strain and plane stress capabilities.
TRAPAX	Fair	Good performance in thick-walled cylinder benchmark trapezoidal requirement; can handle nonaxisymmetric loads.
HEXA1	Poor	Poor performance in cantilevered beam benchmark and modal analysis; existence of spurious lateral displacements; adequate convergence in thick-walled cylinder benchmark.
HEXA2	Fair	Poor rating in cantilevered beam benchmark; adequate performance in thick-walled cylinder and modal analysis.
IHEX1	Fair	Suprisingly poor performance in cantilevered beam and modal analysis; good in thick-walled cylinder. May need "incompatible bending modes" to improve bending capability.
IHEX2	Good	Overall good performance in cantilevered beam benchmark, thick-walled cylinder, and modal analysis.

2. Program Documentation The manuals can be made more readable and user-oriented with simple examples, summary tables, application and usage hints, cost estimates, etc. The User's Guide [13] is a good start.

3. Error Correction Procedure and User Support These areas were the subject of many user complaints. However, the nature of COSMIC/NASTRAN development history, implementation, and maintenance seems to make these areas difficult to change and improve. Recently implemented user support efforts at COSMIC appear to be improving in this respect.

4. Program Architecture The modular concept behind NASTRAN program architecture is flexible but is based on computer core availability in the late sixties and is now difficult to adapt to a time-sharing system and interactive use.

5. DMAP The matrix handling capability and user control offered in DMAP are very flexible and unique among general purpose codes.

6. Constitutive Library Adequate, but deficient for general orthotropic or anisotropic analyses.

7. Eigenvalue Extraction COSMIC/NASTRAN's four eigenvalue extraction methods are the most offered in any code. All seem to work well, except the determinant method.

8. Nonlinear Capabilities COSMIC/NASTRAN offers limited nonlinear analysis capabilities, which are weak compared to many other nonlinear codes currently available.

9. Special Features Special NASTRAN features - such as static analysis with inertia relief, fully stressed design optimization, cyclic symmetry, component mode synthesis, representation of part of a structure by its vibration modes, analyses of control systems, structure/fluid interaction, aeroelasticity, and acoustic cavities - are unique among current competing codes.

10. Automated Multistage Substructuring Analysis AMSS is flexible and

powerful. This highly-developed substructuring capability is matched only by ANSYS among current structural analysis codes.

11. Minicomputer Versions of COSMIC/NASTRAN COSMIC offers a minicomputer version of NASTRAN on a lease basis. Three other minicomputer versions of NASTRAN are also available. These include MSC/NASTRAN, UAI/NASTRAN and PM/NASTRAN.

12. Pre- and Postprocessors for NASTRAN Many interactive graphics pre- and postprocessors have been developed in the past five years for NASTRAN. Among these commercial packages are SDRC/SUPERTAB, McAUTO/FASTDRAW, PDA/PATRAN, GIFTS, MARC/MENTAT, and AOS/GRAFAX.

13. Cost and CPU's versus Mesh Size Both are approximately linear with mesh size (Fig. 36).

Conclusions

1. NASTRAN program architecture is flexible, but has not kept pace with recent developments in computer hardware and operating system software. However, major changes in the architecture would be prohibitively expensive and would require a major rewriting of the program. The gains would probably not justify the expense.

2. NASTRAN is designed for large problems. Small or moderate size problems are expensive compared to other general purpose codes. The lack of self-contained mesh generation capability almost necessitates the use of a preprocessor to develop a finite element mesh. This further reduces the usefulness of the program for small to medium size problems because of the additional step in converting the output of the mesh generation program into NASTRAN data, learning how to use the mesh generator, and the additional control cards. The novice and even the common user are often frustrated by this additional effort.

3. No interactive capability exists. Many of the current general purpose codes can be executed in an interactive mode. It is expected that this trend will become more and more prevalent in the near future. The present program architecture of NASTRAN would be quite awkward to convert to an interactive mode.

4. The documentation is bulky and not user oriented. It could and should be improved.

5. The matrix handling package (DMAP) is very powerful. Better documentation and examples of its use would probably greatly benefit the novice and common user.

6. To improve the efficiency of the finite element library and to reduce confusion to users (especially relatively new ones), some of the older and less effective elements (such as TRSHL, HEXA1, HEXA2) should be removed from the program unless they have unique capabilities that cannot be performed by other elements. Improved elements are needed in some areas (as discussed previously). The myriad of 13 separate membrane and bending elements in COSMIC/NASTRAN - TRMEM, TRIM6, QDMEM, QDMEM1, QDMEM2, TRPLT, QDPLT, TRBSC, TRIA1, TRIA2, QUAD1, QUAD2 - should be revised, consolidated and improved to offer the analyst fewer but better choices. A brief synopsis of each element, its capability and limitations should be included in the Users Manual so that reference to the Theoretical Manual is unnecessary for most analyses. Alternately, the Users Manual could describe the "recommended" elements and the experienced user would have access to the remaining elements if desired.

7. It is our opinion that the only hexahedral elements offered should be isoparametric in formulation, with clearly documented hints on the merits of reduced integration and incompatible bending modes in various applications. The poor performance of IHEX1 on the cantilever beam problem could be greatly improved if incompatible bending mode formulation was added to this

element. Otherwise, the 20-node hexahedron IHEX2 should be used if only one element through the thickness is used when bending loads are present (for example, to represent thick shells). The additional complexity in modeling using a 20-node hexahedron versus an 8-node element results in increased engineering time and greater chance of modeling errors.

8. NASTRAN is primarily a linear code. The nonlinear features are relatively few and not extensive.

9. An organization which uses or intends to use the public domain versions of NASTRAN should be prepared to commit a significant investment for staff for prompt support, consultation, and system (job control) help. Our findings indicate that without this level of support, most organizations are frustrated by the lack of these necessary functions.

10. Error correction in COSMIC/NASTRAN is time-consuming and ineffective. The time lag between when errors are reported and corrected is such that most analysts cannot wait for the response from the NASTRAN subcontractor. Many organizations which use NASTRAN correct errors as they are uncovered and may or may not report these changes to COSMIC or its subcontractor. This process results in many (mostly minor) variations of NASTRAN among the user community, and uniform quality control is virtually impossible. It is incumbent upon the user or his organization to verify the accuracy of the program at each installation.

11. In our opinion, NASTRAN is a program that should be maintained for public usage. While the program is in some respects relatively outdated, we feel that the program is still extremely versatile and serves a very useful purpose. One of the strongest arguments in favor of this is the fact that NASTRAN has been used by such a large number of analysts over the years. Such extensive usage is one of the best methods of verifying a program. Also, this large community of users is familiar with the program and its capabilities. This body of expertise is a very valuable asset. The high degree of modularity of the program will allow for the addition of new elements and new analysis procedures without adversely affecting the existing program. Verification of new features is relatively simple compared to some other general purpose codes because of this modularity.

12. The selection of a general purpose program for use by a company or organization must include the following factors (A) Cost, (B) Capability (including element library and analysis methods), and (C) User Support. The cost of a program includes not only the initial cost of the source code (or the royalty fee for commercial programs) and computer time, but the cost of maintaining the program on the user's system. For example, implementing new features that are needed, error correction, and other maintenance functions can be time-consuming and expensive. Second, the capability of the program should not be static, but must change as new developments in element theory, analysis methods, etc., are developed. Third, user support is very important. If possible, the principal developers of the program should be available for consultation when problems arise. It is extremely inefficient for even an expert user to find and correct programming errors, and this effort probably is impossible for most users. It is our opinion that all of these functions should be provided by a single organization, if possible. Such an organization is also needed to plan the future developments and additions that will be necessary if NASTRAN is to survive as a viable program.

REFERENCES

1 Wilkes, M. V., "Computers into the 1980's," Electronics and Power, January 1980, pp. 67-71.

2 Scarrott, G. G., "From Computing Slave to Knowledgeable Servant: Proc. Royal Society, (London), Vol. 369A, December 1979, pp. 1-30.

3 Mueller, G. E., "The Future of Data Processing in Aerospace," Aeronautical Journal, April 1979, pp. 149-158.

4 "Trends in Computing: Applications for the 80's," Fortune, 19 May 1980, pp. 29-70.

5 Surgarman, R., "Superpower Computers," IEEE Spectrum, April, 1980, pp. 28-34.

6 Darby, M. J., "The Expanding Bubble Market," Electronics Industry, February 1980, pp. 38-47.

7 "A Brief Description of MSC/NASTRAN," MSR-54, April 1978, (MSC).

8 Morgan, M. J., Field, E. I., and Herting, D. N., "Recent Enhancements to COSMIC/NASTRAN," SAP User's Conference, University of Southern California, June 1978.

9 "The NASTRAN Theoretical Manual(Level 17.5)," NASA SP221 (05) Dec. 1978, (COSMIC, 112 Barron Hall, University of Georgia, Athens, GA 30602).

10 "The NASTRAN User's Manual (Level 17.5)," NASA SP222 (05), Dec. 1978.

11 "The NASTRAN Programmer's Manual (Level 17.5)," NASA SP223 (3 & 4), 1979.

12 "The NASTRAN Demonstration Manual (Level 17.0)," NASA SP224 (04), Dec. 1977.

13 Field, E. I., Herting, D. N., and Morgan, M. J., "NASTRAN User's Guide (Level 17.5)," Prepared by Universal Analytics, Inc. (Playa Del Rey, California) for Langley Research Center, NASA DR-3146, June 1979.

14 McCormick, C. W., "MSC/NASTRAN Basic Training Manmual," MSR-46, 15 July 1977, MacNeal-Schwendler Corporation, 7442 N. Figueroa Street, Los Angeles, CA 90041.

15 Schaeffer, H. G., MSC/NASTRAN Primer: Static and Normal Modes Analysis, April 1979, Schaeffer Analysis, Inc.16 "MSC/NASTRAN, Applicatio

17 Fredriksson, B., and Mackerle, J., "Overview and Evaluation of Some Versatile General Purpose Finite Element Computer Programs," Second World Congress on Finite Element Methods, 23-27 October 1978, Bournemouth, England.

18 Dunder, V. F., and Belonogoff, G., "Comparing Finite Element Programs in Engineering," Conference on Finite Element Methods and Engineering, sponsored by the MacNeal-Schwendler Corporation, 13-14 March, 1980, Pasadena, CA.

19 Bath, K. S., and Wilson, E. L., Numerical Methods in Finite Element Analysis, Prentice-Hall, Englewood Cliffs, New Jersey, 1976.

20 Field, E. I., Herting, D. N., Herendeen, D. L., and Hoesly, R. L., "The Automated Multi-Stage Substructuring System for NASTRAN," NASTRAN: User's Experiences, NASA TM X-3278, Fourth NASTRAN User's Colloquium, NASA Langley Research Center, 9-11 September, 1975.

21 Herting, D. N., and Hosely, R. L., "Development of an Automated Multi-Stage Modal Synthesis System for NASTRAN." Sixth NASTRAN User's Colloquium, Lewis Research Center, 4-6 October, NASA Conference Publication 2018, 1977, pp. 435-448,

22 Herting, D. N., and Morgan, M. J., "A General Purpose, Multistage, Component Modal Synthesis Method," 20th AIAA/ASME/ASCE/AHS Structural Dynamics and Materials Conference, 6 April 1979, St. Louis, Missouri.

23 DeSalvo, G. J., "ANSYS Verification Manual," Swanson Analysis Systems, Inc., 1 April 1979, Box 65, Houston, Pennsylvania 15342.

24 Robinson, J., "Element Evaluation - A Set of Assessment Points and Standard Tests," Second World Congress on Finite Element Methods, 23-27 October, 1978, Bournemouth, England. Published as Finite Element Methods in the Commercial Environment, ed. J. Robinson, Robinson and Associates, Horton Road, Woodlands, Wimborne, Dorset BH21, England.

25 Robinson, J., "A Single Element Test," Computer Methods in Applied Mechanics and Engineering, Vol. 1, 1976, pp. 191-200.

26 Robinson, J., and Haggenmacher, G. W., "LORA - An Accurate Four Node Stress Plate Bending Element," Int'l. J. Numerical Methods in Engineering, Vol. 14, 1979, pp. 287-312.

27 Robinson, J., and Blackham, S., "An Evaluation of Lower Order Membranes as Contained in the MSC/NASTRAN, ASAS, and PAFEC FEM Systems," Conference on Finite Element Methods and Technology (Sponsored by MSC), Pasadena, CA 13-14 March, 1980.

28 Padovan, J., and Chang, T. Y., "Evaluation of ADINA: Part I (Theory and Programming Descriptions); Part II (Operating Characteristics)," University of Akron, Akron, Ohio 44325, June 8, 1980.

29 Narayanaswami, R., "New Triangular Shallow Shell Finite Element," Old Dominion University, Technical Report 74-T7, November 1974.

30 Narayanaswami, R., "Addition of Higher Order Plate and Shell Elements into NASTRAN Computer Program," Old Dominion University, Technical Report 76-719, December 1976.

31 Potvin, A. B., Exxon Production Research Company, Private Communication, March 10, 1980.

32 Grafton, P. E., and Strome, D. R., "Analysis of Axisymmetric Shells by the Direct Stiffness Method," J. AIAA, Vol. 1, No. 10, October 1963, pp. 2342-2347.

33 Jones, R. E., and Strome, D. R., "A Survey of Analysis of Shells by the Displacement Method," Proc. First Conference on Matrix Methods in Structural Mechanics, Wright-Patterson Air Force Base, Ohio, 26-28 October, 1965, AFFDL-TR-66-30 (AD 646300), pp. 205-229.

34 Hetenyi, M., Beams on Elastic Foundation, University of Michigan Press, Ann Arbor, 1946.

35 Timoshenko, S. P., Strength of Materials, Vol. II, 3rd. ed., Van Nostrand, 1956.

36 Clough, R. W., "Comparison of Three Dimensional Finite Elements," Proc. of Symposium of Application of Finite Element Methods in Civil Engineering, sponsored by the American Society of Civil Engineers, Vanderbilt University, Nashville, Tennessee, November 1969, pp. 1-26.

37 Zienkiewicz, O. C., The Finite Element Method, McGraw Hill, (U.K.), 1977, Chapter 6.

38 Gallagher, R. H., Finite Element Analysis - Fundamentals, Prentice-Hall, 1975, Chapter 10.

39 Desai, C. S., and Abel, J. F., Introduction to the Finite Element Method, Van Nostrand Reinhold, 1972, pp. 166-169.

40 Wilson, E. L., Taylor, R. L., Doherty, W. P., and Ghaboussi, J., "Incompatible Displacement Models," Numerical and Computer Methods in Structural Mechanics, ed., S. J. Fenves, et al., Academic Press, 1973.

41 Drake, S. K., et al., "Three-Dimensional Finite Element Elastic Analysis of a Thermally Cycled Double-Edge Wedge Geometry Specimen," Air Force Wright Aeronautical Laboratories, Technical Report AFWAL-TR-80-2013, March 1980.

42 Jones, J. W., Fong, H. H., and Blehm, D. A., "Evaluation of the NASTRAN General Purpose Computer Program," Report to ONR, August 1980.

Analysis and Design of Reinforced Concrete Structures

C. S. Krishnamoorthy

Indian Institute of Technology

INTRODUCTION

In the design of concrete structures engineers have to follow the pertinent code of practice used in their countries. This makes it difficult to develop general software for the design of concrete structures which can be adopted in many countries, as in the case of analysis programs. It also explains the reason for the development of a number of programs in different countries oriented to specific code requirements.

The software for the computer aided design of reinforced concrete structures can be grouped into the following categories: 1. analysis, 2. design, and 3. automatic detailing. In this review some of the widely used programs are discussed as general and special purpose programs depending on their use. Thus this review aims to give an overall view of the scope of the software available for reinforced concrete design and to indicate the trends for future development.

ANALYSIS PROGRAMS

For the analysis of concrete structures engineers usually resort to programs based on linear elastic analysis. Most of these programs use the finite element method of analysis. However, it is well known that the behavior of concrete structures at higher load levels is nonlinear and a rigorous nonlinear/inelastic analysis is required in such cases. But there are not many programs available that would consider satisfactorily all the characteristic nonlinear behavior of concrete structures and at the same time be commercially viable for practical use.

General Purpose Linear Analysis Programs

There are a number of finite element analysis package programs available. These are described in Refs. [1-2]. It has been noted that SAP IV (recent versions being SAP V and SAP VI) is moderate in size, efficient, and computationally economical, leading to its wider use. It has been implemented on many computer systems, and there is an increasing trend toward making it available on mini-computer systems.

The program package STRUDL II, developed at M.I.T., has been aimed at providing an integrated analysis and design package [3]. The analysis segment of the package is a large finite element system and includes several options and facilities for the user with regard to static and dynamic analysis of structural systems. The design capabilities of this package are discussed later.

The general purpose finite element programs, when applied to the analysis of reinforced concrete structures, require consideration of the reinforcements as separate bar elements. This poses problems of discretization increasing the computing time. Recent research in this area has shown that special finite elements called "reinforced concrete element" can be formulated incorporating steel as an integral part of the concrete element [4,5]. The program FEPACS1 described in Ref. [6] is applicable to linear and nonlinear analysis of reinforced concrete framed structures. A further development in this area for three-dimensional linear stress analysis is reported in Refs. [7,8], and the program CONSAP based on this work is described below.

Program CONSAP

(CONcrete Structures Analysis Program)

Category: Three-dimensional stress analysis of reinforced concrete structures.

Authors: C. S. Krishnamoorthy, Professor in Civil Engineering, at Indian Institute of Technology, Madras 600 036, India. Also, M. Inbasakaran and V. G. Pandarinathan, Assistant Professors in Civil Engineering at Coimbatore Institute of Technology, Coimbatore 641014, India.

Capability: The program is a three-dimensional linear elastic stress analysis of concrete structures. Reinforcement oriented in any direction is considered as an integral part of the 8- and 20-noded isoparametric element. The program can be used for the stress analysis of nuclear containment vessels, beams curved in plan, stress concentration, and other problems.

Method: The analysis is by the finite element method. It uses a numerical integration procedure for computation of stiffness. The equation solver uses Gauss elimination with an active column storage scheme.

Programming Language: FORTRAN IV

Documentation: Ph.D. thesis of M. Inbasakaran to be submitted in the Department of Civil Engineering, I.I.T., Madras 600 036.

Input: The input data required for the structure and element are the same as that for the SAP Program. Additional input data are required for the global coordinates and area of each reinforcing bar within the element following the element data.

Output: Stress at any point in concrete and axial stress in the reinforcement

General Purpose Nonlinear Analysis Programs

There are a number of programs available for nonlinear analysis of structural systems, and the nonlinear effects may be due to geometric and/or material behavior. Programs like NONSAP [2] and other systems consider these effects in a general way. But in the case of concrete structures nonlinearity is due to a nonlinear constitutive relation for concrete under various stress states, change of topology due to progressive cracking of concrete due to low tensile strength, and yielding of concrete and steel under ultimate load conditions.

A few of the programs have recently been developed from research efforts in this direction. Bathe et al. [9] have considered the nonlinear effects characteristic of concrete structures in the recent addition to the ADINA Program [10]. However, the program development in this area has not yet reached the stage for commercial exploitation.

Special Purpose Elastic Analysis Program

Special purpose programs oriented to solving specific structures are attractive to the users because of their simplicity, their small size, and the capability of operation on small computer systems available in design offices. There are a number of such types of programs available for the analysis of two- and three-dimensional frames, framed structures with shear walls, flat slab systems, and other structures [11]. A few of the programs are described below.

Analysis of Plane Frame Shearwall Structures

Category: Elastic analysis of plane multistory frame shearwall structures under lateral and gravity loads.

Author: Portland Cement Association
Old Orchard Road
Skokie, Illinois 60076

Date: 1971

Capability: PCA program handles linear static elastic analysis of a plane rectangular frame or several such frames linked together, when subjected to gravity and/or lateral loads. The effect of the finite width of members, shear deformations in columns, and partial fixity factors with respect to rotation, as well as vertical displacement for the bases of the lowest story columns, are included in the program.

Method: Direct stiffness method in the form of a tri-diagonal frame stiffness matrix is used in the formulation.

Limitations: The program is limited to a maximum of three linked frames, each having a maximum of 60 stories and 10 column lines.

Input: Frame dimensions, member properties, and loads

Output: Input echo of frame dimensions, member properties and loads, joint displacements, and member end forces

Availability: Available in IBM 1130 · 16K and IBM 360 versions under a nondisclosure licensing agreement with PCA, Illinois

Analysis and Design of Slab Systems

Category: Analysis and Design of interior or exterior two-dimensional equivalent frames for flat plate systems

Author: Portland Cement Association
Old Orchard Road
Skokie, Illinois 60076

Date: 1976

Capability: The program offers scope for the analysis and design of flat plates, flat slabs, waffle slabs, two-way slabs, and continuous beams. Both interior and exterior frames can be handled. Analysis and design are carried out for four combinations of vertical loads and four combinations of wind moments combined with vertical loads. Options are available to use either the working stress method or the strength design method.

Method: Uses the equivalent frame method of analysis and follows the provisions of Section 13.4 of ACI 318-71

Limitations: An interior or exterior frame consisting of maximum of 12 spans and 2 cantilevers can be designed. Slab thickness is assumed to be constant for all spans of a particular frame.
Input: Span dimensions, slab widths, column size, loading conditions, and design specifications
Output: Printout of center-line moments and shears: punching and moment transfer shear investigation at critical sections, reinforcement requirements, and material quantity estimates
Hardware: IBM 1130, 60-K core, IBM 360/370, 220-K core capacity, and CDC 6600 130K octal word capacity
Typical Running Times: For IBM 1130, it ranges from 1 to 4 minutes per span.
Availability: Available under nondisclosure licensing agreement with PCA, Illinois

Program ETABS

Categories: Three-dimensional static and dynamic analysis of building systems
Authors: E. L. Wilson, J. P. Hollings, and H. H. Dovey
University of California
Berkeley, California 94720
Date: 1975
Capability: The program analyzes the frame and shearwall building subjected to both static and earthquake loadings. Beams and girders may be nonprismatic, and bending and shear deformations are included. Finite beam and column widths, shear panels, and diagonal elements are considered in the formulations. The static loads may be combined with a lateral earthquake input which is specified as a time-dependent ground acceleration or an acceleration spectrum response. Nonsymmetric, nonrectangular buildings which have frames and shearwalls located arbitrarily in the plan can be considered.
Method: The stiffness matrix method is used, considering the frame and the shearwall as substructures in the basic formulation assuming the floor diaphragms are rigid in their own planes. For dynamic analysis the mass of the building is lumped at each floor level.
Programming Language: FORTRAN IV
Documentation: Three Dimensional Analysis of Building Systems (Extended Version)
by E. L. Wilson, J. P. Hollings, and H. H. Dovey
Report No. EERC 74-13, 1975
Earthquake Engineering Research Center
University of California
Berkeley, California 94720
Availability: CDC version is available from NISEE, Davis Hall,
University of California
Berkeley, California 94720
IBM version available from University of Southern California,
Los Angeles, California 90007
Atten: Professor V. I. Weingarten
Civil Engineering Department

Special Purpose Inelastic Analysis Programs

With the introduction of limit state design concepts for the design of concrete structures it has become increasingly necessary to develop programs capable of analyzing the structure under the ultimate load conditions; i.e., at the limit state of collapse. As pointed out earlier, a general nonlinear analysis program is very expensive for use in practical design situations. Hence simplified approaches have been used to consider the inelastic effects under the ultimate load conditions. A recently developed program, CONFAP [12], uses the mathematical programming technique providing a computationally efficient algorithm for the inelastic analysis of reinforced concrete frames.

Program CONFAP

CONcrete Frame Analysis Program

Category: Inelastic analysis of reinforced concrete plane framed structures
Authors: D. R. Mosi and C. S. Krishnamoorthy
Civil Engineering Department
Indian Institute of Technology
Madras 600 036, India
Date: 1979
Capability: The program calculates inelastic analysis of moments, shears, and axial forces in continuous beams and plane-framed structures under ultimate load conditions. Loads may be uniform, or point loads on the members, or acting at the joints.
Method: It is based on Macchi's method [13] of "imposed rotation", which assumes that inelastic rotations are concentrated at critical sections and moment-rotation law is tri-linear. Kaneko's Linear Complementarity Problem formulation [14] and L.C.P. Solver is used in the unified program.
Programming Language: FORTRAN IV
Documentation: CONFAP - Computer Program for Inelastic Analysis of Reinforced Concrete Framed Structures - User's Manual by D. R. Mosi and C. S. Krishnamoorthy - CAD/UM-7, Sept. 1979, Structural Engineering Division, Civil Engineering Department, I.I.T., Madras, India
Input: Input data similar to elastic analysis program - structure data, joint, element, and load data. M-θ relations for critical sections and can also be given in tabular form.
Output: Results of elastic analysis, inelastic rotations, and inelastic moments at all critical sections
Software Operations: Batch processing
Hardware: IBM 370/155, 384 K core
Typical Running Time: A typical two-bay, six-story frame takes 146 seconds on IBM 370/155
Availability: Civil Engineering Department
Attn: Professor C. S. Krishnamoorthy
Indian Institute of Technology
Madras, India 600 036

DESIGN PROGRAMS

The programs oriented to the design of concrete structures can be grouped as those dealing with the design of individual elements and those for integrated systems having the capability of designing all the components of a structure.

There are a number of programs that have been developed for the design of reinforced concrete (R.C.) beams and columns (rectangular and circular) with various types of arrangements of reinforcements. A recent review [15] gives an account of these types of programs.

One of the large programs with an integrated design capability is STRUDL II [16]. It is a very large subsystem operating under the ICES Basic system. Through the use of commands the engineer has the ability to direct the computer to perform the analysis and design of R.C. structures. It has special facilities for the treatment of typical orthogonal reinforced concrete buildings. The capability for proportioning members includes the design of beams, flat slabs, columns, one-way slabs, or joist floors. The output consists of the required cross-sectional dimensions, the amount of longitudinal reinforcement at critical sections, and the spacing of stirrups, ties, or spirals. A complete description of all reinforcements, including bar lengths, will be printed if requested. STRUDL II uses the ACI Building Code for the design and detailing procedures.

GENESYS is another large system similar to STRUDL II. It was developed in England, and it can be implemented on many computer systems [1]. The subsystem "RC-BUILDING" offers a capability for automatic analysis and design of reinforced concrete buildings [17]. The design procedures follow the British Code of Practice.

DETAILING OF CONCRETE ELEMENTS

Recent advances in computer graphics have had an enormous impact on software development for engineering practice. It is recognized that the detailing of reinforced concrete is one of the most tedious tasks in the whole design process. Hence programs offering scope for automatic detailing and drawing are important to the users. As mentioned earlier, since the detailing practice is governed by the national codes of practice it is difficult to make these programs portable for use in other countries like the analysis programs.

It is significant to note the development carried out at Loughborough University by Professor L. L. Jones and his associates in the development of LUCID, a structural detailing system providing a lead in this direction. A brief description can be found in Ref. [18].

FUTURE DEVELOPMENTS

In this review the programs that are widely used for analysis and design are discussed, and specific requirements for concrete structures are also mentioned. The major areas which require emphasis in the future development of software can be summarized as follows:

1. With the recent advances in computer hardware and the emergence of powerful mini-computers, large-scale analysis programs can be made operational in these systems so that design offices may find it economical to use them. Such efforts for the SAP Program are reported in Ref. [19].

2. While most of the codes of practice recommend ultimate strength design of sections, the analysis of the structures is still based on linear elastic analysis, as a rigorous nonlinear/inelastic analysis is still very expensive. There is a need for formulating simplified approaches resulting in the use of efficient algorithms, so that programs may be developed to provide a realistic analysis of concrete structures and to be commercially viable.

3. The limit state design of concrete structures recommended by many codes of practice requires analysis under ultimate load conditions and a check on the serviceability conditions under working loads for deflection, crack width, and spacing. Future development of programs should include these requirements so that designers can be relieved of the tedious calculations that satisfy the code regulations.

4. There is considerable interest in the use of optimization techniques for the economical design of structural systems. A recent survey [20] has pointed out the need for comprehensive package programs for the optimal design of structures. In the case of concrete structures, numerical stability of the optimization problem solvers and efficiency in programming require further research and development.

5. In the development of large design packages for reinforced concrete structures, there is a need to make use of efficient data base management and modular programming techniques. This would enable general software to include analysis, optimization, design, and detailing segments in different modules so that only the design and detailing segments need be modified to suit the national codes of practice, thus making the packages usable in different countries. A general package may also provide a facility for automatic drawing of reinforcement details for concrete elements.

REFERENCES

1 Perrone, N., and Pilkey, W., ed., Structural Mechanics Software Series, Vol. 1, University Press of Virginia, Charlottesville, 1977.

2 Perrone, N., and Pilkey, W., ed., Structural Mechanics Software Series, Vol. 2, University Press of Virginia, Charlottesville, 1978.

3 IUG-ICES STRUDL Operations Manual and Applications Manual, Vols. I and II, ICES Users Group, Rhode Island, 02920, U.S.A.

4 Colville, J., and Abbasi, J., "Plane Stress Reinforced Concrete Finite Elements," Journal of the Structural Division, Proceedings of the American Society of Civil Engineers, ST5, May 1974, pp. 1067-1083.

5 Krishnamoorthy, C. S., and Panneerselvam, A., "A Finite Element Model for Nonlinear Analysis of Reinforced Concrete Framed Structures," The Structural Engineer, London, Vol. 55, No. 8, Aug. 1977, pp. 331-338.

6 Krishnamoorthy, C. S., and Panneerselvam, A., "FEPACS1 - A Finite Element Program for Nonlinear Analysis of Reinforced Concrete Framed Structures," Computers and Structures, Vol. 9, 1978, pp. 451-461.

7 Krishnamoorthy, C. S., and Inbasakaran, M., "A New Eight Node Solid Element for Analysis of Concrete Structures," Proceedings of the Third SAP Users Conference, University of Southern California, Los Angeles, June 1978.

8 Inbasakaran, M., Pandarinathan, V. G., and Krishnamoorthy, C. S., "Three Dimensional Finite Element Linear Analysis of Reinforced Concrete Structures," Proceedings of the 5th International Conference on Structural Mechanics in Reactor Technology, Berlin, Aug. 1979.

9 Bathe, K. J., and Ramaswamy, S., "Three Dimensional Nonlinear Analysis of Concrete (and Rock) Structures," M.I.T. Report (private communication).

10 Bathe, K. J., "Static and Dynamic Geometric and Material Nonlinear Analysis using ADINA," M.I.T., Report No. 82448-2, May 1977, Acoustics and Vibration Laboratory, Department of Mechanical Engineering, M.I.T., Cambridge, Massachusetts.

11 Fintel, M., Computer Program Developments by the Portland Cement Association, P.C.A., Skokie, Illinois, 1977.

12 Krishnamoorthy, C. S., and Mossi, D. R., "CONFAP - A Computer Program for Inelastic Analysis of Reinforced Concrete Framed Structures," to appear in Computers and Structures.

13 Macchi, G., "Méthode des Rotations Imposées," Structures Hyperstatiques, Comité Européen du Béton, No. 53, 1966, pp. 3-48.

14 Kaneko, I., "A Mathematical Programming Method for the Inelastic Analysis of Reinforced Concrete Frames," International Journal for Numerical Methods in Engineering, Vol. 11, 1977, pp. 1137-1154.

15 ACI Committee 118, "Review of Computer Program Abstracts," American Concrete Institute Journal, Dec. 1978, pp. 680-683.

16 ICES STRUDL II, Engineering User's Manual, Vol. 3, Reinforced Concrete Structures, Department of Civil Engineering, M.I.T., Cambridge, Report R70-30, June 1970.

17 Wyche, G. A., "'RC-BUILDING'- A GENESYS Subsystem for RC-Detailing - The Construction and Management of the Data Base," Proceedings of the International Symposium on Computer-Aided Structural Design, University of Warwick, Vol. 2, 1972, pp. A 2.18-2.30.

18 Jones, L. L., "LUCID - A Structural Detailing System," Proceedings of the International Symposium on Computer-Aided Structural Design, University of Warwick, Vol. 2, 1972, pp. H2.1-2.17.

19 Miura, H., and Brentano, L., "A Super-minicomputer Version of SAP 6," Proceedings of the Third SAP Users Conference, University of Southern California, Los Angeles, June, 1978.

20 Krishnamoorthy, C. S., and Mossi, D. R., "A Survey on Optimal Design of Civil Engineering Structural Systems," Engineering Optimization, Vol. 4, No. 2, 1979, pp. 73-88.

Small Computers

John A. Conaway

Schaeffer Analysis, Inc.

INTRODUCTION

There is a wide range of structural mechanics software in common use [1, 2]. Part of this diversity is a result of the rich variety of applied mathematics used to solve structural analysis and design problems. At one end of the spectrum are the governing differential equations which arise out of continuum mechanics and the theory of elasticity. The most popular method for solving these equations on a digital computer is the finite element method (FEM). Finite difference methods, used commonly in axisymmetric shells, heat transfer, and wave propagation problems, are another approach to the systematic solution of the governing differential equations.

At the other end of the spectrum are simple analysis formulas based on restrictive assumptions which can be shown to give good results for specific geometries and boundary conditions. The same level of simple formulas is evident in specialized design software which embodies codes and regulations stipulated by engineering societies and other standards agencies.

An examination of the computer requirements for this wide range of software indicates that a similarly diverse mix of hardware may be appropriately applied to the solution of structural mechanics problems. FEM, for example, requires much more computer resources than simple design formulas. A relatively fast central processor with long word lengths and/or double precision arithmetic is needed to solve the large FEM matrix equations efficiently and accurately. A substantial mass storage is also needed to handle the large amount of information calculated by the FEM program. For programs involving simple design formulas, slower processors are adequate and word accuracy is not a problem. The design programs are generally small enough to fit into main memory; they utilize in-core solution algorithms, and a limited amount of information is calculated by the program.

When digital computers were first introduced to structural engineering, they were very expensive resources relative to the salaries of the engineers who used them. Good economics dictated that these mainframes be centrally located. Other pressures for centralization were the large physical size of the machines, stringent environmental requirements, and the need for systems support personnel who were computer experts. The difficulty of programming early computers spurred the concept of a centralized EDP group located close to the mainframe.

In the mid-sixties, IBM introduced the 1130, an early small computer. Civil engineers quickly realized that this machine could be used to run small design programs. The IBM 1130 became popular in engineering consulting companies, where it still may be found today. This was the first application of a less expensive computer to the lower end of the range of structural mechanics software. It occurred, conveniently, at the same time as many student engineers began to be exposed to higher-level computer languages via new texts and elective courses [3]. But the 1130 was still large, slow, and expensive by today's standards.

In the late 1960s, the first modern minicomputer, the DEC PDP-8, was introduced. The new class of machines which it represented was first used in business, laboratory, educational, and manufacturing operations. Minicomputers were the first computers to be installed in close proximity to the user. This was possible because of their relatively low cost, minimal environmental requirements, and small size. It wasn't until the mid-1970s, that minicomputers began to be used heavily in engineering. They were, at that time, applied to the less computationally intensive problems associated with small analysis and design programs and FEM pre- and postprocessing.

In 1978, a new class of computers was introduced; the supermini. These machines did away with many of the restrictions which made it impossible for early minicomputers to be applied to the top end of the range of structural mechanics software. The nominal supermini is a 32-bit word computer with high speed, floating point arithmetic, a large physical memory capacity, and extensive virtual memory addressability. Superminis have been used to solve computationally intensive structural problems such as finite element analysis [4,5].

In 1972, the first microprocessors were introduced, starting another trend which has impacted the mode of structural engineering computing. Programming primarily in the BASIC language, engineers have installed hundreds of small design programs on microcomputers in the last few years. These computers are not only easily accessible in the user's workplace, but are increasingly found as "personal" computers in the home. The first generation microcomputers required several dozen chips to form a computer. Through the technology of large-scale integration, the density of functions has been increased such that microprocessors are now manufactured on one chip. The new fourth-generation microprocessors, introduced in 1980, produce "minicomputer-like" capabilities at very low cost. Low-end structural mechanics software is expected to migrate to these devices in the near future.

AN ECONOMIC CLASSIFICATION OF COMPUTERS

It has been noted by several authors that classification of computers is becoming difficult because of the proliferation and overlap of machine characteristics [2, 6, 7, 8]. A few years ago, it was possible to think of a microcomputer as a very small, slow, computing device with 8-bit word architecture. Similarly, a mini was a larger, more expensive, 16-bit machine, and a supermini was a still larger and more expensive 32-bit machine. At the time, this type of characterization was an over-simplification, but it is totally meaningless today.

Sixteen-bit "microcomputers" such as the DEC LSI-11 were the first major violation of this simple classification scheme. Confusion is also caused by the low-priced 32-bit "superminis" now available from such companies as Perkin-Elmer, Prime, and DEC. These machines are less expensive, and sometimes smaller, than many 16-bit "minis" which are still on the market. The new "microprocessors" on a chip typified by the Motorola 68000 have similar capabilities to existing "minis."

To avoid semantic confusion, a simple cost-based classification is proposed as follows;

	Classification	Complete System Cost ($1,000's)
Large Computers	SUPERCOMPUTER$	5,000 - 14,000
	MAINFRAME$	350 - 5,000
Small Computers	SUPERMINI$	150 - 350
	MINI$	20 - 150
	MICRO$	4 - 20

A small computer is defined here as a device whose system cost, including peripherals, is less than $350,000 and which occupies a space (excluding peripherals and add-on memory) of 150 cubic feet or less. These machines are often operated without trained computer personnel and require little or no environmental restructuring upon installation. They are normally supplied with an operating system that provides for high-speed local interaction via alphanumeric and graphic terminals.

It is assumed that computers having a complete system cost of less than $4,000 are unsuitable for engineering work at this time [9]. This limit can be expected to decrease somewhat as new, more powerful processors become available at the bottom of the micro$ range. The lower limit is somewhat inflexible, however, due to the peripheral equipment that is required for useful engineering work (i.e., mass storage, tape or disc input, graphic display devices, and hard copy). Table 1 lists popular hardware in each cost-based category.

Table 1 Computer Hardware for Structural Mechanics

SUPERMINI$	IBM 4341	SUPERCOMPUTER$	CDC CYBER 205
	DEC VAX 11/780		CRAY 1
	PRIME 750		CDC CYBER 203
	DG MV/8000		CDC STAR-100
	PERKIN ELMER 3240		CDC CYBER 76
	SEL 32/7760		
	HARRIS 800		
MINI$	DG NOVA	MAINFRAME$	IBM 303X
	HP 1000/3000		CDC CYBER 17X
	DEC PDP 11/34, 11/44		UNIVAC 1110
	PRIME 250		IBM 370
	PERKIN ELMER 3220		IBM 360
	WANG 2200		UNIVAC 1108
			CDC 6600

MICRO$
- DG MICRO NOVA
- HP 85, 9825, 9835, 9845
- DEC PDP 11/03, 11/23
- RADIO SHACK TRS-80
- COMMODORE PET
- APPLE II, III
- OHIO SCIENTIFIC CHALLENGER
- CROMENCO

MODES OF OPERATION OF SMALL COMPUTERS

The availability of easily accessible small computers is radically modifying the way structural engineering software is developed and utilized. Installation of the computer close to the user allows high baud-rate communications that are not attainable with remote computers. This is extremely important in interactive program development. It also provides real productivity improvements in input data debugging and output interpretation utilizing interactive graphics.

Processing of structural mechanics problems on local small computers has been accomplished in three basic modes; dedicated, hierarchical, and distributed, as illustrated in Fig. 1. In the simplified schematics shown, rectangles represent computers and circles represent graphic or alphanumeric terminal devices.

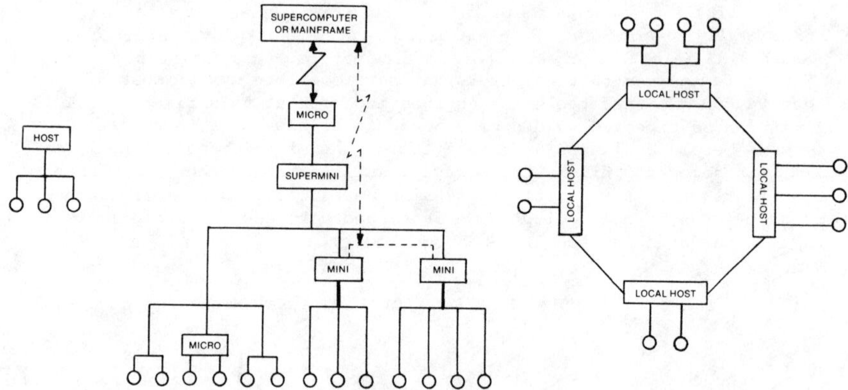

a. Dedicated b. Hierarchical c. Distributed

Fig. 1 Modes of processing

DEDICATED PROCESSING

In dedicated processing, the micro, mini,or supermini host is run in a standalone configuration analogous to traditional mainframe installations. The basic difference is that the computer is a special purpose, rather than general purpose, resource. It is dedicated to running a small number of related programs or a single program for a small number of users. The users may be linked by discipline only, or they may all be members of the same project to which the computer is assigned. Examples that are encountered frequently are small design programs on desktop micro$, FEM pre- and postprocessing on mini$, and FEM on supermini$.

Although the small computer is usually much slower than a mainframe performing the same function, it may give better turnaround times. The mainframe is a shared resource with users competing for a slot. It is typical that in-house mainframe$ are used for business as well as engineering processing. Since payroll and other important business functions often take precedence over engineering work, the structural engineer cannot always gain access to his fast mainframe on a timely basis.

In some situations, it does make sense to put business and structural software on a dedicated small computer. Small consulting firms often run project management and financial software along with design programs on a small machine[10, 11].

HIERARCHICAL PROCESSING

Hierarchical computing schemes are usually implemented by large organizations who have previously installed centralized computers. This allows the addition of local small computers while protecting existing capital investments and organizational structures. Small consulting firms may also use their own small computers in a hierarchical scheme with service bureau mainframes.

In hierarchical processing, structural software is placed on the computer which provides the best mix of cost-effectiveness and responsiveness. In general, the software with more interactive requirements should be placed on the small local computer, and more long-running, batch type software placed on larger machines. Small design programs, for example, can be run on a desktop micro, which can also be used as a terminal to access finite element programs on a larger machine.

DISTRIBUTED PROCESSING

Dedicated and hierarchical processing utilizing structural mechanics software on small computers is well established. Distributed processing, however, is new to the world of engineering computing. In this mode, physically separate computers are linked via communications lines and networking software that allows interaction at higher levels than simple file transfer. With distributed processing, large companies may access distributed engineering data bases through linked machines in order to manage complex evolving designs. The Integrated Program for Aerospace Vehicle Design (IPAD), sponsored by the U.S. National Aeronautics and Space Administration (NASA), is the forerunner of commercial systems which will use distributed processing in structural engineering[12]. In this mode of processing, nonengineering functions requiring networking, such as electronic mail and project control, can be integrated with engineering functions such as FEM superelement analysis and CAD/CAM.

In a distributed processing environment, the configuration and location of small computers is intimately associated with the desirable functional interaction between groups in the design process.

STRUCTURAL MECHANICS SOFTWARE

Structural mechanics software may be obtained from authors or distributors (see Appendix I), user groups, and software distribution agencies. The following agencies distribute structures software in the USA.

1. ASIAC - Aerospace Structures Information and Analysis Center, AFFDL/FBR, Wright Patterson Air Force Base, Dayton, OH 45433
2. CEPA - Society for Computer Application in Engineering, Planning and Architecture, Inc., 358 Hungerford Drive, Rockville, MD 20850
3. COSMIC - Computer Software Management and Information Center, 112 Barrow Hall, University of Georgia, Athens, GA 30602
4. NESC - National Energy Software Center, 9700 South Cass Avenue, Argonne, IL 60439
5. NISEE - National Information Service for Earthquake Engineering, 519 Davis Hall, University of California, Berkeley, CA 94720

At the present time, ASIAC, NESC, and NISEE distribute software only for large computers. COSMIC handles many structural mechanics programs, but only two FEM codes are now distributed for small computers. CEPA has a library of several hundred programs for IBM 1130's and at least 60 programs for modern small computers [13]. The American Consulting Engineers Council also publishes a catalog of developers and users of civil engineering software [10]. This catalog lists a large number of structural analysis and design software packages that operate on small computers, many of which are available from the developers.

The total number of programs for the analysis and design of structures is enormous. Large numbers of programs are available even for relatively specialized structures. Schelling and Neery, for example, have identified 222 different programs used by USA and Canadian highway agencies for bridge design [14]. Of these, however, 180 were internally developed programs having inadequate user and theoretical documentation for general use.

It is beyond the scope of this study to give an accounting of all structural mechanics software. Six representative software categories will be examined: (1) general purpose finite element analysis (FEM), (2) pre- and postprocessing for FEM, (3) special purpose FEM, (4) finite difference analysis, (5) piping analysis, and (6) miscellaneous specialized analysis and design programs.

Emphasis has been placed on the discussion of documented and supported programs which are actively maintained and enhanced. A few programs are included which maintain a respectable level of popularity without these desirable characteristics. Most of the programs listed are available commercially through the burgeoning structural software industry.

The tables of structural mechanics software which follow deal with the availability of programs on small computers. The numbers listed under distributor refer to the list of contacts in Appendix 1 where information regarding the capability of software may be obtained. References [1, 15, 16, 17] contain additional assessments of the capabilities of many of the programs listed.

A substantial number of programs which were found to be in various stages of conversion to small computers are not included in the tables.

GENERAL PURPOSE FINITE ELEMENT ANALYSIS

A program that is based on the finite element method may be considered "general purpose" when it exhibits a large range of analytical capabilities (i.e., statics, dynamics, buckling, heat transfer, etc.), a substantial element library, and a large problem-solving capacity. The world market for general purpose FEM software is dominated by approximately 20 popular programs. Almost all of the well-known FEM programs now operate on at least one small computer, as illustrated in Table 2.

All of the programs listed have been converted to run on supermini$ since the introduction of these machines in 1978. General purpose FEM programs run most comfortably on large supermini$ in the $250,000 to $350,000 price range. Downsized versions of these machines are available for as little as $36,000, but they are generally too slow to perform large-scale FEM analysis. These smaller machines are more suitable for solving small prototype problems and pre-and postprocessing.

Table 2 also indicates that a few general purpose FEM programs have been implemented on 16-bit word mini$ such as the HP-1000 and PDP-11. This does not appear to be a trend since elaborate program overlaying is

Table 2 General Purpose Finite Element Programs on Small Computers

PROGRAM	DISTRIBUTOR	DEC VAX	PRIME	PERKIN ELMER 32XX	DEC PDP-11	HP-1000	HARRIS 500/800	DG ECLIPSE	MODCOMP CLASSIC
ADINA	1	●							
ANSYS	2	●	●				●		
ARGUS	3	●							
ASAS	4	●	●						
ASKA	5	●	●						
BERSAFE/BERDYNE	6	●	●						
EISI/EAL	7	●	●						
COSMIC/NASTRAN	8	●							
MSC/NASTRAN	9	●							
PM/NASTRAN	10		●						
UAI/NASTRAN	11			●					
NISA	12	●	●			●			
MARC	10		●						
PAFEC	13	●	●	●					
SAP IV	*	●	●			●			
SAP 6, 7	14	●	●				●		
SESAM 69, 80	15	●							
SPAR	8	●	●						
GTSTRUDL	16	●							
SUPERB	17	●							
TPS-10	18	●	●	●	●	●		●	●

*Note: There are sèveral versions of the SAP IV program available. Distributors may be contacted through the computer manufacturer.

required, word accuracy is a problem, and these machines are too slow for solving reasonable sized problems. At the present time, no truly general purpose FEM programs have been implemented on micro$.

PRE- AND POSTPROCESSORS FOR GENERAL PURPOSE FEM PROGRAMS

Interactive graphics is used frequently in the development of data for FEM programs and the review of output from them. Most of the developers of FEM software listed in Table 2 supply interactive graphics pre- and postprocessing software for their own analysis programs. Most of these processors are separate pieces of software. A few are closely integrated with the analysis package which can also be run interactively. In most cases these pre- and postprocessors are available on the same computers as the parent analysis program.

In addition, there are many stand alone pre- and postprocessing programs which are designed to communicate with several finite element programs. Some major software in this category which runs on small computers is listed in Table 3.

The traditional host for stand alone pre- and postprocessing has been the mini. More recently they have also been moved to supermini$. A strong motivation for having these programs on larger machines is coresidence with the FEM analysis software. This eliminates the need for file transfer between computers before and after the analysis is performed. In some instances, where there are a large number of finite element problems being solved, the supermini replaces the mini as a dedicated computer for preprocessing.

Table 3 Pre- and Postprocessors for General Purpose Finite Element Analysis

PROGRAM ↓	DISTRIBUTOR	COMPUTER → DEC VAX	PRIME	DEC PDP-11	HARRIS 500	HP 1000/3000	DG ECLIPSE
DISPLAY/DIGIT	12	●	●	●		●	
FASTDRAW	19	●				●	
FEMALE	20			●			
FEMGEN	21	●	●	●			
GIFTS	22	●	●	●			●
MENTAT	10	●	●	●	●		
PATRAN	23	●					
SUPERTAB	17	●	●	●			

FEM PREPROCESSING FROM CAD/CAM SYSTEMS

There are several programs and turnkey hardware/software systems that perform automated drafting and/or tool path calculations. While these systems do not contain structural mechanics software per se, some do provide interfaces from their geometric data base to other structural programs, notably piping and finite element analysis. Links to finite element analysis have been defined by the CAD/CAM developer or there are joint relationships with suppliers of preprocessing software such as the programs shown in Table 3.

Integrating the CAD/CAM system with finite element analysis is extremely important to industries which design complex structures with difficult geometries (i.e., automotive, aerospace, shipbuilding, etc.). In these industries, the impact of finite element analysis on preliminary design has been minimal. Often a detailed analysis is only performed on the final design, and often after it has gone into production. Utilizing integrated CAD/CAM and FEM, engineering drawings are replaced by electronic information stored on a data base. This eliminates costly recreation of geometry, allowing sophisticated analyses of the latest designs earlier in the design process.

Table 4 lists popular CAD/CAM software and turnkey systems which can be used to generate structural geometry prior to finite element analysis.

Mini$ and supermini$ are used as local hosts for CAD/CAM graphic workstations. In the past, turnkey CAD/CAM system developers have used mini$ exclusively. Recently, several major vendors have announced that they are upgrading CAD/CAM hosts to supermini$. This will allow FEM to be performed in the CAD/CAM system environment.

Table 4 CAD/CAM Software and Turnkey Systems in a Small Computer Environment

SYSTEM/PROGRAM ↓	DISTRIBUTOR	COMPUTER → DEC VAX	PDP-11	CGP-100/200	DG ECLIPSE	IBM 43XX	PERKIN ELMER 32XX	PRIME	SEL
AD-2000	24	●				●	●	●	●
CADAM	25					●	●		
CADD	26		●			●			
DDM	27				●				
CADDS	28			●					
DOGS	13	●					●	●	
GS-2000	29	●			●				
IMAGE	30		●						
UNIGRAPHICS	31		●		●				

SPECIAL PURPOSE FINITE ELEMENT ANALYSIS

Special purpose FEM programs are defined here as having one or more of the following characteristics relative to the general purpose programs previously discussed:

1. limited analytical capability
2. small element library
3. small problem size capacity

It is beyond the scope of this study to perform a detailed investigation of special purpose FEM programs. One large segment of this category, spaceframe analysis, is populated by hundreds of little-known programs. Some of this software is included below in the discussion of libraries of small design programs.

Spaceframe programs provide a good example of the motivation for special purpose FEM on small computers. They are used primarily in civil engineering applications where it is traditional to use simplified structural models and to isolate specific components to be evaluated against design codes (e.g., AISC, API, etc.). This approach leads to large numbers of small finite element models which can be successfully and efficiently run on small computers. Rammant describes the developer's motivation relative to special purpose FEM software [18] as:

1. filling the gap between pocket calculators and traditional computers
2. democratizing FEM to a broader public
3. facilitating the application of FEM to preliminary design

A few representative special purpose FEM programs are listed in Table 5. Some of those programs utilize new ways of setting up or solving the finite element matrix equations. Most of them are new programs that are designed for operation on small interactive computers. This represents a departure from past FEM developments conceived in batch mainframe environments [19].

Table 5 Special Purpose Finite Element Analysis on Small Computers

PROGRAM ↓	DISTRIBUTOR	COMPUTER → DEC VAX	PRIME	DEC PDP-11	INTERDATA 8/32	DG NOVA ECLIPSE	HP 3000	WANG 2200	HP 9845	DG MICRO NOVA	RADIO SHACK TSR-80	CROMEM CO	TEKTRONIX 4051
AXISHELL	32								●	●			
COMET-PR1	33	●											
ESA	34							●					
FEMBAS	35								●				●
FES DEC	36							●	●				
F.E. TAPE/FESPAC	37	●		●									
HERCULE	38	●	●										
MISES 3	32		●		●	●	●						
SAP-80	39	●									●	●	
TWODEPEP	40	●											

FINITE DIFFERENCE ANALYSIS

Finite difference analysis was developed prior to the invention of the digital computer to solve differential equations in engineering mechanics. Many of the problems previously solved by finite differences are now solved using finite element methods. There are still many modern finite difference programs based on energy formulations, however. Finite difference methods are used heavily in the analysis of shells and in heat transfer and flow problems. They dominate in the solution of problems involving shock wave propagation.

The number of commercially available, supported, finite difference programs is quite small. In the U.S.A., most finite difference software is developed by government laboratories and is available to qualified users through dissemination organizations such as ASIAC, COSMIC, and NESC. A review of the finite difference programs distributed by these organizations indicates that none of them are supplied on small computers. This is probably due to a number of factors including:

1. lack of competition in federally sponsored and distributed software
2. the large computer hardware at government laboratories
3. the requirement for large mainframes or supercomputers to run two- and three-dimensional shock wave problems.

The only finite different programs which were found to be operating on small computers, at the time of this writing, were the BOSOR 4 and BOSOR 5 shell codes (see Appendix I, entry 14 for distribution information).

PIPING ANALYSIS

Several general purpose FEM programs in Table 2 contain elements which may be used to analyze piping systems. These programs are often used to include effects that are not treated in most special purpose piping software (i.e., plasticity, transient dynamics, compression-only supports, local stress concentrations, etc.). The great majority of piping analysis, however, is performed with special piping programs.

Preprocessor programs are often used in piping design to determine the loads and pressure distributions on the piping system. The piping analysis program then calculates stresses according to specific design codes (e.g., ASME, ANSI, etc.). Many of the piping analysis programs now use the finite element method to determine pipe deformations, but they are more efficient and user friendly for pipe problems than the general purpose FEM software.

The geometry of piping systems is often obtained using CAD/drafting software and the same relationship exists between CAD and the analysis programs as described in the discussion of FEM preprocessing. In fact, because of the simplified topology in piping systems and the tremendous need to manage the design and construction of facilities containing miles of piping, CAD is much more developed for piping than for general structures.

Table 6 lists some piping analysis programs and associated software for developing input loads that run on small computers. Most of the analysis software is now operational on supermini$. Some additional pressure distribution software that runs on mini$ and micro$ is contained in the design libraries discussed below.

Table 6 Piping Analysis Software on Small Computers

PROGRAM	DISTRIBUTOR	DEC VAX	PRIME	WANG 2200
ADINAP	41	●	●	
ADLPIPE/DIS	41	●	●	
NUPIPE	42		●	
PIPANAL	43	●	●	
PIPERUP	42		●	
PIPLIN	43	●	●	
PIPELINE	44	●		
PRTHRUST	42		●	
TRIFLEX	45		●	
TRHEAT	42		●	
WATERNET	46			●
WAVENET/ FLOWNET	47	●	●	

OTHER SPECIALIZED DESIGN AND ANALYSIS SOFTWARE

There are hundreds of computer programs which perform analysis and/or design of specialized structures or components of structures [1, 10, 13, 14]. Most of these programs contain a small amount of coding and do not require extensive computation, high-precision arithmetic, or large amounts of storage. Many programs of this class are implemented on mini$ and micro$. Reference [11] is a good source of information about how these programs are used in civil engineering, particularly on desktop micro$.

It is beyond the scope of this study to attempt a detailed accounting of these programs. Instead, a review of some popular collections or libraries of small design programs available from one source is provided. Specialized design libraries are usually oriented toward either civil or mechanical design although they often contain programs that can be used in both functions. The mechanical libraries typically contain programs for rotating machinery, gear trains, bearings, pressure vessels, heat exchangers, etc. Civil engineering libraries are normally oriented toward buildings, bridges, roadways, surveying, hydrology, and project control.

Table 7 lists some specialized design libraries that are implemented on small computers. There is some overlap with previous categories of software discussed. Some of the programs contained in these libraries are based on finite element solution procedures and could have been discussed under special purpose FEM. Programs which perform a Hardy-Cross network analysis of piping to determine pressure/velocity distributions could also have been discussed under piping analysis.

Table 7 illustrates that specialized design programs are implemented on many different small computers and, unlike other categories of structural engineering software, there are a substantial number installed on micro$.

Table 7 Specialized Design Libraries on Small Computers

LIBRARY	DISTRIBUTOR	SMALL COMPUTERS															SOFTWARE CAPABILITY									
		DEC VAX	PRIME	DEC PDP-11	WANG 2200	HP 1000	HP 9845/85	PERKIN ELMER	HARRIS 500	NORTH STAR	MODCOMP CLASSIC	GENERAL AUTOMATION	DG NOVA, ECLIPSE	DG MICRONOVA	OLIVETTI	HEATHKIT	TRUSSES/FRAMES	PLATES	CYLINDERS/SPHERES	BEARING/SHAFTS ROTATING MACHINERY	PRESSURE VESSELS / FLANGES	HEAT EXCHANGERS	SURVEYING COORDINATE GEOMETRY	CIVIL DESIGN	PROJECT/COST CONTROL	PIPE NETWORKS FLOW ANALYSIS
	46		●																		●			●		
MDL	17	●		●													●			●						
	48					●																●				
	49		●	●													●	●	●	●						
GENESYS	50		●	●				●									●		●					●	●	
	51				●		●										●	●					●	●	●	●
AUTO/STEEL DESIGN	52	●		●													●							●		
CIVIL ENGINEERING	53			●													●						●	●	●	●
	54			●	●												●	●						●		
	55						●										●							●	●	
	56									●	●	●					●							●	●	●
PROFESSIONAL ENGINEERING	57												●	●			●						●	●	●	
	58									●							●							●	●	
	59				●												●							●		
	60														●		●						●	●	●	
	61															●	●				●					
	62									●							●									
	63	●	●																	●						

AUXILIARY SOFTWARE

In order to run engineering software on any computer, some auxiliary software is required. Minimally, the operating system must support functions required by the engineering application. Also, since most engineering applications are written in a high-level language, compilers are required to convert the program into a language that can be recognized by the computer. In addition, other auxiliary software may be necessary to successfully integrate the engineering software into the design process (e.g., graphic terminal drivers, interactive editors, telecommunications software, etc.).

Most of the auxiliary software needed to execute structural mechanics software in a small computer environment will not be discussed further here. It should be noted, however, that this software defines the characteristics of the man-machine interface for a particular system. In the more traditional engineering software environment (i.e., in-house mainframes or service bureaus) the user interface is defined and managed by experts assigned to the centralized computer facility. In small computers, the burden of defining the interface lies with the user unless it has been previously accomplished by a software vendor or turnkey system supplier.

Although auxiliary software has become available at an amazing pace for new computers, many of them, particularly in the micro$ range, do not have adequate high-level language compilers. Table 8 lists compilers that are available for some small computers. This table does not, however, indicate the potential problems associated with the available compilers. Bennett and Goodno [20] have encountered compiler inadequacies on micro$ that would force extensive modifications to existing FORTRAN software. Prospective users should be careful of engineering programs that are distributed in source code. Many software distributors claim their programs are written in "standard" or "machine independent" higher-level languages. This does not ensure that the software will successfully compile on a new computer without modification.

Table 8 Higher-Level Languages on Small Computers

LANGUAGE ↓ / COMPUTER →	DEC VAX	PRIME	PERKIN ELMER 32XX	SEL	HARRIS 500/800	DG ECLIPSE	DG NOVA	PDP-11	HP-1000	HP-45B/85	WANG VS	WANG VP	TRS-80
FORTRAN	•	•	•	•	•	•	•	•	•				•
BASIC	•	•	•	•	•	•	•	•	•	•	•	•	•
PASCAL	•		•	•	•	•	•		•				
PL 1	•	•				•							
APL					•		•						
RPG	•	•	•		•	•					•		

SUMMARY AND FUTURE EXPECTATIONS

Figure 2 summarizes the computer availability of structural mechanics software. Although a few mini versions have been produced, general purpose FEM programs run predominantly on supercomputer$, mainframe$, and supermini$. In the future, these programs will move onto machines in the mini$ price range. While it is possible to run general purpose FEM programs now on small 32-bit machines (i.e., DEC VAX 11/750, PRIME 250, and PERKIN ELMER 3220), these computers are too slow to effectively handle medium to large-scale problems. At the present time, the speeds of these machines recommend them more for pre- and postprocessing than analysis. The requirement for very large problem solutions will keep general purpose FEM software on large computers in the near future.

Pre- and postprocessors for finite element analysis currently operate on mainframe$, supermini$ and mini$. Mini$ such as the DEC PDP-11 are the most popular delivery vehicle for pre- and postprocessing software to date. These programs can be expected to shift to 4th-generation micro$ as soon as sufficient auxiliary software is available for these machines. Installations on mainframes will diminish as service bureaus move to distributed mini$ and graphic workstations.

The CAD software, which is used to create the geometric description of a structure, exists primarily on mainframe$ and mini$ with a few recent installations also being made on supermini$.

Strong evidence suggests that the turnkey CAD/CAM vendors will move to supermini$ for optional hosts shortly, while scientific service bureaus will distribute CAD software on supermini$ and mini$. Host supermini$ will allow the turnkey vendors to offer systems that will perform analysis and pre- and postprocessing as well as traditional CAD/CAM functions. Distributed smaller computers will allow the service bureau to provide low-cost, high-speed graphics for CAD and pre- and postprocessing to front end their mainframe networks. Most of the CAD/CAM processing in the 1980s will take place on small computers, although central data bases and large superelement FEM projects will remain in the mainframe environment for some time.

Special purpose FEM programs and other specialized design software reside currently on machines all the way from large mainframe$ to micro$. As small machines proliferate it will make very little sense to retain this software on large computers. Mini$ and micro$ will be the most popular delivery vehicles in the future, with the selection being based on required resources.

Finite difference programs are, almost exclusively, run on large computers today. Many of these programs, particularly the hydrodynamic shock codes, will continue to demand the maximum performance available. Some commercially available programs which do not require large computers, such as the heat transfer codes, will migrate to supermini$ in the near future.

Piping analysis programs have historically been implemented on mainframe$. Recently, there have been many conversions of these programs to supermini$. Because of the relatively small wave fronts involved in piping matrices, it should be expected that these programs will run comfortably on 32-bit mini$ such as the DEC VAX 11/750, PRIME 250, and Perkin Elmer 3220.

In a short period of time, small computers have made a significant impact in structural engineering. The implementation of engineering software on small machines has been so rapid that it is appropriate to describe it as a revolution. Intelligence regarding the development of new computers and workstation devices would suggest an increasing acceleration of this trend in the future[21, 22].

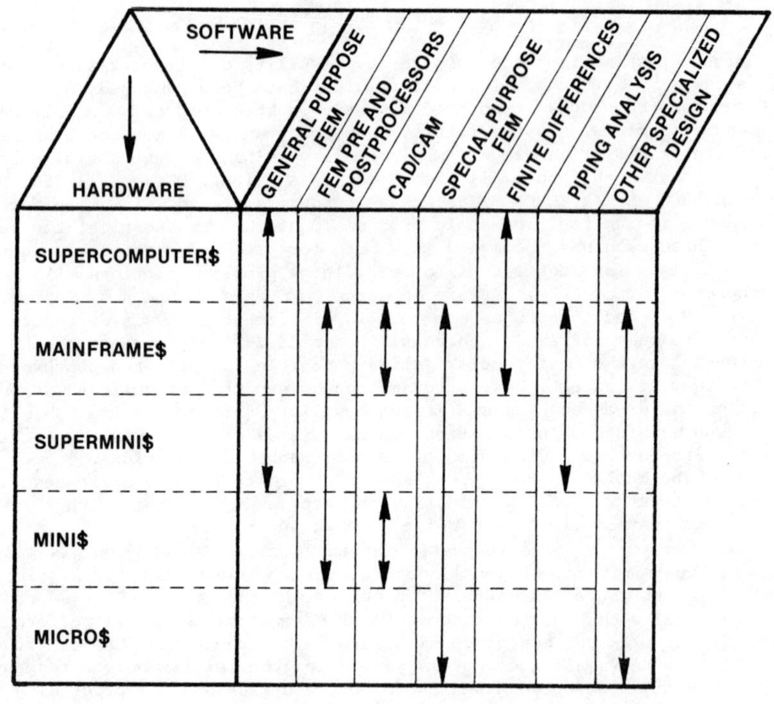

Fig. 2 Predominant computer environments of structural mechanics software

The small-computer revolution in engineering is a subset of an immense revolution in development of computers and related technologies. The miniaturization and concomitant reduction in cost of purchase and operation of computers is proceeding at a steady pace with no indications of slackening in the near future[4]. As in any revolution, the standards by which things are measured are short lived. The cost-based classification scheme proposed herein will only have meaning for a few years as prices of computers continue to plummet. The concept of large versus small computer itself is doomed to rapid extinction since all computers will ultimately be "small." Astounding predictions of the dividends from very large scale integration (VLSI) indicate that processors, equivalent to today's supercomputer$,will appear on one chip by 1985[21].

Acceptance of distributed small computers by engineers will be rapidly accelerated by the convergence of several technologies in the 1980s. Engineers will be increasingly exposed to personal computers and the computerized "office-of-the-future." Some futurists are seriously suggesting that engineers and other information workers will soon begin to telecompute via computers from their homes as many programmers are already doing[23].

By 1985, the office-of-the-future software is expected to appear along with structural mechanics software in the integrated engineering workstation (IEW) [22]. The IEW will allow the engineer to access both types of software from a nearby station and eventually from his own work area. Optional functions will include electronic mail, word processing, voice recognition input, color graphics, hard copy, and communications to more powerful computers. Software installed on the workstation computer will allow the engineer/designer to perform computer-aided drafting, FEM pre- and postprocessing, and execution of specialized analysis and design programs locally.

REFERENCES

1 Pilkey, W., Saczalski, I., and Schaeffer, H., ed. Structural Mechanics Computer Programs - Surveys, Assessments, and Availability, University Press of Virginia, Charlottesville, 1974.

2 Conaway, J., "Structural Engineering Software on Small Computers," ASME Paper No. 80-C2/Aero-7, 1980.

3 McCracken, D., A Guide to FORTRAN IV Programming, John Wiley, New York, 1965.

4 Conaway, J., "The Economics of Structural Analysis on Superminis," ASCE, Proceedings of the Seventh Conference on Electronic Computation, 1979, pp. 374-385.

5 Storaasli, O., "Using SPAR Structural Analysis on a Minicomputer," ASCE, Proceedings of the Seventh Conference on Electronic Computation, 1979, pp. 363-373.

6 Swanson, J., "Present Trends in Computerized Structural Analysis," Journal of Computers and Structures, Vol. 10, 1979.

7 Brentano, L., "Computers in a Civil Engineering Office," ASCE, Proceedings of Computing in Civil Engineering, June 1978, pp. 37-52.

8 Lipetz, M., "Sources of Computers for Small Engineering Firms," ASCE, Proceedings of Second Conference on Computing in Civil Engineering, June 1980, pp. 592-603.

9 Wilson, E., "Role of Small Computers in Structural Engineering," ASCE, Proceedings of the Seventh Conference on Electronic Computation, August 1979, pp. 331-339.

10 ACEC Computer User's Group Software and Hardware Catalog, American Consulting Engineers Council, Washington, D.C., USA.

11 Johnson, K., ed., Engineering Computer Application Newsletter (ECAN), Engineering Computer Applications, Inc., Englewood, CO, USA, Nov. 1979-Sept. 1980.

12 Fulton, R., "IPAD Project Overview," Proceedings of National Symposium on IPAD - NASA Conference Publication 2143, Denver, Sept., 1980, pp. 1-20.

13 CEPA Cut-off Abstracts, Society for Computer Applications in Engineering, Planning, and Architecture, 1980.

14 Schelling, D., and Neary, D., "Current Bridge Design Oriented Computer Practices," ASCE, Proceedings of the Seventh Conference on Electronic Computation, 1979, pp. 813-828.

15 Fredriksson, B., and Mackerle, J., "Structural Mechanics Finite Element Computer Programs - Surveys and Availability," LITH-IKP-R-054, Linkoping Institute of Technology, Linkoping, Sweden, Sept. 1975.

16 Dunder, V., and Belonogoff, G. "Comparing Finite Element Programs in Engineering," The MacNeal Schwendler Corporation, Proceedings of Conference on Finite Element Methods and Technology, Pasadena, March 1980.

17 Noor, A., "Survey of Computer Programs for Solution of Nonlinear Structural and Solid Mechanics Problems," Journal of Computers and Structures, Vol. 13, 1981, pp. 426-465.

18 Rammant, J., "Micro-Computer Finite Element Analysis in Practice," S. A. Computas, Proceedings of International Conference on Application of the Finite Element Method, Oslo, May 1979.

19 Wilson, E., "SAP-80 Structural Analysis Programs for Small or Large Computers," presented at CEPA 1980 Fall Conference, Newport Beach, Oct., 1980.

20 Bennett, C., and Goodno, B., "Structural Analysis on Microcomputers," Proceedings of the Second Conference on Computing in Civil Engineering, ASCE, Baltimore, June 1980, pp. 488-496.

21 Brentano, L., "Hardware Configurations and the Engineer," presented at Century II Aerospace Conference, ASME, San Francisco, Aug. 1980.

22 "Integrated Workstations 1978-1985," Quantum Sciences Corporation, New York, 1978.

23 Toffler, A., The Third Wave, William Morrow and Co., Inc., New York, 1980.

APPENDIX I

DISTRIBUTORS OF STRUCTURAL MECHANICS SOFTWARE ON SMALL COMPUTERS

The following contact information for software distributors is listed in the order that the programs are discussed above. The number assigned to each contact corresponds to the numbers listed under "distributor" in the tabular listings of program availability. In cases where the North American distributor is different than the main distributor, both are listed.

1. Professor K. J. Bathe
Massachusetts Institute of Technology
Room 3-365
Cambridge, MA 02139
USA
Tel: (617) 253-6645

2. Dr. John A. Swanson
Swanson Analysis Systems, Inc.
Box 65
Houston, PA 15342
USA
Tel: (412) 746-3304
TWX: 510-690-8655

3. Dr. Derek Yates
Merlin Technologies, Inc.
977 Town and Country Village
San Jose, CA 95128
USA
Tel: (408) 247-4003

4. Dr. R. K. Henrywood
Atkins Research and Development
Woodcote Grove, Ashley Road
Epsom, Surrey, U.K.
Tel: 03727-26140
TELEX: 23497

(or, in North America)

Dr. Anthony Firmin
H. G. Engineering, LTD.
260 Lesmill Road
Don Mills
Ontario, M3B2T5
Canada
Tel: (416) 447-5535
TELEX: 06-966807

5. IKOSS GmbH
Vaihinger Str. 49
D-7000 Stuttgart 80
West Germany
Tel: (0711) 714006
TELEX/TWX: 7255 490 IKOS

6. Mr. Graham Marshall
C.E.G.B.
Berkeley Nuclear Laboratories
Gloucestershire, England
Tel: Dursley 810451 Ext. 221
TELEX: 43227

7. Dr. Donald Whetstone
Engineering Information Systems
5120 Campbell Ave., Suite 240
San Jose, CA 95130
USA
Tel: (408) 379-0732

8. Mr. Steve Horton
COSMIC
112 Barrow Hall
University of Georgia
Athens, GA 30602
USA
Tel: (404) 542-3265

9. Dr. Joseph Gloudeman
The MacNeal-Schwendler Corporation
7442 North Figueroa Street
Los Angeles, CA 90041
USA
Tel: (213) 254-3456
TWX: 910-321-2492

10. Mr. H. Dale Seamons
Marc Analysis Research Corp.
260 Sheridan, Suite 200
Palo Alto, CA 94036
USA
Tel: (415) 326-7511
TWX: 910-373-2013

11. Dr. Anthony P. Capelli
Universal Analytics, Inc.
7740 W. Manchester Bldg.
Playa del Rey, CA 90291
USA
Tel: (213) 822-4422

12. Dr. Kant S. Kothwala
Engineering Mechanics Res. Corp.
P.O. Box 696
Troy, MI 48099
USA
Tel: (313) 968-1606

13. Mr. Alan Austin
PAFEC, Ltd.
Strelley Hall
Main Street, Strelley
Nottingham, NG8 6PE
England
Tel: 0602-292291

(or, in North America)

Mr. J. Ed Akin
PAFEC Engineering Consultants,Inc.
601 Concord Street
Knoxville, TN 37919
USA
Tel: (615) 524-7447

14. Ms. Linda Walbert
SAP Users Group
Denney Research Bldg., USC
University Park
Los Angeles, CA 90007
USA
Tel: (213) 743-5508

15. Mr. Andreas Mourud
A. S. Computas
Veritasveien 1
P.O. Box 310
N-1322 Hovik, Norway
Tel: OSLO 129292
TWX/TELEX: 16192

16. Dr. Leroy Z. Emkin
GTICES Systems Laboratory
School of Civil Engineering
Georgia Institute of Technology
Atlanta, GA 30332
USA
Tel: (404) 894-2260
TWX/TELEX: 542507 GTRI OCA ATL

17. Structural Dynamics Research Corporation
2000 Eastman Drive
Milford, OH 45150
Tel: (513) 576-2400

18. Herr Groth
T-Programm GMBH
Gustav-Werner-Str. 3
D-7410 Reutlingen
West Germany
Tel: (0 71 21) 23 43 01
TWX/TELEX: 07 29 891

(or, in North America)

Mr. Manny Velivasakis, P.E.
Lev Zetlin Associates
95 Madison Avenue
New York, NY 10016
Tel: (212) 889-3130
TWX/TELEX: 237785

19. Mr. Ted F. McFadden
MCAUTO
Dept. K161/270A
P.O. Box 516
St. Louis, MO 63166
USA
Tel: (314) 233-0431

20. Mr. P. Jeanes
SIA Ltd.
23 Lower Belgrave Street
London, SW 1
England
Tel: 01-730-4544 X234
TWX/TELEX: 916635

21. Mr. Steven Jordan
Jordan, Apostal, Ritter Assoc, Inc.
Administration Bldg. 7
Davisville, RI 02854
USA
Tel: (401) 294-4589

22. Dr. Hussein A. Kamel
Interactive Graphics Engrg. Lab
University of Arizona
College of Engineering
AME Bldg. 16, Room 210A
Tucson, AZ 85721
USA
Tel: (602) 626-1650

23. Mr. Lou Crain
PDA Engineering
1740 Garry Ave., Suite 201
Santa Ana, CA 92705
USA
Tel: (714) 556-2800

24. Mr. Patrick Hanratty
Manufacturing & Consulting Services
3195A Airport Loop Drive
Costa Mesa, CA 92626
USA
Tel: (714) 540-3921

25. Mr. Dick Bennet
Lockheed, Burbank
Building 67, Plant A-1
Department 8034
Burbank, CA 91501
USA
Tel: (213) 847-2304

26. Mgr., CAD/CAM Planning and Marketing
MCAUTO
Dept. K507
P.O. Box 516
St. Louis, MO 63166
USA
Tel: (314) 232-6265

27. Dr. David J. Albert
CALMA Company
5155 Oldsides
Santa Clara, CA 95050
USA
Tel: (408) 727-0121

28. Computervision Corp.
201 Burlington Road
Bedford, MA 01730
USA
(contact local sales office)

29. Mr. Terry Bennett
Auto-Trol Technology Corp.
12500 N. Washington Street
Denver, CO 80233
USA
Tel: (303) 452-4919

30. Mr. David Vitiello
Applicon, Inc.
32 Second Avenue
Burlington, MA 01803
USA
Tel: (617) 272-7070
TWX/TELEX 94-9345

31. Mgr., CAD/CAM Planning and Marketing
MCAUTO Dept. K507
P.O. Box 516
St. Louis, MO 63166
USA
Tel: (314)232-6265

32. Dr. Heinz Pircher
Technishe Datenverarbeitung
A-8010, Graz
Luthergasse 4, Austria

33. Dr. B. A. Szabo
Washington University Technology Associates
8049 Litsinger Road
St. Louis, MO 63144
USA
Tel: (314) 889-6378

Dr. J. P. Rammant
SCIA
Attenrodestraat 6
3385 Meensel-Kiezegem
Belgium
Tel: 016/63 20 44

(or in USA)

Computational Mechanics
P.O. Box 4174
Irvine, CA 92716

35. Advanced Engineering Consultants AB
Box 3044
S-580 03 Linkoping,
Sweden

(or, in North America)

Dr. Anthony Firmin
HG Engineering, Ltd.
260 Lesmill Road
Don Mills, Ontario, M3B2T5
Canada
Tel: (416) 447-5535
TELEX: 06-966807

36. Engineering Computer Services,Ltd.
Piccadilly, Tamworth, Staffs
B78 2ER, England

(or, in North America, see last entry)

37. Mr. Trevor J. Thickett
Computational Mechanics
125 High Street
Southhampton, Hampshire
SO1 0AA, England
Tel: (0703) 21397

38. Monsieur M. Maury
SOCOTEC
"Les Quadrants"
3 Avenue du Centre
78182 St Quentin en Yuelines
Cedex, France
Tel: 043 99 13

39. Dr. Edward L. Wilson
1050 Leneve Place
El Cerrito, CA 94530
USA
Tel: (415) 524-4056

40. Mr. Thomas J. Benner
IMSL, Inc.
6th Floor NBC Building
7500 Bellaire Blvd.
Houston, TX 77036
USA
Tel: (713) 772-1927 IMSL INC HOU
TWX/TELEX: 79-1923

41. Mr. I. W. Dingwell
A D Little, Inc.
20 Acorn Park
Cambridge, MA 02140
USA
Tel: (617) 864-5770
TWX/TELEX: 921436

42. Mr. Tom Vinson
Quadrex Corporation
1700 Dell Avenue
Campbell, CA 95008
USA
Tel: (408) 866-4510
TWX: 910-590-2438
TELEX: 35-2031

43. Dr. Row
Structural Software Development
1930 Shattuck Avenue
Berkeley, CA 94704
Tel: (415) 849-3458

44. Mr. W. J. Reilley
McAuto
Dept. K246
P.O. Box 516
St. Louis, MO 63166
Tel: (314) 232-6526

45. AAA Technology and Specialties Co., Inc.
P.O. Box 37189
Houston, TX 77036
USA
Tel: (713) 789-6200
TWX; 910-881-2425

46. Fitech, Ltd.
Mississippi State University
Drawer KJ
Mississippi State, MS 39762
USA
Tel: (601) 325-3828

47. Mr. Ronald T. Bradshaw
85 Central Street
Waltham, MA 02154
USA
Tel: (617) 894-4090

48. Gulley Computer Associates
2300 E. 14th
Tulsa, OK 74104
USA
Tel: (918) 932-3628

49. Dr. Walter Pilkey
Structural Members Users Group, Ltd.
P.O. Box 3958
University Station
Charlottesville, VA 22903
USA
Tel: (804) 296-4906

50. Mr. T. ON. Maxwell
Genesys Limited
Lisle Street
Loughborough, LE11OAY
England
Tel: 0509 39185/8
TELEX: 341747

51. Mr. Gary Koser
ECOM Associates
5678 W. Brown Deer
Milwaukee, WI 53223
USA
Tel: (414) 354-0243

52. Mr. Fred C. Graves
Synercom Technology
P.O. Box 27
Sugarland, TX 77478
USA
Tel: (713) 491-5000
TELEX: 775619

53. CONCAP Computing Systems
7700 Edgewater Dr., Suite 700
Oakland, CA 94621
USA
Tel: (415) 635-5750

54. Mr. John Evans
Structural Programming, Inc.
83 Boston Post Road
Sudbury, MA 01776
USA
Tel: (617) 443-5366

55. Formerly, Hewlett Packard
now, see entry 51

56. Mr. Charles E. Shapler
Shapler Associates
1959 Chalice Way
Toledo, OH 43613
USA
Tel: (419) 475-5114

57. Mr. Douglas F. Burnside
Sys. Comp. Corporation
2042 Broadway
Santa Monica, CA 90404
USA
Tel: (213) 829-9707

58. Mr. Thomas R. Laatsch, PE
John E. Somerville Associates
2020 Riverside Drive
Green Bay, WI 54301
USA
Tel: (414) 437-8136

59. Mr. Henry Acosta
Holquin and Associates, Inc.
5822 Cromo Drive
P.O. Box 12990
El Paso, TX 79912
USA
Tel: (915) 581-1171
TELEX: 749-422

60. Mr. R. W. Muir, PE
Zeiler-Pennock, Inc.
2727 Bryant Street
Denver, CO 80211
USA
Tel: (303) 455-3322

61. Mr. Douglas B. Nickerson
Stress Analysis Associates
4529 Angeles Coast Highway,
Suite 104
La Canada, CA 91011
USA
Tel: (213) 684-2478

62. Mr. Joseph Inatome
Computer Mart
560 West 14 Mile Road
Clawson, MI 48017
USA
Tel: (313) 542-4862

63. Mr. William Jansen
Northern Research and Engineering
Corp.
39 Olympia Avenue
Woburn, MA 01801
USA
Tel: (617) 935-9050

PAFEC Compared with Other Major Finite Element Codes

J. E. Akin

B. R. Dewey

University of Tennessee

INTRODUCTION

There are many commercially available finite element codes. Some that were developed outside the USA are now becoming popular in this country. Among these are the free format Programs for Automatic Finite Element Calculations (PAFEC) and the supporting PAFEC Interactive Graphics System (PIGS), which were designed for easy use and for efficiency on the superminis such as the VAX and Prime machines. However, they have also been implemented on all major machines including the CRAY.

Since PAFEC is not well known in the USA we will summarize its features and compare it with U.S. codes of similar capability. The tabular comparisons will primarily be made with ANSYS, MARC, NASTRAN, NISA, and SUPERB. These can generally be placed in two groups: those designed for easy use (PAFEC, NISA,and SUPERB) and those with extra computational power for advanced or nonlinear applications. The latter group also tends to be designed for batch use on large mainframe computers. There is clearly a need for both approaches.

Most of the codes to be considered have similar computational capabilities. Free format input and a data base management systems are not widespread, however. Most codes have rigid formats, while a minority offer partial free format. That is, they still require blank cards to terminate data and do not allow columns of data to be omitted and thus to assume their default values. PAFEC and NISA are two examples of codes that have these useful default features.

The element library often indicates the special features of a code. ANSYS and MARK tend to offer a wider range of nonlinear elements than the other programs. NISA offers more elements for filament-wound vessels. Most codes include the linear and quadratic elements, but PAFEC also includes the cubic families. The outstanding semi-loof beam and shell family of elements are available only in NISA and PAFEC. All of the programs tend to add new elements as demand requires.

Before presenting the specific comparison tables the features of the PAFEC system will be outlined.

Features of PAFEC

The specific free format data modules available in PAFEC are named in Table 1. With these PAFEC offers the following analysis options:

- General 1-D, 2-D, and 3-D models
- Elastic deflection and stress analysis
- Steady state and transient heat transfer
- Modes and frequencies calculation
- Direct dynamic time integration
- Frequency response analysis, FFT
- Creep analysis
- Substructures
- Hydrodynamic lubrication
- Plastic analysis
- Large deflection analysis
- Reaction calculations

The PAFEC element library contains over 80 elements including:

- Springs, masses, truss elements
- Beams with shear, offset, curvature
- Linear to cubic isoparametric triangles and quadrilaterals for 2-D and axisymmetric options
- Curved shells of revolution
- Linear to cubic isoparametric wedges and hexahedrons for 3-D options
- Quadrilateral and triangular thin and thick plates and facet shells
- Curved semi-loof shells and beams
- Anisotropic, multilayered construction with general material axes
- Convection and conduction elements
- Crack-tip elements
- Gaps and friction elements

The element material properties can be linear, anisotropic, and temperature dependent. Laminated and orthotropic materials can be defined. Creep and plasticity models are available. User-selected and default load increments are included for nonlinear applications.

PAFEC offers extensive mesh generation and data supplementation options. Eight default coordinate systems are available as well as user-defined axes. The isoparametric generation of meshes for 2-D elements, surfaces, and 3-D solids is included in the use of PAFBLOCKS. There are transitions for mesh refinement and user-defined spacing ratios. Several mesh plotting options are included in PAFEC.

The load conditions in PAFEC include:

- Nodal loads, thermal loads
- Element pressure loads
- Time and frequency dependent forces
- Centrifugal and gravity loads
- Nonaxisymmetric loads
- Linear loading combinations

The boundary and support conditions are:

- o Fixed and simple supports
- o Prescribed displacements
- o Sliding boundaries, coupled nodes
- o Generalized constraint equations
- o Local displacement and load directions
- o Time-dependent temperature or heat flux conditions
- o Time-dependent displacements, velocities and accelerations

PAFEC offers extensive warning and error messages in the data validation and geometry checks. Some stop conditions can be overridden by the user. An element frontal solution is usually employed. Both automatic and manual element renumbering are available. Banded solutions can be selected. Automatic and manual masters for dynamic solutions are available.

The PAFEC passive presolution graphics capabilities include

- o input mesh
- o mesh boundary
- o node points
- o restraints
- o property number
- o group numbers
- o exploded mesh
- o axis sets
- o node/element numbers
- o dof arrows
- o frontal position
- o dynamic masters

The passive output plots for static problems include

- o deformed shape
- o displacement components
- o stress vectors
- o failure codes
- o contours of stresses and temperature
- o selected path graphs of displacements, rotations, temperatures, and stresses.

The transient and dynamic output plots include

- o temperature contours at selected times
- o force vs. time or frequency
- o displacement vs. time or frequency
- o velocity vs. time or frequency
- o acceleration vs. time or frequency
- o selection of linear or logarithmic axes

Most of the passive plots allow user-selected windows for more detail.

PIGS- The PAFEC Interactive Graphic System

PIGS is used to display interactively or to modify the PAFEC data base. It accepts cursor and keyboard input. PIGS will add and delete nodes and elements; rotate, window, and zoom in on the mesh; display and change topology; plot deformed shape; list and change nodal coordinates; update PAFEC data base, etc.

User Benefits

PAFEC is a user-oriented, cost-effective, and practical tool for structural, mechanical, and thermal analysis. Particular benefits are:

- o CONTROL module for selective user control and restarts
- o Free format input using short engineering terms and comments
- o Powerful 2-D and 3-D mesh generation
- o Extensive passive graphics output from pre- and postsolution
- o PIGS, interactive graphics available
- o Lubrication analysis package available
- o Comprehensive element library
- o Composite materials and laminates
- o Generalized constraint equations
- o Versatile dynamics capabilities
- o Geometric and material nonlinearities
- o Ability for user to insert own FORTRAN routines
- o Widely used, extensively tested program
- o Modular structure
- o Data base management system

There is an independent users group that supports the more than 150 sites worldwide. They meet yearly to recommend enhancements and changes in PAFEC. The programs are well documented and tested. The available documentation includes Users' and Technical Manuals (Refs. [1] to [8]).

PAFEC is available worldwide through Control Data's Cybernet Services systems. For documentation, training courses, and support in the use of PAFEC and PIGS, contact:

PAFEC Engineering Consultants, Inc.
601 Concord Street
Knoxville, TN 37919 USA
(615) 524-7447

PAFEC Ltd.
Strelley Hall, Strelley
Nottingham NG8 6PE
ENGLAND
0602-292291
(USA direct dial 011-44-602-292291).

CODE COMPARISONS

For simplicity the comparisons of these programs will be made by way of general features summarized in tables. The information is obtained from various sources such as Refs. [9] to [12]. Hopefully the tables are complete but their accuracy is unascertained. Tables 2 and 3 outline the general analysis capabilities and available element families, respectively

When conducting an analysis, data preparation and ease of use are important to the analyst. Table 4 summarizes the common mesh generation features of the above codes. Of course, the graphical representation of the input and generated data are useful. Typical batch or passive graphics options that are available to assist in report preparations are also given in Tables 5 and 6.

The major common areas of finite element analysis [13] are linear static analysis, thermal analysis, linear dynamic and harmonic analysis, and nonlinear procedures. Tables 7 through 10 compare these major areas, respectively. To support these analysis areas some programs also offer special user-supplied control features and/or interactive computing options. For example, PAFEC allows for more than 55 user control statements, such as SKIP.AUTOMATIC.FRONT, and REDUCTION.RESTART. Others are added at each local site.

As mentioned earlier, PIGS allows the data to be viewed or changed interactively. It also includes a dignitizing option. The level 1 options of PIGS are summarized in Table 11 while the general features of interactive codes are given in Table 12.

PROBLEM COMPARISONS

In addition to the above features, a user wants to be assured that a program is well tested, has an active user group, and is continually enhanced. This is true of all of the programs summarized herein. To verify the accuracy of the program, most codes supply sets of test or verification problems. Unfortunately, there is little overlap in the problem sets that would assist in comparing problem results from different codes. The PAFEC test set has about 70 problems.

The ASME guide [9] suggests several verification problems. Some of these are found in the various test sets and thus are available for comparison. The first problem in Ref. [9] is a natural frequency calculation for a space frame with lumped masses. Typical results for this problem are given in Table 13. The second problem was to compute the frequencies of a cantilivered triangular plate [9]. The frequencies obtained with a 10 x 10 triangular grid are given in Table 14.

The next two problems in Ref. [9] involved pressure loads, temperature distribution, and thermal stresses in a thick cylinder. The results for these three calculation sets are given in Table 15. The small differences in these comparison problems are not unexpected. The major differences in codes today are things like ease of use and execution times. The latter are often close but will differ with the solution algorithm utilized. Usually the frontal solvers (e.g., PAFEC, ANSYS) are more economical than bandwidth solvers (e.g., SAP, GIFTS). For example, one benchmark problem with 1,000 dof showed PAFEC to be more than 40 times faster than GIFTS. However, such differences are not common.

CLOSURE

These comparisons have shown that codes such as PAFEC may have additional features that offer benefits to finite element users in the USA. This is especially true when the codes, such as PAFEC, are developed on and designed for the super-mini computers. Machines like the VAX 11/780, Prime 750, Cyber 170, etc., are becoming much more widespread. It may be unwise to "shoehorn" large codes, like NASTRAN, into these machines when other codes offer base management systems designed to give top efficiency on these super-minis.

Table 1 PAFEC Data Modules in Various Levels

1. The EASIDATA Set, Level 1 of PAFEC

AXES
BEAMS
CENTRIFUGAL
CONTROL
CRACK.TIP
DISPLACEMENT.PRESCRIBED
ELEMENTS
ENCASTRE
FLUX
FRONT.ORDERING
GRAVITY
IN.DRAW
LOADS
LOCAL.DIRECTIONS
MASTERS
MASS
MATERIALS
MEMBER.LOADS
MESH
MODES.AND.FREQUENCIES
NODAL.FLUX.SHOCK
NODES
OUT.DRAW
PAFBLOCKS
PLATES.AND.SHELLS
PRESSURE
REACTIONS
REPEATED.FREEDOMS
RESTRAINTS
SIMPLE.SUPPORTS
SPRINGS
STRESS.ELEMENT
TEMPERATURE
THERMAL.SHOCK
TITLE
UNSTEADY.THERMAL.TIMES

2. Level 2 Additional Modules

ARC.NODES
CHANGE.OF.MASS
CREEP.LAW
DAMPING
DELETE
DYNAMICS.GRAPH
FACTOR.LOADS
FORCING
FREQUENCIES.FOR.ANALYSIS
GROUP.OF.SIMILAR.ELEMENTS
HINGES.AND.SLIDES
INCREMENTAL
LINE.NODES
PLASTIC.MATERIAL
REFERENCE.IN.PAFBLOCK
RESPONSE
SELECT.DRAW
SIMILAR.NODES
SINE.LOADING
SINUSODIAL.OUTPUT
TABLES
TABLE.OF.FORCES
TIMES.FOR.THERMAL.STRESS.
CALCULATIONS
VARIABLE.MATERIAL
VELOCITIES.PRESCRIBED
YIELDING.ELEMENTS

3. Level 3 Additional Modules

DEFINE.RESPONSE
FAILURE.CRITERIA
FULL.DYNAMICS.OUTPUT
GENERALIZED.CONSTRAINTS
LAMINATES
OMIT.FROM.FRONT
ORTHOTROPIC.MATERIAL

Table 2 General Capabilities of Program

FEATURE	PAFEC	ANSYS	MARC	NASTRAN	NISA	SUPERB
Free Format Input	o	o			o	o
Mesh Generation	o	o	o	o	o	o
Passive Graphics	o	o	o	o	o	o
Interactive Graphics	o	o	o		o	o
Static Structural Analysis	o	o	o	o	o	o
Direct Integration Dynamics	o	o	o	o	o	o
Modal Superposition Dynamics	o	o	o	o	o	o
Nonlinear Dynamics	o	o	o	o		
Creep	o	o	o			
Plasticity	o	o	o	o		
Large Deflections	o	o	o	o		
Steady State Heat Transfer	o	o	o		o	
Transient Heat Transfer	o	o	o		o	
Hydrodynamic Lubrication	o					
Equation Renumbering	o	o	o	o	o	o
Restart Capability	o	o	o	o	o	o
Generalized Constraints	o	o	o	o		
User Subroutines	o		o	o		

Table 3 Typical Element Families

Element Type	PAFEC	ANSYS	MARC	NASTRAN	NISA	SUPERB
Springs, Masses	o	o	o	o	o	o
Beams, Trusses	o	o	o	o	o	o
Membranes						
Linear	o	o	o	o	o	
Quadratic	o	o	o	o	o	o
Cubic	o				o	o
Plates						
Thick	o		o			
Thin	o	o	o	o	o	o
Shells						
Thick	o		o			
Thin	o	o	o	o	o	o
Sandwich	o	o	o		o	
Semi-Loof Curved	o				o	
Axisymmetric						
Solids	o	o	o	o	o	o
Shells	o	o	o	o	o	o
Nonsymmetric loads	o	o	o		o	
Gap Element	o	o	o			
Solid Elements						
Wedges	o	o				o
Hexahedron	o	o	o	o	o	o
Transition	o	o	o			o
Crack Tip	o	o		o		

Table 4 Mesh Generation Features

FEATURE	PAFEC	ANSYS	MARC	NASTRAN	NISA	SUPERB	UNISTRUC
Element Families							
1-D	o	o	o	o	o	o	o
2-D	o	o	o	o	o	o	o
3-D	o	o	o	o	o	o	o
Shells	o	o	o	o	o	o	o
Data Supplementation	o	o	o	o			
Restraint Generation							
Points	o	o	o	o	o	o	o
Lines	o	o	o	o		o	
Planes	o		o				
Replication							
Nodes	o				o	o	o
Elements	o				o	o	o
Drag Copies							o
Data Validation							
Aspect Ratios	o	o	o		o	o	
Corner Angles	o						
Coincident Nodes	o				o	o	o
Edge Curvature	o						
Shell Planarity	o						o
Local Axes	o	o	o	o	o	o	o
Coordinates							
Cartesian	o	o	o	o	o	o	o
Cylindrical	o	o		o	o	o	o
Spherical	o	o		o	o	o	o
Syntax	o	o	o	o	o	o	o

Table 5 Mesh Graphics Comparisons

Feature	PAFEC	ANSYS	MARC	NASTRAN	NISA	SUPERB
Mesh Plots						
Exploded	o				o	
Unexploded	o	o	o	o	o	o
Dashed Interiors	o				o	
Boundaries Only	o	o			o	o
Mesh Information						
Node Numbers	o	o	o	o	o	o
Node Points	o	o	o	o	o	o
Element Numbers	o	o	o	o	o	o
Front Order	o					
Property Number	o	o			o	o
DOF Vectors	o					
Restraint Vectors	o	o		o	o	o
Axes Used	o			o		
Plot Limits						
By Element Group	o					
By Element Types	o	o	o	o	o	o
Elements Inside Region	o		o	o	o	o
Nodes Inside Region	o	o	o	o	o	o
Elements Outside Region	o					o
Nodes Outside Region	o					o
View Control						
Given Eye Point	o	o	o	o	o	o
Axis Direction on Paper	o	o		o	o	
Four Views of 3D Mesh	o				o	o
Perspective		o				o
Hidden Line Removal		o				

Table 6 Output Graphics Summaries

Feature	PAFEC	ANSYS	MARC	NASTRAN	NISA	SUPERB
Graphs vs. Position						
Displacements	o	o	o			
Principal Stresses	o	o	o			
Temperatures	o	o	o			
Mesh Plots						
Deformed Shapes	o	o	o	o	o	o
Mode Shapes	o	o	o	o	o	o
Displacement Vectors	o					
Dynamic Master Locations	o	o				
Stress Vectors	o					
Principal Stresses Contours	o	o	o	o	o	o
Failure Codes	o					
Temperature Contours	o	o	o			
Temperatures at Time Steps	o	o	o	o	o	o
Displacements at Time Steps	o	o	o		o	
Response Plots						
Force vs. Time	o	o				
Displacement vs. Time	o	o	o	o	o	o
Velocity vs. Time	o	o	o	o	o	o
Acceleration vs. Time	o	o	o	o	o	o
Force vs. Frequency	o	o				
Displacement vs. Frequency	o	o			o	
Velocity vs. Frequency	o	o			o	
Acceleration vs. Frequency	o	o			o	
Linear and Logarithmic Axes	o	o	o	o		

Table 7 Static Linear Stress Capabilities

Feature	PAFEC	ANSYS	MARC	NASTRAN	NISA	SUPERB
Load Conditions						
Nodal Loads	o	o	o	o	o	o
Fourier Harmonic Loads	o	o	o		o	
Pressure Loads	o	o	o	o	o	o
Inertia Loads	o	o	o	o	o	o
Thermal Loads	o	o	o	o	o	o
Swelling Loads		o	o			
Load Combinations	o	o		o		
Support Conditions						
Zero Displacements	o	o	o	o	o	o
Prescribed Displacements	o	o	o	o	o	o
Rigid Links	o	o	o	o	o	
Sliding Interface	o	o	o	o		
Generalized Constraints	o	o	o	o	o	
Local DOF Directions	o	o	o	o		o
Material Options						
Isotropic	o	o	o	o	o	o
Orthotropic	o	o		o	o	o
Temperature Dependent	o	o	o	o	o	o
Laminated	o	o	o		o	

Table 8 Thermal Analysis Capabilities

FEATURE	PAFEC	ANSYS	MARC	NASTRAN	NISA	SUPERB
Type of Analysis						
Steady State	o	o	o	o	o	o
Transient	o	o	o	o	o	
Nonlinear	o	o	o		o	
Initial Conditions						
Uniform	o	o	o	o	o	o
Arbitrary Distribution	o	o	o	o	o	o
Boundary Conditions						
Temperature	o	o	o	o	o	o
Temperature vs. Time	o	o			o	
Nodal Flux	o	o	o	o	o	o
Nodal Flux vs. Time	o	o			o	
Convection	o	o	o	o	o	o
Radiation		o		o	o	
Thermal Mass	o	o	o			
Output						
Temperatures	o	o	o	o	o	o
Nodal Flux Values	o					
Data for Thermal Stress	o	o	o	o	o	o

Table 9 Dynamic Analysis Summary

FEATURE	PAFEC	ANSYS	MARC	NASTRAN	NISA	SUPERB
Type of Analysis						
Time Integration	o	o	o	o	o	o
Frequency Dependent	o	o		o		o
Nonlinear	o	o	o	o	o	
Capabilities						
Natural Frequencies, Modes	o	o	o	o	o	o
Manual Masters	o	o	o	o	o	o
Automatic Masters	o				o	
Mass Elements	o	o	o	o	o	o
Time-Dependent Mass	o					
Damping						
Modal Damping	o		o	o	o	o
Mass Proportional	o	o	o	o	o	
Stiffness Proportion	o	o	o	o	o	
Damping Elements	o	o		o		o

Table 10 Nonlinear Stress Analysis Capabilities

FEATURE	PAFEC	ANSYS	MARC	NASTRAN	NISA	SUPERB
Creep	o	o	o			
Large Deflection	o	o	o		o	
Plasticity	o	o	o	o	o	
Creep - Plasticity		o	o			
Buckling			o	o		
Method of Solution						
Variable Stiffness			o			
Initial Stress	o					
Initial Strain	o	o	o	o	o	
Iteration Within Increment	o	o	o	o	o	
Von Mises Yield	o	o	o	o	o	
Prandtl-Reuss Flow	o	o	o	o		
Primary Strain Hardening	o	o	o		o	
Total Strain Hardening		o	o			
Time Hardening	o	o				
Primary Creep	o	o	o			
Element Library						
Beams, Bars		o	o	o		
Axisymmetric Solids	o	o	o	o	o	
2-D Solids	o	o	o	o	o	
3-D Solids		o	o	o	o	

Table 11 Summary of PIGS Commands

COMMAND	DESCRIPTION
ADD NODES	to the mesh
ADD PICTures	of new data to screen
ANALYZE	select analysis menu
BOUNDARY	outline is to be plotted
CLEAR SCreen	and redraw menu
COORDS	of a node are to be modified
DASH INTerior	lines only
DASHED	lines are to be used
DEFORMed	shape is to be plotted
DRAW	the mesh after clearing screen
ELEM ADD	add new elements to mesh
ELEM DELetion	is requested
ELEM LABels	are to be plotted
ELEM SELected	are to be plotted
EXPERT	user, reduce prompting
FILE PAFEC	data set with a new name
FIT	the plot to fill the screen
LAST	scale option is requested again
LOADCASE	or mode shape number to be used
NODE LABels	are to be plotted
NORMAL	plot status (curved lines)
NOVICE	use default prompting options
OPTIMIZE	plot for speed (straight lines)
PLOT	next DRAW or ADD PICT on plotter
PROMPT	typed input instead of cursor
RETURN	control to the ROOT menu
ROTATE	view about global or relative axes
SOLID	lines are to be used
STATUS	display is requested
STOP	and exit from PIGS
STORE	updated PAFEC data set
TOPOLOGY	list is typed or modified
TYPEDISPLacements	of a selected node
UNDERFORMed	plot of mesh requested
VIEW	select view menu
WINDOW	an area to fill the screen
ZOOM IN	to given point at double scale
ZOOM OUT	from given point at half scale

Table 12 Interactive Plotting Capabilities

FEATURE	PIGS	ANSYS	DISPLAY	MARC	SUPERB	UNISTRUC
Nodes						
Add, delete	o	o	o	o	o	o
Label	o	o	o	o	o	o
List coordinates	o	o	o	o	o	o
List displacements	o					o
Elements						
Add, delete	o	o	o	o	o	o
Label	o	o	o	o	o	o
Modify topology	o	o	o	o	o	o
Select type or range	o	o	o	o	o	o
Shape plotting						
Undeformed	o	o	o	o	o	o
Deformed	o	o		o		o
Mode	o	o				
Property edits	o	o	o	o	o	o
Rotations						
Screen axes	o	o	o	o	o	o
Model axes	o		o		o	
Views						
Perspective					o	
Windows	o	o	o	o	o	o
Zoom	o		o	o	o	o
Sections		o		o		o
Boundary only	o		o			o
Dashed line	o					
Solid line	o	o	o	o	o	o
Hidden line		o	o	o		
Plots						
Speed option	o					o
Hard copy conversion	o					o

Table 13 Results for ASME Problem 1

	Frequency, Hertz				
SOURCE/MODE	1	2	3	4	5
Test	110	117	134	214	359
PAFEC	111.3	116.1	137.5	216.3	405.3
ANSYS	111.5	115.9	137.6	218.0	404.2
SAP6	111.2	115.8	137.1	215.7	404.1

Table 14 Results for ASME Problem 2, 10 x 10 Grid

	Frequency, Hertz		
SOURCE/MODE	1	2	3
Accepted	55.9	210.8	291.9
PAFEC	55.7	212.1	290.9
ANSYS	55.9	210.9	293.5
NASTRAN	55.6	205.5	283.2
SNAP	55.5	205.4	280.7

Table 15 Percent Error in a Thick Cylinder

A) Hoop Stress Due to Pressure

Location	PAFEC	ANSYS	ASKA
Inner	0.15	0.15	0.41
Outer	0.06	0.09	0.20

B) Maximum Error in Temperature

PAFEC	ANSYS	ASKA
0.005	0.02	0.07

C) Hoop Stress Due to Temperature

Location	PAFEC	ANSYS	ASKA
Inner	0.4	0.9	0.02
Outer	0.1	0.7	0.7

REFERENCES

1 Henshell, R. D., "PAFEC Theory, Results," PAFEC Ltd., 1975.
2 Henshell, R. D., "PAFEC Get Started," PAFEC Ltd., 1975.
3 Henshell, R. D,, "PAFEC Easidata," PAFEC Ltd., 1975.
4 Henshell, R. D., "PAFEC Data Preparation Manual," PAFEC Ltd., 1978.
5 Davis, R., "PAFEC Systems Manual," PAFEC Ltd., 1978.
6 Stafford, A., "PAFEC Lubrication Analysis," PAFEC Ltd., 1980.
7 Jones, D. G., "PAFEC Substructures Option," PAFEC Ltd., 1980.
8 Shaw, K. G., "PIGS Users Manual," PAFEC Ltd., 1977.
9 Tuba, I. S., and Wright, W. B., "Pressure Vessel and Piping 1972 Computers Programs Verification," ASME PVP, 1972.
10 De Salvo, G. J., "ANSYS Verification Manual," Swanson Analysis Systems, 1976.
11 Dunder, V. F., and Belonogoff, G., "Comparing Finite Element Programs in Engineering," NASTRAN Users Conference, 1978.
12 Prajapati, G. I., and Weingarten, V. I., "SAP6 Problem Verification Manual," USG, University of Southern California, 1978.
13 Akin, J. E., Applications and Implementation of Finite Element Methods, Academic Press, London, December 1980.

Curving Dynamics Train Models

Robert L. Jeffcoat

INTRODUCTION

When a train negotiates a curve, significant lateral forces against the inner or outer rail may result. These are due in part to the buff and draft forces set up by operation over an irregular path; such "train action" forces are discussed elsewhere in this volume. Modifying these are other forces developed by the individual cars, which are attributable to kinematic accommodation of profiled wheelsets and to imbalance between gravitational and centrifugal forces. This latter group of curving forces is the subject of the analyses considered in this chapter.

It is evident after a little reflection that the net force and moment applied by the track to a car under steady conditions can be easily determined given the magnitude and direction of coupler and other external forces. A more microscopic view, however, is needed to calculate the distribution and dynamic variation of these forces. A car may derail due to a high total lateral load, but a high load on one wheel, possibly of short duration, can have the same effect. Curving models are thus central to studies of safety. They are also used to predict wear, which correlates with slip and which is a significant economic problem in curving territory.

MODELS

Degrees of Freedom

The choice of degrees of freedom for use in a curving analysis depends on the vehicle in question and the range of conditions being studied. A rigid carbody is sufficient for virtually all applications. Lateral and yaw carbody freedom are usually required, plus roll if significantly imbalanced operation is to be treated; a half carbody with fixed (generally nonzero) yaw has been used successfully.

Passenger and locomotive trucks may be reasonable treated as rigid in plan, with yaw and lateral freedom only. North American three-piece freight trucks, on the other hand, require at least three degrees of freedom (lateral, yaw, and warp) for adequate treatment. Additional wheelset degrees of freedom (i.e., primary suspensions to truck frame) are included only if high-frequency vibration and impack are to be modeled.

Nonlinearities

Nonlinearities of three main types appear in curving models: suspension elements (friction, slack, hardening springs, etc.); creep force relationships (formulations such as Kalker's [1] and Johnson's [2]); and wheel-rail contact geometry (from simple dead-band-spring flange representations through detailed constraint analysis). All, none, or some of these effects may be present in a given model.

Track Representation

At a minimum, the track must be represented by a radius of curvature and a super-elevation (which may be set implicitly to zero if desired). Quasi-steady and dynamic analyses allow these to be specified as functions of position in the curve. Track roughness, expressed as variations in gage, crosslevel, alignment, and superelevation which are superimposed on the curve, are sometimes allowed. One important use of track irregularities is to investigate vehicle response to high rail misalignment during negotiation of a curve above balance speed.

Most models assume that this geometry applies to a pair of rigid rails. Track compliance is introduced when it is important to reproduce the details of wheel-rail transients and impacts, since the rigid rail assumption predicts unrealistically high forces. In all cases known to the author, track compliance is modeled (if at all) as a set of springs acting at each wheel; crosscoupling through the track among the several wheelsets is not considered. Since the effect of lateral track compliance is insignificant while the wheel is running on its tread, a common practice is to model the rail as a rigid geometric curve, and to add a stiff lateral spring with a deadband to represent the stiffness after flange contact.

SOLUTION METHODS

Domain

It is useful to refer to three "domains" in which curving problems can be posed:

1. Steady: Curving is assumed to continue indefinitely at a constant radius and speed; all vehicle components move in strictly circular paths. If curvature or imbalance varies through a curve, the vehicle adapts instantaneously to each condition.
2. Quasi-steady: A general curve is traversed, starting from arbitrary initial conditions, but acceleration of the vehicle is ignored. This is equivalent to neglecting the vehicle inertia; the resulting response is kinematically determined.
3. Dynamic or time domain: The full dynamic equations of vehicle motion are used to analyze response to arbitrary track input. The analysis is typically by simulation (time domain), but other methods are possible.

The choice of domain has a clear effect on the cost of solution. For an equivalent system model, going from dynamic to quasi-steady solution reduces the number of dynamic equations to be solved (e.g., integrated) by half; they are replaced by algebraic constraint equations. Similarly, the steady-state assumption allows one to replace the remaining dynamic equations with the same number of static algebraic equations, which need be solved at only one instant of time. It should be noted, however, that the complexity involved in solving a set of nonlinear algebraic equations is typically greater than in integrating the corresponding dynamic equations.

Friction Center Method

The friction center method was developed [3,4] to analyze steady curving of stiff trucks on curvatures sufficiently high so that guidance is by flange contact, with at least some wheels slipping. Under the steady-state assumption, all truck components are moving in uniform circular arcs. The rigidity of the truck then makes it easy to calculate the magnitude and direction of tread slip at each wheel. (These four slip velocities are tangent to circles about a common center, whence the name of the method.) Tread friction forces, which act opposite to slip velocities, are thus determined. Flange forces, acting parallel to the axles, can then be calculated from the requirement of lateral force and yaw moment balance. The remaining longitudinal force resultant is finally balanced by varying the assumed location of the friction center.

The advantage of the friction center method is that it reduces the problem to be solved to a single-dimensional search for the friction center location along the truck centerline. The concept has been extended to flexible trucks [5] and to tansient analysis [6].

Desirable Features

This section touches briefly on several of the more desirable features to be sought in computer programs for curving analysis. It goes without saying that correctness, efficiency, readable source code and documentation, and user-oriented input and output are helpful.

Realistic Wheel-Rail Profile

A simple analysis of curve negotiation for 1:20 conical tapered wheels will indicate that flange contact will occur on quite modest curves (the order of 2 degrees) even in the absence of imbalance. For this reason, it is essential that curving models incorporate more than a simple cone representation for wheel-rail geometry. A conical tread plus some abrupt flange action beyond a specified clearance is appropriate. The most widely used representation of this kind treats the rail as a stiff lateral spring acting against the wheel. Although individual implementations vary, two main objections can be raised concerning the rail spring model: first, that it does not adequately represent the abrupt change in force due to spin creep and reorientation of the normal load vector; and second, that it does not give rise to a sudden longitudinal force as a result of flange slippage. Either effect may give rise to unrealistically low forces and sluggish response.

Some programs use very detailed representations of wheel-rail contact geometry, based either on polynomial approximations or on arbitrary measured data. An intermediate approach is to use simplified relationships for wheel-rail force which, being based on detailed theory, give generally correct relationships among displacement, angle of attack, and forces.

Realistic Creep Relations

Because of the high creep rates associated with flanging in curves (especially transient flanging), a simple linear relationship between creepage and creep force is undesirable. At a minimum, the creep force should be limited to the value given by the coefficient of sliding friction. Other approximations to the creep characteristic can be used (e.g., those of Johnson and Levi-Chartet [7]), but more important than the exact shape of the curve is that combined lateral and longitudinal creepage be properly accounted for. Kalker's complete theory [1] does this, but is seldom incorporated directly in curving analyses. An alternative adopted by Law and Cooperrider involves adjusting the individual calculated creep forces according to the total vector creepage.

Suspension Nonlinearities

It is usual for a vehicle negotiating a curve to be in a region of its suspension characteristics which, if not locally nonlinear, is at least different from what would be predicted based on "centered" measurements: slack is taken up, multiple rate springs are compressed, and friction is significant. For this reason, nonlinear characteristics should be modeled or otherwise taken into account (for example, by relinearizing about the new operating condition).

Coupler Forces

A vehicle rarely negotiates a curve in isolation, and the coupler forces arising from train action very strongly affect curving behavior. It should be possible at least to specify constant coupler forces and angles at each end of the car, and preferably to input these quantities as a function of time (obtained, for example, from a train action simulation).

Efficient Solution Methods

For high-order nonlinear dynamic problems, consideration should be given to efficient integration techniques. Rail vehicle models are mathematically "stiff," i.e., their characteristic frequencies are widely spaced, and this property contributes to very expensive simulations. Techniques to reduce this cost, such as variable-step and multiple-step integration routines, should be explored. The same comment applies to methods for solution of sets of algebraic equations.

CURVING ANALYSES AND PROGRAMS

Table 1 lists the 20 methods for curving analysis which are summarized below. Two of these are reports of analytical results rather than computer programs, but are included for completeness.

Sources

Computer programs are available from several organizations and individuals currently active in the field. With the exception of Track-Train Dynamics, these programs are not intended for formal distribution; the people named below can, however, assist potential users with their inquiries.

Track-Train Dynamics (TTD)

Closely affiliated with the Association of American Railroads, TTD develops programs for general industry use. They are provided as complete, ready-to-run packages including source and object files, test data, and full documentation. The programs conform to good professional software standards. For availability and technical information, contact:

Mr. J. G. Britten
AAR Technical Center
3140 South Federal Street
Chicago, Illinois 60616

or

Dr. V. K. Garg
Track-Train Dynamics
3140 South Federal Street
Chicago, Illinois 60616
(312) 567-3596

Battelle Columbus Laboratories (BCL)

Battelle has developed a number of programs for internal use. Most are considered proprietary, but some were developed under contract to DOT and can be obtained with DOT release. Documentation is not generally available outside BCL. Contact:

Mr. George Doyle
Battelle Columbus Laboratories
505 King Avenue
Columbus, Ohio 43201
(614) 424-6424

Law and Cooperrider

Professors Neil Cooperrider and Harry Law, together with their students, have collaborated in the development of a large number of computer pro-

Table 1 Summary of Curving Analysis

Sequence Number	Program Name	Source	Components	Type Vehicle	Domain	Deg. of Freedom	Method	Linear/Nonlinear	Available?	Documentation?
1	Flexible Truck Steering Anal.	Newl	Trk	Idlz	Stdy	4	Alg	Lin	No	Yes
2	Side Thrust in Curves	JNR	Hveh	Idlz	Stdy	4	Alg	Non	No	Yes
3	SSCUR2: 2 Axle Steady Curving	BCL	Trk	Psgr	Stdy	7	Alg	Non	Yes	Soon
4	2 Axle Steady Curve Neg.	L&C	Veh	Idlz	Stdy	7	Alg	Non	Yes	No
5	Nonlinear Steady Curving, 9-DOF	L&C	Veh	Frt	Stdy	9	Alg	Non	Yes	No
6	Full Car Steady Curving	BCL	Veh	Psgr	Stdy	11	Alg	Non	No	No
7	Full Car Steady Curving	L&C	Veh	Psgr	Stdy	11	Alg	Non	?	No
8	Steady Curving Model, 17-DOF	L&C	Veh	Frt	Stdy	17	Alg	Non	Yes	No
9	SSCUR3: 3 Axle Loco. Curving	BCL	Trk	Loco	Stdy	9	Alg	Non	No	No
10	Quasi-Static Curve Neg.	TSC	Trk	Idlz	Q-st	4	Int	Non	Yes	Yes
11	RTCN: 2,3,4 Axle Rigid Truck	TTD	Trk	Loco	Q-st	10	Fctr	Non	Yes	Yes
12	Half Car Curve Entry	BCL	Hveh	Psgr	Dyn	9	Int	Non	No	No
13	Half Car Curve Entry	L&C	Hveh	Psgr	Dyn	9	Int	Non	?	No
14	Freight Car Curving	TTD	Veh	Frt	Dyn	43	Int	Non	Soon	Soon
15	Dynamic Locomotive Curving	TTD	Veh	Loco	Dyn	59	Int	Non	Soon	Soon
16	Locomotive and Car Curving	TTD	2Veh	Loco	Dyn	?	Int	Non	No	No
17	CURVLOCO: 6 Axle Loco. Curving	L&C	Veh	Loco	Dyn	21	Int	Non	Yes	Yes
18	RVDCADET.2: Freight Car Covariance	TASC	Veh	Frt	Dyn	14	Int	Non	No	No
19	SSCURVE15: Linear Steady Curving, 15 DOF	MIT	Veh	Psgr	Stdy	15	Alg	Lin	Yes	Yes
20	Nonlinear Steady Curving, 6-DOF	MIT	Veh	Psgr	Stdy	6	Alg	Non	Yes	No

grams for DOT. These tend to include detailed wheel-rail geometry, a good approximate creep relationship, and careful kinematic analysis. Documentation of some programs is available as DOT reports, but does not exist for most curving programs. Contact:

Professor N. K. Cooperrider
Mechanical Engineering Faculty
Arizona State University
Tempe, Arizona 85281
(602) 965-3797

or

Professor E. H. Law
304 Riggs Hall
Department of Mechanical Engineering
Clemson University
Clemson, South Carolina 29631
(803) 656-3294

Transportation Systems Center (TSC)

TSC staff members have developed analysis programs in-house, and have also obtained and modified programs from other sources. Contact:

Dr. Herbert Weinstock
DTS-744
Transportation Systems Center
Kendall Square
Cambridge, Massachusetts 02142
(617) 494-2459

The Analytic Sciences Corporation (TASC)

TASC has developed a package of statistically oriented routines which incorporates curving among its inputs. In addition, it maintains a diverse library of computer programs from other sources. This work is under contract to TSC. Documentation will be available in 1980. Contact:

Dr. Fred Blader
The Analytic Sciences Corporation
6 Jacob Way
Reading, Massachusetts 01867
(617) 944-6850

Massachusetts Institute of Technology (MIT)

Ongoing work in the Department of Mechanical Engineering at MIT has led to a number of useful computer programs, some of which are available with documentation. Contact:

Professor David N. Wormley
Room 3-346
Massachusetts Institute of Technology
Cambridge, Massachusetts 02139
(617) 253-2246

Program Summaries

This section gives more detailed information on the programs in Table 1. For an overview of methods for curving analysis, see the paper by Perlman [8]. An excellent survey of computer tools for all aspects of rail vehicle dynamics is given in Ref. [9].

FLEXIBLE TRUCK STEERING ANALYSIS

Category: Curving, analysis, linear
Sequence Number: 1
Program Title: Flexible Truck Steering Analysis
Author:
Newland
Sheffield University
Sheffield
England
Date: 1969
Components Modeled: Truck
Type of Vehicle: Idealized
Domain: Steady
Degrees of Freedom: 4
Method: Algebraic
Linear/Nonlinear: Linear
Creep/Friction Model: Linear
Wheel/Rail Profile: Conical and Flange
Coupler Forces: Yes (truck)
Limitations and Restrictions: Analytical method only
Documentation: ASME Paper No. 69-RR-5

SIDE THRUST OF WHEELS IN CURVES

Category: Curving, analysis, nonlinear, half-vehicle, steady
Sequence Number: 2
Program Title: Side Thrust of Wheels in Curves
Author: Kuneida; Japanese National Railways
Date: 1970
Components Modeled: Half Car
Type of Vehicle: Idealized
Domain: Steady
Degrees of Freedom: 4
Method: Algebraic
Linear/Nonlinear: Nonlinear
Creep/Friction Model: Linear
Wheel/Rail Profile: Conical and Flange
Coupler Forces: No
Limitations and Restrictions: Analytical method only

Documentation: "Quarterly Reports," R.T.R.I., Vol. 11, No. 2, 1970

TWO AXLE STEADY CURVING (SSCUR2)

Category: Curving, nonlinear, vehicle, steady
Sequence Number: 3
Program Title: SSCUR2: Two Axle Steady Curve Negotiation Model
Author: Battelle Columbus Laboratories
Maintenance: Same
Date: 1973
Components Modeled: Truck
Type of Vehicle: Passenger (Metroliner); Freight
Domain: Steady
Degrees of Freedom: 7
Method: Newland's (#1): Iterative algebraic
Linear/Nonlinear: Nonlinear
Creep/Friction Model: Linear Kalker with slip limit
Wheel/Rail Profile: Conical and flange
Coupler Forces: Yes (truck)
Other: Constant centerplate torque; centrifugal force
Programming Language: FORTRAN
Documentation: Not complete; forthcoming TSC report
Comments: Good
Input: Vehicle configuration, speed, truck loads
Output: Prints equations of motion, truck position, forces, L/V ratios
Software Operation: Batch
Hardware: CDC Cyber 73; 41,000 octal
Usage: BCL, TSC
Typical Running Time: 19 sec
Availability: Available from TSC (H. Weinstock, 617-494-2459)
Remarks: Modified and documented under contract DOT-TSC-1051; Similar to #4.

TWO AXLE STEADY CURVING

Category: Curving, nonlinear, truck, steady
Sequence Number: 4
Program Title: Two Axle Vehicle Steady Curve Negotiation
Author: E. H. Law (Clemson University) and N. Cooperrider (Arizona State University)
Maintenance: Same
Date: ca. 1976
Components Modeled: Vehicle (or truck)
Type of Vehicle: Idealized, 2-axle
Domain: Steady
Degrees of Freedom: 7
Method: Iterative algebraic
Linear/Nonlinear: Nonlinear
Creep/Friction Model: Linear Kalker with slip limit
Wheel/Rail Profile: Arbitrary
Coupler Forces: Yes
Programming Language: FORTRAN
Documentation: None

Availability: A source tape is available from E. H. Law, Clemson University (803) 656-3294.
Remarks: Similar to #3

NONLINEAR STEADY CURVING

Category: Curving, nonlinear, freight car, steady
Sequence Number: 5
Program Title: Nonlinear Steady Curving (9-DOF)
Author: E. H. Law (Clemson University) and N. Cooperrider (Arizona State University)
Maintenance: Same
Components Modeled: Vehicle
Type of Vehicle: Freight
Domain: Steady
Degrees of Freedom: 9
Method: Iterative algebraic
Linear/Nonlinear: Nonlinear
Creep/Friction Model: Linear Kalker with slip limit
Wheel/Rail Profile: Arbitrary
Coupler Forces: Yes
Other: Three-piece trucks teated as parallelograms
Limitations and Restrictions: Geometry relations from preprocessor
Programming Language: FORTRAN
Documentation: None
Input: Card image: vehicle and track data
Output: Printout and plot of slip and flange forces, contact points, vehicle position 6
Software Operation: Batch
Hardware: IBM 370
Usage: About 4 users
Availability: A source tape is available from E. H. Law.

NONLINEAR FULL-CAR CURVING

Category: Curving, nonlinear, passenger car, steady
Sequence Number: 6
Program Title: Nonlinear Full-Car Steady Curving (11-DOF)
Author: Batelle Columbus Laboratories
Maintenance: Same
Components Modeled: Vehicle
Type of Vehicle: Passenger (Metroliner)
Domain: Steady
Degrees of Freedom: 11
Method: Iterative algebraic
Linear/Nonlinear: Nonlinear
Creep/Friction Model: Linear Kalker with slip limit
Wheel/Rail Profile: Arbitrary
Coupler Forces: Yes
Programming Language: FORTRAN
Documentation: None
Input: Card image: vehicle and track data
Data file: wheel-rail relationships
Output: Printout of vehicle position, forces

Software Operation: Batch
Usage: BCL only
Availability: Restricted
Remarks: Similar to #7

NONLINEAR FULL-CAR CURVING

Category: Curving, nonlinear, passenger car, steady
Sequence Number: 7
Program Title: Nonlinear Full-Car Steady Curving
Author: E. H. Law (Clemson University) and N. Cooperrider (Arizona State University)
Maintenance: Same
Components Modeled: Vehicle
Type of Vehicle: Passenger (Metroliner)
Domain: Steady
Degrees of Freedom: 11
Method: Iterative algebraic
Linear/Nonlinear: Nonlinear
Creep/Friction Model: Linear Kalker with slip limit (extension may exist)
Wheel/Rail Profile: Arbitrary
Coupler Forces: Yes
Limitations and Restrictions: Geometry relations from preprocessor
Programming Language: FORTRAN
Documentation: None
Input: Card Image: vehicle and track data
Data File: wheel-rail relationships
Output: Print out of vehicle location, forces
Software Operation: Batch
Hardware: IBM 370
Usage: About 4 users
Availability: A source tape is available from E. H. Law.
Remarks: Similar to #6. Said to have been used to model freight cars also.

NONLINEAR STEADY CURVING

Category: Curving, nonlinear, freight car, steady
Sequence Number: 8
Program Title: Nonlinear Steady Curving Model (17-DOF)
Author: E. H. Law (Clemson University) and N. Cooperrider (Arizona State University)
Maintenance: Same
Components Modeled: Vehicle
Type of Vehicle: Freight
Domain: Steady
Degrees of Freedom: 17
Method: Iterative algebraic
Linear/Nonlinear: Nonlinear
Creep/Friction Model: Linear Kalker with slip limit
Wheel/Rail Profile: Arbitrary
Coupler Forces: Yes
Programming Language: FORTRAN

Documentation: None
Input: Card image: vehicle and track data
Data file: wheel-rail relationships
Output: Printout and plot of vehicle position, creep and flange forces
Software Operation: Batch
Hardware: IBM 370
Usage: About 4 users
Availability: A source tape is available from E. H. Law.

LOCOMOTIVE STEADY CURVING (SSCUR3)

Category: Curving, nonlinear, locomotive, steady
Sequence Number: 9
Program Title: SSCUR3: Three Axle Locomotive Truck Steady Curving Model
Author: Battelle Columbus Laboratories
Maintenance: Same
Components Modeled: Truck
Type of Vehicle: Locomotive
Domain: Steady
Degrees of Freedom: 9
Method: Newland's (#1): iterative algebraic
Linear/Nonlinear: Nonlinear
Creep/Friction Model: Linear Kalker with slip limit
Wheel/Rail Profile: Conical and flange
Coupler Forces: Yes (truck)
Other: Constant centerplate torque; centrifugal force
Programming Language: FORTRAN
Documentation: Not complete
Comments: Good
Input: Vehicle configuration, speed, truck loads
Output: Printout of equations of motion, truck position, forces, L/V ratios
Software Operation: Batch
Hardware: CDC Cyber 73
Usage: BCL only
Availability: Restricted
Remarks: Adapted from #3

QUASI-STATIC CURVING

Category: Curving, nonlinear, truck, quasi-steady
Sequence Number: 10
Program Title: Quasi-Static Curve Negotiation Model
Author: Perlman and Weinstock; TSC
Maintenance: Same
Date: 1975
Components Modeled: Truck
Type of Vehicle: Idealized
Domain: Quasi-steady
Degrees of Freedom: 4
Method: Integration
Linear/Nonlinear: Nonlinear (linear suspension)
Creep/Friction Model: Cubic approximation (Ref. [2])
Wheel/Rail Profile: Polynomial

Coupler Forces: No
Other: Knife-edge rails
Programming Language: FORTRAN
Documentation: Interim Report No. FRA-ORPD-75-56
Availability: Contact H. Weinstock, (617) 494-2459, at TSC.

RIGID TRUCK CURVE NEGOTIATION (RTCN)

Category: Curving, nonlinear, locomotive, quasi-steady
Sequence Number: 11
Program Title: RTCN: 2,3,4, Axle Rigid Truck Curve Negotiation Model
Author: Track-Train Dynamics
Maintenance: Same
Components Modeled: Truck
Type of Vehicle: Locomotive
Domain: Quasi-steady
Degrees of Freedom: 10 (lateral and yaw, frame and wheelsets)
Method: Friction center (iterative algebraic)
Linear/Nonlinear: Nonlinear
Creep/Friction Model: Linear and slip friction
Wheel/Rail Profile: Cylindrical and flange
Coupler Forces: Yes (truck)
Programming Language: FORTRAN
Documentation: Technical Rept. (R-206), Program Rept. (R-205), and User's Manual (R-204) from The Association of American Railroads, 3140 South Federal Street, Chicago, Illinois 60616
Comments: Good
Input: Card: truck data, traction/braking, buff/draft, curvature
Output: Printout of flange and tread forces, friction center location
Software Operation: Batch
Hardware: IBM 370; 600 K byte
Usage: Significant; about 10 users
Typical Running Time: 10 sec (3031), single case
Availability: Readily available from TTD: source, object, data tapes, and documentation. Contact J. G. Britten, AAR Technical Center, 3140 South Federal Street, Chicago, Illinois 60616. The cost is $50 for the tape, and $8 for all documents.
Remarks: Outgrowth of GM-EMD model

NONLINEAR HALF CAR CURVE ENTRY

Category: Curving, nonlinear, passenger car
Sequence Number: 13
Program Title: Nonlinear Half Car Curve Entry Model
Author: E. H. Law (Clemson University) and N. Cooperrider (Arizona State (University)
Maintenance: Same
Components Modeled: Half Car
Type of Vehicle: Passenger
Domain: Dynamic
Degrees of Freedom: 9

Method: Integration
Linear/Nonlinear: Nonlinear
Creep/Friction Model: Extended Kalker (simplification with vector force limit)
Wheel/Rail Profile: Arbitrary
Coupler Forces: Yes
Programming Language: FORTRAN
Documentation: None
Input: Card: vehicle and track data
Data file: wheel-rail relationships
Output: Printout and plot of states and forces
Software Operation: Batch
Hardware: IBM 370
Usage: About 4 users
Availability: Contact E. H. Law, (803) 656-3294
Remarks: Similar to #12

FREIGHT CAR CURVING

Category: Curving, freight car, nonlinear
Sequence Number: 14
Program Title: AAR Freight Car Curving Model
Author: Track-Train Dynamics
Maintenance: Same
Date: 1978
Components Modeled: Vehicle
Type of Vehicle: Freight
Domain: Dynamic
Degrees of Freedom: 43
Method: Integration
Linear/Nonlinear: Nonlinear
Creep/Friction Model: Nonlinear (Johnson)
Wheel/Rail Profile: Conical and flange
Coupler Forces: Yes
Other: Track compliance in detail
Limitations and Restrictions: No carbody yaw; no superelevation
Programming Language: FORTRAN
Documentation: Not complete. See ASME Paper No. 76-WA/RT-14
Usage: Internal TTD and AAR plus about 2 others
Availability: Restricted pending completion of documentation. Contact J. G. Britten, AAR Technical Center, 3140 South Federal Street, Chicago, Illinois 60616.
Remarks: Adapted from K. R. Smith's work at IIT.

LOCOMOTIVE CURVING

Category: Curving, locomotive, nonlinear
Sequence Number: 15
Program Title: AAR Dynamic Locomotive Curving Model
Author: Track-Train Dynamics
Maintenance: Same
Date: 1979
Components Modeled: Vehicle
Type of Vehicle: Locomotive (6 axle)
Domain: Dynamic

Degrees of Freedom: 59
Method: Integration
Linear/Nonlinear: Nonlinear
Creep/Friction Model: Linear
Wheel/Rail Profile: Conical and flange
Programming Language: FORTRAN
Documentation: Not complete
Output: Printout and plot of states, forces, L/V ratios
Software Operation: Batch
Usage: Internal TTD and AAR
Availability: Restricted pending completion of documentation. Contact J. G. Britten, AAR Technical Center, 3140 South Federal Street, Chicago, Illinois 60616.

LOCOMOTIVE AND CAR CURVING

Category: Curving, nonlinear, locomotive
Sequence Number: 16
Program Title: AAR Dynamic Curving of a Locomotive and Car
Author: Track-Train Dynamics
Maintenance: Same
Date: 1979
Components Modeled: Locomotive and one car
Type of Vehicle: Locomotive, passenger (baggage)
Domain: Dynamic
Method: Integration
Linear/Nonlinear: Nonlinear
Creep/Friction Model: Linear
Wheel/Rail Profile: Conical and flange
Coupler Forces: Internal
Programming Language: FORTRAN
Documentation: None
Output: Printout and plot of states, forces, L/V ratios
Software Operation: Batch
Usage: Internal TTD and AAR
Availability: Restricted

NONLINEAR LOCOMOTIVE CURVING (CURVLOCO)

Category: Curving, nonlinear, locomotive
Sequence Number: 17
Program Title: CURVLOCO: Nonlinear Six Axle Locomotive Curving Model
Author: E. H. Law (Clemson University) and N. Cooperrider (Arizona State University)
Maintenance: Same
Date: 1978
Components Modeled: Vehicle
Type of Vehicle: Locomotive (6 axle)
Domain: Dynamic
Degrees of Freedom: 21 plus 6 axle rotation variables
Method: Integration
Linear/Nonlinear: Nonlinear
Creep/Friction Model: Extended Kalker

Wheel/Rail Profile: Arbitrary
Coupler Forces: Yes
Other: Deterministic track geometry can be superimposed
Limitations and Restrictions: Geometry relations from preprocessor
Programming Language: FORTRAN
Documentation: User's Manual (brief)
Comments: Good
Input: Card: vehicle and track data, creep data
Data file: wheel-rail relationships
Output: Printout and plot of states, forces, L/V ratios
Software Operation: Batch
Hardware: IBM 370
Usage: Heavy use by about four users, with various modifications
Typical Running Time: 30 min. (3031)
Availability: Source tapes and User's Manual are available from N. K. Cooperrider, (602) 965-3797.
Remarks: Corrections and modifications appear occasionally from ASU or TSC

FREIGHT CAR COVARIANCE (RVDCADET)

Category: Curving, nonlinear, freight car, stochastic
Sequence Number: 18
Program Title: RVDCADET.2: Freight Car Covariance Analysis
Author: The Analytic Sciences Corporation
Maintenance: Same
Date: 1978
Components Modeled: Vehicle
Type of Vehicle: Freight
Domain: Dynamic; steady-state option
Degrees of Freedom: 14
Method: Integration of quasi-linearized system
Linear/Nonlinear: Nonlinear
Creep/Friction Model: Linear with slip limit
Wheel/Rail Profile: Implicit arbitrary, idealized
Coupler Forces: Yes
Other: Trucks treated as parallelograms. May be operated in deterministic or stochastic mode.
Limitations and Restrictions: Multiplicative, piecewise-linear flange force representations; must be extracted from separate analysis.
Programming Language: FORTRAN
Documentation: Should be available in 1980
Comments: Good
Input: Card image: vehicle characteristics, track geometry, covariances
Output: Printout of plot of states, forces (time history of statistics)
Software Operation: Batch
Hardware: IBM 370 (3031)
Usage: TASC only
Typical Running Time: 30 min. (stochastic), 10 min. (deterministic), 2 min. (steady state)
Availability: Late 1980, from TASC or TSC. Contact Dr. Fred Blader, TASC (617) 944-6850
Remarks: Time varying curvature is treated as yaw offset plus differential velocity of rails.

LINEAR STEADY CURVING (SSCURVE15)

Category: Curving, linear, steady
Sequence Number: 19
Program Title: SSCURVE15: 15-DOF Linear Steady Curving Model
Author; Charles Bell; MIT
Maintenance: Same
Date: 1979
Components Modeled: Vehicle
Type of Vehicle: Passenger
Domain: Steady
Degrees of Freedom: 15
Method: Solution of simultaneous linear equations
Linear/Nonlinear: Linear
Creep/Friction Model: Linear
Wheel/Rail Profile: Conical; linearized stiffness
Coupler Force: No
Other: Generalized shear and bending stiffness among wheelsets
Programming Language: FORTRAN
Documentation: User's manual
Input: Vehicle characteristics, track geometry, flange clearance
Output: Maximum curvature for flange-free curving
Software Operation: Batch
Hardware: DEC VAX
Usage: About 4 users
Typical Running Time: Less than 0.5 sec per case
Availability: Contact Charles Bell, 3-351, MIT, Cambridge, MA 02139, (617) 253-3772. Source tapes are available.

NONLINEAR STEADY CURVING

Category: Curving, nonlinear, steady
Sequence Number: 20
Program Title: 6-DOF Nonlinear Steady Curving Model
Author: Charles Bell; MIT
Maintenance: Same
Date: 1980
Components Modeled: Vehicle
Type of Vehicle: Passenger
Domain: Steady
Degrees of Freedom: 6
Method: Iterative algebraic
Linear/Nonlinear: Nonlinear
Creep/Friction Model: Linear
Wheel/Rail Profile: Conical tread; hard flange
Coupler Forces: No
Other: Generalized shear and bending stiffness among wheelsets
Programming Language: FORTRAN
Documentation: None
Input: Vehicle characteristics, track geometry, flange clearance
Output: States, forces
Software Operation: Batch
Hardware: DEC VAX
Usage: MIT only at this time
Typical Running Time: Less than 1 sec per case

Availability: Contact Charles Bell, 3-351, MIT, Cambridge, MA 02139 (617-253-3772). A source tape is available.
Remarks: Extension of No. 19. Development continues.

SUMMARY

A number of analytical and computer methods exist to study the behavior of rail vehicles in curves. Of these, only the friction center method has achieved any degree of general acceptance; the technique is used in several of the programs reviewed here, and it has been widely used as a design tool. Newer methods for steady curving analysis which employ more detailed representations of the geometric and creep relationships exist, but are not readily available and useful to the industry. The situation with regard to dynamic curving is even less settled, because there is as yet no model of transient wheel-rail interaction which is sufficiently comprehensive and well validated to be relied upon.

In general, curving models are not well validated by experimental results. Steady curving analyses yield qualitatively correct behavior but should not be treated as better than about 20% accurate in predicting individual wheel/rail forces. Dynamic curving models are also accurate as to overall low-frequency response; their prediction of high frequencies and impacts varies tremendously with the details of the model, however, and cannot be trusted. Unfortunately, it is just this impact regime which dominates safety and track deterioration. Dr. Garg of Track-Train Dynamics and Professor Sweet of Princeton University have recently presented some informal results which show encouraging correlation between analytical and test data (field and laboratory, respectively). Nevertheless, transient curving analysis remains an underdeveloped but important area.

ACKNOWLEDGMENTS

In compiling this information, I was greatly helped by discussions with Messrs. Donald Ahlbeck (BCL), Charles Bell (MIT), Paul Berry (TASC), Neil Cooperrider (ASU), V. K. Garg (AAR/TTD), Harry Law (Clemson), Harvey Lee (TSC), Robert Prause (BCL), and Herbert Weinstock (TSC).

REFERENCES

1 Kalker, J. J., "On the Rolling Contact of Two Elastic Bodies in the Presence of Dry Friction," Doctoral thesis, Technische Hogeschool, Delft, The Netherlands, 1967.

2 Johnson, K. L., "The Effect of a Tangential Contact Force Upon the Rolling Motion of an Elastic Sphere on a Plane," J. Appl. Mech. (ASME), Vol. 86, Ser. E, p. 339, December 1958.

3 Koci, L. F., and Marta, H. A., "Lateral Loading Between Locomotive Truck Wheels and Rail Due to Curve Negotiation," ASME Paper No. 65-WA/RR-4, November 1965.

4 Bolt, D. W., "Dynamics of Railway Vehicles on Curved Track," B. M.E. thesis, General Motors Institute, 1975.

5 Muller, C. Th., "Dynamics of Railway Vehicles on Curved Track," Proc. I. M. E. , Vol. 180, Pt. 3F, 1966, p. 45.

6 Minchin, R. S., "The Mechanics of Railway Vehicles on Curved Track," J. Inst. Engrs. (Australia), Vol. 28, 1956, p. 179.

7 Hobbs, A. E. W., "A Survey of Creep," Report No. DYN/52, British Railways Research Department, Derby, England, April 1967.

8 Perlman, A. B., "Computational Methods for the Prediction of Truck Performance in Curves," ASME Paper No. 76-WA/RT-15, December 1976.

9 Johnson, L., et al., "Truck Design Optimization Project Phase II: Analytical Tool Assessment Report," Report No. FRA/ORD-79/36, Wyle Laboratories, Colorado Springs, August 1979.

Lateral Stability of Trains

J. A. Hadden

Columbus Laboratories

INTRODUCTION

In recent years there has been a dramatic upsurge in research in North America in the rail vehicle area. This has spawned the application of sophisticated analytical methods to the study of rail vehicle dynamics. As a result, a substantial number of digital computer programs have been developed to study rail vehicle lateral stability. In this chapter, several of these programs are compared and evaluated with respect to their capabilities, availability, and documentation.

A major obstacle in preparing this review was the lack of formal documentation of many existing computer programs. This may be attributed partly to the fact that rail vehicle dynamics is a relatively new field of research in North America. Many computer programs that have been developed remain specifically for a given task and a given group of users, and have not yet been "tailored" for general use by others.

Another problem that may be attributed partly to the newness of this field is the lack of sufficient experimental data to validate fully the computer programs. Consequently, the best validation for some programs is to show similar model behavior with other previously developed models and with qualitative observations of vehicle behavior. In spite of this shortcoming, these computer programs generally have proved valuable in at least predicting trends in vehicle behavior. With more complete, quantitative validation, these programs should become powerful design tools for the railroad industry. A breakdown of the analysis methods used presently to evaluate rail vehicle lateral stability is shown in Table 1. The elements of this chart are discussed in detail in the next section.

BACKGROUND

General Vehicle Dynamic Behavior

The lateral stability of a rail vehicle represents one aspect of the overall dynamic behavior. Other aspects of dynamic behavior include curve entry and curve negotiation characteristics and the response to stochastic and deterministic excitation from the track, wind, and other vehicles.

Table 1 Breakdown of Analytical Methods Used In Digital Computer Programs To Examine Rail Vehicle Lateral Stability

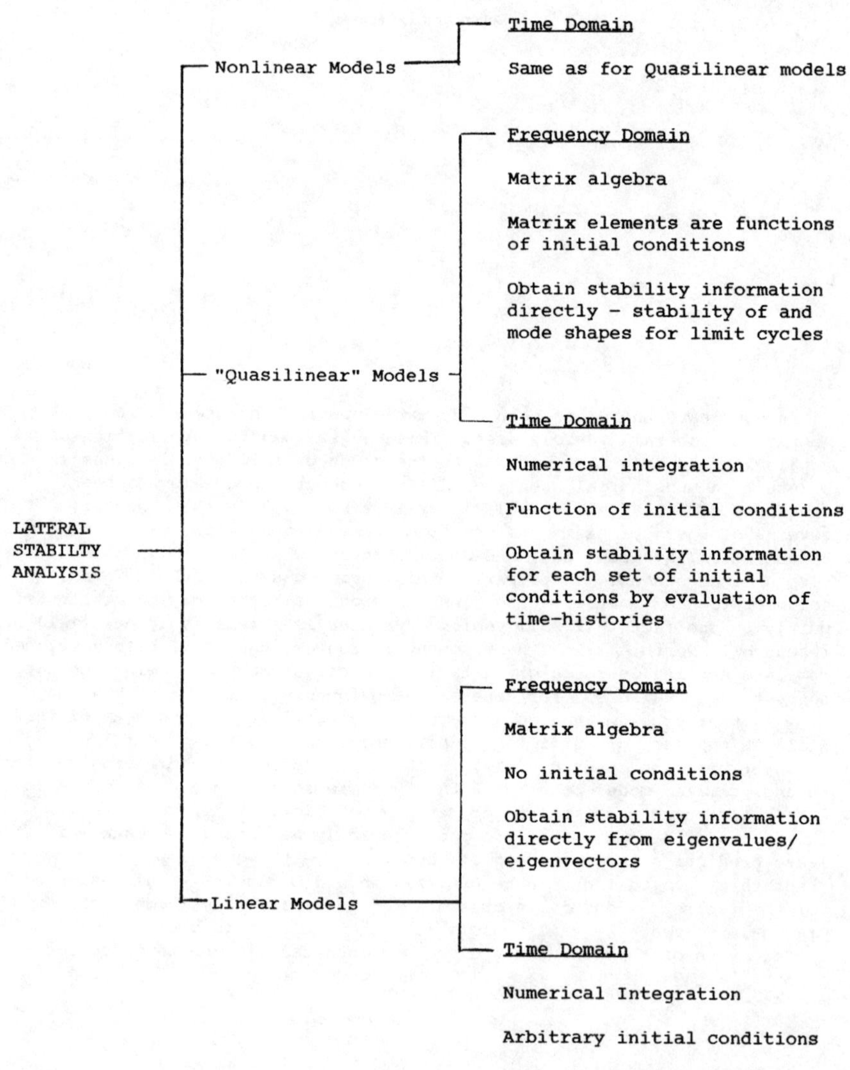

A lateral, or "hunting," instability problem in conventional rail vehicles is caused by the nature of the wheel/rail interaction. Hunting is characterized by coupled yaw and lateral oscillations of the wheelsets which increase in amplitude until repeated flanging of the wheels on the rail occurs. There exists a "critical speed" above which the response to an arbitrary small perturbation is manifested in hunting oscillations. These oscillations, which are coupled with motions of the rest of the vehicle, are sustained in a "limit cycle" condition at wheelset lateral amplitudes equal to the flange clearance. Above the critical speed, the wheels will climb the rail and derailment may occur. Below the critical speed, the oscillatory response will either die out or decrease to a relatively safe, small-amplitude limit cycle condition.

It is possible that for certain worn or unconventional wheel profiles sustained limit cycle oscillations will occur without flanging. For new wheels, however, the limit cycle condition exists only for the flanging condition.

Nonlinear Modeling

The hunting behavior described previously is inherently nonlinear due primarily to the nonlinear wheel/rail geometry (including flanging) and wheel/rail contact forces. Suspension nonlinearities, friction, stops, and clearances throughout the rail vehicle also contribute to the nonlinear performance. Therefore, the most accurate model of rail vehicle lateral dynamics would include realistic representations of these nonlinearities. For this approach, the only analytical method that can be used is that of numerical integration of the nonlinear equations of motion. The response of a nonlinear system is generally a function of the initial conditions. Thus, a reasonable range of initial conditions must be prescribed to obtain a set of time-domain solutions that represents the range of behavior expected in practice.

Depending on the purpose of the study, and the time and costs involved to exercise a large, nonlinear, time-domain model, several times may not be justified. These are motivating factors for the use of approximate methods in lateral stability analyses. By making reasonable approximations, computer time and costs can be cut substantially and still the program will provide sufficiently accurate results. Linear and quasilinear modeling are two classes of approximate methods which are discussed in the following sections.

Linear Modeling

A linear rail vehicle stability model consists of a set of second-order, constant-coefficient, homogeneous differential equations. To obtain this type of model, several simplifying assumptions are made, including those in the following list.

1. All displacements are small enough so that second and higher order quantities in the variables may be neglected.
2. Friction elements may be approximated by linear elements, such as by calculating an equivalent viscous damping coefficient.
3. Equivalent linear springs may be used to approximate small displacement behavior of nonlinear spring elements.
4. Nonlinear wheel/rail geometry terms may be represented by neglecting terms higher than first order in the Taylor series expansion for the particular terms. Flanging cannot occur.

5. The possibility of sliding of the wheels on the rails is neglected; pure creepage occurs between the wheels and rails.

6. All stops and clearances are either neglected or accounted for in linear suspension terms.

7. The vehicle is traveling at a constant forward speed (this assumption is used for linear, quasilinear, and nonlinear stability models).

These assumptions may impose substantial limitations on the validity of the models, as determined by the degree of nonlinear characteristics inherent in the actual rail vehicle. However, by making intelligent choices for the linearized model's parameters, qualitative trends in behavior usually can be identified. Thus, a primary benefit of the linear stability model is to illustrate the basic dynamic behavior of rail vehicles.

An attractive feature of linear models is that the stability characteristics are independent of the initial conditions. Thus, arbitrary initial conditions may be prescribed for time-domain simulations of a linear model. Then, the stability characteristics can be extracted by evaluation of the displacement time-histories. It should be emphasized that the linear stability characteristics are amplitude independent, due to the general nature of linear systems.

A major benefit of stability analysis with linear models is that frequency domain techniques can be used conveniently. Specifically, stability information is provided directly by solution of the eigenproblem. The sign of the real part of the eigenvalues determines the stability of the system (positive real part means divergence) as a function of vehicle speed. The imaginary part of the eigenvalues are the damped natural frequencies for the corresponding eigenvectors or "modes" (a zero imaginary part implies a nonoscillatory mode). The system damping ratio for each mode can be calculated from the real and imaginary parts. Finally, relative magnitude and phase relationships between the degrees of freedom of the system for each mode are provided by the eigenvectors. The frequency-domain solution usually is faster and cheaper to exercise on the computer than is the time-domain solution. These savings typically are more substantial for larger models.

"Quasilinear" Modeling

The application of quasilinearization (or describing function) techniques to rail vehicle stability analysis is an area of relatively recent interest. The essence of these techniques is that the fundamental nonlinear characteristics of the system are included, while the mathematical form of the system allows the application of frequency-domain analysis, the benefits of which were explained in the previous section. Specifically, quasilinearization consists of approximating a nonlinear function by one or more gains that are a function of the input signal amplitudes. In contrast, linearization consists of approximating the nonlinear function by a single gain that is amplitude independent. The stability of the quasilinear rail vehicle model is described typically in terms of stable and unstable limit cycle oscillations, which are a function of the amplitude and/or frequency of motion.

General Comments

It should be noted that almost all lateral dynamics time-domain simulations may be used to determine rail vehicle stability characteristics. However, the manipulations necessary to extract these characteristics are usually cumbersome and costly. The nature of rail vehicle lateral dynamics allows the use of convenient frequency-domain techniques to approximate stability characteristics. Thus, this review is restricted to the class of frequency-domain stability models.

It should also be noted that this review is by no means complete. Some existing computer programs have been omitted from consideration, mainly because of lack of sufficient information on the programs' details. However, the sample of programs presented is believed to be representative of the range of analytical capabilities that presently exists in the field of rail vehicle dynamics.

SURVEY OF COMPUTER PROGRAMS

CU/ASU Freight Car Lateral Stability Models

Categories: Hunting, lateral stability, freight car stability, wheel profile assymmetries, loading asymmetries, wheelset interconnection, torsionally flexible wheelsets

Authors: E. H. Law
Department of Mechanical Engineering
Clemson University
Clemson, South Carolina 29632

N. K. Cooperrider
Department of Mechanical Engineering
Arizona State University
Tempe, Arizona 85282

J. A. Hadden (23 degree-of-freedom model only)
Battelle
Columbus Laboratories
505 King Avenue
Columbus, Ohio 43201

Maintenance: Authors

Date: Development of 17 and 19 degree-of-freedom (DOF) models comprised latest update (1976-7)

Capabilities: Series of four models, having 9, 17, 19, and 23 DOF. Programs calculate eigenvalues (frequency and damping) and eigenvectors (mode shapes) for the system equations. 9 DOF model specialized to roller bearing freight trucks and rigid car body. Other programs include capability to simulate plain bearing, passenger, "radial" (interconnected wheelsets), and unconventional trucks. Twenty-three DOF model also includes torsionally flexible wheelsets. Seventeen DOF model includes wheel profile and loading asymmetries. Nineteen and twenty-three DOF models include first torsional and lateral bending modes of car body. Models approximate nonconical wheel profiles at an assumed wheelset displacement amplitude.

Method: QR Algorithm, as described by Wilkinson [1] and Marcotte [2]

Limitations and Restrictions: Linear systems only. Asymmetries in 17 DOF model are limited to fore and aft loading, and to identical wheel profiles on each axle. Relative roll between car body and bolsters does not exist. 9 DOF model truck representations are limited to roller bearing freight or rigid trucks.

Programming Language: FORTRAN
Documentation: User's manuals are in preparation. Equations of motion and/or model derivations are presented in Refs. [3,4].
Input: Mass, damping, and stiffness parameters; physical dimensions; and vehicle speeds
Output: Real and imaginary parts of eigenvalues, damping ratios, and relative magnitudes and phase angles between displacements for each eigenvalue
Software Operation: Batch
Hardware: Programmed for IBM 370/165-II and UNIVAC 1110
Usage: Developed for the U.S. Department of Transportation (DOT) Federal Railroad Administration (FRA) under Contract DOT-OS-40018 in a joint effort by Clemson University and Arizona State University
Typical Running Time: Unknown
Availability: Dr. E. H. Law
Department of Mechanical Engineering
Clemson University
Clemson, SC 29632

Program TRKHNT II

Categories: Hunting, lateral stability, passenger truck stability, wheelset interconnection, torsionally flexible wheelsets
Descriptive Program Title: Linear Passenger and Radial Truck Hunting Model
Author: G. R. Doyle
Applied Dynamics and Acoustics Section
Battelle - Columbus Laboratories
Columbus, Ohio 43201
Maintenance: G. R. Doyle
Date: 1974; latest update in 1978 - revisions made to include radial truck model
Capability: 9 DOF model of a single passenger truck with torsionally flexible wheelsets and suspension interconnection between wheelsets; can represent passenger, rigid, and "radial" trucks.
Method: Solution of eigenproblem, based on Ref. [5]
Limitations and Restrictions: Linear systems only. Rigid truck frame disallows modeling of conventional 3-piece freight truck. No car body flexural degrees of freedom. Conical wheels only. No asymmetries.
Programming Language: FORTRAN
Documentation: Not available. Model described and equations of motion (without wheelset interconnection capability) presented in Ref. [6]
Input: Mass, damping, and stiffness parameters; physical dimensions; vehicle speeds
Output: Real and imaginary parts of eigenvalues, relative magnitude and phase angles between displacements for each eigenvalue
Software Operation: Batch
Hardware: Program designed for CDC 6400
Usage: Used at Battelle for several sponsored research programs over past several years
Typical Running Time: 10 sec
Availability: Author

Program CARHNT II

Categories: Hunting, lateral stability, passenger car stability, torsionally flexible wheelsets
Descriptive Program Title: Linear Passenger Car Hunting Program
Authors: R. H. Prause and G. R. Doyle
Applied Dynamics and Acoustics Section
Battelle - Columbus Laboratories
Columbus, Ohio 43201
Maintenance: G. R. Doyle
Date: 1974
Capability: 21 DOF model of complete passenger rail vehicles with torsionally flexible wheelsets
Method: Solution of eigenproblem, based on Ref. [5]
Limitations and Restrictions: Linear systems only. Rigid car body model disallows car body flexural motions. Conical wheels only. No asymmetries.
Programming Language: FORTRAN
Documentation: Not available. Model described and equations of motion presented in Ref. [6]
Input: Mass; damping and stiffness parameters; physical dimensions; and vehicle speeds
Output: Real and imaginary parts of eigenvalues, and relative magnitudes and phase angles of displacements for each eigenvalue
Software Operation: Batch
Hardware: Programmed for CDC 6400
Usage: Used at Battelle for several sponsored research programs over the past several years.
Typical Running Time: 30 sec
Availability: Authors

Program DYNALYST II

Categories: Hunting, lateral stability, rail vehicle dynamic response, component mode synthesis
Descriptive Program Title: Computer Program for Stability and Dynamic Response Analysis of Linear Rail Vehicle Systems
Authors: T. K. Hasselman and A. Bronowicki
J. W. Wiggins Company
1650 South Pacific Coast Highway
Redondo Beach, California 90277
Date: 1974; several revisions were made in 1975-76, including force response capability, improved plotting capability, and a computer matrix generator.
Capability: Stability analysis, and forced response to deterministic and random excitation. Flexible car body modeling. Up to 25 DOF models. Capable of simulations of freight and passenger vehicles and locomotives. Plot routine for frequency and system damping vs. speed. Two preprogrammed rail vehicle models, consisting of 8 DOF truck and 14 DOF complete vehicle. Gneral program can accommodate asymmetries, nonconical wheel profiles.
Method: Component mode method (Ref. [7]). Component masses are defined independently. Constraint relations are defined to combine components into complete vehicle, with editing capability for deletion of characteristics associated with large eigenvalues.
Limitations and Restrictions: Linear systems only. Preprogrammed models

limited to rigid truck frames and rigid car body, no asymmetries, and conical wheels only. No car body roll in 14 DOF model. General purpose program limited to 25 DOF.
Programming Language: FORTRAN
Documentation: Complete (Ref. [7])
Input: Required inputs into preprogrammed vehicle models include vehicle mass, stiffness, and damping characteristics; physical dimensions; and vehicle speed. General purpose program requires programming of user's specific equations of motion.
Output: Stability information is presented in the form of a listing of the complex eigenvalues and associated normalized values (real and imaginary parts) for each vehicle component and the assembled vehicle. Plot options include frequency and damping ratio vs. speed, plotted on a Calcomp plotter for each conjugate pair of eigenvalues.
Software Operation: Batch. Uses three working files, which may be tapes or discs.
Hardware: Programmed for CDC 6600, requiring a maximum of 163 K of core.
Usage: The program was developed by the J. W. Wiggins Company for DOT.
Typical Running Time: Unknown
Availability: Through Transporation Systems Center, Cambridge, MA.

Freight Car Hunting Model

Categories: Hunting, lateral stability, freight car stability
Descriptive Program Title: Freight Car Hunting Model
Authors: T. W. Cheung, V. K. Garg, and G. C. Martin
Association of American Railroads (AAR)
3140 South Federal Street
Chicago, IL 60616
Maintenance: AAR
Date: 1974
Capability: 25 degrees of freedom. Primary suspension elements between wheelsets and truck. Truck models can represent freight, rigids and passenger, and unconventional trucks.
Method: QR double step method and inverse iteration (Ref. [5])
Limitations and Restrictions: Linear systems only. Conical wheels only. Rigid car body model. No asymmetries.
Programming Language: FORTRAN
Documentation: Complete (Ref. [8])
Input: Mass; damping and stiffness characteristics; physical dimensions; and vehicle speeds. Also must specify stiffness matrix inversion option (yes or no), depending on accuracy desired for high-frequency response.
Output: Eigenvalues, damping ratios, and eigenvectors (in terms of normalized magnitudes and phase angles) for system equations
Software Operation: Batch
Hardware: Programmed for IBM 370/158
Usage: Program was developed for AAR
Typical Running Times: 171-184 seconds per run (one vehicle speed) for compilation (126 sec), link edit (4 sec), and execution (45-53 sec)
Availability: Director, Technical Center
Association of American Railroads
3140 South Federal Street
Chicago, IL 60616

Locomotive Truck Hunting Model

Categories: Hunting, lateral stability, locomotive stability, three-axle trucks
Descriptive Program Title: Locomotive Truck Hunting Model
Authors: V. K. Garg, P. W. Hartmann, and G. C. Martin
Association of American Railroads
3140 South Federal Street
Chicago, IL 60616
Date: Unknown
Capability: Linear stability program, accommodating models of 2 , 7, 9, 17, and 21 DOF. These consist of a wheelset, two-axle truck, three-axle truck, four-axle locomotive, and six-axle locomotive, respectively.
Method: QR double step method and inverse iteration (Ref. [5]).
Limitations and Restrictions: Linear systems only. Conical wheels only. Rigid truck frame and rigid car body only. Symmetrical wheel profiles only.
Programming Language: FORTRAN
Documentation: Complete (Ref. [9])
Input: Mass, damping and stiffness characteristics, physical dimensions, vehicle speeds, choice of model, option for English or metric units, matrix inversion option, diagnostics printout options
Output: Eigenvalues (real and imaginary parts), frequency (Hz), damping ratios, and normalized eigenvectors (magnitude and phase angle)
Software Operation: Batch
Hardware: Programmed for IBM 370/158
Usage: The program was developed for use at General Motors Electro-Motive Division and AAR.
Typical Running Times: Compilation =66.0 sec
Link Edit = 4.0 sec
Execution (per train speed) = 0.3 sec (2 DOF)
2.0 sec (7 DOF)
3.0 sec (9 DOF)
20.0 sec (17 DOF)
30.0 sec (21 DOF)
Availability: Association of American Railroads
3140 South Federal Street
Chicago, IL 60616

Program FDM

Categories: Frequency response, freight car stability, Nyquist stability
Descriptive Program Title: Frequency Domain Model
Author: Southern Pacific Transportation Company
Technical Research and Development Group
One Market Plaza
San Francisco, CA 94105
Maintenance: Author
Date: 1976
Capability: 13 degree-of-freedom linear freight car model. Frequency response to deterministic or random forcing from track. Nyquist stability plots. Conical and concave wheel profiles. Suspension loading and wheel/rail geometry asymmetries. Car body fundamental torsional mode is included.
Method: Solution of 13 simultaneous equations of motion as function of frequency (Ref. [10]).
Limitations and Restrictions: Linear systems only. Rigid truck or roller

bearing freight truck only. Requires track deflection data in format of TDOP test track data measured by DOT track geometry cars (available through National Technical Information Service (NTIS) on NTIS Tape PB 249 794/9WT). Tapes must be converted to proper form using a peripheral program.
Programming Language: FORTRAN
Documentation: Complete (Ref. [10])
Input: Mass, damping and stiffness characteristics, vehicle speeds, track geometry characteristics, physical dimensions, wheel profile type, friction forces (automatically converted to equivalent viscous damping)
Output: 21 response variables, as a function of frequency, option of Calcomp (or equivalent) plots of Nyquist diagram, Power spectral density plots, and time-domain plots.
Software Operation: Batch
Hardware: Programmed for IBM 370/168. Requires 194 bytes of memory.
Usage: Developed by and for use in Truck Design Optimization Program (TDOP).
Typical Running Time: 6 to 9 minutes of CPU time for execution for each simulation
Availability: Author

Quasilinear 9 DOF Freight Car Model

Categories: Hunting, lateral stability, limit cycles, quasilinearization, freight car dynamics
Descriptive Program Title: Quasilinear 9 DOF Freight Car Model
Authors: N. K. Cooperrider
Department of Mechanical Engineering
Arizona State University
Tempe, AZ 85292

J. K. Hedrick
Department of Mechanical Engineering
Massachusetts Institute of Technology
Cambridge, MA 02139
Maintenance: Authors
Date: 1977
Capability: Describing function approximations to system geometries and suspension nonlinearities. Computes existence and stability characteristics of limit cycle oscillations. Can examine dry friction, flanging, nonlinear creep, and nonconical wheel geometry effects.
Method: Iterations on vehicle speed and limit cycle frequency for a specified amplitude of wheelset motion to arrive at eigenvalues/eigenvectors for limit cycle condition (Ref. [11, 12]).
Programming Language: FORTRAN
Documentation: Instructions are presented in Ref. [11].
Input: Mass, damping and stiffness characteristics, physical dimensions, describing functions for nonlinearities, range of vehicle speeds and amplitudes of motion
Output: Tabularized describing function data, amplitudes, speed, and frequency of limit cycles
Software Operation: Batch
Hardware: Programmed for UNIVAC 1110
Usage: Program was developed under Contracts DOT-OS-40018 and DOT-TSC-902 to the Federal Railroad Administration and the Transportation Systems Center, respectively.
Typical Running Time: Unknown
Availability: Authors

COMPARATIVE EVALUATION OF PROGRAMS

A summary and comparison of the characteristics of the computer programs described in the previous section are presented in Table 2. Several of these characteristics are described in detail below.

Model Validation

Very few attempts have been made to validate rail vehicle stability models by matching a model's analytical predictions with experimental results. For the most part, model validation has consisted of comparing model behavior to either qualitative rail vehicle behavior or to the behavior of other existing models. Because of the wide range of parameter values that may represent an actual rail vehicle (due to the large variations that exist in wheel/rail contact force characteristics, wheel profile shapes, track conditions, effective stiffnesses and damping coefficients throughout the vehicle, etc.), combinations of parameters usually can be chosen to match the critical speed and the shape of the "hunting" mode, as a function of the vehicle speed range (rather than at the critical speed only).

From the available documentation of the programs reviewed here, it appears that experimental data were used in a formula validation effort only for the CU/ASU models and the FDM model. For the FDM model [10], time-histories and output PSD's were used from test data on a refrigerator car to check the model performance. An experimental program was performed with an instrumented hopper car and parameter identification techniques were used with some success in an attempt to validate the CU/ASU model [13]. The results of these latter tests give a good indication of the problems which are encountered when attempting to validate rail vehicle models.

Time and Costs

Detailed time and cost data on several of the programs were not obtained. However, based on the nature of the computer methods, it appears that almost all of the eigenproblem-type programs should solve the system equations in under about 3 CPU minutes per simulation (one vehicle speed). The required computer time increases with the number of model degrees of freedom. Thus, there exists a trade-off between model detail and time/cost. The 25-DOF AAR/TTD Freight Car Model is the largest of the models examined and thus is expected to require the most computer time of the eigenproblem-type programs that were considered here. Of course, computer times are based on the specific computer characteristics, computer language characteristics, etc., and times would be expected to vary for a given program on different computers.

The FDM program requires the most time of the programs examined (based on available information). This is because the primary purpose of the program is to compute frequency response characteristics due to forced excitation. These computations generally require a longer computer execution time than the eigenproblem solution does for the same model.

Computer cost may be considered as being proportional to computer time.

Versatility

Of the "special features" listed in Table 2, the ability to model asymmetries is more important than the flexible car body feature, from a stability stand-

Table 2 Summary and Comparison of Digital Programs for Rail Vehicle Lateral Stability Analyses

	Model Class			Domain		Vehicle Class			
Program Name	Linear	Quasilinear	Nonlinear	Time	Frequency	Freight	Passenger (1)	Six Axle Locomotive	Unconventional
DYNALYST II	X				X	(4)	X	(4)	(4)
TRKHNTII	X				X	---	X	---	X
CARHNT II	X				X	---	X	---	---
CU/ASU 9-DOF	X				X	X	---	---	---
CU/ASU 17-DOF	X				X	X	X	---	X
CU/ASU 15-DOF	X				X	X	X	---	X
CU/ASU 23-DODF	X				X	X	X	---	X
AAR/TTD Freight Car Model	X				X	X	X	---	X
AAR/TTD Locomotive Model	X				X	---	X	X(2)	---
FDM	X				X	X	---	---	---
9-DOF Quasilinear Model		X			X	X	---	---	---

Table 2 Summary and Comparison of Digital Programs for Rail Vehicle Lateral Stability Analyses (cont.)

Program Name	Special Features: Flexible Car Body	Special Features: Asymmetric	DOF	Stability Data: Eigen Problem Solution (Direct)	Stability Data: Manual Reduction	Plot Option	Time, per Simulation (sec)	User's Manual	Other Documentation
DYNALYST II	(4)	(4)	8,14	X		X	60	X	X
TRKHNTII	---	---	9	X		---	10	---	X
CARHNT II	---	---	21	X		---	30	---	X
CU/ASU 9-DOF	X	X	17	X		---	---		X
CU/ASU 17-DOF	X	---	19	X		---	---		X
CU/ASU 15-ODF	X	---	19	X		---	---		X
CU/ASU 23-DOF	X	---	23	X		---	---		X
AAR/TTD Freight Car Model	---	---	25	X		X	171-184	X	X
AAR/TTD Locomotive Model	---	---	2,7,9 17,21	X		X	90-100	X	X
FDM	X	X	13		(3)	X	360-540	X	X
9-DOF Quasilinear Model	---	---	9	X	---	---	---	---	X

(1) Most passenger car truck models can also depict 4-axle locomotive/trucks

(2) Also depicts 4-axle locomotive.

(3) Output is Nyquist diagram.

(4) General program can depict rail vehicles other than passenger and 4-axle locomotive types, with up to 25-DOF flexible car bodies and asymmetries.

point. This is supported by analyses conducted with the CU/ASU 17 DOF [14] and 23 DOF [4] models. The analyses indicated that the critical speeds of hopper and flat car models were negligibly affected by the car body's lateral and torsional bending stiffness, while the existence of wheel/rail profile asymmetries can have a dramatic effect on stability.

Thus, from the standpoint of the range of asymmetries that can be modeled, the FDM program appears to be the most versatile, followed closely by the CU/ASU 17 DOF program. In terms of the range of truck types that can be modeled, the CU/ASU 17, 19, and 23 DOF models, and the AAR/TTD freight and locomotive models are most versatile. It should be noted that the DYNALYST II program offers the most overall versatility in terms of general programming capability. This is, the program can accept the user's equations of motion for a variety of vehicle models. However, the preprogrammed models provided by DYNALYST II are not as versatile as the models mentioned above.

The 9 DOF Quasilinear Program provides the most versatility for roller bearing freight car models, since it provides the most accurate depictions of nonlinear effects such as wheel/rail geometry and dry friction, of the models listed in Table 2.

Plot options in various forms are provided for the DYNALYST II, AAR/TTD, and FDM models.

Documentation

The most complete and usable documentation is provided for the DYNALYST II, AAR/TTD, and FDM models. The documentation for most of the other models consists of (1) presentation and/or derivation of the equations of motion, (2) detailed schematics of the models, and/or (3) program listings and general discussions of the program capabilities and usage. User's manuals for some of the programs are forthcoming.

CONCLUSIONS

Due to the wide range of rail vehicle types and operating conditions which exist, and the specialized needs of the program users, it is inappropriate to rank the computer programs in terms of performance. Each program offers features that may make it a suitable choice of a given user.

There is a definite need for the development of test programs and analytical methods for the accurate validation of rail vehicle models in general. Until then, many existing computer programs may be suitable only for predicting qualitative trends in vehicle behavior. These efforts will help to establish clearly the range of validity of linear and quasilinear models for evaluating rail vehicle lateral stability.

REFERENCES

1 Wilkinson, J. H., The Algebraic Eigenvalue Problem, Oxford University Press, London, 1965.

2 Marcotte, P. P., "Lateral Dynamic Stability of Railway Bogie Vehicles," MS Thesis, University of Sheffield (England), May 1972.

3 Law, E. H., et al., "General Models for Lateral Stability Analysis of Railway Freight Vehicles," Report No. FRA-OR&D-77-36, PB 272371/AS, June 1977.

4 Hadden, J. A., "The Effects of Truck Design and Component Flexibility on the Lateral Stability of Railway Freight Vehicles," MS Thesis, Department of Mechanical Engineering, Clemson University, 1976.

5 Gard, J., and Brebner, M. A., "Algorithm 343, Eigenvalues and Eigenvectors of a Real General Matrix [F2]," Communications of the ACM, Vol. 11, No. 12, December 1968, pp. 820-826.

6 Doyle, G. R., and Prause, R. H., "Hunting Stability of Rail Vehicles with Torsionally Flexible Wheelsets," Journal of Engineering for Industry, Vol. 99, No. 1, February 1977, pp. 10-17.

7 Hasselman, T. K., and Bronowicki, A., "Dynalist II, A Computer Program for Stability and Dynamic Response Analysis of Rail Vehicle Systems," Volume I: Technical Report, Volume II: User's Manual, Volume III: Technical Report Addendum, and Volume IV: Revised User's Manual, Report No's. FRA-OR&D-75-22.I, II, III, IV,

8 Cheung, T. H. W., Garg, V. K., and Martin, G. C., "User's Manual Freight Car Hunting Model," AAR/TTD, Report R-251,

9 Garg, V. K., Hartmann, P. W., and Martin, G. C., "User's Manual Locomotive Hunting Model," AAR/TTD Report R-227.

10 "TDOP-Phase I Frequency Domain Model," by Southern Pacific Transportation Co., Report FRA/ORD-78-12, Vol. III (PB278700), Feb. 1978.

11 Hull, R. L., "An Investigation Into Nonlinear Railway Vehicle Response," MS Thesis, Department of Mechanical Engineering, Arizona State University, Tempe, Arizona, May 1977.

12 Hedrick, J. K., et al., "The Application of Quasi-linearization Techniques to Rail Vehicle Dynamic Analysis," Report No. FRA/OR&D-78/56, November 1978.

13 Fallon, W. J., "An Investigation of Railcar Model Validation," MS Thesis, Department of Mechanical Engineering, Arizona State University, Tempe, Arizona, May 1977.

14 Tuten, J. M., et al., "Lateral Stability of Freight Cars with Axles Having Different Wheel Profiles and Asymmetric Loading," Journal of Engineering for Industry, Vol. 101, No. 1, February 1979, pp. 1-16.

Programs for Train Dynamics

Sam Shum

Conrail

INTRODUCTION

One major area of concern to the railroad industry, the supply industry, and the government is the safe operation of the rail system. The railroad suffers losses of many millions of dollars worth of equipment, lading damages and losses, and personal injuries every year from accidents, derailments, and over-the-road and yard operations. Concerned parties, including the Federal Railroad Administration, the Association of American Railroads, the Railway Progress Institute, the Transportation Development Agency, universities, and railroad and supply industries, have pooled their resources for the formation and development of the Track Train Dynamics Programs, which have been functioning for about ten years. The Track Train Dynamics Program has addressed itself to many facets of the railroad problem; the computer modeling of train dynamics is one of the many areas that has achieved considerable success.

A moving freight train interacts with the track in three directions: longitudinal, lateral, and vertical. Locomotives provide tractive efforts for train motions, while braking provides for retardations. Couplers transmit drafting or buffing forces to cars from locomotives and maintain the trains intact. Starting and stopping, accelerating or braking, the existence of slacks, coupled with varying resistances due to grade and/or curvature changes set up differential velocities among neighboring vehicles. These phenomena of run-in or run-out actions generate in-train dynamic forces which, when high enough, can result in train separation, lading and equipment damage, derailments, and/or personal injuries.

Railroads have train operations over curvatures, turn-outs, and cross-overs on main lines and in-yard services. Some have relatively higher running speeds on level tangent territories than others. The lateral stability of trains in curve negotiations or in diverging on a turn-out or cross-over is a subject of concern. Hunting is a phenomenon which involves the lateral stability of equipment above certain critical speeds. Occasionally there is a train derailing on a curve, a cross-over, or a turn-out that many other trains have successfully negotiated. On-site derailment investigations may not always be able to uncover the exact cause or causes of accidents. A life reconstruction of the sequence of events for the derailment may be costly and impractical and will introduce further delays in the traffic flow. Moreover, it may not always be possible to gain additional information to explain the cause of the accident through this kind of endeavor; therefore, recommendations for preventing similar happenings are not always be available.

Railroads are interested in learning of the results of tests or analyses which can compare the performance of one design with another. For example, in hump yard operations, thousands of freight cars every day experience impact forces in the process of recoupling during classifications. The amount of lading and/or equipment damage could potentially be reduced through selection of the optimum suspension characteristics and shock absorbing devices for controlling the bouncing, pitching motions and the impact forces on the car body. Even over-the-road in-train dynamic forces could set up car body vertical motions and vibrations which can be responsible for many concealed damages on lading shipped over the rail.

The railroad and the supply industry are faced with the need for analysis tools which can shed more insight into the many problems of railroad operations. Specifically, computer modeling of train stabilities offers a better understanding of the interactions of train handling, train makeup, and equipment and track designs for a safer and a more profitable operation of the rail service.

Train Dynamics Models

The Train Dynamics Models developed through the Track Train Dynamics Program, the FRA, and other research efforts may be classified into three areas:

1. Models which specifically address the longitudinal train dynamics
2. Models which deal with the lateral dynamics
3. Models which cover areas of vertical dynamics

Table 1 summarizes various computer models in the area of train dynamics with a brief description of the basic applications of each and is followed by a more in-depth discussion of each computer model.

PROGRAM SUMMARIES

Train Operations Simulator (TOS)

Categories: Freight train performance, diesel-electric locomotives, longitudinal coupler force, L/V ratio, speed,and distance
Descriptive Program Title: Train Operations Simulator (TOS)
Authors: N. W. Luttrell, R. K. Gupta, R. M. Low G. C. Martin
Association of American Railroads
3140 South Federal Street
Chicago, Illinois 60616
Maintenance: Association of American Railroads
Date: Currently available
Capability: This program can simulate the performance of a freight train powered by diesel-electric locomotives over a piece of railroad with any combination of curvature and grades. Operation capabilities

Table 1 Train Dynamics Models

Train Dynamics	Model	Model Application	Program Language	Core Space Execution (K Bytes)	Availability
Longitudinal	Train Operations Simulator (TOS)	Train handling and train makeup analyses; derailment investigation; track and signal spacing design.	Fortran	216	AAR
	Detailed Longitudinal Train Action	Same as TOS model; evaluation of shock absorbing devices such as EOC and sliding sills in controlling train actions.	Fortran	About 400	AAR*
	Quasi-Static Lateral Train Stability Model (QLTS)	Establish train makeup guidelines; designs for curvature, crossovers, turn-outs, minimum tangent length in reverse curves and spiral lengths.	Fortran	292	AAR
Lateral	Detailed Lateral Train Stability Model	Train operation and train makeup guidelines; track design evaluation.	Fortran	---	AAR*
	Detailed Vertical Train Stability Model	Evaluation of suspension characteristics in controlling vertical stability lading acceleration analysis.	Fortran	156	AAR*
Vertical	Longitudinal Vertical Train Action	Same as Detailed Vertical Train Stability Model; study of effect of impacts on train vertical stability.	Fortran	64	WU,** FRA

* Model being finalized at the Association of American Railroads
** WU - Washington University; FRA - Federal Railroad Administration

include any combination of throttle and various modes of braking manipulations. The program has been applied for derailment investigation, train makeup studies, power selection, a train-handling training tool, signal spacing,and track layout designs.

Method: Based on the available tractive effort from locomotives and the total resistance acting against the train using the Davis Resistance formula, dynamic braking characteristics, and air brake forces from WABCO's freight train braking characteristics, the net force on the train is calculated. This net force determines whether the train will accelerate, decelerate, or remain at a constant speed. By numerical integration, train velocity and distance are determined. The relative velocities between neighboring vehicles, together with the amount of coupler slack, govern the buff and draft actions in the train and the magnitude of drawbar forces calculated according to draft gear characteristics.

Limitations and Restrictions: The drawbar forces and L/V ratios are quasi-dynamic and are good approximatins. They should not be considered as being absolutely exact.

Only one remote consist may be placed within the train close to the rear end. Only ABD valves are correctly handled during brake release. The program shows much quicker than actual release on AB valves. It does not have the provision for ABDW brake valves. Simulation of cyclic braking involving complete release is not accurate, and brake pipe leakage is assumed to be evenly distributed throughout train.

An undesired emergency with remote-control units cannot be simulated. The program cannot give correct results simulating an undesired emergency after a partial service brake application without having the previous brake application completed on the whole train.

The program does not give a complete echo of the input data. The user should not assume that data as input are absolutely correct.

Programming Language: FORTRAN

Documentation: Users, Technical, and Programming Manuals are available [1-4]. The Users Manual is written to be user oriented. However, due to the complexity of data for the Standard Library, locomotive and freight car characteristics, train handling commands, and track curvature and profile data, beginning users without railroad background may find it difficult to prepare data for simulation.

Input: Input may be divided into four areas:

1. Track Data: Curvature data includes degree of curve, length of spiral and curve, and superelevation. Profile data includes mileage and elevation.
2. Train Consist Data: Data required are for locomotive and freight cars. If different from those in the Standard Library (which comes with the program) the user must input various geometric parameters as well as the brake valve type, brake shoe type, and shoe forces. For locomotives not in the Standard Library, data such as tractive effort and dynamic braking characteristics are required.
3. Train Operations Command: These include commands such as speed, throttle, and brake pipe reductions and brake releases, independent and dynamic brake application, etc.
4. Title Information: This is one card stating the title that the users wish to appear on output.

Output: This is given in three sections:

1. Train Consist Data: The number of locomotives, number of cars, train length, and tonnages and a list of primary characteristics of each vehicle.

2. Power Summary: The tractive effort and dynamic braking characteristics including HP on rail and transition speed.
3. Performance Printout:
   (a) Time, station name, and mile post location of front end of train
   (b) Speed limit and actual train speed
   (c) Locomotive throttle setting and amperage
   (d) Train brake setting, brake pipe and brake cylinder pressures
   (e) Maximum value and location of drawbar and L/V ratio
   (f) Fore and aft drawbar forces and L/V ratios on vehicles selected by user for each print interval
   (g) A summary for maximum buff, draft, and L/V with corresponding location in train for the simulation
   (h) An indication of whenever there are changes in operation commands, grade, and/or curvatures.

Software Operation: The program is available for both batch and time-sharing modes. For the batch mode all input data with the necessary Job Control Language are on punched cards. The time-sharing option is available on the DEC-20 computer located in-house at the Technical Center of the AAR in Chicago. To adopt the time-sharing mode on other computers may require slight modifications.

Hardware: The program was developed on an IBM 370/158 machine requiring 216 K bytes of core storage. This program can be run on other computers with minor modifications.

Usage: To date, more than 50 organizations, including government agencies, the supply industry, research organizations, universities, and railroads have purchased this program. It has been used extensively by several major railroads in the United States. Some comments by users are given in another section of this report.

Typical Running Time: A typical stopping simulation for a freight train at 50 to 60 MPH requires about 1 minute of IBM 360/168 CPU time. Simulation using the automatic mode requires approximately twice as much time as the manual modes. A typical simulation consumes about 1/3 as much CPU time as simulation time on an IBM 360/168 computer.

Availability: TOS is available to the general public for a fee of $50.00.

Contact: Director - Technical Center
Association of American Railroads
3140 South Federal Street
Chicago, Illinois 60616

The fee covers the magnetic tape of the program and the documentation available at the time of the purchase.

Quasi-Static Lateral Train Stability Model (QLTS)

Categories: Train consists in curve negotiation, lateral stability, L/V ratio, coupler angles, buff, and draft

Descriptive Program Title: Quasi-Static Lateral Train Stability Model (QLTS)

Authors: L. R. Thomas, R. D. MacMillan, G. C. Martin
Association of American Railroads
3140 South Federal Street
Chicago, Illinois 60616

Maintenance: Association of American Railroads

Date: Currently available. Updated versions are only available to individual railroads accessing the AAR computer.

Capability: The program simulates the lateral stability of a train consist in curve negotiations under buff or draft drawbar forces. It calculates derailment tendencies through L/V ratios of rail-roll-over and wheel climb and coupler lateral angles. The program can be used for evaluation of long car - short car, loaded and empty combinations of train consists. It has been used for the determination of minimum tangent lengths between reverse curves, the effect of spiral lengths in curve negotiation, and the establishment of guide-lines for train makeup, and it has been applied as a design tool for freight car geometric considerations.

Method: Based on the geometric interaction of track configuration with vehicle arrangement, the amount of buff or draft forces, the train speed and the amount of superelevation in a curve, this program computes the equilibrium condition using a coupler model and a vehicle model. The resultant lateral loading at bolster centers at equilibrium is used to calculate L/V ratios of rail roll-over and wheel climb.

Limitations and Restrictions: This is a quasi-static model which does not provide for inertial force considerations. A maximum of 2500 feet of track or 100 vehicles can be simulated. The only available alignment control types for locomotives is M380/381 and for freight cars is on E-60 square-butt coupler with M-17A draft gear and an F-butt type coupler. Maximum drawbar force on vehicles must be less than 450,000 lbs. There is no lateral coupler swing limit and the user must manually check each calculation of the coupler angle against the maximum allowable for the equipment. The L/V ratios calculated do not take into account the coupler arm's contacting strikers.

Programming Language: FORTRAN IV

Documentation: User's Technical and Progamming Manuals are available through the Association of American Railroads [5-7]. Due to the simplicity of the model, all documentation is self-explanatory. These manuals are easy to follow for those users who have some back-ground in freight car geometric parameters and spirals and super elevation of curves.

Input: The input is in three parts:

1. Track Data: Requires lengths of tangent, lead and trail spirals, length and degree of curve, and amount of superelevation
2. Train Operation Data: Includes speed of train, drawbar force, start and stop times, and interval of simulation
3. Train Consist Data: Includes bolster (truck) center distance, length between bolster center and coupler pin, coupler length, maximum lateral offset of bolster center from track center line, type of alignment control, vehicle weight, and the net lateral load at the leading outer wheel of each vehicle.

Output: There are two sections of output:

1. Track Generator: The track generator gives an echo of the input data and generates the X-y coordinates, and the angle to the origin of the track centerline. It shows the radii of curvature and the superelevation for every chord length as defined by the user.
2. Results of Equilibrium: Every calculation time-step gives an echo of the input geometry of each vehicle. In addition, the following are calculated:
   (a) Location of vehicle on track
   (b) Bolster lateral displacement and reactions

(c) Coupler lateral angles and couple pin reactions
(d) Centrifugal and superelevation forces
(e) Alignment control moments if present
(f) Drawbar force on each vehicle and L/V ratios for rail roll-over and wheel climb

Software Operation: Both batch and time-sharing modes are available.

Hardware: This program was developed on the IBM 370/158 machine requiring 292 K bytes of core for execution. Only minor modifications, if any, are required to operate on other computers.

Usage: There are relatively few users for this program. They are mainly from railroads. At one time, this program was heavily used to determine critical consists in train makeups, minimum tangent length, and effect of spiral lengths in curves. The Transportation System Center has used a modified version of this program to generate a Buff Stability Index and the Southern Pacific Transportation Company has utilized information generated from this program to improve train makeup.

Typical Running Time: Typical running time on an IBM 370/158 machine varies from a few CPU seconds to over a minute, depending on the length of the train consist, the train speed, and the calculation interval specified by the user.

Availability: This program is available to the general public for $50.
contact: Director
Technical Center of the Association
of American Railroads
3140 South Federal Street
Chicago, Illinois 60616

The fee covers the cost of the program on magnetic tape with sample input data and the costs of all documentation available at the time of purchase.

Detail Vertical Train Stability Model (VTS)

Categories: Vertical train stability, vertical forces, motions, and displacements

Descriptive Program Title: Detailed Vertical Train Stability Model

Authors: T. B. Raidt, K. L. Shum, G. C. Martin, V. K. Garg
Association of American Railroads
Track Train Dynamics Phase II
3140 South Federal Street
Chicago, Illinois 60616

Maintenance: Association of American Railroads

Date: Currently unavailable. The program is being finalized.

Capability: The program can be used as an analysis tool for the vertical forces and motion due to the longitudinal in-train dynamic forces which, when they become larger, can cause vertical coupler disengagement and/or car body separation from trucks. It can be used for train makeup evaluations in terms of vertical stability.

Method: This is a two-dimensional model developed to study the vertical and pitching motions and forces of ladings and trucks in a train consist under the action of in-train longitudinal forces. Car bodies, trucks, and lading are assumed to be rigid masses interconnected by a nonlinear spring and damper system. The equations of motion describing the force-acceleration relationship are numerically integrated using a modified Euler's method which yields velocites and displacements.

Limitations and Restrictions: The current version of the program does not have the capability of train operation simulation. In train dynamics, drawbar forces can be obtained through simulations using either the Train Operations Simulator (TOS), or the Detailed Train

Action Model (DTAM), or through field tests. These forces may then be used as input horizontal coupler forces. Not more than ten vehicles in a train consist can be simulated.

Programming Language: FORTRAN IV

Documentation: To date, only the User's and Technical Manuals are available [8,9]. The User's Manual is fairly easy to follow. The use of sample input cards and illustrations and suggested values for various input parameters is advantageous. A Technical Manual with illustrations helps the user gain insight into the model. It also compares the simulated versus test results.

Input: There are four sections of input:

1. Consist data which includes the number of cars, first and last car numbers, and train speed
2. Car data by geometry, weight, stiffness, and snubber damping force, coupler slacks, mass moment of inertia in pitching, and coefficient of friction
3. Horizontal coupler force acting at the front and rear end of simulated consist as a function of time
4. Simulation data, which includes time duration of simulation, integration time step, and plot option

Output: There are seven sections of output:

1. Echo of input data
2. Car body acceleration, velocity, and displacement
3. Coupler horizontal and vertical force and vertical slippage
4. Truck horizontal and vertical reactions and vertical displacement
5. Lading acceleration, velocity and displacement, friction, and end wall forces
6. Plot option echo
7. Draft gear characteristics

Plot output is also available if desired

Software Operation: Batch modes in cards. No pre- or postprocessors are available.

Hardware: The program was developed on an IBM 370/158 computer requiring 156 K bytes of core for execution. A total of five input, output, logical units are required in this program.

Usage: There are a limited number of users from railroads.

Typical Running Time: A typical 1 second run-in simulation on a seven car consist uses about 20 seconds of IBM 370/158 CPU time.

Availability: The program is being finalized. It will be available soon for $50 through the Director - Technical Center
Association of American Railroads
3140 South Federal Street
Chicago, Illinos 60616

The fee covers costs of the magnetic tape of the program and all documentation available at the time of purchase.

Detailed Longitudinal Train Action Model (DTAM)

Categories: Longitudinal coupler forces, train operation, speed, distance

Authors: G. C. Martin, W. E. Plouffe, S. Ahmed, H. Antezak and H. Tideman
Association of American Railroads
3140 South Federal Street
Chicago, Illinois 60616

Maintenance: Association of American Railroads

Date: Soon available. The program is being finalized.

Capability: The program handles simulations of freight train longitudinal train actions due to train handling, profile, and grade changes. The program can be used for performance evaluation of end-of-car cushioning devices and sliding sill equipment in controlling in-train dynamic forces.

Method: The program can be classified into 3 subprograms by function. The Standard Library Program prepares vehicle data for standard locomotives and freight cars and stores the characteristics of equipment in the Standard Library, which may be saved for future runs. The Run Library Program constructs files for profile, curvature, consist, and station data. All data prepared by the Standard Library and Run Library Programs are input to the Detailed Train Action Model's Forward Integration Program which computes the acceleration of the train for each time step based on the net force and mass of the system. Numerical integration for velocity and displacement can be utilized through Hamming's, Runge-Kutta fourth order, or Beta method of integration. Relative velocities of neighboring vehicles, together with the amount of coupler slack form the basis for computing longitudinal coupler forces from draft gear characterisics.

Limitations and Restrictions: The program does not consider effects of track irregularities, worn wheels, and stuck brakes. All drawbar forces are assumed to be acting only in the direction of travel of the train. Only Mark-50 draft gear characteristics have been modeled in the program. Users, however, have been provided the option of inputting characteristics of any cushioning device.

Programming Language: FORTRAN IV

Documentation: User's, Technicals and Progamming Manuals are available [10-12]. The DTAM User's Manual describing the Standard Library, the Run Library, and the Forward Integration program, is somewhat confusing to first-time users, not because of the way the manual was written, but because of the complexities of the idea of three programs in one. Beginning users without prior exposure to the concept of a Standard Library are strongly urged to attend one of the AAR-TTD seminars for further explanation of the program. The Technical Manual is quite technical and contains the validation of the DTAM program against SP Steel Coil Train Tests comparing stop distance, time, and coupler forces. The section illustrating tested drawbar forces versus relative car positions indicated a high degree of nonlinearities of energy dissipation exhibited by draft gears and hence explains why it is difficult to accurately model a draft gear. The Programming Manual is voluminous and attempts to illustrate program logic in great detail.

Input: The Standard Library data should be available as part of the program package. Unless this is missing from the magnetic tape delivered, it is not necessary to input any data for the Standard Library Program. Input to the Run Library Program consists of track data including station name and speed limit, curvature and profile data, vehicle geometric and brake characteristics, train brake pipe pressure, and tractive effort and dynamic characteristics for non-standard power units. Input to the forward integration simulator includes the number of vehicles in the train, speed, throttle, and brake handling sequence, the condition of the rail, the integration time step, and instructions for how often braking and grade routines should be called.

Output: Output consists of an initial echo of input data including station and speed limit, curvature and profile data, train brake characteristics, and the vehicle listing showing all data used; this is followed by program debugging aids of initial forces and displacements of vehicles and various indices for error analysis. The main output of the DTAM are time and speed of the train and the mile post and distance reached by the front locomotives, throttle setting and amperage reading on locomotives, train line pressure, and independent brake setting. On vehicles specified by the user, the program outputs the vehicle location with the grade and curvature information, brake pipe and cylinder pressure, maximum and minimum front and rear drawbar forces. The program also indicates the maximum drawbar force and the location for each print interval. Plot outputs are also available.

Software Operation: Batch mode only; all input data is on punched cards; no pre- or postprocessors are available.

Hardware: The program was developed on an IBM 370/158 machine requiring bout 400 K bytes of core for execution.

Usage: There are limited users only because the program is still not released.

Typical Running Time: DTAM requires about 15-20 IBM 370/158 CPU minutes for typical stopping simulations on a medium length train using the R-K integration scheme. Simulation time increases with train length and decreases with the use of Hamming's method and bigger time-steps for integration. However, the user is advised not to sacrifice program accuracy and integration stability by going to too large an integration time step, nor should he decrease the integration time-step unnecessarily, which will end up with cumulative truncation errors.

Availability: This is not currently available to the public. The program is in its final stage before release. When approved, the program should be available through the

Director
Technical Center of the Association
of American Railroads
3140 South Federal Street
Chicago, Illinois 60616

Longitudinal - Vertical Train Action Model

Categories: Railroads, accident, collision, derailment, coupler override
Descriptive Program Title: Longitudinal - Vertical Train Action Model
Author: K. Y. Sheng
Maintenance: School of Engineering and Applied Science
Washington University
St. Louis, Missouri 63130
Date: June, 1976

Capabilities: The program can be used for the simulation of the longitudinal - vertical motion of railroad cars during impact. The model is capable of modeling friction draft gears and hydraulic cushioning devices.

Method: Each freight car is modeled as rigid masses connected by springs and dampers having degrees of freedom in the longitudinal, vertical, and pitching directions. The underframe of each car is represented by a linear spring in series with the draft gear spring, which is represented by a hysteresis loop with different loading and unloading stiffnesses. Depending on the amount of coupler slack and the displacement, the horizontal coupler force is calculated from the draft gear characteristics. Vertical coupler force, vertical and horizontal truck forces, and lading dynamics are also computed. The program utilizes the fourth order Runge-Kutta for numerical integrations.

Limitations and Restrictions: The program does not provide for the consideration of plastic deformation of underframes under impact conditions.

Programming Language: FORTRAN

Documentation: Theoretical Manual and User's Guides are available [13]. Both theoretical and user's sections of the manual are relatively straightforward. Output is denoted in terms of program variables.

Input: There are three types of data to be input:

1. Train Consist Data: Total number of cars and number of impacted cars with selection of degree of freedom, coulomb of viscous for track vertical damping, and plot option
2. Simulation Data: Impact speed, program input boundaries, time steps for point and plot outputs
3. Vehicle Geometric, Weight Data: Inertia and stiffness parameters

Output: Output is in three sections.

1. I/O logical units and word storage size
2. Echo of the input data including total number of cars, impact car, and impact speed. Simulation control data including step size, initial and final time, print and plot time steps. Vehicle parameters for all the cars, and draft gear and underframe characteristics.
3. For each print step it gives the horizontal coupler force, coupler displacements, relative displacements between adjacent cars, horizontal and vertical truck forces, coupler offsets, and truck separations and coupler disengagement, if any.

Software Operation: Batch mode

Hardware: This program was developed on an IBM 360/65 computer requiring 64 K bytes for execution with NSIZE = 1000. No pre- or postprocessor is available.

Usage: The number of users is unknown.

Typical Running Time: For a 0.04 second simulation, it took about 2.8 IBM 360/65 CPU seconds for execution.

Availability: A document which contains the listing of the program is available from

National Technical Information Service
Springfield, Virginia 22161

ACKNOWLEDGMENT

The author acknowledges the support of C. P. Popma, A.V.P. Quality Control and Mechanical Engineering, G. A. Thelon, Director of Mechanical Engineering, and G. C. Martin, former Director of Mechanical Engineering of Consolidated Rail Corporation, in the preparation of this chapter. Further, J. L. Hamilton's aid is also deeply appreciated.

REFERENCES

1 Luttrell, N. W., Gupta, R. K., Low, E. M., and Martin, G. C., "Train Operations Simulator - User's Manual," AAR-TTD publication, R-198.

2 Low, E. M., and Garg, V. K., "Train Operations Simulator - Technical Documentation," AAR-TTD publication, R-269.

3 Low, E. M., and Garg, V. K., "Train Operations Simulator - Programming Manual," AAR-TTD publication, R-359.

4 Low, E. M., and Garg, V. K., "Validation of Train Operations Simulator Computer Program," AAR-TTD publication, R-335

5 Thomas, L. R., MacMillan, R. D., and Martin, G. C., "Quasi-Static Lateral Train Stability Model User's Manual," AAR-TTD report, R-207.

6 Thomas, L. R., MacMillan, R. D., and Martin, G. C., "Quasi-Static Lateral Train Stability Model Technical Documentation," AAR-TTD report, R-209.

7 Thomas, L. R., MacMillan, R. D., and Martin, G. C., "Quasi-Static Lateral Train Stability Model Programming Manual," AAR-TTD report, R-208.

8 Raidt, J. B., Shum, K. L., Martin, G. C., and Garg, V. K., "Detailed Vertical Train Stability Model User's Manual," AAR-TTD report, R-261.

9 Raidt, J. B., Shum, K. L., Martin, G. C., and Garg, V. K., "Detailed Vertical Train Stability Model Technical Documentation," AAR-TTD report, R-261.

10 Martin, G. C., Plouffe, W. E., Ahmed, S., Antczak, H., and Tideman, H., "Detailed Longitudinal Train Action Model User's Manual," AAR-TTD report, R-220

11 Martin, G. C., and Tideman, H., "Detailed Longitudinal Train Action Model Technical Documentation," AAR-TTD report, R-221.

12 Low, E. M., and Garg, V. K., "Detailed Longitudinal Train Action Model Programming Manual," AAR-TTD report, R-296.

13 Sheng, K. Y., "Theoretical Manual and User's Guide for Longitudinal - Vertical Train Action Model by Washington University," Report FRA/ORD, 76/278.

PART III

REVIEWS OF COMPUTATIONAL MECHANICS TECHNOLOGY

Structural Mechanics Software Evaluation: A Bigeneric Diagnostic Framework

Robert E. Nickell

Applied Science & Technology

INTRODUCTION

In a previous report [1], a set of general criteria was described for critically evaluating structural mechanics software. These criteria were oriented toward an external intervention mode of evaluation -- that is, the rules are designed to permit a skilled individual with no previous experience with a particular structural software package to systematically and logically characterize the package. The documentation, algorithms, program architecture, and program performance on selected exercises are each examined objectively, with the external intervenor selected both for competence and independence from the developer/user community.

Another approach to critical software evaluation is receiving increased emphasis. This approach can be described as internal intervention, implying that the software is able to deduce the quality of results obtained through some type of systematic application of internally programmed criteria. The most popular notions relate to self-adaptive mesh refinement and a posteriori error estimation.

The external and internal intervention modes of evaluation should be considered complementary, since they address different parts of the problem. Both are outlined here. First, the general criteria and some detailed examples of externally oriented evaluation are given. Then some thoughts and preliminary results from internally oriented evaluation are offered. The conclusion is reached that a combination of third-party (not the developer and not the user) and self-generated (by the software) evaluation are pivotal ingredients in any overall structural mechanics software quality assurance plan.

EXTERNAL EVALUATION CRITERIA

The state of the art of external evaluation of software is described well by Andrew and Taig [1], who describe the process in quasi-legal terms as certification. They state that "complete certification of large scale computer programs is the elusive goal of all software engineers." They hasten to add, however, that such a goal may not be practical at present;

instead, the more universal approach is to certify the software probabilistically. This should be interpreted to mean that a sample space is created from verification solutions generated by the developer and qualification solutions generated by various second-party users. (Verification is used here in the sense of testing the theory coded in the software for correctness; qualification is used in the sense of a second party trying to explore the application of the software to a particular problem area in a production configuration.) This sample space then permits some confidence estimate that different, but somewhat related, problems can be successfully solved.

Only recently have efforts been initiated to formalize third-party intervention into this probabilistic certification process. Such formalized intervention was suggested by Dr. Ruth M. Davis, then under secretary of defense for research and advanced development, who stated [2] to a Congressional subcommittee in April 1979 that the key software problems within DoD were software reliability and computer systems accountability. Dr. Davis described several examples that illustrated the lack of reliability and proposed a major DoD initiative to rectify the situation, closing with the phrase: "I see an immediate need for this type of initiative in DoD because we cannot rely on the consumer computer market to produce software of adequate quality." The theme in this statement is that quality control and reliability should be taken beyond the usual developer/user axis to include third-party intervention (or evaluation). One such effort at third-party intervention is described next.

The Interagency Software Evaluation Group (ISEG), [3], is composed of representatives from a number of U.S. government agencies with an interest in improved reliability of applications software. The ISEG has also encouraged information exchange with the industrial and academic communities in order to provide better definition and wider applicability of the evaluation effort. For the present, only structural mechanics software is being considered for evaluation, primarily because the fluid mechanics and heat transfer fields do not yet reflect an advanced state of software development for second-party usage.

With active participation from the Army, Navy, and Air Force laboratories and contractors, a list of potential structural software packages to be evaluated was generated. The list was screened according to availability (how rapidly and independently could a third party -- not the developer or a member of the user community -- obtain the software and make it operational), documentation (a users' manual, at a minimum, but hopefully including theoretical background and example problems), and verification (sufficient use by second parties and a sufficient number of solved examples which could be reproduced by the evaluator, so that correct coding of the principal functional characteristics is assured). The screening rules were developed prior to, but are in general agreement with, recommendations by Andrew and Taig [1] regarding the initial screening of candidate software by a major company. Those packages that survived the screening were then organized into general groupings, with the ISEG as a body making the final decision on the particular software to be evaluated.

The general purpose production code NASTRAN was selected for evaluation, which is currently underway and scheduled for completion in September 1980. The nonlinear research code ADINA was also selected and its evaluation is essentially complete. The nonlinear, special purpose shell code STAGS is in the very early stages of evaluation, while the linear code SAP is scheduled for evaluation within the coming year. These four structural software packages cover a broad spectrum of users and applications; therefore, a correspondingly broad set of evaluation criteria were sought which could be generally applied to all of the candidate software.

The third parties that conduct these evaluations must, of course, possess certain qualifications. Many of these will become apparent as the evaluation criteria are introduced and discussed. As a minimum, however, experience as both a developer and a user is essential. Conflict of interest, such as that of a developer of software competitive with the product being evaluated, should be avoided. Also, independence from the "closed" user community for that software is required. The term closed, in this sense, refers to a second party who is dedicated to the use of the subject software to the exclusion of other codes.

The evaluation criteria were discussed in Ref. [3] under four groupings: (i) documentation; (ii) functional description; (iii) architectural description; and (iv) advanced evaluation exercises. They are summarized here for completeness.

Henrywood [4] has provided an excellent summary of the documentation requirements for a major finite element code. A slightly modified list is given here. Of greatest importance is a user's manual which, in its most primitive form, merely outlines the input data, with perhaps a few comments or explanations aimed at the most prevalent user input errors. There is an equal propensity for an overly complex user manual and one which is too meager. Second, the technical (or theoretical) manual provides the background for the algorithms and procedures adopted by the developer. Often, this may be a collection of journal articles but, more properly, it should be focused more toward the subject software. Third, a set of verification and, if possible, qualification examples should be included. Fourth, a programmer's manual is essential if the software is to be maintained by a second party or if the software is operational on more than a single system. In addition, the theoretical and programmer's manuals provide the basic information from which the functional and architectural descriptions are derived.

In addition to quantity, the documentation should be evaluated for quality, especially as it pertains to end use reliability. It should be recognized, however, that documentation in itself cannot hope to address the major sources of unreliability. Nevertheless, standards have been adopted for documentation [5].

The functional and architectural descriptions are a part of the evaluation in order to help mitigate two sources of unreliability; the application of the software to a problem involving a combination of functions for which it was not intended, and the application of the software to a problem for which it was intended, but in a configuration that it cannot support. A practical approach to both of these descriptions is through the definition of data bases and libraries.

A finite element software package manipulates data bases associated with nodal points, elements, and volume integration points. Typical nodal point data bases include coordinates, kinematic constraints, concentrated loads, and values of displacement, velocity, acceleration, temperature, etc. A typical element data base would be the connectivity, but could also include distributed loads and local matrices (if a frontal solver is used, for example). Integration point data bases usually include stress and strain information. Another data base, quite apart from those associated with nodal points, elements, and volume integration points, is a logical data base that enables the package to select the proper combination of components from its resident libraries.

These libraries include, but need not be limited to, the following:

1. The geometric library, which consists of the element strain-displacement options (both linear and nonlinear representations), the kinematic boundary condition options, coordinate transformations, and

generalized kinematic constraint conditions; additional features, such as a coordinate update option that enables the program to handle both full Lagrangian and updated Lagrangian reference systems, might be offered; it should be pointed out that an essential feature of any general purpose structural code is the ability to incorporate generalized kinematic constraints between different portions of the element library (e.g., beam, plate, or shell elements enforcing a plane section constraint on a series of continuum elements);

2. The constitutive library, which consists of the various material property models available to the user, ranging from linear, isotropic elasticity to nonlinear, anisotropic elastic-plastic-creep behavior; if the constitutive and geometric libraries are kept properly independent, each constitutive capability will be available for any geometric configuration; one of the underlying principles of general purpose coding is to maintain this independence;

3. The procedures library, which contains the range of analysis options open to the user; typical examples are linear static analysis, linear dynamic analysis (either by mode superposition or by a variety of direct integration operators), eigenvalue extraction (whether for dynamics or for linearized buckling analysis), nonlinear static analysis, nonlinear dynamic analysis, linear elastic fracture mechanics, fluid-structure interaction analysis, thermostructural analysis, and limit analysis; it should be noted that solution and accuracy-preserving strategies, such as in-core or out-of-core solution, iteration, and equilibrium load correction, are considered to be part of the procedures library.

With these data bases and libraries defined, the code architecture can be seen to be a form for accepting input from the user in order to create some of the data bases, for manipulating and recreating data bases through the exercise of the resident libraries, and the delivery to the user of the appropriate output data bases.

The third-party evaluator then can determine what the code is able to do, producing a functional description, and how the code is trying to implement these functions, producing an architectural description. The highest level of modularity -- the preprocessor, the analysis module, and the postprocessor -- have functions and architecture readily outlined in these terms. The preprocessor may include any or all of the following features:

a) Reading and printing of input data, with possible format conversion, depending upon the freedom or rigidity of the input format;

b) Automatic generation of portions of the nodal point and element data bases, with possible interpolants and smoothing algorithms designed to provide some control over mesh condition number (vertex angle acuity) and aspect ratio (in matter of fact, the combination of mesh aspect ratio and deformation gradients are needed in order to properly allocate mesh spacing; the deformation gradients are, of course, unknown at the preprocessing stage);

c) Creation of other data bases for use in the analysis module, such as material properties or element data subsets;

d) Creation of special file structure required by the input data, such as restarting or plotting, or for storage of geometric and material information, coefficient assembly and/or equation-solving; files for two or more distinct analysis modules would be included in this item;

e) Initialization of constants, flags, logical variables, and arrays;

f) Preanalysis plotting, aimed at verifying the mesh geometry, boundary conditions, material properties (constitutive representations, such as creep laws or elastic-plastic stress-strain laws, can be plotted in order to expose any regions of error or omission), or other input features.

Many modern preprocessors are interactive, interrogative, and are self-contained with respect to documentation. For example, the user may be creating a portion of the input data base interactively, with the pre-processor interrogating the user intermittently and providing a display of the necessary documentation at decision points in the preparatory process.

The analysis module contains the connective coding that permits the data bases and libraries to interact. An excellent framework for the submodularization necessary to carry this out is given by Nagy [6]. His Fig. 1 and the corresponding section on modularity are the starting point for the evaluation.

Postprocessing modules remain in a relatively primitive state, in comparison to preprocessing and analysis capabilities. As a convenience to the user, almost all commercial and many research structural software packages provide plotting files of stresses, strains, displacements, etc., that can be accessed by the local plotting devices. In recent years, there has been an upsurge in the development of postprocessors to evaluate the results from one or more analyses against design allowables, providing the user with a direct confirmation of structural integrity. Some attention has been paid to printed output formatting, aimed at producing results in a form that can be put directly into a reporting document. However, very little progress has been made toward a self-contained evaluation of the analysis results, aimed at providing the user with a quantitative assessment of the reliability of the structural model. In some cases, however, this type of postprocessing is available and merits special attention in the code evaluation.

The functional and architectural descriptions form a reference point for systematically and intelligently enlarging the probabilistic certification sample space, which was defined previously as the space of developer verification solutions combined with second-party qualification solutions. A third-party evaluator now enters into the phase of advanced evaluation exercises. Previously, in Ref.[3], these exercises were discussed in terms of discretization checks, energy checks, efficiency comparisons, and so forth. While these may be desirable goals, a more practical and modest aim should be to develop pathological examples that probe the boundaries of the sample space.

Pathology can be isolated, e.g., testing a time integration operator for stability and accuracy by gradually increasing the time step size, or changing system properties gradually so that two dynamic eigenvalues become less distinct and the extraction capability of an eigenvalue subroutine can be tested. Also, pathology can be combined, such as exercising constitutive and finite deformation options simultaneously, in order to test the logical flow.

The above general criteria for third-party evaluation of structural mechanics software represent the state of the art for external assurance of reliability and supplement two other components of the software quality assurance program -- developer software engineering and second-party (user) statistics.

INTERNAL EVALUATION CRITERIA

The external evaluation methodology provides a significant improvement in reliability through the efforts of a skilled third party concerned with the quantity and quality of the documentation, the description of the functional characteristics of the software, the architectural robustness of the coding, and the pathological enlargement of the sample space of correct solutions obtained with the software. The latter item follows the current trend toward quasi-legal certification by probabilistic means, whereby the demonstration (verification) solutions offered by the developer are combined with the successful solutions obtained by a wide variety of second-party users to form a sample space. A different problem then has a measurable outcome for successful solution.

Even though the software has been certified probabilistically in this fashion, the different (but related) problem may not yield a correct solution because of input or modeling error. In order to extend the certification process somewhat farther, additional "third-party" intervention is needed, this time by the software itself. The developer can provide a preprocessor, for example, which interrogates the user's input file, with appropriate "evaluation criteria" and corresponding messages to help the user modify the input, if required. Some modest attempts to develop such interrogative and evaluative preprocessors are underway.

Another example is provided by built-in error controls and slightly adaptive solution strategies, especially in nonlinear problems. Hibbitt and Karllson [7] have implemented one such strategy in a nonlinear dynamics code. A single-step, modified Newmark implicit time integration method provides a predicted set of displacements, velocities, and accelerations at the end of the time step of concern. Because the modified Newmark method represents a continuous distribution of kinematic quantities throughout the time step, as a function of initial values at the beginning of the step and values at the end of the step, out-of-balance residual forces can be computed at the middle of the interval. If the residuals are large, in comparison to incremental loads or changes in inertial forces, the solution could be iterated or the time step could be reduced. Similarly, if the residual forces are small, the time step could be increased.

Other measures of error may eventually lead to adaptive procedures. Until recently, for instance, an exercise to test the algorithm for integrating the rate equations of plasticity had to be indirect; that is, the error was inferred by examining successive iterates of the effective plastic strain increment or the unbalanced force residuals or some other indirect measure of accuracy. However, a systematic approach to error evaluation was suggested by Krieg and Krieg [8] for elastic-perfectly plastic materials and has been extended by Schreyer et al. [9] for work hardening materials. Error is measured, for the elastic-perfectly-plastic case, entirely in terms of angular deviation along the yield surface between the approximate and exact solutions, as seen by viewing the stresses on the Π-plane (along the hydrostatic axis). An additional parameter, the percentage difference in yield surface radius, arises from the inclusion of work hardening.

One of the assumptions implied in both the Krieg and Krieg and Schreyer et al. works is that iteration of the rate equation integration procedure is not considered. For example, the conventional approach, the tangent stiffness method, was not analyzed. Instead, a tangent stiffness predictor with radial return to the yield surface was evaluated and compared an explicit radial return method. Various subincrementation strategies, which serve no purpose for iterated tangent stiffness calculations, are used to improve the accuracy of the two methods. The iterated tangent stiffness, however, is successively corrected so that the stiffness reflects the current estimates of the normal to the yield surface. A mean, or average, normal is used for the condition when a stress point moves from inside to outside the yield surface in a load increment. Improved accuracy might be obtained by enforcing a mean normal for starting points on the yield surface as well.

Irrespective of the deficiencies of these recent investigations, the error measurements in terms of angle and yield surface modulus might someday be used as direct convergence parameters, rather than the indirect measures currently employed, for iterated tangent stiffness elastic-plastic calculations. Relatively simple modifications would permit a scaling of the load incrementation, as well, should the incremental solution fail to converge adequately after two or three iterations.

Our intent here, however, is not to review all the possible direct and indirect measures of error in finite element computation. Instead, an evaluation criterion that uses the finite element solution to glean information on its quality, in terms of discretization error, is offered. In order to maintain some agreement with generally accepted terminology, the criterion is referenced as an adaptive mesh adjustment and refinement technique.

Adaptive mesh adjustment and refinement has been a research topic for several years, with most of the contributions attributable to applied mathematicians, rather than engineering software developers. Because the adaptation strategies depend upon computed values of equilibrium or momentum error residuals [10] and upon adjustment/refinement criteria from approximation theory and error analysis, the engineering community has been reluctant to adopt and extend the procedures.

In this treatment we set forth an experiential framework, based on numerous finite element calculations of problems with linear and quadratic continuum element formulations, both in solid and fluid/thermal mechanics. The technique was originally conceived purely as a means for evaluating the relative convergence properties of various elements in general purpose structural software element libraries and was thought to be a means for upgrading the quality of element library evaluation to the point reached by some of the previous examples, each of which tests a feature of the analysis procedures library.

Methods for evaluating the procedures library of finite element/difference computer programs have become quite sophisticated in comparison to geometric (element) libraries. Standardized single element tests have been described by Robinson [11] for membrane and plate elements, consisting of combinations of nodal point load and constraint conditions designed to exercise the fundamental deformation modes. For instance, a four-node quadrilateral membrane element has eight degrees of freedom, and, therefore, the stiffness matrix has eight eigenvalues. If the element is properly formulated, three of these eigenvalues will be virtually zero, corresponding to rigid body modes (two in-plane translations and a rotation about the membrane normal). The remaining eigenmodes correspond to constant strain deformation modes -- two extensional modes and a shear mode -- and linear strain, in-plane flexural modes.

Robinson also discusses convergence, concentrating on monotonicity, and the hierarchy of rigid-body and deformation modes, with single-element examples to exhibit desired and undesired behavior. The Irons [12] patch test for multielement relative completeness examination is also described.

These tests are extremely useful. However, we choose here to adopt a procedure that accomplishes all of these examinations simultaneously and, when coupled with adaptive mesh strategies, holds the promise of providing automatic convergence to the user of finite element software. We will apply the procedure to a simple example through two different element formulations, in order to illustrate how the promise might be achieved in practice. No sophistication is attempted; instead, only simple concepts are developed.

The procedure is defined here as an element library test procedure. First, the element stiffness matrix is computed, without the application of nodal point constraints. The possibility of element constraints, such as those required to satisfy incompressibility in a Navier-Stokes fluid formulation, should be retained. The element stiffness will nominally be positive, semi-definite at this point, because the rigid-body behavior has been retained. In some cases, the element "stiffness" matrix may not be positive, semi-definite because of some type of hybrid, or mixed, formulation. Typical examples are the finite element fluid formulations which contain both the momentum and continuity equations in the global (integral) system, thereby including both velocity and pressure as nodal point variables. The rank and positivity of the matrix will be determined as a by-product of an eigenvalue/eigenvector analysis.

The number of rigid-body modes that are required is known. For example, a two-dimensional plane element requires two translations and a rotation; an axisymmetric element has one translation (parallel to the z-axis) and a rotation in the r-z plane; a three-dimensional continuum element has three translations and three rotations; etc. For some element formulations, more than the required number may be observed. A classic example is the underintegrated four-node isoparametric quadrilateral. Rather than the 2x2 Gaussian integration pattern for volumetric strain energy evaluation, a single centroidal evaluation may be used. Such underintegration is popular because it cuts the cost of element assembly by 75% and eliminates merely the two linear strain, in-plane flexural modes. However, the elimination of these two deformation modes adds two more rigid-body modes, which will be characterized as zero-energy modes, which can produce spurious behavior, such as "keystoning." a mechanism that propagates through the mesh, clouding the interpretation of results.

If more than the required number of rigid-body modes is found, misuse of the element is possible. Generally, knowledge of these additional rigid-body modes can lead to simple schemes for controlling unwanted distortion. Some negative eigenvalues may be found, such as the pressure modes in a mixed Navier-Stokes element.

The relative completeness of the element, i.e., the hierarchy of eigenmodes without any missing deformation modes, is a by-product of this analysis. In addition to the required rigid body modes, a set of constant straining modes is essential. Beyond that, higher-order elements should represent the complete set of linear straining modes, and so on. Needless to say, the identification of a given eigenmode with a particular strain pattern can be nontrivial if the element shape is severely distorted. A rectangular shape (e.g., rectangle, box, etc.) is preferred for these tests.

It follows, from this discussion, that two element formulations can be compared in terms of their respective eigenvalue spectra. For example, two membrane quadrilateral elements with differing formulations will, in general, have different eigenvalue spectra. The convergence characteristics can be compared, to some extent, by the "softness" of the individual spectra. A bilinear isoparametric quadrilateral membrane element with a 10:1 aspect ratio (E=1000, ν=0.3) would compare, as shown in Table 1, unfavorably with a biquadratic isoparametric quadrilateral membrane element. The reduction in the lowest extensional mode (in the long direction) is not dramatic, only dropping from 99.909 to 66.160, about 30%. However, the lowest shearing mode dropped by a factor of five and the lowest longitudinal bending mode dropped by a factor of 400. Note, in fact, that for this geometry -- an elongated rectangle -- that the lowest deformation mode is extension for the bilinear element but becomes longitudinal bending for the biquadratic element. This information will be useful in the multiple-element studies, to be discussed subsequently.

Table 1 Element Stiffness Eigenvalue Comparisons Isoparametric Membrane Element

(Δx=10., Δy=1., E=1000., ν=0.3)

	Bilinear	Biquadratic
Lowest x-extensional mode	99.909	66.160
Lowest y-extensional mode	10,999.	1,759.3
Lowest shearing mode	3,884.6	692.85
Lowest longitudinal bending mode	1,318.7	3.1515

The relative stiffness of the deformation mode eigenvalues can be misleading as an indicator of convergence. In order to understand the situation more clearly, a cantilever beam of aspect ratio 10:1 was analyzed through a pair of bilinear isoparametric plane stress models -- a 4x2 and an 8x2, with the two elements through the thickness capturing the bending displacement field -- and a pair of biquadratic isoparametric plane stress models -- a 1x1 and a 2x1, where one element through the thickness represents the bending displacement. After the approximate solutions were found, the strain energy within each element was projected onto the individual element deformation modes.

Since the discretizations were uniform, the eigenvalues and deformation mode shapes were identical for each element in a particular mesh; the projected energies varied, however, from element to element. For the 4x2 and 8x2 bilinear meshes, the lowest deformation mode in both cases was longitudinal extension, and the eigenvalue increased from 199.26 to 393.39 as the mesh spacing decreased (in accord with the inverse dependence of extensional stiffness on element length), while at the same time the strain energy projection increased. This contradicted the second mode findings. The eigenvalue for the second mode (combined longitudinal bending and shear) decreased from 714.29 to 467.03 as the mesh spacing decreased, in accord with improved modeling of the bending curvature. Strain energies projected onto this mode tended to be highest near the root of the cantilever, gradually decreasing to near zero at the tip. The percentage of strain energy in the bending/shear mode decreases as the mesh is refined, while the percentage of extensional strain energy rises.

The situation varies only modestly for the two biquadratic grids. In this case the lowest mode is a pure bending mode, with quadratic displacement (constant curvature) along the length and with plane sections remaining planar through the thickness. This deformation mode contains virtually the entire strain energy of the structure, but actually increases from 3.15 to 19.05 as the mesh is refined.

From a close examination of these results, three conclusions with respect to convergence, accuracy, and adaptive grid strategies can be reached. First, a convergent mesh is a mesh with the strain energy concentrated in the lowest element deformation modes. These modes need not be the constant straining modes, unless the deformation pattern is such that element aspect ratios of unity are necessary for convergence. Second, an attempt should be made to balance the effort expended by each element in the mesh; thus, elements with relatively small amounts of strain energy in an element should be a signal to adjust the sizes. Finally, adjustments in the element sizes may lead to either increases or decreases in deformation mode eigenvalues, and could possibly lead to an interchange of mode ordering. The crucial item is the gradual projection of greater and greater percentages of strain energy onto the lowest modes.

Therefore, a procedure for automatic evaluation of results and self-adaptive grid adjustment/refinement emerges. The first step following the initial analysis is the projection of strain energy onto the individual element deformation modes. Then, keeping the number of elements constant, the mesh should be adjusted to balance the element strain energies. The formula for balancing -- whether to change one element dimension or another -- is derived from a knowledge of the deformation modes with the bulk of the strain energy. Then, for those elements with strain energies not concentrated in the lowest deformation modes, subdivision is necessary.

For completeness, we point out that the bilinear element representation converges to an extensional strain and bending/shear mode combination, both of which have nearly the same eigenvalue, the lowest of the non-rigid body modes. The biquadratic element converges to a single mode a longitudinal bending mode. These observations apply to cantilever beams.

Perhaps the only disadvantage of projecting the strain energy onto the element deformation modes is the cost of computing the eigenvalues and eigenvectors. This disadvantage may be more apparent than real, because the element eigenvalue problem lends itself naturally to an inexpensive iterative solution. For example, trial eigenvectors can be readily determined for rectangular, bilinear isoparametric elements, and even though most elements in a given mesh may differ from this ideal, the differences should hardly affect the speed of convergence of generalized Rayleigh quotient methods, such as those outlined by Turinsky [13], Shavitt et al. [14], and Nickell [15].

SUMMARY

We have presented a two-step extension of current procedures for improving the reliability of applications software, in this case structural mechanics software. The current procedure is defined as an implied probabilistic approach to reliability, since a large body of second parties (users) with a variety of solved problems are needed to supplement the demonstration problems supplied by the developer. This sample space of successfully solved problems provides a measure of confidence that additional problems can also be solved successfully. Building upon the quality assurance that this implied probabilistic approach provides (together with sound software engineering by the developer), we have introduced third-party intervention in two ways: (i) external third-party intervention by a qualified evaluation team, which concerns itself with the software documentation, descriptions of the intended functional capabilities of the software and the programming architecture to achieve these goals, and extension of the probabilistic sample space through pathological evaluation exercises; and (ii) internal intervention by the software itself.

Examples of internal intervention are numerous, and only a few were specifically discussed, primarily those concerned with automatic error control with the analysis procedures library. The main point, however, is the introduction of an adaptive mesh adjustment/refinement procedure that can be readily incorporated into existing software modules or into proposed software, through modest additional effort in the postprocessor. Using the trial solution as data input, the method projects the strain energy onto each of the element deformation eigenmodes. Two steps are then followed; (a) criteria for balancing the strain energy can be used to adjust the existing mesh, thus improving the solution; and (b) rules that state that "the bulk of the strain energy should be concentrated in the lowest deformation modes" can be enforced, leading to mesh refinement.

As with all adaptive techniques, the form of application will depend upon whether a linear or nonlinear problem is being analyzed. For a nonlinear problem, the mesh can be adjusted and adapted prior to the next step in the solution. For a linear problem, the cost of resolution is perhaps unwarranted. Instead, the output can contain a description of the regions of the mesh that are underdiscretized or overdiscretized, together with estimates of the changes required to obtain an efficient, accurate solution.

More work is needed to test out the method. In particular, the numerical criteria for adjustment and refinement will be based upon linear interpolation and element area scaling. Also, the efficiency of the iterative deformation mode eigenvalue/eigenvector scheme should be proven.

ACKNOWLEDGMENTS

This work was supported under contract N00014-79-C-0620 with the Office of Naval Research, Arlington, Virginia. Many thanks are due to Dr. N. Perrone for his encouragement and support. Thanks are also due to Mr. Randy James, for some of the calculations, and to Mrs. Dianne Torncello, for preparation of the manuscript.

REFERENCES

1 Andrew, L. V., and Taig, I. C., "Selection of Structural Analysis Computer Programs," AGARD Report No. 670, Jan. 1979.

2 Davis, R. M., "Statement on Computer Sciences," Subcommittee on Research and Development, Committee on Armed Services, 96th Congress, April, 1979.

3 Nickell, R. E., "The Interagency Software Evaluation Group: A Critical Structural Mechanics Software Evaluation Concept," Report No. PT-U78-0246, Pacifica Technology, Del Mar, California, Aug. 1978.

4 Henrywood, R. K., "The Design, Development, Documentation and Support of a Major Finite Element System," Computer Aided Design, Vol. 5, July 1973, pp. 160-165.

5 "Recommended Programming Practices to Facilitate the Interchange of Digital Computer Programs," ANS-STD. 3-1971; American National Standard Guidelines for the Documentation of Digital Computer Programs, ANSI-N413-1974;"Guidelines for Considering User Needs in Computer Program Development," ANS 10.5 Draft, July 1978.

6 Nagy, D. A., "Software Engineering for Finite Element Analysis," J. Struct. Div., Proc. ASCE, Vol. 104, No. ST8, Aug. 1978, pp. 1287-1298.

7 Hibbitt, H. D., and Karllson, B. I., "Analysis of Pipe Whip," Paper No. 79-PVP-122, ASME, New York, 1979.

8 Krieg, R. D., and Krieg, D. B., "Accuracies of Numerical Solution Methods for the Elastic-Perfectly Plastic Models," J. Pressure Vessel Technology, Vol. 99, Trans. ASME, No. 4, Nov., 1977, pp. 510-515.

9 Schreyer, H. L., Kulak, R. F., and Kramer, J. M., "Accurate Numerical Solutions for Elastic-Plastic Models," Paper No. 79-PVP-107, ASME, New York, 1979.

10 Carey, G. F., and Humphrey, D. L., "Residuals, Adaptive Refinement and Iterative Solution in Finite Element Computations," in Finite Element Grid Optimization, ed. M. S. Shepard and R. H. Gallagher, PVP-38, ASME, New York, 1979.

11 Robinson, J., "Element Evaluation - A Set of Assessment Points and Standard Tests," in Finite Element Methods in the Commercial Environment, ed. J. Robinson, papers presented at the Second World Congress on Finite Element Methods, 23-27 October 1978, Bournemouth, Dorset, England, pp. 218-247.

12 Irons, B. M., and Razzaque, A., "Shape Function Formulations for Elements Other than Displacement Models," Proceedings, International Conference on Variational Methods in Engineering, Vol. 1, University of Southampton, England, Sept. 1972.

13 Turinsky, P. J., "The Super-Variational Technique Revisited," J. Math. Anal. Appl., Vol. 33, 1971, pp. 605-615.

14 Shavitt, I., Bender, C. F., Pipano, A., and Hosteny, R. P., "The Iterative Calculation of Several of the Lowest or Highest Eigenvalues and Corresponding Eigenvectors of Very Large Symmetric Matrices," J. Comp. Phys., Vol. 11, 1973, pp. 90-108.

15 Nickell, R. E., "Nonlinear Dynamics by Mode Superposition," Comp. Meth. Appl. Mech. Engr., Vol. 7, 1976, pp. 107-129.

Integration Methods for Stiff Systems

Michael Chi

John Tucker

CHI Associates, Inc.

INTRODUCTION

This chapter deals with numerical integration methods that can efficiently handle stiff systems, especially those arising from modern structural dynamics. These methods are needed in conjunction with the lumped mass or finite element methods to determine the responses of a complex structure due to a moderate amount of loading. The emphasis is placed on those applications which involve both material and geometrical nonlinearities. Due to the difficult and complex nature of the subject matter, this present work must be considered as tentative and exploratory. No attempt was made to compile either an exhaustive bibliography or a detailed account on all methods in existence.

MATHEMATICAL PRELIMINARIES

Stiff Systems [1, 2, 3, 4, 5]

The stiffness of a system is measured by the velocity difference between its fastest and slowest components. Given a system $\dot{y} = Ay$, A is a constant matrix, since the system is linear and autonomous, the eigenvalues of the system will be constants and, in general, complex numbers. A convenient measure of the stiffness of the system is the ratio between the largest and smallest moduli of the eigenvalues. For nonlinear systems $\dot{y} = f(y)$, the Jacobian $\partial f/\partial y$ varies with time, and often rather rapidly. The stiffness of a system must be defined for each short interval of time.

To put it formally, a system is said to be stiff in an interval I, if for $t \in I$, the eigenvalues $\lambda_j(t)$, $j = 1, \ldots, p$, of its Jacobian satisfy

a. $\text{Re}\, \lambda_j(t) < 0,\ j = 1, \ldots, p$

b. $M \gg m$, where $M = \max_{1 \le j \le p} \left| \text{Re}\lambda_j(t) \right|$

and $$m = \min_{1 \leq j \leq p} | \mathrm{Re}\lambda_j(t) |.$$

The ratio M/m is called the stiffness ratio. A system is very stiff if the stiffness ratio is in the order of thousands, or even millions.

It should be noted that partial derivatives in the Jacobian must be continuous and bounded in an appropriate region. If so, the Lipschitz constant L, which is defined as the norm of the Jacobian, can also be a measure of stiffness, and a stiff system is sometimes referred to as a system with a large Lipschitz constant.

The stiffness of a system has a great bearing in choosing an integration algorithm to solve it. Further discussion of this shall appear in a later section.

Types of Errors

Any numerical computation, being approximate in nature, will engender a variety of errors. Among these are the round-off error, the starting error, and the truncation errors. A brief discussion of each error type is given as follows.

There are two categories of truncation errors: the global and the local. The global truncation errors originate from the discretization of the continuous operator, e.g., to approximate the original differential equations by the finite element discretization. In general, the global truncation error can be minimized by using the smallest element sizes permitted by consideration of the economy and convergence. The local truncation error is that which is introduced at each time step via the interpolation polynomial(s) used for the approximation. For example, a fourth-order Runge-Kutta method employs a fourth-degree polynomial to approximate a given function. The numerical difference between the given function and the approximate polynomial produces the local truncation error.

The starting error is that which is introduced in the very first step of the numerical solution. If a numerical method requires a great precision in the starting sequence, it is crucial that accurate values be obtained at this point. For this reason, a separate method may be needed in the initial phase of the numerical solution to furnish a good starting value. This approach has, in fact, been used in some programs.

The round-off error is caused by the inexact machine representation of the numbers involved in the numerical process. How numbers are stored and manipulated varies from computer to computer, and accordingly the propagation of a round-off error is machine-dependent.

Stability

The work "stability" pertains to the control of the growth of extraneous solutions introduced by replacing the differential equations by the higher-order difference equations in the numerical method. The simplest and most natural kind of control is through an artificial damping factor which causes extraneous solutions to die out in the limit with the decrease in step sizes.

In numerical integration, one is primarily interested in two types of stability: the absolute and the relative stability. The region of absolute stability of a method is that set of λh for which the sequence $\{y_n\}_0^\infty$ is bounded. The definition refers to a simple test equation

$$\dot{y} = \lambda y \tag{1}$$

with a solution $y(t_m)$ at $t = t_m$.

In the above sequence, y_n, $n = 0,1...$, is an approximate solution of the test equation relative to the exact solution $y(t_n)$. The relative stability region of a method is defined as the region in which the extraneous eigenvalues introduced by the method are no larger than the true eigenvalues of the system.

In some problems, the prescribed accuracy requires a time step which is small enough to automatically ensure stability; in such cases the relative stability is no longer a limiting factor for the step size, leaving the truncation error to be a paramount factor of consideration.

Stability of Some Classical Integration Methods [1, 2]

Since the problem of stability is vital in the selection of integration methods, it is relevant to introduce those modern concepts of numerical stability which can be used to judge the merit of a newly developed method. It is pertinent to describe the stability of some classical methods. Three integration methods are selected for illustration: the implicit trapezoidal, backward implicit Euler, and explicit Euler method.

It can be shown that the stability region for the implicit trapezoidal method consists of the entire left half-plane, $Re(\lambda h) < 0$. Thus, it is said to have an "unbounded" region of absolute stability (see Fig. 1a). Regardless of how large the step size chosen for the calculation, the numerical results will not have a runaway error growth. In such a case we must watch for accuracy since, in most cases, as the step size increases, the accuracy of the results invariably deteriorates.

With this in mind, it is pertinent to inquire whether if it possible to have a larger region of absolute stability than the left half-plane, and if so, to determine if it is more advantageous. The answer to the former question is affirmative, an easy example being the backward Euler method, whose stability region consists of the exterior of a circle of radius one with its center at one on the real axis (Fig. 1b). The extension of the stability region over a large area into the right half-plane tends to produce artificial damping which can change the nature of the solution, and in extreme cases can cause components to die out in the numerical solution while, in the exact solution, they should be growing in time. Also, in nonlinear problems, some time-dependent eigenvalues which have large moduli are forced to move quickly from left to right in the complex plane.

In the other extreme, the region of absolute stability of the explicit Euler method consists of the interior of a circle of radius one, centered at -1 (see Fig. 1c). As is true for nearly all explicit linear multistep method which have inherently small stability regions, violently unstable results can be frequently expected when applied to a stiff system.

Modern Theories of Numerical Stability Criteria [10, 1, 24, 13]

Motivated by these considerations, Dahlquist advocated that a method for stiff problems ought to have a region of absolute stability at least as large as that of the implicit trapezoidal method. This he referred to as "A-stability" and defined it formally as follows:

> "A numerical method is said to be A-stable if its region of absolute stability contains the whole of the left half-plane of $Re(\lambda h)$."

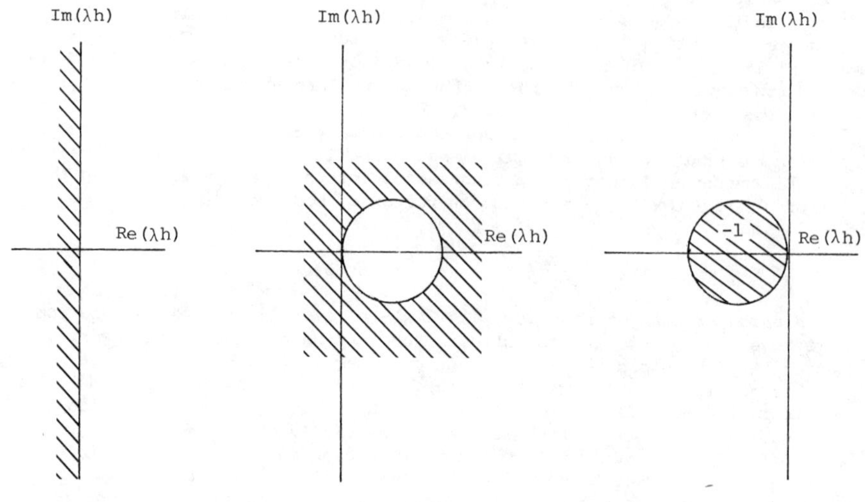

a. Implicit trapezoidal method
b. Backward Euler method
c. Explicit Euler method

Fig. 1

Thus, a linear multistep method is A-stable if all approximate solutions y_n tend to zero when the method is applied with fixed $h > 0$ to the test problem $\dot{y} = \lambda y$, $\mathrm{Re}(\lambda) < 0$.

A-stable methods are fairly stable, but not nearly stable enough for nonlinear stiff problems. They are comparable to the implicit trapezoidal method in regard to their potential for producing large truncation errors in a stiff system. To illustrate, the principal local truncation error of the trapezoidal method is $\frac{h^3 d^3 y}{12 dt^3}$, which can be sizable if $\frac{d^3 y}{dt^3}$ is large. For a stiff system this will happen in an interval in which the transient solution is sizable in magnitude. Also, for a test equation with a large $|\mathrm{Re}\lambda|$ it can be shown that the numerical solutions reduce only very slightly in magnitude between two successive iterations; that is, $|y_{n+1}/y_n|$ is almost unity for any step of appreciable size. The implication is that the amount of calculation effort may be excessive for practical applications.

On the other hand, A-stability is prohibitively demanding. For example, it can be shown that no explicit linear multistep method can be A-stable, nor can a high-order implicit one. This excludes many popular method, including the popular explicit Runge-Kutta method, whose stability region is shown in Fig. 2. It can be seen that this region is not much larger than that of the explicit Euler method. For stiff systems, the permissible time step must be very small and the computation cost becomes very high.

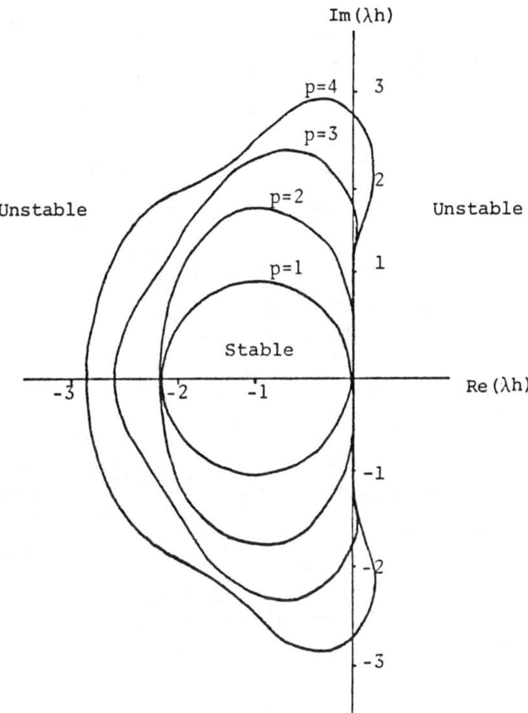

Fig. 2 Stability Region of the Runge-Kutta Method of p-Order

The following example [10] illustrates the instability in numerical results when such methods are used in a stiff system.

$$\begin{aligned} \dot{y}_1 &= 100\ (y_2 - y_1) \\ \dot{y}_2 &= y_3 \\ \dot{y}_3 &= -y_2 \end{aligned} \qquad (2)$$

and at t = 0, $y_1 = y_2 = y_3 = 0$. It can be verified that the eigenvalues of this linear system are -100, i, -i, and the first solution is $y_1 = \text{Sin } t - 0.01 \text{ Cos } t + 0.01 \exp(-100\ t) / 1.001$. It is obvious that the exponential term in y_1 decays rapidly to less than 10^{-6} after the first 0.1 unit of time. Thus, the largest eigenvalue quickly loses its dominance. However, the step size must be kept very small in subsequent times to avoid instability. The following are results at t=3 for the classical fourth-order

Runge-Kutta method:

h	0.015	0.020	0.025	0.030
$y_1(t)$	0.1510	0.1510	0.15094	6.7×10^{11}

It is seen that the use of a step size, $h = 0.025$ gives a good result whereas the use of $h = 0.030$ creates violent instability. For many methods the step size is limited due to stability requirements by the following expression:

$$\max_j \lambda_j h \leqq C \tag{3}$$

in which C is a method-dependent constant and is 2.7 for the fourth-order Runge-Kutta method. In the above example, the threshold step size is 0.027.

In an effort to strengthen A-stability conditions, Ehle proposed the [2]
notion of L-stability, which is defined as follows:

A one-step method is said to be L-stable if

(a) it is A-stable

(b) it yields $y_{n+1} = E(\lambda h)\, y_n$, $|E(\lambda h)| \to 0$ as $Re(\lambda h) \to -\infty$

It is evident that L-stability implies A-stability but not vice versa. Research to date indicates that very few methods can pass the requirement of L-stability (see Table 1).

Table 1 Stability of Method for Linear Systems

Method or Program	L-Stable	A-stable	Stiffly Stable
4th-order explicit Runge-Kutta			
Explicit Euler (forward)			
Implicit Trapezoidal		X	
Implicit Euler (backward)	X	X	X
Explicit Central Difference			
Newmark β Implicit		X (for β=¼)	
Newmark β Noniterative		X (for β=¼)	
Wilson θ		X (for θ=½)	
Houbolt (3rd-order implicit)		X	
Park (3 step, Gear Variant)			X
Runge-Kutta, Semi-implicit (Michelsen)	X	X	X
Runge-Kutta Type, implicit (Cash)	X	X	
Predictor-corrector 4th order (Cash)		X	
Explicit 5th-order Devoglaere (Fu)			

Table 1 (cont.)

Method of Program	L-Stable	A-stable	Stiffly Stable
Explicit Nonlinear methods (Lambert)	X	X	
Gear P-C Program (stiff option)			X
Adams-Bashforth-Moulton PECE (DE/STEP)			

One useful notion, developed by Gear [2], is the "Stiffly Stable" condition:

A numerical method is said to be stiffly stable if

a. its region of absolute stability contains R_1,

b. it is accurate for all $\lambda h \in R_2$ when applied to the scalar test equation $\dot{y} = \lambda y$, $\mathrm{Re}(\lambda) < 0$

where

$R_1 = \{\lambda h \mid \mathrm{Re}\,(\lambda h) < -a\}$

$R_2 = \{\lambda h \mid -a \leq \mathrm{Re}\,(\lambda h) \leq c,\ -b \leq \mathrm{Im}(\lambda h) < b\}$

and a, b, and c are positive constants. (See Fig. 3.)

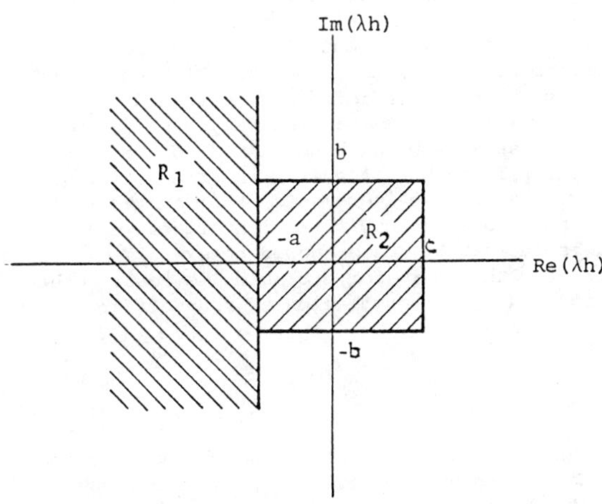

Fig. 3 Region of a stiffly stable method

The stiff stability is derived from the known fact that those fast components which represent rapidly decaying terms in transient solutions correspond to values of λh lying in R_1. Thus, the remaining lower eigenvalues will lie in R_2 if the step size h is suitably chosen. In this manner, the slower components will be computed accurately as well as "stably." In a similar vein, it is not important to represent the fast-decaying terms accurately as long as they can be somehow made to decay with sufficient rapidity and, in consequence, be represented "stably."

The stiffly stable condition is in certain regards weaker than the A-stable condition. For example, it does not require the inclusion of the entire left half-plane, i.e., the boundary of its region is allowed to be a distance away from the imaginary axis. In another sense, it is stronger than the A-stable condition, since it includes as its stability region a rectangular area in the neighborhood of the origin. A method can be A-stable or even L-stable, but not be stiffly stable. It is instructive to point out that an implicit Runge-Kutta method is A-stable but not stiffly stable; its unstable region, although small, encroaches too closely on the origin (see Ref. [32]). Linear explicit multistep methods do not satisfy stiffly stable conditions. Thus, these methods are inefficient in solving stiff systems [12].

The concept of numerical stability is under intensive study and in the process of development. Recently, the notion of P-, H-, and Q-stability [12, 13] have arisen. However, to the best of the author's knowledge, they are in the purely theoretical stage and no practical properties have been uncovered.

We have studied some modern notions of numerical stability and have determined that the state-of-the-art has not yet reached a satisfactory point. It is expected that it shall develop rapidly in the next few years. At this juncture, we remark that pure theory gives only a qualitative guidance in the selection of a candidate method for a particular application. This is because selection of an integration method is more aptly derived from actual experience which can only be obtained by painstakingly conducting numerical experimentation. It is pertinent then to discuss how instability can be detected in a computation process. Instability is usually indicated by an exponential growth of errors. This growth usually starts with an oscillation, which will grow if the amount of damping in the method is not sufficient. If the oscillations become violent, the process is said to be unstable. Let us take the predictor-corrector method as an example with P_{ij} and C_{ij} the predicted and corrected values of the ith component and jth time increment, respectively. We can monitor the sign changes of the difference between these values, $d_{ij} = P_{ij} - C_{ij}$. Suppose that we use a counter I_j such that every time the difference d_{ij} disagrees in sign in two successive time increments, the counter is advanced by one. We can confirm that an oscillatory situation arises when I_j registers three and instability is indicated. Care should be exercised to select a d_{ij} substantially greater than zero for a conclusive test. Otherwise, a false alarm may be triggered by the cumulation of roundoff errors in the absence of instability.

Order vs. Stability

In recent years research has concentrated on the development of the variable-order methods. The order of a method is, in general, one less than the order of the stepwise truncation error of the formula. For example, if a method has a truncation error of $O(h^5)$ per step, it is termed a fourth-order method. It can be verified that, in a nonstiff system, other factors being equal, the greater the order of the method, the greater the accuracy that can be achieved for a given step size. When a variable order procedure is applied to a stiff problem, an increase in the order of the numerical method will generally result in a decrease in the size of the region of stability. Thus, an increase in order may place a given step size outside the reduced region of stability. Thus, whenever the accuracy requirement calls for an increased order, the stability requirement must call for a reduced time step size. Any variable order program must contain a procedure to vary the step size in conjunction with a change of order. Also, for stiff systems, a low-order method, frequently less than three, is preferable.

Explicit vs. Implicit Methods

As stated before, a structural dynamics problem will frequently lead to a stiff system of ODEs. Since the explicit methods cannot even satisfy conditions of A-stability, their application to stiff ODE systems will be costly and often lead to a violent instability condition.

An implicit method, therefore, is preferable for stiff problems [14]. In an implicit formulation, it is necessary to solve a set of implicit difference equations, which take the form of simultaneous algebraic equations denoted by $F(y) = 0$. In many structural dynamics problems, $F(y)$ is nonlinear and the stiffness of the differential system carries over into it, causing the ordinary iterative approach to converge extremely slowly, if at all. (The reason for this is that stiffness imposes very severe restrictions on step size.) A more powerful method such as Newton's iteration method is often recommended. The formulation of this method is:

$$y^{(n+1)} = y^{(n)} - J^{-1}(y^{(n)})\, F(y^{(n)}) \tag{4}$$

where $J(y^{(n)})$ is the Jacobian matrix. In a strict sense, Newton's method calls for the reevaluation and inversion of the Jacobian matrix at each iteration, which requires unacceptable amounts of computing time and memory core space. It is more expedient to hold the Jacobian constant for a number of iteration steps such that the Jacobian is only reevaluated if the computation fails to converge after three or so iterations. If this is followed, the method is commonly known as a "Newton-like" method. Experience has shown that for many problems, its results are satisfactory, especially if the Jacobian varies slowly. One must be sure that the iteration method is convergent. From a computational point of view, the proof of convergence is not as important as its rate. That is to say, the iteration algorithm must produce a solution which converges after a reasonably small number of iteration steps.

In carrying out the iteration for solving implicit difference equations, one can use a piecewise linearization technique, i.e., the time-varying Jacobian $J(y)$ can be assumed to be a constant matrix within a sufficiently small time increment. To invert the Jacobian, the most popular method is perhaps the "LU decomposition" method, which is a special case of the Gaussian elimination scheme. In this method the Jacobian is first decomposed into a product of a lower triangular matrix L and an upper triangular matrix U. The original problem is then reduced to the solution of a pair of equations, namely $Ux = w$ and $Lw = b$. Decomposition is easily accomplished and is available through standard FORTRAN program library packages.

INTEGRATION METHODS FOR STIFF, NONLINEAR EQUATIONS

In this chapter, a number of the better known and more efficient methods for integrating nonlinear, stiff equations are discussed. To provide a better perspective, these methods are conveniently grouped into three classes. The first is the Newmark type, which employs a second derivative formulation and is popular in the engineering community. It is actually a collection of several methods of diverse origins and several other methods can be considered variants on it, among which are the Houbolt and Wilson methods. Unfortunately, the Newmark family is not yet well known to mathematicians, and its stability and error estimates have not been investigated thoroughly, especially for nonlinear problems.

The second class of methods is the Adams type, which employs a first derivative formulation. Its properties have been thoroughly studied. The best known and well-documented of program packages is the DE/STEP program, which is perhaps the most powerful of all in dealing with nonstiff to moderately stiff problems. Programs developed on the basis of Adams methods include Gear's DIFSUB which incorporates his second, third,and higher-order formulas, which were formulated specifically for stiff problems. These second and third order formulas were the basis of Park's method, while DIFSUB is the progenitor of the latest, more improved programs, such as DVOGER and GEAR. This last program stimulated the development of the highly advanced program, EPISODE.

The third class of methods is the Runge-Kutta type, which also employs a first derivative formulation. The classical explicit version has poor stability properties and is inefficient. The implicit version is somewhat better but the semi-implicit version is highly respectable. Among the latter's variants are Cash's L-stable method and the Michelsen variable step method.

If not for their small stability region, explicit methods would have been generally favored because they are easy to formulate and efficient to execute. Several approaches have been used to improve the stability properties of explicit methods. For example, Fu's artifical damping method is appealing, not only because it has the improved stability but also because it has a second derivative formulation, a rare find among the mathematical literature. Another is the Euler method with interpolation. The third uses rational functions in the interpolation which is the only nonlinear formulation discussed in this report. These latter stable explicit nonlinear methods, as they are known, have not been sufficiently developed but show considerable promise to become power methods of the future.

Newmark Beta Method [7, 9, 15 through 28]

The Newmark Beta method has been perhaps the most widely used integration procedures for structural dynamics problem. Due to the natural kinematic interpretation of its variables, the Newmark method is commonly known as the "generalized acceleration" method. The formulation is as follows:

$$\begin{aligned} \dot{y}_{n+1} &= \dot{y}_n + (1 - \gamma)\,\ddot{y}_n h + \gamma \ddot{y}_{n+1} h \\ y_{n+1} &= y_n + \dot{y}_n h + (\tfrac{1}{2} - \beta)\ddot{y}_n h^2 + \beta \ddot{y}_{n+1} h^2 \end{aligned} \tag{4}$$

Due to the second derivative nature of the above equations, the method is ideally suited for dynamical problems.

Two parameters β and γ, are employed in the formulation. The parameter, γ, or rather $\gamma - \frac{1}{2}$, is proportional to the artificial damping that the method introduces into the system. It has been found through numerical experimentation that, by using an adjustable damping parameter, the Newmark Beta method can be just as effective but more more flexible than its variants, such as the Houbolt and the Wilson θ methods. The parameter β governs the shape of acceleration assumed between nodal points; for example, when β is zero, the formulation degenerates into the standard central difference formulas which were discussed by Levy and Kroll in 1951. For β = 1/12, it becomes the method developed in 1949 by Fox and Goodwin [19]which has the lowest truncation error. For β = 1/8, the acceleration is a step function with an initial value for the first half of the time and a final value for the second half of the time interval. For β = 1/6, the method is known as the "linear acceleration" method, which has a pleasing feature in that velocity and acceleration are both continuous. In the case of β = 1/4, the acceleration profile is constant, equal to the mean value of the initial and final accelerations, similar to a method introduced in 1928 by Timoshenko. From this vantage point the generalized acceleration method of Newmark is really a group of several powerful methods of diverse origins.

The Newmark Beta Method has different stability and convergence properties, depending on the assigned value of β. Let the smallest natural period be denoted by T; then the permissible time step h for a linear system are as follows:

β	0	1/12	1/8	1/6	1/4
Convergence Limit h/T	∞	0.551	0.450	0.389	0.318
Stability Limit h/T	0.318	0.389	0.450	0.551	∞

It is seen that β = 0, the procedure is unconditionally convergent but has a poor stability, i.e., it may become unstable when the time step is large. In the other extreme, for β = 1/4, the opposite is true, i.e., the procedure is unconditionally stable but a large time step produces high truncation errors which may cause convergence problems as was proved for a one degree of freedom system by Newmark, and verified for multi-degree of freedom systems as shown by Nickell [9]. In applications, a compromise of convergence and stability must be made.

The performance of this method depends also on the iteration process, the variable time step control procedure and the type of nonlinearity. The accuracy and stability in nonlinear problems are not known and can best be studied by numerical experimentation. For practical application, the following remarks may be useful.

Central Difference Method [1, 7, 9, 15, 20, 24, 25, 26, 28, 30, 31]

This is the case of β = 0 and is the only explicit procedure among the various versions of the Newmark method. For this reason, some numerical instability is a commonplace occurence. The method is advantageous in terms of ease of formulation, savings in memory space,and computational simplicity. Limited experience shows that it gives good results in comparison with other reliable methods for simple nonlinear systems, as long as the step size is kept small. If a large step is used, the accuracy of its result left a lot to be desired.

In the case of stiff nonlinear system, as is the case in most structural dynamics problems, the central difference method is not recommended.

Constant Average Acceleration Method [1, 2, 3, 7, 9, 10, 17, 19, 20, 21, 22, 23, 24, 25, 26, 27, 28, 29, 32, 34, 35, 36, 37, 38, 39, 40, 41]

In this method, $\beta = \frac{1}{4}$ and the resultant numerical procedure for 2nd-order ODEs is equivalent to the well-known trapezoidal rule for integration of first-order ODEs. The $\beta = \frac{1}{4}$ method is perhaps the most extensively used method in structural analysis. A moderate amount of damping (e.g., γ=0.55), is recommended for solving stiff systems.

For nonlinear problems, the stability properties of the method have not been studied, although it is known to be at least conditionally stable. The stability factor should be carefully considered, especially when softening springs are involved. For stiff nonlinear problems, the method can be effective provided that a variable time step algorithm is used.

Methods Using Intermediate Values of Beta [7, 15, 19, 20, 21]

For $0 < \beta < \frac{1}{4}$, the stability properties of the procedure are discussed by Hughes [21] and Goudreau and Taylor [20], who alluded that the stability region is somewhere between the two extreme values of β.

Newmark Beta Method - "Non-Iterative" Version [16, 23, 29]

This method is the "explicit" version of the Newmark Beta method. It was developed at the suggestion of Belystschko [16] who observed that the implicit terms in the original Newmark formulation can be made explicit by a straightforward algebraic manipulation, of which the formulation, when $\beta = \frac{1}{2}$, is:

$$\dot{y}_{n+1} = \dot{y}_n + \tfrac{1}{2}h\ (\ddot{y}_n + y_{n+1})$$

$$\dot{y}_{n+1} = (K^e)^{-1}M\ [\ \frac{1}{h^2\beta}\, y_n + \frac{1}{h\beta}\, \dot{y}_n + (\frac{1}{2\beta} - 1)\ddot{y}_n\ ] + (K^e)^{-1}\ F_{n+1} \qquad (5)$$

$$\text{where } K^e = K - \frac{1}{h^2\beta}\, M$$

Because the method is derived from the basic implicit method with no simplifying assumptions added, it inherits all the niceties of the implicit method despite its appearance of explicitness. Furthermore, since it is in fact explicit, the difference equations can be solved directly without the need of iteration, which can be a source of instability. However, the necessity of updating and inverting the stiffness matrices can become a laborious and time-consuming process.

In light of the proven excellent performance of this method on linear as well as some nonlinear systems, it is highly recommended. The installation of a suitable variable time step procedure should greatly enhance its effectiveness in dealing with the complex stiff systems.

Variants of the Newmark Method

Houbolt Method [9, 15, 20, 24, 25, 26, 28, 30, 38, 42]

The Houbolt method can be obtained by replacing the acceleration expression in the Newmark formulation by a third-order backward difference, and the velocity expression by Gear's third-order method. This method requires a separate starting algorithm; Houbolt has recommended one which is equivalent to the linear acceleration method of the Newmark family. The formulation is as follows:

$$v_{n+1} = \frac{1}{6h} (11y_{n+1} - 18y_n + 9y_{n-1} - 2y_{n-2})$$
$$a_{n+1} = \frac{1}{h^2} (2y_{n+1} - 5y_n + 4y_{n-1} - y_{n-2}) \tag{6}$$

Because of its backward-difference formulation, a considerable storage space is needed during its execution to accommodate the past displacement vectors. This method is unconditionally stable for linear systems. For nonlinear systems, the built-in artificial damping may be used to avoid a runaway oscillation. The damping should not be too large or distortions and phase shifts in the solution may result. In order to minimize the effects of artificial damping, and to revive the high-frequency components, sufficiently small time steps should be used. This, of course, increases the cost of the computational effort.

The Houbolt method was quite popular in earlier days when there were relatively few numerical integration schemes available. In the present time, it has lost some of its favor. Since its procedure is in part identical to a well-developed Gear's method it is superseded by the latter. The Houbolt method is inflexible in that its artificial damping property is fixed. The Newmark method which uses a variable damping coefficient γ is a recommended substitute

The Wilson Θ Method [9, 29, 24, 25]

This method is basically a version of the Newmark method, using $\beta = 1/6$. In an effort to compensate for the spurious oscillation inherent in discrete approximations to continuum problems, Wilson introduced a factor θ as the artificial damping. The basic approach is to use a linear acceleration method for a double interval and then to proceed step by step in a manner of a predictor-corrector method. The formulation is as follows:

$$\ddot{y}_{n+\theta} = \theta\ddot{y}_{n+1} + (1 - \theta)\ddot{y}_n, \quad k = \theta h \qquad \text{Predictor}$$
$$y_{n+\theta} = y_n + k\dot{y}_n + k^2 y_n/2 + k^3(\ddot{y}_{n+1} = y_n)/6h$$

(7)

$$\dot{y}_{n+1} = \dot{y}_n + h(\ddot{y}_{n+1} - \ddot{y}_n)/2 \qquad \text{Corrector}$$
$$y_{n+1} = y_n + h\dot{y}_n + h^2 (\ddot{y}_{n+1} + 2\ddot{y}_m)/6$$

The Wilson method has been generalized somewhat by Farhoomand into a third-order difference equation. Both methods are unconditionally stable and have considerable artificial damping. In fact, it can be shown that the damping is far more than is usually needed to control the spurious oscillation of the discrete approximation.

The Runge Kutta Variants [13, 43, 44, 45, 46]

Runge-Kutta methods are probably the best-known class of methods. One version, the fourth-order explicit, is perhaps the most popular, at least for rigid body mechanics. For stiff problems in continuum mechanics, however, the method lacks efficiency because its stability region is very small, a problem it shares with other standard explicit methods.

To have a practical application to stiff problems, it has been determined that a method should preferably be L-stable, i.e., stable for a large region of the complex plane and accurate in some neighborhood of its origin. The implicit Runge-Kutta formulas have been found to be merely A-stable. They also suffer from the serious disadvantage of requiring that complicated nonlinear implicit equations be solved at each time step. To overcome this latter difficulty at least partially, methods have been developed that are compromises between the implicit and explicit varieties. These methods are known as the semi-implicit methods.

Cash's L-stable Method [11]

Although semi-implicit Runge-Kutta methods are much more efficient from a computational point of view, most of them are still only A-stable. Cash's method is unique, being the only semi-implicit Runge-Kutta method which is L-stable. Its formulation is:

$$y_{n+1} = y_n + h(\tfrac{1}{4}k_2 + \tfrac{1}{2}k_3 + \tfrac{1}{4}k_4) \tag{7}$$

where

$$\begin{aligned} k_2 &= f(t_{n+1} - \frac{1}{3}h,\ y_{n+1} - \frac{1}{3}h\,k_1) \\ K_3 &= f(t_{n+1} - \frac{1}{3}h,\ y_{n+1} - \frac{1}{12}h\,k_1 - \frac{1}{4}h\,k_2) \\ K_4 &= f(t_n, y_n) \text{ and } K_1 = f(t_{n+1}, y_{n+1}) \end{aligned} \tag{8}$$

In common with the classical Runge-Kutta methods, the solution of Cash's method at the point t_{m+1} is obtained from the solution at the point. t_n, using evaluations of the function $f(y,t)$ within the range (t_n, t_{n+1}). Thus, it is possible to solve a system of algebraic equations for a single unknown y_{n+1} instead of for a large system as is the case for implicit methods. A predictor-corrector method is included in Cash's paper for the solution of such an algebraic system.

Michelson's Third-Order, Variable-Step Method [47]

This semi-implicit Runge-Kutta method was based on the ideas of Caillaud and Padmanabhan, using a third-order formula. They developed a system which was stable but inaccurate. Michelson, however, recognized the method's potential and improved it by incorporating an efficient variable step procedure.

If the system to be integrated is $\frac{d}{dt}(y) = f(y)$ with $y(t_n)$, let the Jacobian A be given as $A_{ij} = \partial f_i/\partial y_j|_{y = \dot{y}_n}$. Then the solution y_{n+1} at time $t_n + h$ is found from:

$$k_1 = h(I-haA)^{-1}f(y_n)$$
$$k_2 = h(I-haA)^{-1}f(y_n + b_2k_1) \qquad (9)$$
$$k_3 = h(I-haA)^{-1}(b_{31}k_1 + b_{32}k_2)$$
$$y_{n+1} = y_n + R_1k_1 + R_2k_2 + k_3$$

where

$$a^3 - 3a^2 + \frac{3}{2}a - \frac{1}{6} = 0, \quad a = 0.4358...$$
$$b_2 = 0.75$$
$$b_{31} = \frac{-1}{6a} \quad (8a^2 - 2a + 1)$$
$$b_{32} = \frac{2}{9a} \quad (6a^2 - 6a + 1) \qquad (10)$$
$$R_1 = \frac{11}{27} - b_{31}$$
$$R_2 = \frac{16}{27} - b_{32}$$

The Gear Family of Methods [1-3, 24-26, 35, 38, 39, 42, 43, 45, 48-62]

Gear was among the first to recognize the need to develop a package specially designed to deal with stiff nonlinear problems. For this he implemented the basic Adams type of integration scheme with variable order and variable step capabilities. Being a variable order method, it can cope with a wide range of error requirements and can also keep the number of function evaluations well below the number required by other methods. This is especially significant in the application to structural mechanics problems, in which these functions are usually very complicated. Another advantage of this method, in common with all Adams methods, is that it lends itself to interpolation at intermediate points. As Hull [44] has stated, "There is no doubt that a program library should contain a variable-order, variable step Adams method." For stiff problems, Gear-type methods would be a logical choice.

Gear developed the original version of his method into a computer program, DIFSUB.

DVOGER [2, 3, 35, 37, 39, 48, 49, 51, 51, 52, 56, 59, 60, 63]

One of the latest versions of DIFSUB is known as DVOGER. It is in the EMSL package, and has also been tested for nonstiff problems with favorable results.

Three disadvantages of DVOGER have been noticed so far. One is that it uses a Taylor series representation to store information. There is considerable evidence that the conventional divided difference approach is better. Another drawback is that DVOGER is less efficient than other methods when the eigenvalues of the Jacobian are close to the imaginary axis. Also, for extremely stiff systems, a second-order algorithm with an effective step length adjustment procedure could perform more efficiently than a complex multiorder method, especially when the number of function evaluations is low.

EPISODE [48, 55, 56, 64, 65]

Hindmarsh, recognizing DVOGER's limitations, first developed a modified version of the program, which he named GEAR in honor of its originator. Then in 1975 Hindmarsh and Byrne [19] announced that they had developed a new program, EPISODE (Effective Package for the Integration of Systems of Ordinary Differential Equations; formerly, the E stood for Experimental). Similar in some ways to the original programs developed by Gear, EPISODE provides options for the use of implicit multistep methods, i.e., a generalized Adams method for nonstiff problems, or of a generalized backward differentiation scheme for the solution of stiff problems. It also uses a dynamic variable-order formulation for both stiff and nonstiff problems. However, in constrast to GEAR, which stipulates that a step size is changed by an interpolation scheme, EPISODE uses a truly variable-step algorithm in which the step size can be varied from step to step, if needed.

EPISODE was designed to overcome the deficiencies in previous programs in dealing with the instability of nonsmooth problems, i.e., problems with rapidly changing characteristics. However, Enright and Hull have reported that EPISODE requires frequent updating of the Jacobian matrix which must itself be accompanied by a new LU-decomposition. For large stiff problems, this can be very costly.

Park's Method [8, 25, 26, 38]

In the course of evaluating a few of Gear's stiffly stable methods with other methods which were used for the solution of structural dynamics problems, Park discovered that Gear's two-step methodology was only slightly better than Houbolt's while his three-step method was unstable for the frequency ranges in interest. He deduced that the two-step method with high numerical damping in the system has an improved stability while the three-step method of higher order gives a better accuracy. By combining the two methods, Park theorized that he would obtain a method which would be accurate and stable for the low frequency range and stable for high frequency components. The formulation is:

$$v_{n+1} = 1/6h\ (10y_{n+1} - 15y_n + 6y_{n-1} - y_{n-2}) \tag{11}$$

He has shown that this new method yields good results but exhibits a slight phase shift from the known exact solution, while the two and three-step Gear-originated methods undershoot and overshoot the exact solution respectively.

Other Predictor-Corrector Methods

DE/STEP Program [41, 44, 49, 57-60]

This program is a sophisticated ODE solver composed of a driver, DE, and a modified divided difference variable-order Adams-Bashforth-Moulton type variable-step code, STEP. The originators, Shampine and Gordon [41], have thoroughly documented all aspects of the program in their book. Among DE/STEP's advantages is its ability to detect both stiffness and discontinuities. DE recognizes and responds to requests for high accuracy through implementation of a propagated roundoff error control algorithm, and the degree of accuracy is thus dependent only on the limitations of the computer itself. The DE/STEP program in problems of extreme stiffness has a built-in algorithm which lowers the order of the interpolation for improved stability properties. For moderately stiff problems, the program gives a warning signal, advising the use of a stiff system solver.

One deficiency of DE/STEP may present a problem in its application. In order to use DE/STEP in an existing program or as a subroutine in a new program, it is necessary to supply a derivative evaluation algorithm to determine the Jacobian matrix. It may prove to be complicated to provide linkages for such an algorithm to a complex, dynamic program.

Cash's A-Stable High-Order Predictor-Corrector Method [33, 66]

Cash recently modified the standard linear multistep methods into a higher-order A-stable method. His third-order method was merely of theoretical interest and was not useful in practical application. In his fourth-order method he employs the backward Euler method as a predictor and the trapezoidal rule as a corrector. The solution is, therefore, not computed directly but is generated by an iterative procedure, which will remain A-stable if not used more than a specified number of times. Based on limited experience, it is believed that this method is superior to the trapezoidal rule.

The formulation is:

$$y_{n+1} + 9y_n - 9y_{n-1} - y_{n-2} = 6h(f(t_n, y_n) + f(t_{n-1}, y_{n-1})) \tag{12}$$

which, when written iteratively, becomes

$$y_n^{(p)} - y_{n-1}^{(p)} = \frac{h}{2}(f(t_n, y_n^{(p)}) + f(t_{n-1}, y_{n-1}^{(p)}) - \frac{1}{12}D^2y_n^{(p-1)} + \frac{1}{12}D^2y_{n-1}^{(p-1)}$$

$$\text{where} \quad D^2y_n^{(o)} = y_{n+1}^{(o)} - 2y_n^{(o)} + y_{n-1}^{(1)} \tag{13}$$

Unfortunately, the method is complex to formulate and costly to program. The iteration scheme which ensures its A-stability is particularly intricate and requires extensive support procedures. Therefore, it is not possible to recommend the method until it has been tested more thoroughly.

Stable Explicit Methods

Fu-deVogelaer [67]

The original deVogelaer Method was designed for the numerical integration of a system of second-order differential equations without explicit first derivatives. Fu then extended the scope of the method so that it can sovle large systems of equations. The Fu-deVogelaer method, being an explicit method, requires a minimal amount of storage locations and is also relatively easy to program. Its accuracy is quite impressive, having a truncation error of the fifth order. The Fu-deVogelaer method is claimed to be twice as fast as the Runge-Kutta-Gill method. In a transient vibration problem of a Timoshenko beam, the method was found to be as accurate as Hamming's modified predictor-corrector method but required significantly less running time.

Fu's contribution to the method was the addition of a damping term. This permits the modeling of the internal material viscosity and the control of numerical oscillation. In applying this method to actual problems, the step size is often determined by the accuracy consideration rather than the stability consideration. This is in contrast to ordinary explicit methods in which the step length is almost invariably controlled by stability considerations. When the Fu-deVogelaere method was used to study two-dimensional wave propagation in axisymmetric and plane strain problems, it demonstrated that its integration scheme was capable of treating a suddenly applied load and could also be used to provide static finite-element solutions. In its present form, the methods employs a fixed time step algorithm, but this can easily be modified to a variable step version.

Modified Euler Explicit Method [45, 68]

Richards, Lanning, and Torrey [68] modified Euler's original method by changing it into a variable-step procedure, which meant that a much larger step size could be used without instability resulting. The method, therefore, appears to combine the simplicity of the Euler method with the economy of using the large time step lengths usually associated only with unconditionally stable implicit methods.

The basis of the method is the replacement of the calculated value of y = f(y) with an interpolated value, provided the following condition is satisfied:

$$\frac{f(y_n)\ f(y_{n+1})}{\| f(y_n) \| \ \| f(y_{n+1})} < -1/8 \tag{14}$$

The interpolated value is defined by:

$$s = \frac{f(y_n)\ [f(y_n) - f(y_{n+1})]}{\| f(y_{n+1}) - f(y_n) \|^2} \tag{15}$$

Nonlinear Explicit Methods [69, 70]

Research endeavors previously concentrated on reducing the computational complexity of implicit linear multistep methods to make them acceptable for solving stiff systems, but at best, success was only marginal. Recently, however, efforts have been directed toward developing a class of explicit methods with improved stability properties. Being explicit, these methods are inherently simple to use and they should be effective in solving stiff systems since their greater stability regions permit larger time steps in integration. Known as the explicit nonlinear methods, they have the economic advantage, in common with all explicit methods, of requiring no matrix inversions.

The strategy of explicit nonlinear methods is based on local extrapolation through the use of rational functions instead of polynomial, as in the linear methods. First, we shall define a nonlinear method. A method for the numerical solution of an IVP.

$$\dot{y} = f(y,t) \qquad y(t_o) = y_o \tag{16}$$

is said to be nonlinear if, when applied to the test equation,

$$\dot{y} = Ay, \quad A = \text{a dense matrix}$$

it yields a nonlinear difference equation in the discrete variable

$$y_n = y(t_n), \; t_n = t_o + nh$$

To date, stability analysis of explicit nonlinear methods has been made only for the scalar test equation; that for the vector test equation remains to be done. It has been determined that control of local truncation errors is difficult and, in fact, the notion of a principal local truncation error cannot be logically carried over directly from that used in linear methods. This results in a lack of error control and good results can only be obtained through use of small time steps, even though the stability consideration would allow much larger time steps. The possible application of explicit nonlinear methods to stiff systems has not been thoroughly studied and is, therefore, not adequatley understood. It has been found that sometimes they work well for linear problems with high stiffness ratios but poorly for low or medium stiffness ratios. It has been conjectured that these methods may serve as excellent "predictors" but that a more accurate method must be developed to serve as a "corrector." Such a combination may ultimately evolve into a powerful tool for the solution of stiff systems.

CONSIDERATIONS FOR VARIABLE TIME STEP SCHEMES [12, 31, 40, 46, 53, 57, 58, 63]

A practical integration method must be efficient and accurate. It is obviously necessary to take as large a time step as possible without producing unacceptable error. This is not possible for a stiff problem in which the frequency of the fastest component may be a thousand or more times larger than the frequency of the slowest one. A fixed time step suitable for the fast period would give more than adequate accuracy for the slow period but would be vastly inefficient. On the other hand, if the time step were chosen on the basis of slow components, then the solution would be entirely inadequate for the fast-moving period of motions. Since a structural dynamic research frequently yields a stiff problem, a variable step program is a must for its solution. An automatic step size control is a necessary part of any variable step integration program.

Variable time step control algorithms are based on the error estimate. [4, 5, 62] The error can be estimated through an analytical representation of the numerical formula of integration such as a Taylor expansion in which the first neglected term in the expansion is then assumed to be the dominant source of error. The error can be conveniently related there in terms of a given power of the step size.

To illustrate the general procedure we shall present the following, which is taken from Kurokawa [40].

To fix ideas, let us use the implicit trapezoidal method to integrate the differential equations $\dot{y} = f(y,t)$. The formulation is

$$y_{n+1} = y_n = \frac{h}{2} (\dot{y}_{n+1} + \dot{y}_n) + D \qquad (15)$$

where $y_n = y(t_n)$ and $\dot{y}_n = f(y_n, t_n)$, $t_{n+1} = t_n + h$, h = step size, and D = error term of the (trapezoidal) formulation.

Using the Taylor expansion we obtain

$$y_{n+1} = y_n + h\dot{y}_n + \frac{h^2}{2} \ddot{y}_n + \frac{h^3}{3!} \dddot{y}_n + D(h^4) \qquad (16)$$

which, with the consideration of example (15) can be written as:

$$D + \frac{h}{2} (\dot{y}_{n+1} + \dot{y}_n) = h\dot{y}_n + \frac{h^2}{2} \ddot{y}_n + \frac{h^3}{3!} \dddot{y} + 0(h^4) \qquad (17)$$

On the other hand, differentiating (16) gives

$$\dot{y}_{n+1} = \dot{y}_n + h\ddot{y}_n + \frac{h^2}{2} \dddot{y}_n + 0(h^3)$$

which can be rewritten as

$$\frac{h}{2} (\dot{y}_{n+1} + \dot{y}_n) = h\dot{y}_n + \frac{h^2}{2} \ddot{y}_n + \frac{h^3}{4} \dddot{y}_n + 0(h^4) \qquad (18)$$

Subtracting (18) from (17) we obtain the error term D to be

$$D = -\frac{1}{12} h^3 \dddot{y}_n + 0(h^4) \qquad (19)$$

If y is sufficiently smooth, a backward difference formula states

$$\dddot{y}_n = \frac{1}{h^2} (\dot{y}_{n-2} - 2\dot{y}_{n-1} + \dot{y}_n)$$

or (20)

$$D = -\frac{h}{12} (\dot{y}_{n-2} - 2\dot{y}_{n-1} + \dot{y}_n) + 0(h^4)$$

A variation of the above-mentioned method was introduced recently for general purpose integrators. It was apparently inspired by the popularity of modern variable-order methods. In this algorithm, the same integration polynomial is used but the calculations are done for different orders. The difference of the results by the different order method is then used as a measure of the local truncation error. This algorithm was first implemented for the Runge-Kutta method but it should be equally applicable to other methods, such as Adams methods.

Another fairly common decision procedure for step size control is based on the number of iteration cycles. In this method, a first integration step size is chosen, and using it, a certain parameter such as acceleration is predicted or estimated. The numerical integration then proceeds with the chosen step size. The result is then used to determine the new value of the same physical parameter. The difference between these two values (i.e., the estimated vs. the calculated) is used as a measure of the truncation error. If the error is too large to be tolerated, the procedure is repeated, using half of the original step size, and half again until the result is acceptable. If the error is too small, the step size is doubled until a satisfactory result is obtained. The number of halvings or doublings is recorded by a counter whose subsequent total will be compared with a threshold value. If the threshold is more than a constant multiple of the number of iterations, then the step size of the next integration step shall be increased. If it is less than a fraction of the number of iteration cycles used, the step size of the next integration shall be decreased. If neither is the case, the step size for the next integration shall be unchanged. This algorithm has been used for step size control in am Implicit Newmark Beta program.

To carry the method a step further, we can use this logic to regulate the time step in a standard predictor-corrector method. Suppose that the predicted value of the jth component of the solution at the ith integration step is P_{ij} and the corrected value of its counterpart is C_{ij}, then the absolute value of their difference $C_{ij} - P_{ij}$ is a measure of the local truncation error. In application of this method it is crucial to have a reasonably good estimate of the parameter which is used for error estimation. Usually, the standard procedure of comparing the predictor and corrector results would be adequate. Care should be exercised when an explicit formula is used as a predictor. Due to its poor stability property, the predicted vlaue may be grossly in error when the step size is outside its stability region. This consideration is perhaps especially important for nonlinear systems. It is well known that the nonlinear system can have nonunique solutions; if a starting value in a solution process is not near the solution itself, the iteration may lead to a wrong result.

Perhaps the most commonly used variable step technique for linear multistep methods is one which previous values of the function f in the differential equation $\dot{y} = f(y,t)$ are used. In this method the step size is changed by integrating the interpolating polynomial through those previous values of the function f, and estimating the local error as well as the effect of a change in the step size on future estimated errors.

This method has the following advantages:

1. The actual error is more likely to vary continuously with the prescribed local truncation error.
2. It is easier to increase the step size when the round-off error is affecting the accuracy of the result, and not merely the truncation error.

The main disadvantage of this algorithm lies in the additional cost for determining prior to the integration process the weighting coefficients which must be applied to the previous values of f. This cost should not be excessive for stiff systems since the integration order is already low for stability and efficiency reasons, and hence the number of previous values of f required is relatively small.

CONCLUSION

A plausible but paradoxical phenomenon occurs in the use of linear multistep methods; the computing time remains the same regardless of the prescribed accuracy. The reason is that in stiff problems stability, rather than accuracy, is the deciding factor of the step size. It turns out that inside the stability region, the propagation error is always damped out and the variable-step algorithm will call for an increase of the step size; outside the stability region, the error will grow rapidly and the algorithm will reduce the step size. The net result is that the chosen step size will be such that the process operates always in the proximity of the boundary of the stability region. The prescribed accuracy in such cases has virtually no effect on the step size determination.

In this condition, the order of the integration method has no effect; that is, for a variable order method, a low-order procedure will work as well as a high-order one. The reason is the same as before, i.e., the step size of a stiff system is decided by stability, rather than accuracy. Since the higher-order method is usually more laborious, a low-order method will usually turn out to be more efficient. It is then simpler sometimes to use even a fixed-order method, provided that a sophisticated step size adjustment algorithm is incorporated into it.

REFERENCES

1 Dahlquist, G., and Bjorck, A., Numerical Methods, Prentice-Hall Inc., Englewood Cliffs, New Jersey, 1974.

2 Gear, C. W., Numerical Initial Value Problems in Ordinary Differential Equations. Prentice-Hall, Inc., Englewood Cliffs, New Jersey, 1976.

3 Lambert, J. D., Computational Methods in Ordinary Differential Equations, John Wiley and Sons, New York, 1973.

4 Curtis, A. R., "Solution of Large, Stiff Initial Value Problems, The State of the Art," in Numerical Software - Needs and Availability, ed. D. Jacobs, Academic Press, New York, 1978, pp. 257-278.

5 Lambert, J. D., "The Initial Value Problem for Ordinary Differential Equations," in Numerical Software - Needs and Availability, ed. D. Jacobs, Academic Press, New York, 1977, pp. 451-500.

6 Forsythe, G. E., and Moher, C. B., Computer Solution of Linear Algebraic Systems, Prentice-Hall, Inc., Englewood Cliffs, New Jersey, 1976.

7 Newmark, N. M., "A Method of Computing for Structural Dynamics," Proc. Am. Soc. Civ. Engrs., Vol. 85 (EM), 1959, pp. 67-94.

8 Park, K. C., "Evaluating Time Integration Methods for Nonlinear Dynamics Analysis," Symposium on Mathematical Aspects of Finite Elements in Partial Differential Equations, ed. C. De Boor.

9 Nickell, R. E., "On the Stability of Approximation Operators in Problems of Structural Dynamics," Int. Journal of Solid Structures, Vol. 7, 1971, pp. 301-319.

10 Dahlquist, G., "Problems Related to the Numerical Treatment of Stiff Differential Equations," Invited Paper, International Computing Symposium, 1973, published in International Computing Symposium 1973, ed. A. Gunter et al., North-Holland Publishing Co., 1974, pp. 307-314.

11 Cash, J. R., "A Class of Implicit Runge-Kutta Methods for the Numerical Integration of Stiff Ordinary Differential Equations," J. Assn. Comp. Mach., Vol. 22, No. 4, 1975, pp. 504-511.

12 Robertson, H. H., "Some Factors Affecting the Efficiency of Stiff Integration Routines," in Numerical Software - Needs and Availability, ed. D. Jacobs, Academic Press, New York, 1978, pp. 279-302.

13 Burrage, K., and Butckher, J. C., "Stability Criteria for Implicit Runge-Kutta Methods," Siam J. Numerical Analysis, Vol. 16, No. 1, February 1979.

14 Shampine, L. F., "Implementation of Implicit Formulas for the Solution of ODEs," Siam J. Sci. Stat. Comput., Vol. 1, No. 1, March 1980.

15 Chan, S. P., Cox, H. L., and Benfield, W. A., "Transient Analysis of Forced Vibrations of Complex Structural-Mechanical Systems," J. R. Aeronaut- Soc., Vol. 66, 1962, pp. 457-460.

16 Chiapetta, R. L., Belytschko, T., and Rouse, J., "A Computer Code for Dynamic Stress Analysis of Media Structure Problems with Nonlinearities (SAMSON)," Air Force Weapons Laboratory, AFWL- TR-72-104, IIT Research Institute Project J6254, 1972.

17 Dunham, R. S., Nickell, R. E., and Stickler, D. C., "Integration Operators for Transient Structural Response," Computers and Structures, Vol. 2, 1972, pp. 1-15.

18 Enright, W. H., "Second Derivative Multistep Methods for Stiff Ordinary Differential Equations," Siam J. Numerical Analysis, Vol. 11, No. 2, 1974, pp. 321-331.

19 Fox, L., and Goodwin, E. T., "Some New Methods for the Numerical Integration of Ordinary Differential Equations," Proc. Camb. Phil. Soc. Math. Phys., Vol. 45, 1949, pp. 373-388.

20 Goudreau, G. L., and Taylor, R. L., "Evaluation of Numerical Integration Methods in Elastodynamics," Computer Meth. in Appl. Mech. and Eng., Vol. 2, 1972, pp. 69-97.

21 Hughes, T. J. R., "A Note on the Stability of Newmark's Algorithm in Nonlinear Structural Dynamics," Int. J. Num. Meth. Eng., Vol. 11, No. 2, 1977, pp. 383-386.

22 Liniger, W., and Willoughby, R. A., "Efficient Integration Methods for Stiff Systems of Ordinary Differential Equations," Siam J. Numer. Anal., Vol. 8, No. 1, 1970, pp. 47-66.

23 Mondkar, D. P., and Powell, G. H., "Finite Element Analysis of Nonlinear Static and Dynamic Response," Int. J. Num. Meth. Eng., Vol. 11, 1977, pp. 499-520.

24 Nickell, R. E., "Direct Integration Methods in Structural Dynamics," J. Eng. Mech., ASCE, Vol. 99, No. 2, 1973, pp. 303-317.

25 Park, K. C., "Evaluating Time Integration Methods for Nonlinear Dynamics Analysis," invited paper at the Applied Mechanics Symposia Series, ASME Winter Annual Winter Meeting, Finite Element Analysis of Transient Nonlinear Structural Behavior, Houston, Texas, 1975.

26 Park, K. C., "An Improved Stiffly Stable Method for Direct Integration of Nonlinear Structural Dynamic Equations," J. App. Mech., Vol. 42, No. 2, 1975, pp. 464-470.

27 Stricklen, J. A., and Haisler, W. E., "Survey of Solution Procedures for Nonlinear Static and Dynamic Analyses," SAE Proceedings, P-52, International Conference on Vehicle Strutcural Mechanics, 1974, pp. 1-17.

28 Weeks, G., "Temporal Operators for Nonlinear Structural Dynamics Problems," J. Eng. Mech., ASCE, Vol. 98 (EMS), 1972, pp. 1087-1104.

29 Belytschko, T., Schoeberle, D. F., "On the Unconditional Stability of an Implicit Algorithm for Nonlinear Structural Dynamics," J. of Appl. Mech., 1975, pp. 1-5.

30 Houbolt, J. C., "A Recurrence Matrix Solution for the Dynamic Response of Elastic Aircraft," J. Aeronaut. Sci., Vol. 17, 1950, pp. 540-550.

31 Park, K. C., and Underwood, P. G., "A Variable Step Central Difference Method for Structural Dynamics Analysis - Part I, Theoretical Aspects," Computer Methods in Applied Mechanics and Engineering, North Holland Publishing Co., Vol. 22, 1980, pp. 241-258.

32 Boggs, P. T., "The Solution of Nonlinear Systems of Equations by A-Stable Integration Techniques," SIAM J. Numer. Anal., Vol. 8, No. 4, 1971, pp. 767-785.

33 Cash, J. R., "A Class of Iterative Algorithms for the Integration of Stiff Systems of Ordinary Differential Equations," J. Inst. Math. App., Vol. 19, 1977, pp. 324-335.

34 Enright, W. H., "Optimal Second Derivative Methods for Stiff Systems," ed. R. A. Wolloughby, in Stiff Differential Systems, Plenum Press, New York, 1974, pp. 111-121.

35 Enright, W. H., and Hull, T. E., "Comparing Numerical Methods for the Solution of Stiff Systems of ODEs Arising in Chemistry," in Numerical Methods for Differential Systems, ed. L. Lapidus and W. E. Schiesser, Academic Press, New York, 1976, pp. 45-66.

36 Hodgkins, W. R., "A Method for the Numerical Integration of Nonlinear Ordinary Differential Equations with Greatly Different Time Constants," Conf. on the Numerical Solution of Differential Equations, ed. J. L. Morris, Springer-Verlag Lec. Notes in Math #109, 1969, pp. 172-177.

37 Hull, T. E., "Numerical Solution of Initial Value Problems for Ordinary Differential Equations," Numerical Solutions of Boundary Value Problems for Ordinary Differential Equations, ed. A. K. Aziz, Academic Press, New York, 1975, pp. 3-27.

38 Jensen, P. S., "Stiffly Stable Methods for Undamped Second Order Equations of Motion," SIAM J. Numer. Anal., Vol. 13, No. 4, 1976, pp. 549-563.

39 Johnson, A. I., and Barney, J. R., "Numerical Solution of Large Systems of Stiff Ordinary Differential Equations in Modular Simulation Framework," Numerical Methods for Differential Systems, ed. L. Lapidus and W. E. Schiesser, Academic Press, New York, 1976, pp. 97-124.

40 Kurokawa, K., "The Automatic Integration of Stiff Differential Equations by the Implicit Trapezoidal Rule," Bull Electrotech. Lab., (Japan), Vol. 39, No. 6, 1975, pp. 429-448.

41 Shampine, L. F., and Gordon, M. K., Computer Solution of Ordinary Differential Equations: The Initial Value Problem, W. H. Freeman and Co., San Francisco, 1975.

42 Cash, J. R., "On the Integration of Stiff Systems of O.D.E.'s Using Extended Backward Differentiation Formulae," Numer. Mathematics, Vol. 34, No. 3, 1980.

43 Chau, L. O., and Lin, P-M., Computer Aided Analysis of Electronic Circuits: Algorithms and Computational Techniques, Prentice Hall, Englewood Cliffs, N. J., 1975.

44 Enright, W. H., Hull, T. E., and Lindburg, B., "Comparing Numerical Methods for Stiff Systems of O.D.E.'s," BIT, Vol. 15, pp. 10-48.

45 Lapidus, L., and Seinfeld, J. H., Numerical Solution of Ordinary Differential Equations, Academic Press, New York, 1971.

46 Kaps, P., and Rentrop, P., "Generalized Runge-Kutta Methods of Order Four with Stepsize Control for Stiff Ordinary Differential Equations." Numer. Mathematics, Vol. 33, 1979, pp. 55-68.

47 Michelson, M. L., "An Efficient General Purpose Method for the Integration of Stiff Ordinary Differential Equations," AIChE Journal, Vol. 22, No. 3, 1976, pp. 594-597.

48 Byrne, G. D., et al., "Panel Discussion of Quality Software of ODE's," in Numerical Methods for Differential Systems, ed. L. Lapidus and W. E. Schiesser, Academic Press, New York, 1976.

49 Davenport, S. M., Shampine, L. F., and Watts, H. A., "Comparison of Some Codes for the Initial Value Problem for Ordinary Differential Equations," in Numerical Solutions of Boundary Value Problems for Ordinary Differential Equations, ed. A. D. Aziz, Academic Press, New York, 1975, pp. 349-353.

50 Gear, C. W., "DIFSUB for Solution of Ordinary Differential Equations," Comm. ACM, Vol. 14, No. 3, 1970, pp. 185-190.

51 Gear, C. W., "The Automatic Integration of Ordinary Differential Equations," Comm. ACM., Vol. 14, No. 3, 1970, pp. 176-179.

52 Gear, C. W., Tu, K. W., and Watanabe, D. C., "The Stability of Automatic Programs for Numerical Problems," in Stiff Differential Systems, ed. R. A. Willoughby, Plenum Press, New York, 1974, pp. 111-121.

53 Gear, C. W., and Tu, K. W., "The Effect of Variable Mesh Size on the Stability of Multistep Methods," J. Numer. Anal., Vol. 11, No. 4, 1974, pp. 1025-1043.

54 Gourlay, A. R., and Watson, H. D. D., "An Implementation of Gear's Algorithm for CSMP III," in Stiff Differential Systems, ed. R. A. Willoughby, Plenum Press. New York, 1974, pp. 123-133.

55 Hindmarsh, A. C., and Byrne, G. B., "EPISODE: An Experimental Package for the Integration of Systems of Ordinary Differential Equations," Lawrence Livermore Laboratory Report UCID-30112, 1975.

56 Hindmarsh, A. C., and Byrne, G. B., "Application of EPISODE: An Experimental Package for the Integration of Systems of Ordinary Differential Equations," in Numerical Methods for Differential Systems: Recent Developments in Algorithms, Software and Applications, ed. L. Lapidus and W. E. Schiesser, Academic Press, New York, 1976, pp. 147-166.

57 Krough, F. T., "Algorithm for Changing the Step Size," Siam J. Numer. Anal., Vol. 10, No. 5, 1973, pp. 949-965.

58 Krough, F. T., "Changing Stepsize in the Integration of Differential Equations using Modified Divided Differences," in Proc. of the Conf. on the Numer. Sol. of Ord. Diff. Eq., ed. A. Dold and B. Eckmann, Springer-Verlag Lec. Notes in Math No. 361, 974, pp. 22-71.

59 Shampine, L. F., "Stiffness and Non-stiff Differential Equation Solvers," in Numerische Behandlung von Differentialgleichungen, Tagung in Mathematischen Forschungsinstitut Oberwolfach, Vol. 9, No. 14, June 1974, Ismn 27 Birkhauser Verlag, Basel and Stuttgart, 1975.

60 Shampine, L. F., Watts, H. A., and Davenport, S. M., "Solving Nonstiff Ordinary Differential Equations - The State of the Art," SIAM Rev, Vol. 18, No. 3, 1976, pp. 376-411.

61 Willoughby, R. A., "International Symposium on Stiff Differential Equations: Introduction," in Stiff Differential Systems, ed. R. A. Willoughby, Plenum Press, New York, 1974, pp. 1-19.

62 Stetler, H. J., "Interpolation and Error Estimation in Adamc PC Codes," SIAM J. Numer. Anal., 1979, pp. 311-323.

63 Robertson, H. H., and Williams, J., "Some Properties of Algorithms for Stiff Differential Equations," J. Inst. Math. Applics., Vol. 16, 1975, pp. 23-34.

64 Byrne, G. D., Hindmarsh, A. C., et al., "A Comparison of Two ODE Codes: GEAR and EPISODE, Computers and Chemical Engineering, Vol. 1, 1977, pp. 133-147.

65 Byrne, G. D., Hindmarsh, A. C., et al., "Comparative Test Results for Two ODE Solvers: EPISODE and GEAR," Argonne National Laboratory Report ANL-77-19, Argonne, Ill., March 1977.

66 Cash, J. R., "High Order Methods for Numerical Integration of Ordinary Differential Equations," Numer. Mathematics, Vol. 20, 1978, pp. 385-409.

67 Fu, C. C., "A Method for the Numerical Integration of the Equations of Motion Arising from a Finite Element Analysis," J. App. Mech., Trans. ASME, September 1970, pp. 599-605.

68 Richards, P. L., Lanning, W. D., and Torrey, M. D., "Numerical Integration of Large, Highly Damped Nonlinear Systems," SIAM Rev., 1965, pp. 376-380.

69 Lambert, J. D., "Nonlinear Methods for Stiff Systems of Ordinary Differential Equations," in Proceedings of Conference on the Numerical Solutions of Differential Equations, ed. A. Dold and B. Eckmann, Springer-Verlag Lecture Notes in Mathematics, No. 363, 1973.

70 Lambert, J. D., "Two Unconventional Classes of Methods for Stiff Systems," in Stiff Differential System, ed. R. A. Willoughby, Plenum Press, New York, 1974.

Additional References Not Listed In Chapter

1 Bickart, T. A., and Rubin, W. B., "Composite Multistep Methods and Stiff Stability," in Stiff Differential Systems, ed. R. A. Willoughby, Plenum Press, New York, 1974, pp. 21-36.

2 Chambers, T., "The Use of Numerical Software in the Digital Simulation Lnguage PHSP," in Numerical Software - Needs and Availability, ed. D. Jacobs, Academic Press, New York, 1978, pp. 237-253.

3 Delves, L. M., "Numerical Software for Integral Equations," in Numerical Software - Needs and Availability, ed. D. Jacobs, Academic Press, New York, 1978, pp. 303-323.

4 Felippa, C. A., and Park, K. C., "Direct Time Integration Methods in Nonlinear Sructural Dynamics," Computer Methods in Applied Mechanics and Engineering, North Holland Publishing Co., Vol. 17, No. 18, 1979, pp. 277-313.

5 Hindmarsh, A. C., "Preliminary Documentation of GEARID: Solution of Implicit Systems of Ordinary Differential Equations with Banded Jacobian," Lawrence Livermore Laboratory Report UCID-30130, February 1976.

6 Krough, F. T., "A Test for Instability in the Numerical Solution of Ordinary Differential Equations," J. Assoc. Comp. Mach., Vol. 14, No. 2, 1967, pp. 351-354.

7 Lax, P. D., and Richtmyer, R. D., "Survey of the Stability of Linear Finite Difference Equations," Commun. Pure Appl. Math., Vol. 9, 1971, pp. 267-293.

8 Skappel, J., "Attempts to Optimize the Structure of an ODE Program," in Conf. on the Numerical Solution of Differential Equations ed. J. L. Morris, Springer-Verlag Lecture Notes in Mathematics, No. 109, 1969, pp. 243-248.

9 Thompson, S., "A Comparison of Available Software for the Numerical Solution of Stiff Ordinary Differential Equations," Babcock and Wilcox, Report NPGD-TM-368, Power Generation Group, Nuclear Power Generation Division, P.O. Box 1260, Lynchburg, Va., 24505 June 1977.

Assessment of Freight Car Computer Models

Arnold J. Gilchrist

Wyle Laboratories

N. T. Tsai

Federal Railroad Administration

INTRODUCTION

The Federal Railroad Administration (FRA) is currently sponsoring programs to improve the safety, efficiency, and productivity of rail freight transportation. One of these programs is the Truck Design Optimization Project (TDOP), Phase II. As part of this effort, experimental and analytical studies are being conducted by Wyle Laboratories to define the performance capabilities of conventional (Type I) freight car trucks and various innovative (Type II) freight car truck designs. In carrying out the analytical evaluations of freight car trucks, it was necessary to make an assessment of several computer models which have been developed by various researchers over a number of years. The purpose of this paper is to report the results of the assessments of these computer models.

The models assessed were selected on the basis of their applicability to one or more of the four performance regimes that characterize freight car trucks. These four performance regimes are:

1. Lateral Stability, which refers to the tendency of a truck to oscillate (hunt) with severe lateral and yawing motions while operating at high speeds on tangent track.
2. Curve Negotiation, which measures the ability of a truck to track through a curve with a minimum of flange contact and wear on the rail and on the wheels.
3. Ride Quality, which is defined as the normal vibration environment that both the lading and the truck components are exposed to during nonextreme in-service operation.
4. Trackability, which is the ability to maintain adequate loads for guidance on all wheels during extremes of in-service operation. Subsets of this regime include harmonic roll and bounce, curve entry and exit, and load equalization.

SURVEY OF PROGRAM DESCRIPTIONS

To identify suitable computer programs which would meet the needs of the TDOP analytical effort, a formal survey of pertinent literature was performed. The literature survey was based largely on three excellent summaries of existing analytical tools [1,2,3]. These, plus recent technical papers and descriptions of concurrent research projects, provided the necessary information for the preliminary survey.

The survey was limited to either completed or nearly completed computer programs. In many cases, methods rather than actual models were discussed in the literature. Since our objective was to assemble existing analytical models, we did not review analytical methods in detail unless a program source code, which implemented the method under discussion, was indicated. Simplified engineering models (e.g., single degree-of-freedom systems) were also not included in the survey. While engineering models are highly useful in providing insight and have been, in fact, used frequently in TDOP analyses, the purpose of this paper is to review more comprehensive candidate tools for possible validation.

After the preliminary survey, all but the clearly unsuitable analytical models were studied in greater detail. Where formal program documentation was available, it was obtained and reviewed. When attempts were made to obtain models thought to be available, some problems were encountered, such as: a number of programs were tied to a particular set of equipment, such as hybrid computers; other programs were proprietary; still others were programs from foreign sources for which no contact was readily available. In all, some 59 programs were surveyed. Of these, 19 were selected as being applicable to the needs of TDOP and suitable for more detailed evaluations.

The set of models evaluated generally includes both linear frequency domain simulation approaches and nonlinear time domain simulations within each performance regime. The models are identified according to the performance regime in Table 1. Two of the 19 programs evaluated were auxiliary or subroutine programs which describe the contact geometry of the important wheel/rail interface. These two subroutine programs are compatible with a number of the comprehensive vehicle simulations which treat the wheel/rail geometry.

A description and summary of the capabilities of each of the 19 programs is given below.

FREIGHT CAR HUNTING MODEL

Category: Linear frequency domain dynamic analysis of full vehicle lateral stability.

Authors: T. H. W. Cheung, V. K. Garg, G. C. Martin
Association of American Railroads
3140 S. Federal Street
Chicago, Illinois 60616

Date: 1977

Capability: The model is a 25 degree-of-freedom (dof) linear representation of a freight car with standard trucks. This program uses matrix methods to solve for eigenvalues and eigenvectors (natural frequencies and mode shapes) from which critical hunting speeds are obtained.

Table 1 Models Selected for Detailed Assessment

MODEL	PRIMARY PERFORMANCE REGIME
Freight Car Hunting (AAR)	Lateral Stability
Lateral/Vertical Model (AAR)	Lateral Stability
17 dof Eigenvalue (Law & Cooperrider)	Lateral Stability
HUNTCT (Wyle)	Lateral Stability
Freight Car Curving Model (AAR)	Curve Negotiation
9 dof Steady State Curving Model (Law & Cooperrider)	Curve Negotiation
17 dof Steady State Curving Model (Law and Cooperrider)	Curve Negotiation
DYNALIST II (TSC)	Ride Quality
FULL (TSC)	Ride Quality
HALF (TSC)	Ride Quality
FLEX (TSC)	Ride Quality
LATERAL (TSC)	Ride Quality
Freight Car Frequency Domain Model	Ride Quality
Flexible Body Railroad Freight Car Model (AAR)	Trackability
FRATE (MITRE)	Trackability
FRATE 11 (Wyle)	Trackability
FRATE 17 (Wyle)	Trackability
SUPPORTING SUBROUTINES	
WHRAIL, Symmetric Wheel/Rail Geometric Constraint Routine (Law & Cooperrider)	Lateral Stability Subroutine
WHRAILA, Asymmetric Wheel/Rail Geometric Constraint Routine (Law & Cooperrider)	Lateral Stability Subroutine

Model Description: The configuration for this lumped mass model is shown in Fig. 1. (Note: All of the illustrations that appear in these summaries have been extracted from the appropriate source documents cited in the list of references.) The model represents a freight car with Type I trucks having 25 degrees of freedom. Each truck model consists of a pair of side frames which are connected by linear spring and damping elements to the bolster and wheelsets. The carbody is a single rigid mass element. The wheelsets are modeled assuming symmetric wheels and are characterized by a single effective value of conicity. The track is assumed to be completely rigid and thus does not enter into the formulation.

The linear representation assumes small amplitude displacements. The equations of motion for the system are derived using Newtonian methods. It is assumed that the model could be modified to reflect Type II trucks; however, this may require additional documentation from AAR on the specific means by which the system equations are implemented in the program.

Limitations: The model assumes small amplitude displacement and linearized equations. The validity diminishes as the amplitude of lateral motions exceeds flange clearance.

Programming Language: FORTRAN IV

Documentation: Documentation exists in the form of a User's Manual [4], which provides an excellent description of the general theory forming the basis of the program, as well as sample input and program results. Additionally, the appendixes of the manual provide a helpful discussion.

Operating Systems: Model was developed for IBM operating system but has been adapted for CDC and Interdata usage.

Availability: Program can be obtained from AAR.

Assessment: The Freight Car Hunting Model shows promise as a useful tool for establishing general relationships between truck and carbody parameters and lateral stability. Quantitative results may be somewhat in error due to the linear approximations used in the solution. The model uses matrix manipulations to obtain natural frequencies and mode shapes, and hence critical speeds, for a 25 dof truck/body representation. The computer program is straightforward and generally well documented, although additional clarification on the implementation of system equations in the programming would be useful.

LATERAL/VERTICAL MODEL

Category: Nonlinear time domain dynamic analysis of lateral and vertical forces at the wheel/rail interface

Authors: Y. H. Tse and G. C. Martin
Association of American Railroads
3140 S. Federal Street
Chicago, Illinois 60616

Date: 1977

Capability: The model is a 14 dof representation of a freight car truck and a half carbody. Time domain integration is used to solve the nonlinear equations of motion. The intent of the model is to make a determination of the approximate ratio of lateral to vertical forces at the wheel/rail interface in order to obtain an indication of the potential for wheel climb and derailment.

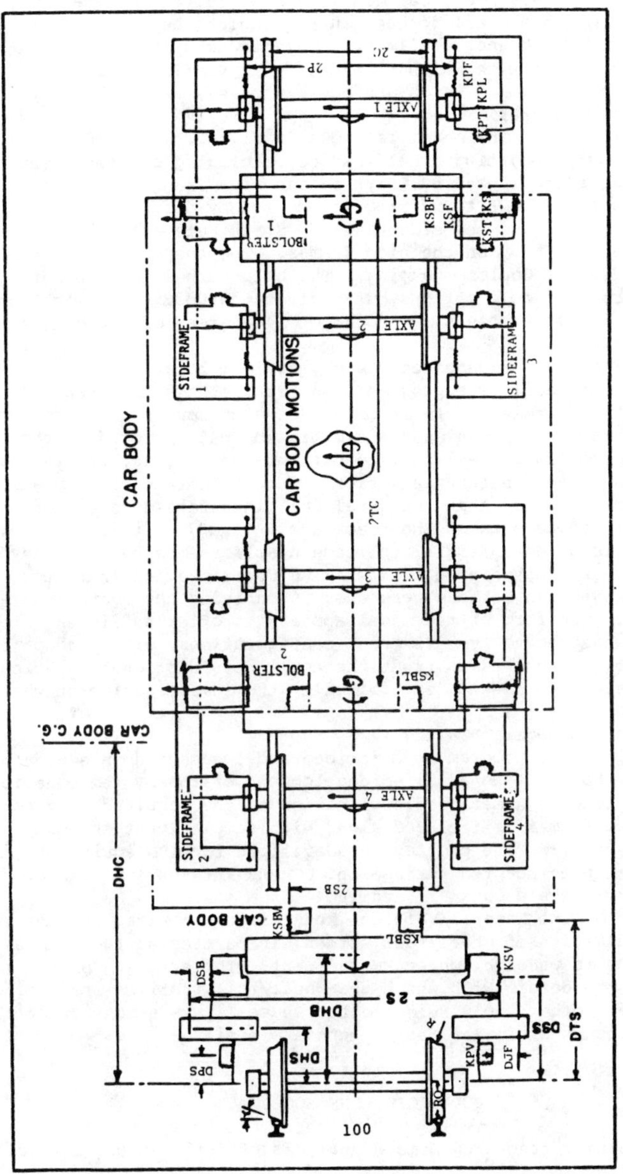

Fig. 1 Freight Car Hunting Model configuration

The Lateral/Vertical Model is best suited for the investigation of wheel/rail forces, in particular the interactions leading to wheel climb and derailment. The strength of the model is in the detail with which the wheel/rail profiles are defined; however, other tools, which are easier to use, treat the profiles in a similar manner.

Model Description: The model is shown in Fig. 2. The model includes one truck supporting a half carbody including bolster. The two wheelsets are linked by inertia-less side frames. The truck stiffness with respect to warping is modeled by diagonal spring elements connecting the side frames. Spring elements also support the half carbody on the side frames. The suspension model also provides for Coulomb damping. The half carbody accounts for vertical and roll motions but neglects carbody yaw, pitch, and lateral displacements. A total of 14 degrees of freedom is included in the model.

The model focuses on the geometrical relationship between wheel and rail. The program requires the user to define the wheel and rail profiles in terms of a series of fourth order polynomial segments. The technique is similar to that employed in the Law and Cooperrider wheel/rail constraint subroutines, but is coarser and requires greater user effort to precalculate polynomial coefficients. Other than the wheel/rail interface description, no additional aspects of the track are included in this model. The model is based on small amplitude displacements but does involve nonlinear suspension elements. The documentation indicates that Newtonian methods were used in deriving the system equations. The form of the model appears to offer sufficient flexibility to be adapted to Type II truck configurations, with perhaps extra attention required to treat the nonlinear functional relationships.

Limitations: Application is limited to the investigation of wheel/rail forces.

Programming Language: FORTRAN IV

Documentation: The program is described and documented in a user's manual [5], but no detailed development of the system equations is included. A detailed explanation of the required program input and its format is included along with sample input and output.

Operating System: The program was developed for IBM equipment but has been adapted for use on CDC and Interdata machines.

Availability: The program is available from AAR.

Assessment: The Lateral/Vertical Model is best suited for the investigation of wheel/rail forces, in particular the interactions leading to wheel climb and derailment. The strength of the model is in the detail with which the wheel/rail profiles are defined; however, other tools selected for Phase II assessment treat the profiles in a similar manner, and are easier to use.

17 DOF EIGENVALUE MODEL

Category: Linear frequency domain analysis of full vehicle lateral stability.

Authors: N. K. Cooperrider, Arizona State University, Tempe, Arizona; E. H. Law, Clemson University, Clemson, South Carolina

Date: 1977

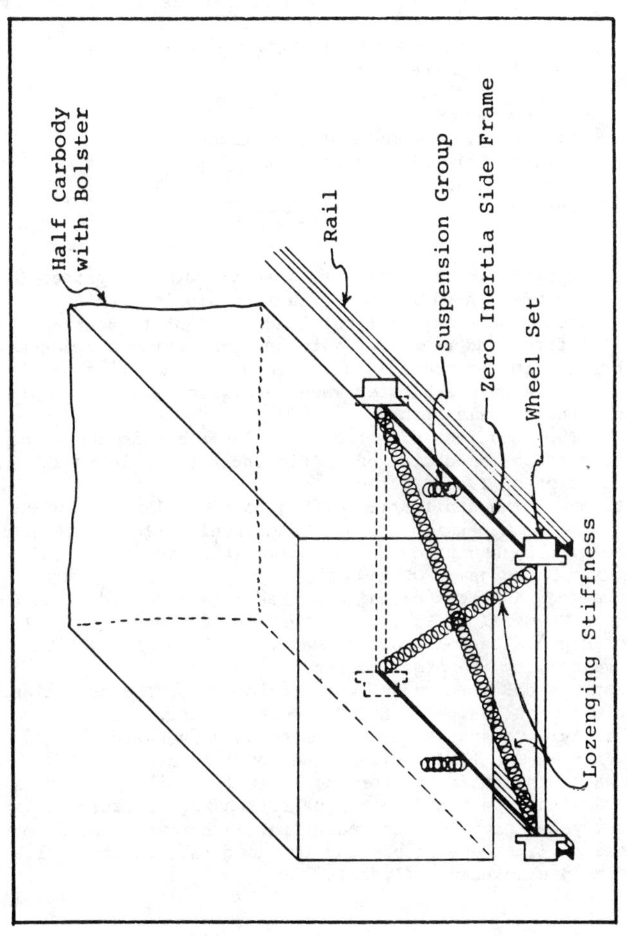

Fig. 2 Lateral/Vertical Model configuration

Capability: The 17 dof Eigenvalue Model can be applied in the lateral stability investigation. The natural frequencies and mode shapes obtained from the eigenvalue analysis can be related to critical hunting speeds and damping factors.

Model Description: The model consists of a single rigid mass representing the carbody. The carbody is supported on two trucks, each having two wheelsets. The 17 degrees of freedom include:

Lateral displacement of each wheelset	4
Yaw of each wheelset	4
Warp of each truck	2
Yaw of each truck	2
Lateral displacement of each truck	2
Carbody lateral displacement	1
Carbody roll	1
Carbody yaw	1
TOTAL:	17

Gravitational stiffness, spin creep, and gyroscopic terms are included in addition to the more significant terms. The model can accommodate asymmetrical loading front to rear and nonidentical front and rear wheelsets and suspension parameters. Also included in the model is a provision for modeling bending and shear connections between wheelsets, such as those implemented in a radial axle truck.

The equations of motion are linear and homogeneous. The formulation is considered sufficiently flexible to allow the representation of Type II trucks.

Limitations: The application of the model is limited by the linearization of suspension elements and wheel/rail contact geometry and by the assumption of small amplitude motion.

Programming Language: FORTRAN IV

Documentation: A user's manual [6] has been released since the TDOP Phase II model evaluations. The user's manual covers the 17 dof Eigenvalue Model as well as other lateral stability models developed by the same authors.

Operating System: The model was developed for IBM operation. It has been adapted for CDC and Univac use.

Availability: Contact E. H. Law, Clemson University.

Assessment: The 17 dof Eigenvalue Model is a linear frequency domain program for performing lateral stability analyses of freight cars with Type I and most Type II trucks. Because it is linear, it may not provide close quantitative agreement with test data. However, its ease of use and low cost make it attractive for doing preliminary analyses.

HUNTCT

Category: Nonlinear time domain computer simulation of a complete rail vehicle

Author: M. J. Healy
Wyle Laboratories
Colorado Springs, Colorado, 80915

Date: 1978

Capability: As a comprehensive freight car model, the program can be used to investigate a number of performance areas. Specifically, the model is best suited for examining the detailed motions resulting from truck hunting and the forces produced in curve entry and exit. Since it is a time domain solution, it is suitable for investigations of detailed motions and forces as well as the identification of critical speeds and mode shapes.

Model Description: A description of the model appears in Fig. 3. The model provides the option of representing the carbody as a rigid mass or as a flexible body. With the basic rigid carbody representation, the model has 21 degrees of freedom. When the flexible carbody option is used, an additional degree of freedom is included for each natural mode of carbody flexure considered. The truck is currently modeled as a single mass with vertical, lateral, yaw, and roll degrees of freedom. The truck model also provides for coupling between wheelsets in the yaw sense (lozenging stiffness). A lumped mass having lateral and yaw degrees of freedom is included for each wheelset. Vertical and roll motions of the wheelset are constrained by the wheel/rail geometry with the assumption of no wheel liftoff. Detailed calculations of the wheel/rail interface are carried out for each wheelset. The effective track mass, stiffness, and damping in the vertical sense are lumped with the truck.

The nonlinear equations of motion are developed using Newtonian methods. The equations are formulated to correspond to physical components of the actual rail cars and trucks so that the model can be adapted to include more or less detail.

Limitations: Some preprocessing to obtain input data is necessary. For example, the carbody bending and torsional mode shapes must be obtained for program input if the flexible carbody option is employed.

Programming Language: FORTRAN IV

Documentation: No documentation has been published.

Operating System: Program was developed for CDC and Interdata use.

Availability: Contact Gordon Bakken, Wyle Laboratories, Colorado Springs, Colorado, 80915.

Assessment: The HUNTCT Model provides a potentially useful means of examining the details of the track/train dynamic interactions in the time domain. The program will have its primary benefit in its application to the lateral stability and curve entry and exit studies. The model accounts for many nonlinearities in representing the truck. The basic number of degrees of freedom is 21 with additional degrees added for each mode of carbody flexibility represented. The model has been developed and used extensively by Wyle Laboratories, the TDOP Phase II Contractor. Some preliminary validation has been carried out, but additional validation with Phase II data is required.

FREIGHT CAR CURVING MODEL

Category: Nonlinear analysis program which uses time integration techniques to simulate the dynamic curving behavior of railroad freight cars

Author: K. R. Smith
Electro-Motive Division, General Motors Corp.
La Grange, Illinois

Date: 1975, later revised by AAR.

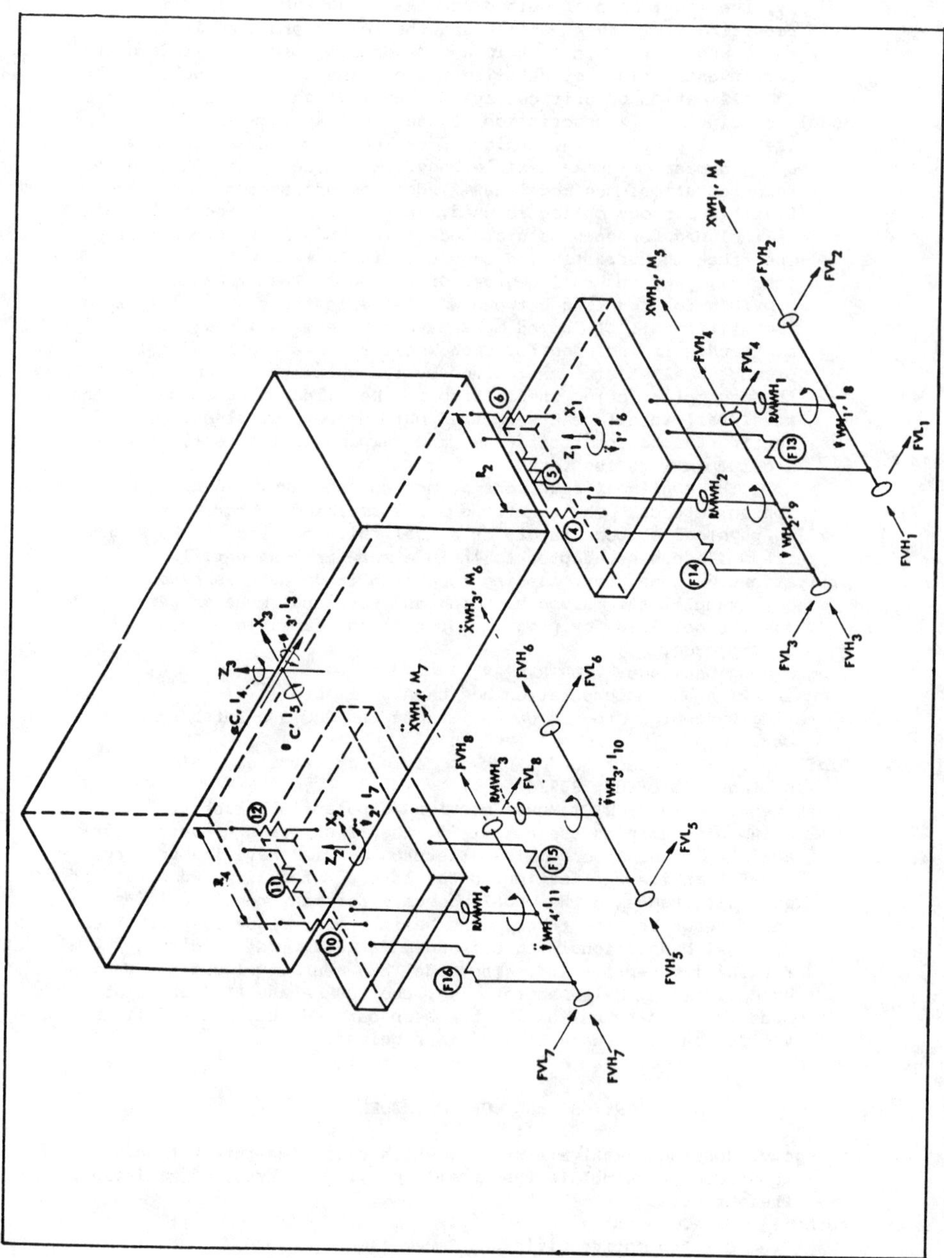
FVH_1
FVL_1
FVH_2
FVL_2
FVH_3
FVL_3
FVH_4
FVL_4
FVH_5
FVL_5
FVH_6
FVL_6
FVH_7
FVL_7
FVH_8
FVL_8
XWH_1, M_4
XWH_2, M_3
$\ddot{X}WH_3, M_6$
$\ddot{X}WH_4, M_7$
$RAWH_1$
$RAWH_2$
$RAWH_3$
$RAWH_4$
F13
F14
F15
F16
4
5
6
10
11
12

Capability: The Freight Car Curving Model has been specifically developed to investigate curve negotiation including the dynamics of curve entry and exit. Nonlinearities included are spring bottoming, clearances, and Coulomb damping.

Model Description: The program employs 43 degrees of freedom to represent the dynamics of a freight car. Each truck is represented by five masses. These are the bolster, the two side frames, and the two wheelsets. Each of those masses has four degrees of freedom consisting of lateral, yaw, vertical, and roll motions. Thus, there are 20 degrees of freedom associated with each truck. The remaining three degrees of freedom are associated with the rigid carbody which is free to translate laterally and vertically and to roll. The masses in the model are connected by nonlinear springs and dampers. Spring characteristics, for instance, may be defined to represent bottoming and free clearance.

The rails are characterized by effective lateral and vertical stiffness and damping elements. The track can be divided into tangent, spiral, or constant curvature segments.

The equations of motion for the system are determined by applying Lagrange's equation for a nonconservative holonomic system. The result is 43 second-order differential equations. The solution of these equations gives the time response of the system to the given input of track curvature. Because of the Lagrangian derivation of the equations, the modification of the program to represent Type II trucks may be difficult.

Limitations: The model is fairly expensive to use for parametric investigations since the time integration of many degrees of freedom is required. Track curvature is idealized.

Programming Language: FORTRAN IV

Documentation: The program is described in technical papers presented by Smith and Willis [7], Garg and Singh [8], and in the 1975 M.S. thesis of Smith [9].

Operating System: The model was developed for IBM operation.

Availability: The program is available from AAR.

Assessment: The Freight Car Curving Model provides the capability of detailed simulation of curve negotiation dynamics. The model is a nonlinear, 43 degree-of-freedom representation. Time integration is used to solve the equations of motion. The level of detail in the simulation offers the possibility of good validation with test results; however, no validation has been carried out to date. Because of the complexity of the model, it is relatively costly to use. The Lagrangian derivation of equations makes it difficult to modify the program to account for the differences of advanced trucks.

9 AND 17 DOF STEADY STATE CURVING MODELS

Category: Nonlinear models which can be used to study the curving behavior of a freight car in terms of forces and displacements developed in a constant radius turn. The 9 dof model represents a standard three-piece roller bearing truck. Additional degrees of freedom in the 17 dof version allow more detailed study of standard trucks and allow representation of various features of advanced truck design.

Author: N. K. Cooperrider
Arizona State University
Tempe, Arizona

E. H. Law
Clemson University
Clemson, South Carolina

Date: 1978

Capability: These models are specifically oriented toward the curve negotiation performance regime. Their main usefulness is in calculating estimates of the slip and flange contact boundaries for nonlinear vehicles.

Model Description: The 9 degrees of freedom considered in the simpler model are lateral, yaw, and warp motion for each of two trucks and lateral, yaw, and roll motion for the carbody. The carbody is assumed to be rigid. In addition to the 9 degrees of freedom in the simpler model, the 17 dof Steady State Curving Model includes lateral and yaw freedom for each of the four wheelsets. Nonlinearities which are considered include wheel/rail geometric constraint functions and suspension elements. The wheel/rail geometric constraints are handled by either the symmetric wheel/rail constraint subroutine or the asymmetric wheel/rail constraint subroutine which are assessed elsewhere in this chapter. The creep force versus displacement relationship is considered to be linear and can be expressed in terms of Kalker's creep coefficients. The track is assumed to be rigid.

The equations for steady state curving result in a nonlinear matrix equilibrium problem which is solved by iteration for a given value of cant deficiency.

Limitations: The 9 dof version is limited primarily to standard freight car trucks. Both models are limited to the analysis of flange-free contact curving.

Programming Language: FORTRAN IV

Documentation: No formal documentation is known to exist for these programs although the technique is described in an ASME paper by the programs' authors [10].

Operating System: The programs were developed for IBM operation but have been adapted for Interdata use.

Availability: Contact E. H. Law, Clemson University

Assessment: The 9 and 17 dof Steady State Curving Models are nonlinear models which predict the steady state curving behavior of freight cars with Type I and some Type II trucks. Their main usefulness is in calculating estimates of the slip and flange contact boundaries including the effects of nonlinear vehicle suspension elements. The solution technique is computationally efficient and relatively inexpensive to use. The shortcoming of the models which may limit their usefulness is the inability to predict steady state performance during flange contact.

DYNALIST

Category: General purpose computer program which solves systems of linear second-order differential equations. Dynamic models of freight cars with up to 50 degrees of freedom can be analyzed both in the time and frequency domains. DYNALIST can be applied to a number of performance regimes including lateral stability, trackability (harmonic roll and bounce subset), and ride quality.

Authors: T. K. Hasselman and A. Bronowicki
J. H. Wiggins Company
Redondo Beach, California

Date: 1976

Capability: Because of its generality and its ability to perform both time and frequency response analysis, this program can be used in a variety of different applications. DYNALIST, like other linear frequency domain models, can be used to produce estimates of critical hunting speeds. The limitation in this regard is in the ability to represent inherently nonlinear trucks with a linear model. In the linear time domain DYNALIST can be used to estimate harmonic roll behavior.

Although linear modeling may be overly simplifed for obtaining quantitatively accurate results for hunting and harmonic roll phenomena, linear models are likely to be sufficient for ride quality analysis. Hence, DYNALIST can readily be applied to this performance area. The flexibility of DYNALIST should prove particularly useful in comparing the effects of Type I versus Type II trucks.

Model Description: The DYNALIST II program has no particular model structure, but instead the program allows the user to define the structure by means of the input. The structure may be composed of rigid bodies, wheelsets with lateral degrees of freedom, model mass elements, springs, and dampers. Flexible bodies can also be included by using an appropriate modal representation. The program determines the equations of motion for the system defined by the user in the general form.

$$[M]x + [C]x + [K]x = F(t)$$

Note that the mass, damping, and stiffness matrices $[M]$, $[C]$, and $[K]$ may be asymmetric. The model is limited to a total of 50 degrees of freedom. The forcing function F(t) can be harmonic, periodic, or random in character. The capability of simulating arbitrary periodic inputs allows the respresentation of transient responses.

Limitations: The model is restricted to linear analysis.

Programming Language: FORTRAN IV

Documentation: A four-volume documentary report [11] is available.

Operating System: The program is operable on CDC equipment.

Availability: Contact Federal Railroad Administration, Office of Research and Development, Washington, D.C.

Assessment: This program provides a general means of creating a linear model for analyzing freight car dynamics. DYNALIST can best be exploited in performing ride quality and harmonic roll investigations, areas in which linear analysis can be applied with the least idealization.

DYNALIST has been used previously for freight car modeling and has also been validated by comparison of its results with "textbook" sample cases.

A background in dynamic modeling is needed for using DYNALIST to define model structures. Otherwise, the thorough documentation enables the program to be easily used by the unfamiliar.

FULL, HALF, FLEX, AND LATERAL

Category: These four models constitute a suite of programs which are intended to provide a comprehensive modeling capability for freight car dynamic behavior. Although these models are linear and sufficiently simple so that they could be duplicated by appropriate DYNALIST modeling, the group has been included because they are fully developed, available, and fairly well documented.

The four models are described as follows:

1. FULL is a linear frequency domain model of the vertical dynamics of a rail vehicle. It is a relatively simple model with six degrees of freedom.
2. HALF is a linear frequency domain model focusing on wheel/rail vertical forces with a half vehicle model which includes a track compliance representation.
3. FLEX is a linear frequency domain model of the vertical dynamics of a rail vehicle; it differs from FULL in that carbody bending is included to a first mode approximation and a lumped mass is included to account for lading.
4. LATERAL is a linear frequency domain model of the lateral dynamics of a rail vehicle. Its focus is on ride quality rather than lateral stability.

Authors: A. B. Perlman and F. P. DiMasi
Transportation Systems Center
Cambridge, Massachusetts

Date: 1975

Capabilities:

1. FULL vertical ride quality analysis
2. HALF vertical wheel/rail forces
3. FLEX vertical ride quality, carbody/lading interactions
4. LATERAL lateral ride quality analysis

Limitations: The four programs are restricted to linear frequency domain analysis.

Programming Language: FORTRAN IV

Documentation: The programs are documented in a single volume [12].

Operating System: The original programs were developed for DEC PDP-10 operation. The programs have been adapted for use on CDC equipment.

Availability: Contact F. P. DiMasi, Transportation Systems Center, Cambridge, Massachuetts.

Assessment: FULL, FLEX, and LATERAL are simple models which can be used as tools for the preliminary evaluation of ride quality using efficient frequency domain techniques. HALF is a very simplified representation of the complex dynamics of wheel/rail vertical forces. Its results must be interpreted with a great deal of caution.

FREIGHT CAR FREQUENCY DOMAIN MODEL

Category: The Freight Car Frequency Domain Model program represents a freight car by 13 degrees of freedom. The objective of the program is to calculate lateral stability characteristics and, to a lesser extent, to predict vehicle motions in regimes such as the harmonic roll excitation.

The model was developed by Southern Pacific Transportation Company (SPTCo.) in conjunction with the testing carried out in the initial phase of the TDOP program. Although the frequency domain model requires linearity in the representation, an attempt was made to characterize some nonlinear suspension elements as linear on a rational basis using describing function techniques.

Authors: Southern Pacific Transportation Company
Technical Research and Development Group
San Francisco, California

Date: 1976

Capability: The model primarily addresses lateral stability but in theory should also predict general truck and carbody motions including a first-order representation of vertical car bending.

Model Description: The 13 degrees of freedom of this model include three degrees for each truck:

Yaw of the side frame pairs	2
Yaw of the bolsters	2
Lateral displacement of the side frames	2

The remaining degrees of freedom are associated with the two lumped masses representing the carbody. See Figs. 4a and 4b. The use of two half carbody masses connected by springs allows a first-order representation of carbody bending and torsion. The other degrees of freedom are:

Roll of each half carbody	2
Relative pitch of the two half carbodies	1
Vertical displacement of each half carbody	2
Yaw of the combined half carbodies	1
Lateral displacement of the combined half carbodies	1

Other forces and moments accounted for in this model are those due to the usual springs and dampers, gyroscopic moments, moments due to center of gravity offset of the carbodies, gravity restoring forces from the wheel/rail interactions, and creep forces generated at the wheel/rail interface.

The wheel/rail interface is idealized by assuming that the wheel and rail have constant but different radii of transverse curvature at the contact point. The representation results in a single value of effective conicity which can be used in the linear representation.

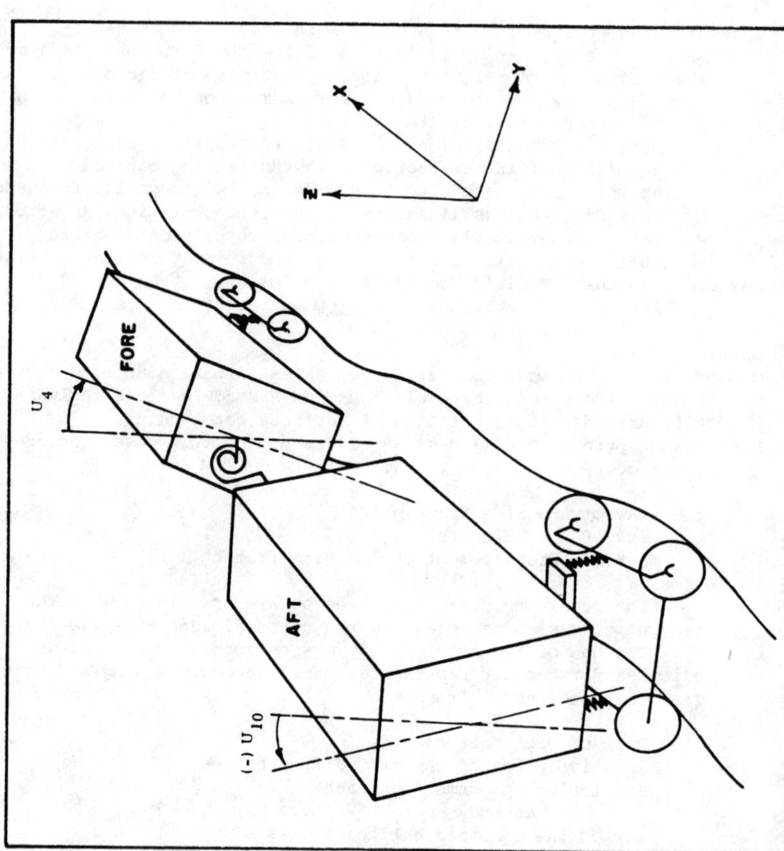

Fig. 4a Freight Car Frequency Domain Model - roll of the half carbody

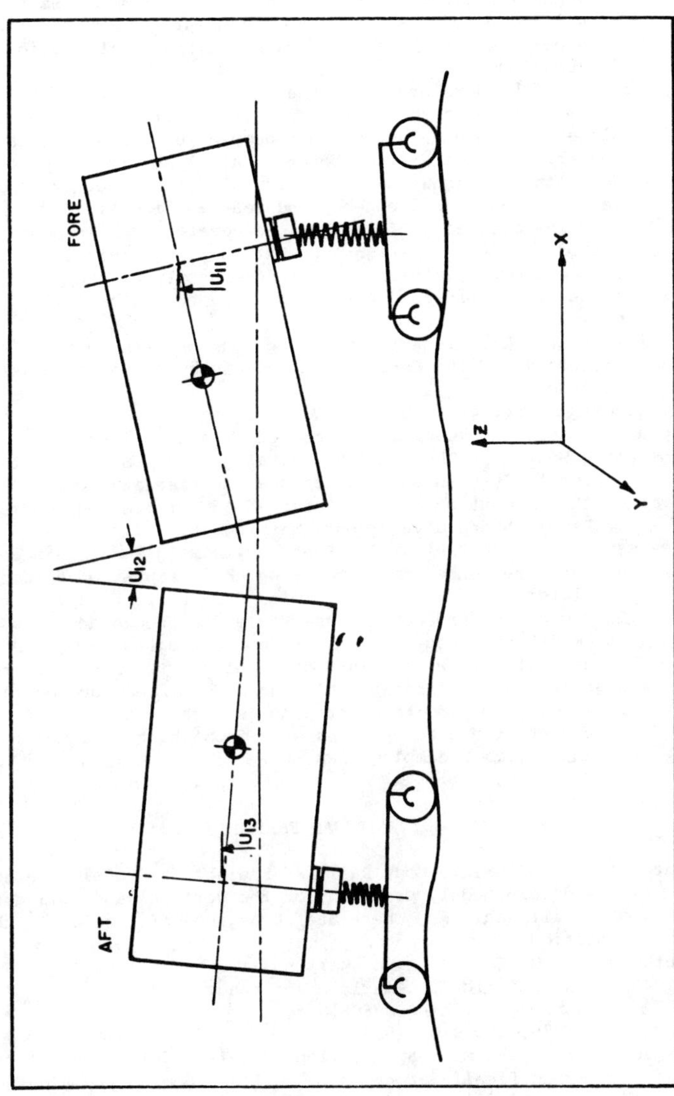

Fig. 4b Freight Car Frequency Domain Model - relative pitch and vertical displacement of half carbodies

The representation of the track input is made by decomposing actual track measurements of the TDOP Phase I test sites into a 200-term Fourier series at frequencies from 0.1 Hz to 20 Hz at 0.1 Hz increments. Time domain solutions are obtained by superposition of the individual solutions of the various forcing frequencies.

In the development of the Frequency Domain Model, an attempt was made to characterize the nonlinear Coulomb damping elements by equivalent viscous damping elements in a rational manner. The coefficient for an equivalent viscous damper was determined by equating the energy dissipated per cycle of oscillation at a given frequency and peak amplitude.

The equations of motion were developed using Newtonian methods. The derivation of equations (not their implementation in the program) was verified independently by the MITRE Corporation, which provided a technical review in the initial stages of TDOP.

Limitations: The linearizing assumptions concerning the wheel/rail interface and the Coulomb damping elements are the chief limitations of the model.

Programming Language: FORTRAN IV

Documentation: The model is documented in a formal report [13].

Operating System: The model was developed for IBM use. It has successfully been adapted for use on Interdata equipment.

Availability: Contact Federal Railroad Administration, Office of Research and Development, Washington, D.C.

Assessment: The Freight Car Frequency Domain Model is a linearized frequency domain model which attempts to represent the lateral and vertical dynamics of a freight car. A total of 13 degrees of freedom are used to model trucks and carbodies. The model has been used to make comparisons with TDOP Phase I test data but with only poor results. The model has received a great deal of scrutiny which has identified fundamental technical flaws contributing to discrepancies with test data [14]. For the most part, the discrepancies stem from the quasilinearization of the friction damping elements.

FLEXIBLE BODY RAILROAD FREIGHT CAR MODEL

Category: The Flexible Body Railroad Freight Car Model is a nonlinear time domain model, primarily of the vertical and roll dynamics of a rail vehicle. There are 20 degrees of freedom in the representation.

Authors: Y. H. Tse and E. C. Martin
Association of American Railroads
Chicago, Illinois 60616

Date: 1976, revision 1979

Capability: The main application of this model is in the area of trackability, specifically of harmonic roll and bounce and ride quality. With modifications to generalize track input, the model could be applied to the track twist load equalization subset of the trackability regime. The user has the option of Runge-Kutta or Hamming integration schemes.

Model Description: The model is illustrated in Fig. 5. Note that the carbody flexibility is approximated to a first order by using two lumped masses with a compliant connection between them.

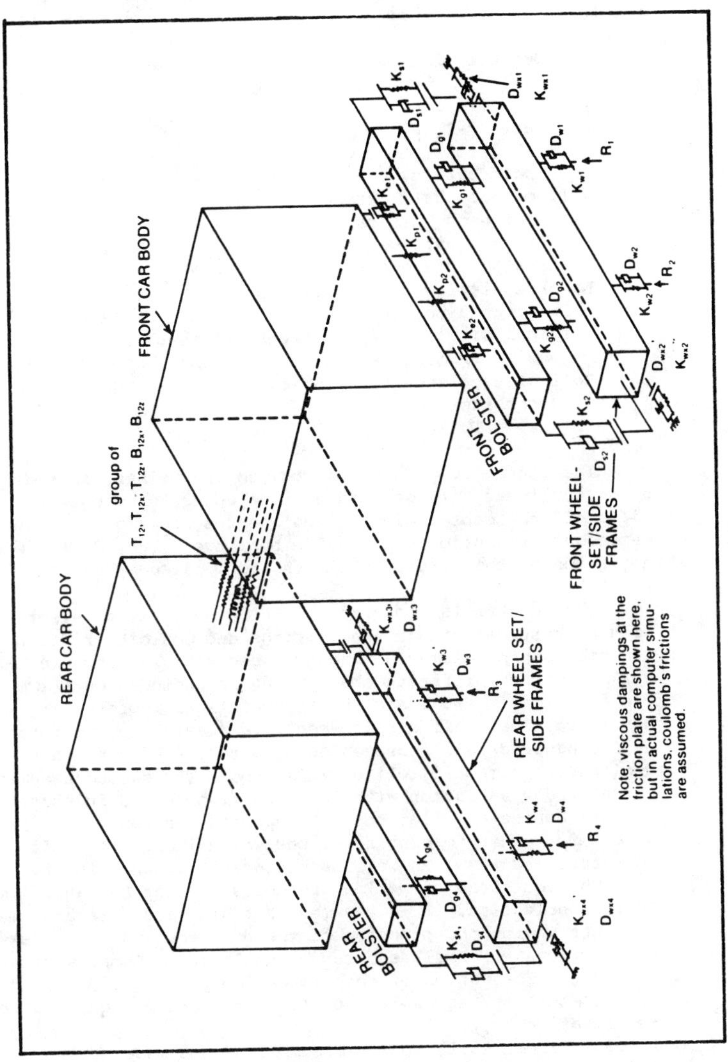

Fig. 5 Flexible Body Railroad Freight Car Model

The two wheelsets of a truck are lumped together with the side frame pairs. The track inputs to such a side frame/wheelset combination are the average of the vertical displacements of the front and rear wheelsets of a truck on each side, left and right.

The degrees of freedom are identified as:

Vertical displacement of each half carbody	2
Lateral displacement of each half carbody	2
Roll of each half carbody	2
Pitch of each half carbody	2
Yaw of each half carbody	2
Vertical displacement of each bolster	2
Lateral displacement of each bolster	2
Roll of each bolster	2
Vertical displacement of front and rear side frame/wheelset combinations	2
Roll of each side frame/wheelset combination	2
TOTAL:	20

The connection of the carbody to the bolster is modeled using nonlinear springs with a force going to zero as the carbody lifts off the center plate. Nonlinear springs are also used to represent the action of the side bearings. They do not exert any force on the carbody until the roll is such that the clearances are taken up.

The bolster is connected to the side frame/wheelset combination by vertical and lateral springs and Coulomb friction elements. Coulomb damping elements also act when gib clearance is taken up. The track stiffness and damping is included on a lumped element basis. Two basic forcing functions representing the static vertical rail displacement are possible. The first assumes half-staggered rail represented by a rectified sine wave which excites the harmonic roll oscillations. The second assumes sinusoidal track variation with left and right rails in phase which excites bounce oscillations. An updated version of the program allows for other forcing functions which include the effects of curvature and ramps as well as user-defined track input.

The equations of motion are derived using Lagrangian methods. In the derivation, it is assumed that displacements are small and that yawing and pitching of the bolsters and side frame/wheelset combinations are small and can be neglected. Because of the Lagrangian derivation of this rather complex model, the adaptation of the model to represent Type II trucks could require a major rederivation.

Limitations: Some small motion assumptions are made. Also, the friction damping elements are idealized. Time integration of large systems of equations such as this tends to be costly for parametric studies, etc.

Programming Language: FORTRAN IV

Documentation: The earlier version of the program is documented in AAR reports R-199, R-200, and R-260. Documentation of the revised version is available from AAR.

Operating System: The program was developed for IBM but has been adapted for CDC and DEC PDP-10 use.
Availability: Contact V. K. Garg, Association of American Railroads, Chicago, Illinois, 60616.
Assessment: The Flexible Body Railroad Freight Car Model is a complex, nonlinear time domain program. It can be applied in the harmonic roll and bounce analyses as part of the trackability investigation and also may be used to study ride quality. With a more general representation of track input, the capability of the model would be extended to cover the load equalization area. The model is best suited to representing Type I trucks. Its ability to represent some Type II trucks is questionable and modifications may be difficult due to the complex Lagrangian derivation of the equations of motion. The program has received independent analytical scrutiny; validation efforts with test data have been made, although results are somewhat marginal. The program is well documented.

FRATE (MITRE VERSION)

Category: The FRATE model is a nonlinear time domain representation of a freight car with provision for modeling lading, specifically Trailer-On-Flatcar (TOFC) configurations. A total of 27 basic degrees of freedom are involved, 11 of which are used to represent the rigid carbody and truck dynamics. The model provides for the modeling of carbody flexibility in terms of normal modes and nonlinear spring and damping characteristics. Each mode included increases the total degrees of freedom by one. The model is an extension of models developed by M. J. Healy of Wyle Laboratories.
Authors: G. Kachadourian, N. E. Sussman, and J. R. Anderes
The MITRE Corporation
Maclean, Virginia
Date: 1978
Capability: FRATE emphasizes the vertical and roll phenomena of vehicles and lading. It is thus suitable for the areas of harmonic roll and bounce and for ride quality. The truck equations are easily related to the actual truck configuration and can be readily modified if required to reflect a Type II assembly.
Model Description: Figures 6a and 6b describe the full FRATE/TOFC configuration. The carbody/truck degrees of freedom are:

Lateral displacement of each truck	2
Vertical displacement of each truck	2
Roll of each truck	2
Lateral displacement of carbody	1
Vertical displacement of carbody	1
Yaw of carbody	1
Pitch of carbody	1
Roll of carbody	1
TOTAL:	11

Each TOFC is represented by two rigid masses (trailer body and wheelset) having eight degrees of freedom. By various program options, one or both of the TOFCs can be eliminated, reducing the extent of the model to represent an ordinary freight car. Similarly, the inclusion of carbody flexibility by specifying its

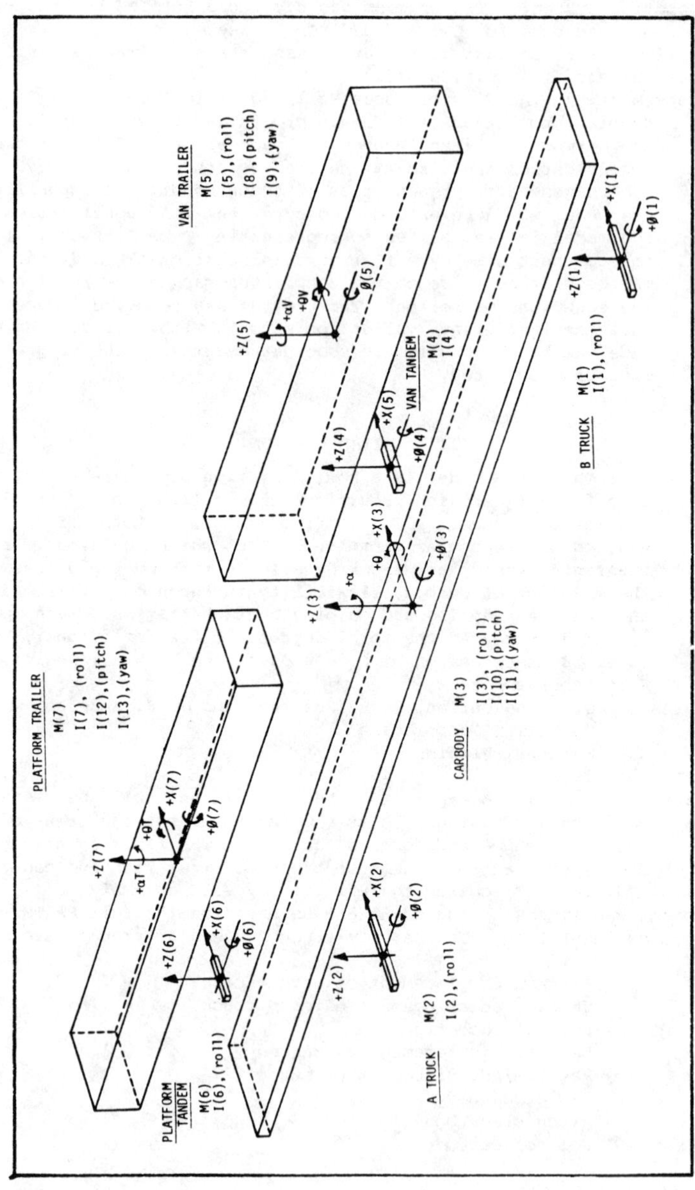

Fig. 6a FRATE/MITRE Model - TOFC, inertia, and degree of freedom notation

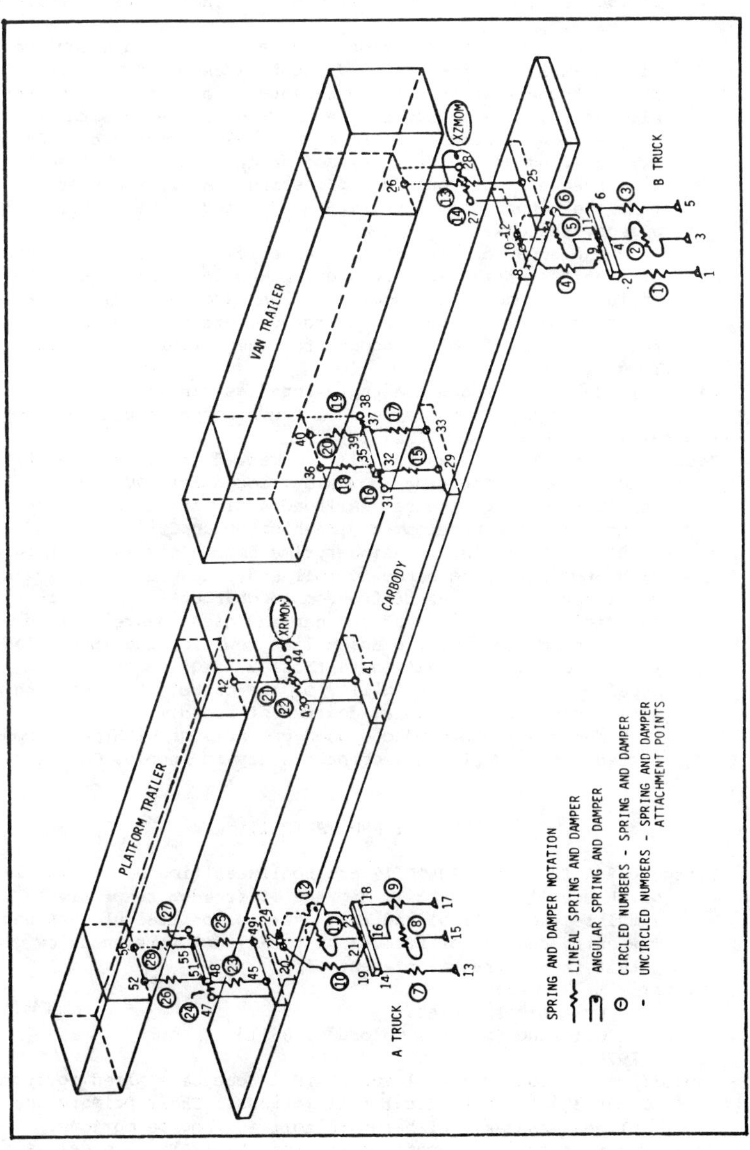

Fig. 6b FRATE/MITRE Model - TOFC, spring damping notation

normal modes is a user option and can be omitted when a rigid carbody representation suffices. Track compliance and damping characteristics are lumped with other truck suspension elements in FRATE.

The vertical excitation is generated by sinusoidal vertical displacements of the left and right sides of each truck. Thus, inputs from front and rear wheelsets of each truck are averaged. Alternately, the trucks can be excited laterally with sinusoidal displacement variations. In either case, the input frequency may be fixed or may be increased or decreased with time to simulate frequency response sweep testing. Also, the user may specify that the sinusoidal input terminate after so many cycles to obtain a decay response.

The equations of motion are derived as a set of second-order differential equations using Newtonian methods. The model includes second-order angular motion terms and is thus valid for angular deflections of up to 10 degrees. The model can quite readily be modified to account for the differences of particular Type II trucks.

Limitations: The trucks are represented as single lumped masses; therefore, detailed analysis of truck components is not possible.

Programming Language: FORTRAN IV

Documentation: The program is well documented in two volumes [15].

Operating System: The program was developed for CDC use.

Availability: Contact Federal Railroad Administration, Office of Research and Development, Washington, D.C.

Assessment: FRATE is a nonlinear time domain simulation program with application to harmonic roll and ride quality analysis. The model uses 11 degrees of freedom to characterize the trucks and rigid body motions of the car and eight degrees freedom are used for each of two assemblies representing sprung lading (e.g., TOFC). In addition to those 27 degrees of freedom, the model provides for flexibility of the carbody by including its normal modes as additional degrees of freedom.

The model has produced good comparisons with tests conducted at the Rail Dynamics Laboratory in Pueblo, Colorado.

FRATE 11 AND FRATE 17

Category: FRATE 11 and FRATE 17 are nonlinear time domain models which use 11 and 17 basic degrees of freedom respectively to simulate the vertical and roll dynamics of freight cars and trucks. The extra degrees of freedom of the 17 dof version allow greater detail in the truck representation.

Author: M. J. Healy
Wyle Laboratories
Colorado Springs, Colorado, 80915

Date: 1976

Capability: Both FRATE 11 and FRATE 17 can be applied to studies of car and truck vertical roll motions. Their primary use is for nonlinear analysis of harmonic roll and bounce motions.

Model Description: The configuration of the FRATE 11 model is identical to that of the MITRE version of FRATE previously discussed without the elaboration of the lading masses and suspension elements. The FRATE 17 model configuration shown in Fig. 7 indicates the additional detail used in representing the trucks.

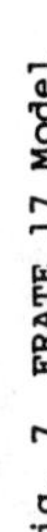

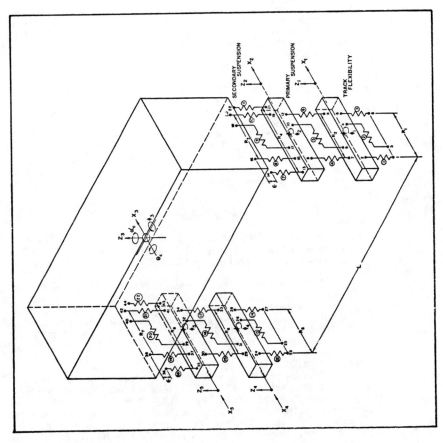

Fig. 7 FRATE 17 Model

In both models the carbody may have flexible modes, each of which adds a degree of freedom to the basic 11 or 17.

Each model accepts vertical excitation of the trucks in the form of sinusoids or optionally tabulated functions of time (or distance for a given forward speed).

The equations of motion for the two models are developed using Newtonian methods. The formulation can be thus easily modified, if necessary, to account for peculiarities of particular Type II truck assemblies.

Limitations: The 11 dof version has a limited representation of the truck which prevents detailed analysis of such phenomena as center plate rocking. The 17 dof version requires smaller time steps; hence, there is an additional cost for a specified simulation time.

Programming Language: FORTRAN IV

Documentation: The models are discussed in an ASME paper [16].

Operating System: The models were developed for CDC use and were later adapted for an Interdata machine.

Availability: Contact Gordon Bakken, Wyle Laboratories, Colorado Springs, Colorado.

Assessment: The FRATE 11 Model is the antecedent of both FRATE/MITRE and FRATE 17. Both FRATE 11 and FRATE 17 can be applied to the analysis of harmonic roll and bounce and ride quality of the lading environment. The models have produced favorable comparisons against actual test data.

WHRAIL/WHRAILA

Category: WHRAIL and WHRAILA are the symmetric and asymmetric versions, respectively, of a subroutine program which determines the geometric constraint functions for a given wheel/rail configuration.

The routines are not dynamic models but rather auxiliary programs which precalculate such wheel/rail constraint relationships as effective conicity, gravitational stiffness, difference in rolling radii, and wheelset roll angle for all practical values of lateral wheelset displacement. The tabulation of these constraint functions serves as input to a number of dynamic models requiring this information.

Authors: N. K. Cooperrider, Arizona State University, Tempe, Arizona; E. H. Law, Clemson University, Clemson, South Carolina

Date: WHRAIL - 1975, WHRAILA - 1977

Capability: The Wheel/Rail Geometric Constraint Routines are presently capable of generating data for three of the preceding models discussed. These are the Lateral Stability Model, HUNTCT, and Law and Cooperrider's 9 and 17 dof Curving Models. With modifications there is no doubt that other models could make use of these routines, especially the curving and lateral stability programs.

Model Description: Fig. 8 shows the basic configuration treated by both the Symmetric and Asymmetric Wheel/Rail Geometric Constraint Routines. Note, however, that in the symmetric case,

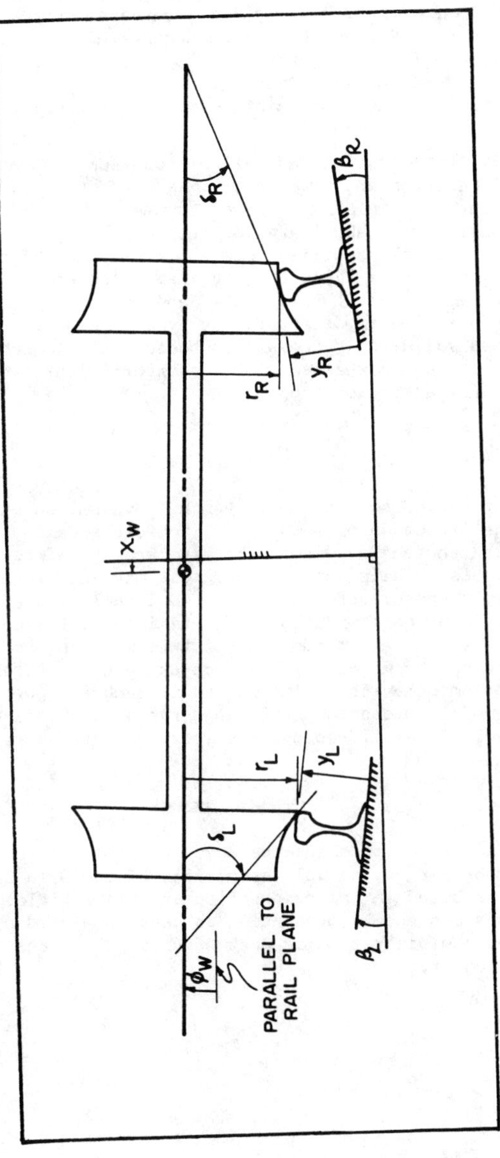

Fig. 8 Geometry for WHRAIL & WHRAILA routines

left and right cant angles, as well as wheel and rail profiles, are identical. The wheelset and rails are assumed to be rigid. The individual wheel and rail profiles are each defined by a series of 15 fourth-order polynomial curve segments.

Limitations: The geometric constraint relationships assume negligible effects of yaw.

Programming Language: FORTRAN IV

Documentation: The constraint routines are documented in two reports [17,18].

Availability: Contact Federal Railroad Administration, Office of Research and Development, Washington, D.C.

Assessment: The Symmetric and Asymmetric Wheel/Rail Constraint Routines are auxiliary routines which support dynamic curving and lateral stability models. From data defining the profile of a wheel and a rail, the routines calculate rolling radii, contact angles, wheelset roll angle, and other important geometrical information important to the dynamic models. The routines have been validated successfully against static laboratory mockups of rails and wheelset. It is an efficient, well-documented, and useful analytical tool.

CONCLUSION

One of the findings of the TDOP model evaluation exercise has been that the direction of future rail vehicle modeling should not necessarily be toward increasingly comprehensive and therefore increasingly complex models. While each added detail may seem to increase realism and completeness, unfortunately each detail also adds to the work load of input determination, results interpretation, and model verification. It is recommended that future modeling be problem oriented, elaborating the model only as much as required to explain reasonably the problem behavior. With regard to such an approach, the survey of the models presented here can serve as a guideline for determining the level of detail necessary to perform various types of analyses.

ACKNOWLEDGMENT

The authors wish to thank the developers of the various programs for their cooperation, as well as members of the Wyle Laboratories staff who contributed in the preparation of this article. The survey of the rail dynamics models presented has been sponsored by the Federal Railroad Administration as part of Phase II of the Truck Design Optimization Project.

APPENDIX A

MODELING OF RAIL VEHICLE DYNAMICS AT THE FRA

In its effort to reduce rail accidents and assist the rail industry, the Federal Railroad Administration (FRA) has long recognized the importance of a fundamental understanding of the basic causes of rail accidents and the dynamic performance characteristics of rail vehicles. Over the past ten years, FRA has conducted research and development programs, most of which were done jointly with the rail industry, on the dynamics of rail vehicle systems, including the well-known cooperative project, Track Train Dynamics (TTD). Part of this effort is directed towards developing computer models that can analyze the dynamic behavior of rail vehicles.

The purpose of this appendix is to summarize the results of FRA activities in the modeling of rail vehicle systems. Since Ref. [19] contains a detailed description of the modeling programs at TTD, this appendix will discuss only FRA activities other than the TTD programs. It should be noted that FRA activities include those carried on at the Transportation Systems Center (TSC), where a major portion of FRA dynamic research is conducted.

A. Programs for Wheel/Rail Contact Geometry and Forces

1. Nonlinear wheel/rail geometric constraints for symmetric wheels and rails (WHRAIL) [17]. This program calculates the wheel/rail contact positions and geometric constraint functions versus wheelset lateral given wheel and rail profiles, rail cant, and rail and wheel gaps.
2. Nonlinear wheel/rail geometric constraints for asymmetric wheels and rails (WHRAILA) [19]. This program has the same capabilities as program WHRAIL but is for asymmetric wheel, rail, and roadbeds.
3. Nonlinear Creep Forces (FORCES) [20]. FORCES calculates creep coefficients and creep forces by Kalker's simplified theory of rolling contact with contact patch geometry and creepage as given.
4. Nonlinear Creep Forces (FORCES - II) [21]. This has the same capabilities as Program FORCES but uses Kalker's "Exact" nonlinear creep theory, which is valid for both equal or unequal elastic bodies in rolling contact.
5. Programs CONFORM and COUNTACT [22, 23, 24, 25]. These calculate the wheel/rail contact stress for conformal and counterformal contact problems given wheel/rail geometry.

B. Rail Vehicle Stability Analysis (Hunting)

1. Linear Analysis with 9 dof, 17 dof, 19 dof, and 23 dof Rail Car Models [6]. Using the technique of eigenvalue analysis, these four models calculate the critical speed and hunting frequency of the rail vehicle.

2. Quasi-linear 9 dof Freight Car Model [26]. Using the technique of describing function analysis, this model calculates the limit cycle conditions of a rail vehicle.
3. Nonlinear 9 dof Freight Car Model [27]. Using commercial integration techniques, this model calculates the hunting behavior of freight cars.
4. Nonlinear 5 dof Hybrid Computer Model [28]. This program calculates the time response characteristics and hunting behavior of freight car with 5 dof half-car model.
5. Program DYNALIST II [11]. This program constructs and analyzes linear models on a modal basis, and computes complex eigenvalues for lateral stability analysis of rail systems up to fifty degrees of freedom.
6. Programs CARHNT, TRKVEH, TRKHNT [29]. These are several programs developed for linear analysis of rail passenger and freight vehicles up to 17 dof.

C. Rail Vehicle Forced Response Analysis

1. Linear 9 dof Freight Car Model [30]. Calculates the frequency domain solution for amplitude ratios, and the PSD and RMS values of vehicle motions in response to alignment and cross-level input spectra.
2. Hybrid, Nonlinear 5 dof Freight Car [28]. This is a nonlinear, five dof, half-car model of a freight car. Output is a graphic display of time histories of selected model variables.
3. Programs FULL, FLEX, HALF, LATERAL [12]. These calculate the frequency response of different linear rail vehicle models up to 15 dof to track surface irregularities.
4. Program FRATE [15]. This is a 34 dof nonlinear time domain model for simulating rail freight vehicle response to track surface irregularities.
5. TDOP Phase I Model [13]. This is a 13 dof model for simulating freight car frequency response which includes the effects of truck instability, friction damping, and flexibility of carbody structure.
6. Rail vehicle response models at Battelle [31]. Several linear models of rail vehicles for analyzing vehicle responses to sinusoidal or random track irregularities are being developed.

D. Rail Vehicle Curving

1. Nonlinear, steady state, curving model of rail vehicle [10]. This calculates steady state curving displacement, wheel/rail contact forces, and stresses with 9 to 17 degrees of freedom, freight car models.
2. Nonlinear curve entry for 27 dof, 6 axle locomotive model [10]. Time histories of state variables and wheel/rail forces are calculated and summary statistics with numerical integration are set forth.

E. Other Rail Vehicle Dynamic Programs

1. Rail vehicle impact program [32]. Longitudinal and vertical motion of railroad cars in impact situations is simulated.

2. Freight element program [33]. Using 27 dof model, this program calculates the dynamic response of a freight element inside a typical freight box car in service condition.
3. DODX Car Models [34]. This simulates stability and forced response characteristics of large capacity freight cars (100 ton to 200 ton), loaded with high center of gravity containers. The model, derived from an AAR model, is a 22 dof, nonlinear, time domain model of railcars equipped with two axle trucks.

In summary, the computer models described here represent only the FRA effort in rail vehicle dynamics. There are several other FRA and AAR projects which are being utilized in the evaluation and validation of related models. It is anticipated that by the year 1981, FRA should have several validated models in rail vehicle dynamics. FRA is also investigating, through its contractors, the utilization of vehicle dynamics models in other areas of application, such as track structure, energy and environment, and yard system design, as well as vehicle analysis and design.

REFERENCES

1 Perlman, A. B., "An Evaluation of Computer Programs for the Analysis, Prediction, and Simulation of Rail Vehicle Dynamics," Transportation Systems Center (TSC) Task Memorandum, RR-515, Rail System Dynamics Program, August 1974.

2 Cooperrider, N. K., and E. H. Law, "A Survey of Railway Vehicle Dynamics Research," Journal of Dynamic Systems Measurement and Control, Trans. ASME, Special Issue on Ground Transportation, June 1974.

3 Breese, R. G., ed., "Track-Train Dynamics Bibliography," AAR, Railway Progress Institute, Chicago, Illinois, 1973.

4 Cheung, T. H. W., Garg, V. K., and Martin, G. C., "User's Manual, Freight Car Hunting Model," AAR Document R-251, February 1977.

5 Tse, Y. H., and Martin, G. C., "User's Manual, Lateral/Vertical Model," AAR Document R-237, February 1977.

6 Hague, I., Law, E. H., and Cooperrider, N. K., "User's Manual for Lateral Stability Computer Programs for Railway Freight Car Models," Report No. FRA/OR&D-80/30, April 1980.

7 Willis, T., and Smith, K. R., "A Mathematical Simulation of the Curve Entry and Curve Negotiation Dynamics of Flexible Two Axle Railway Trucks," ASME Paper No. 76-WA/RT-14, July 1976.

8 Garg, V. K., and Singh, S. P., "Dynamic Curve Negotiation Behavior of a Freight Car," Session 34, Paper E.3, Heavy Haul Railways Conference, Perth, Australia, September 1978.

9 Smith, K. R., "A Mathematical Simulation of the Curve Entry and Curve Negotiation Dynamics of Flexible Two Axle Railway Trucks," M.S. thesis, Illinois Institute of Technology, Chicago, Illinois, 1975.

10 Law, E. H., and Cooperrider, N. K., "Nonlinear Dynamic and Steady State Curving of Rail Vehicles," ASME Winter Annual Meeting, San Francisco, December 1978.

11 Bronowicki, A., and Hasselman, T. K., "DYNALIST II, A Computer Program for Stability and Dynamic Response Analysis of Rail Vehicle Systems," Report No. FRA-OR&D-75-22, July 1976.

12 Perlman, A. B., and DiMasi, F. P., "Frequency Domain Computer Programs for Prediction and Analysis of Rail Vehicle Dynamics," NTIS Report No. FRA-OR&D-76-135.II, Vol. I & II, December 1975.

13 Southern Pacific Transportation Company, "Math Modeling Report, Vol. I, TDOP Phase I," Interim Report, July 1976.

14 Sussman, N. E., "Critique of Frequency Domain Model-Solution Techniques," Report No. FRA/ORD-78/12.IV, February 1978.

15 Kachadourian, G., Sussman, N. E., and Anderes, J. R., "FRATE Vol. I User's Manual; Vol. II Technical Manual" (pre-publication copy), FRA/ORD-78/59, September 1978.

16 Healy, M. J., "A Computer Method for Calculating Dynamic Responses of Nonlinear Flexible Rail Vehicles," ASME Paper 76-RT-5, April 1976.

17 Cooperrider, N. K., Law, E. G., et al., "Analytical and Experimental Determination of Nonlinear Wheel/Rail Geometric Constraints," Report No. FRA-OR&D-76-244, December 1975.

18 Cooperrider, N. K., and Heller, R., "User's Manual for Asymmetric Wheel/Rail Contact Characterization," Report No. FRA/ORD-78/05, December 1977.

19. Garg, V. K., "Computer Models for Railway Vehicle Operations," Rail International, June 1978, pp. 381.

20. Goree, J., and Law, E., "Users' Manual for Kalker's Simplified Nonlinear Creep Theory," Report FRA-ORD-78-06 (PB 279503), December 1977.

21. Goree, J., "Users' Manual on Kalker's 'Exact' Nonlinear Creep Theory," Report FR-ORD-78-50 (PB 287472/AS), August 1978.

22. Paul, B., and Hashemi, J., "Users' Manual for Program CONFORM," Report FRA-ORD-78-40, June 1978.

23. Hashemi, J., and Paul, B., "User's Manual for Program CONNTACT," Report FRA-ORD-78-27, September 1977.

24. Paul, B., and Hashemi, J., "Rail Wheel Geometry Associated with Contact Stress Analysis," Report FRA-ORD-78-41, September 1979.

25. Paul, B., and Hashemi, J., "Numerical Determination of Contact Pressures Between Closely Conforming Wheels and Rails, FRA-ORD-79-41, July 1979.

26. Hendrick, J. K., Cooperrider, N., and Law, E. H., "The Application of Quasi-Linearization Technique to Rail Vehicle Dynamics Analysis," FRA-ORD-78-56, November 1978.

27. Law, E. H., et al., "General Models for Lateral Stability Analysis of Railway Freight Vehicles," FRA-ORD-77-36, June 1977.

28. Malstrom, C., et al., "Hybrid Computation - An Advanced Computation Tool for Simulating the Nonlinear Dynamic Response of Railroad Vehicles," AAR Proceedings of Advanced Techniques in Track/Train Dynamics and Design Conference, September 1978.

29. Doyle, G., and Prause, R., "Hunting Stability of Rail Vehicles with Torsionally Flexible Wheelsets," ASME paper 75-WA/RT-2, 1975.

30. Law, E., et al., "User's Manual of Linear Forced Response of 9 dof Rail Freight Car," to be published in 1980.

31. Ahlbeck, D., and Doyle, G., Jr., "Comparative Analysis of Dynamics of Freight and Passenger Rail Vehicles," Report FRA-ORD-77-04, 1976.

32. Washington University, "Theoretical Manual and User's Guide for Longitudinal-Vertical Train Action Model," Report FRA-ORD-76-278.

33. Shum, K., and Willis, T., "A Mathematical Computer Simulation of the Dynamics of a Freight Element in a Railroad Freight Car," Report FRA-ORD-77-28 (PB 282308), May 1975.

34. Jones, C. T., "Mathematical Modeling of DODX Railcars," FRA-ORD-78-47, February 1980.

Static Reanalysis Methods

Alan Palazzolo

Allis Chalmeers Corporation

Bo Ping Wang

Walter D. Pilkey

University of Virginia

INTRODUCTION

Recently the finite element methods have been playing an even larger role in the design of engineering structures. Typically, based on prior experience with similar structures, an initial design is selected and a mathematical model, e.g., a finite element model, is constructed and used to predict the structural response to anticipated loadings. This model may also be employed to investigate whether changing certain structural parameters can improve response characteristics, while constraints on such quantities as total weight, stresses, and displacements are satisfied. For each trial design, a system of equations must be solved. With current technology, a single solution for a problem with several thousand degrees of freedom is quite affordable in most engineering offices. Typically, however, a structure may undergo hundreds of changes before a final design is achieved. The computational cost of reaching this design may become prohibitively high.

Fortunately, a structural design usually involves only local adjustments in structural parameters and efficient analysis techniques have been developed accordingly. That is, consideration of typical machinery, buildings, support structures, etc. reveals that geometrical constraints restrict a trial design from deviating substantially from some "basic" or "original" design. This basic design defines the so-called unmodified or original systems. Reanalysis is an analysis procedure for treating systems containing alterations to the original system. To improve computational efficiency, reanalysis takes advantage of the analysis already done for the original system.

Reanalysis techniques available for statically loaded structural systems are studied in this chapter. The governing equations, although narrowly banded, may contain thousands of independent degrees of freedom. Modification to the original system may consist of small magnitude changes affecting a large portion of the structure, or relatively large magnitude alterations confined to a small portion of the structure, i.e., local modifications. For efficiency, the former case is best treated by an approximate reanalysis technique. For accuracy, the latter case should be handled by an exact or direct reanalysis method. Both approximate and exact reanalysis methods are surveyed in this chapter.

In general, a local modification will change the structural response of all degrees of freedom. In this chapter, frequent reference is made to that portion of the structure affected by a modification. This is defined to be the portion of the structure which is part of or is connected to the physical modifications.

EXACT REANALYSIS METHODS

Exact reanalysis methods lead to exact expressions for the static equilibrium of a structural system.

Mathematical Background

In most cases, static reanalysis involves modifications to the coefficient matrix and right-hand side vector of a system of simultaneous linear algebraic equations. Considerable attention has been paid to this problem in the mathematical literature. The earliest work in this area seems to be that of Sherman and Morrison [1], who examined the change in the inverse of a square matrix caused by a change in a single row or column of the original matrix. Their results for a change to column s of the matrix A can be summarized as follows. Let

$$\tilde{\underline{B}} = (\underline{A} + \Delta\underline{A})^{-1} = (\underline{A}')^{-1} \tag{2}$$

By definition

$$(\Delta\underline{A})_{ij} = 0 \qquad i = 1,\ 2, \ldots N$$
$$j = 1, 2, \ldots s-1,\ s+1 \ldots N$$
$$\underline{A}' = \underline{A} + \Delta\underline{A} \tag{3}$$

then the elements of $\tilde{\underline{B}}$ can be computed from the elements of $\underline{B}$ via the following equations

$$\tilde{B}_{sj} = \frac{B_{sj}}{\sum_{r=1}^{N} B_{sr} A'_{rs}} \qquad j = 1,\ 2, \ldots N \tag{4}$$

$$\tilde{B}_{ij} = B_{ij} \quad B_{sj} \sum_{r=1}^{N} B_{ir} A'_{rs}, \qquad i = 1, 2, \ldots s-1, s+1, \ldots N$$

$$j = 1, 2, \ldots N \qquad (5)$$

In this case only column s of ΔA is nonnull. The elements of the inverse of the modified matrix are provided by Eqs. (4) and (5).

Sherman and Morrison [2] also considered the change in the inverse of a matrix when a single element of the original matrix is altered. They found that for

$$(\Delta \underline{A})_{ij} = 0 \text{ for all i and j except } (\Delta A)_{r,s} \neq 0 \qquad (6)$$

that

$$\tilde{B}_{ij} = B_{ij} - \frac{B_{ir} B_{sj} \Delta A_{rs}}{1 + B_{sr} \Delta A_{rs}} \qquad i,j = 1, 2, \ldots N \qquad (7)$$

where $\underline{A} + \underline{\Delta A}$ is singular if

$$\Delta A_{rs} = -1/B_{sr} \qquad (8)$$

Woodbury [3] further generalized the results of Sherman and Morrison.

Bartlett [4], developed a general formula using matrix-vector notation which includes the Sherman and Morrison formulas as special cases. The modification matrix here is a degenerate matrix of rank one

$$\Delta \underline{A} = \underline{U}\, \underline{V}^T \qquad N \times N \qquad (9)$$

where $\underline{U}$ and $\underline{V}$ are N x 1 matrices. His results are

$$\tilde{\underline{B}} = \underline{A}^{-1} - (\underline{A}^{-1}U)(\underline{V}^T\underline{A}^{-1})/(1 + \underline{V}^T\underline{A}^{-1}\underline{U}) \qquad (10)$$

which can be easily verified by pre- or postmultiplication by $(A + U\, V^T)$ and using the fact that $V^T A^{-1} U$ is scalar.

Householder [5,6], referencing the works of the preceeding authors, further generalized the matrix inverse modification formulas. In summary

$$\tilde{\underline{B}}_1 = (\underline{A} + \Delta\underline{A}_1)^{-1} = (\underline{A} + \underline{U}\ \underline{s}\ \underline{V}^T)^{-1}$$

$$= \underline{A}^{-1} - \underline{A}^{-1}\ \underline{U}\ \underline{s}\ (\underline{s} + \underline{s}\ \underline{V}^T\underline{A}^{-1}\underline{U}\ \underline{s})^{-1}\ \underline{s}\ \underline{V}^T\ \underline{A}^{-1} \quad (11)$$

$$\tilde{\underline{B}}_2 = (\underline{A} + \Delta\underline{A}_2)^{-1} = (\underline{A} + \underline{U}\ \underline{s}^{-1}\ \underline{V}^T)^{-1}$$

$$= \underline{A}^{-1} - \underline{A}^{-1}\ \underline{U}\ (\underline{s} + \underline{V}^T\underline{A}^{-1}\underline{U})^{-1}\ \underline{V}^T\ \underline{A}^{-1} \quad (12)$$

where $\underline{U}$ and $\underline{V}$ are N x r rectangular matrices, $\underline{s}$ an r x r square matrix, and the indicated inverses exist.

Bennett [7] approaches this problem in a different fashion, using the triangular factorization of a matrix. This decomposition may be represented by

$$\underline{A} = \underline{L}\ \underline{D}\ \underline{W} \qquad N \times N \quad (13)$$

$$\underline{A} + \Delta\underline{A} = \underline{A} + \underline{U}\ \underline{S}\ \underline{V}^T = \tilde{\underline{L}}\ \tilde{\underline{D}}\ \tilde{\underline{W}} \quad (14)$$

where matrices $\underline{L}$ and $\tilde{\underline{L}}$ are lower triangular, matrices $\underline{W}$ and $\tilde{\underline{W}}$ are upper triangular, and matrices $\underline{D}$ and $\tilde{\underline{D}}$ are diagonal. Since when $\underline{A}$ is narrowly banded $\underline{L}$ and $\underline{W}$ are also narrowly banded, Bennett maintains his approach will save computer storage space and reduce the number of arithmetic operations required. This assertion holds when computing the entire inverse of the modified system matrix $\underline{A} + \underline{\Delta A}$, using Eq. (11).

The modification matrix in exact reanalysis approaches is typically very sparse. Submatrices are consequently formed to distinguish between modified and unmodified quantities. The following notation is very useful in the required bookkeeping.

$$(\underline{A})\ \begin{pmatrix} j_1 & j_2 & \cdots & j_p \\ k_1 & k_2 & \cdots & k_V \end{pmatrix} = \begin{bmatrix} A_{j_1k_1} & A_{j_1k_2} & --- & A_{j_1k_V} \\ A_{j_2k_1} & A_{j_2k_2} & --- & A_{j_2k_V} \\ \vdots & \vdots & \ddots & \vdots \\ A_{j_pk_1} & A_{j_pk_2} & --- & A_{j_pk_V} \end{bmatrix} \quad (15)$$

$$(\underline{V})(j_1\ j_2\ \cdots\ j_p) = \begin{bmatrix} V_{j_1} \\ V_{j_2} \\ \vdots \\ V_{j_p} \end{bmatrix} \tag{16}$$

Structural Modification Methods

Three approaches to the static reanalysis problem are

1. The initial strain-initial stress method
2. The inverse adjustment method
3. The sparsity-condensation approach.

The first method was very popular during 1945-1965, prior to the widespread availability of generic finite element method codes using the direct stiffness assembly procedure. This method is used with structural analyses based on action transfer matrices (flexibility-force approach) or displacement transfer matrices (stiffness-displacement approach) [8].

The second method is based on the "adjustment of an inverse matrix" identities of Sherman and Morrison, Woodbury, Bartlett, and Householder. The sparse nature of the stiffness modification matrix is represented here with Boolean matrices.

The third approach condenses the order of the modified system's static equilibrium equation by exploiting the sparsity of the stiffness modification matrix. Although the results of this method and the second method are identical in some cases, the sparsity-condensation approach can incorporate changes to the external force vector as well as to the stiffness matrix.

Initial Strain-Initial Stress Methods

Pipes presented a general initial strain-inital stress modification procedure in Ref. [9]. Initial strain is used in conjunction with flexibility-force structural analyses. The vector of internal forces (stresses) is expressed by

$$\underline{P} = \underline{f}_o\ \underline{F} + \underline{f}_x\ \underline{R} \tag{17}$$

where

$\underline{P}$ = internal forces (stresses)

$\underline{F}$ = external forces

$\underline{R}$ = redundant internal forces

$\underline{f}_o$ = action transfer matrix for unit applied external loads

$\underline{f}_x$ = action transfer matrix for unit redundant forces

The elements of $\underline{f}_o$ and $\underline{f}_x$ are computed by applying unit actions corresponding to system references and calculating the associated member actions. Pipes adds a fictitous initial strain vector to those elements of the original structure which are selected for modification. The original structure is then subjected both to external loads and initial strains. Under these conditions a set of stresses ($\underline{P}_{ho}$) and strains ($\underline{V}_{ho}$) exist within the original structure in those elements which are chosen for modification. Consider the modified system which differs from the original system in that certain element matrices of the unassembled flexibility matrix are altered. A set of stresses ($\underline{P}_{hm}$) and of strains ($\underline{V}_{hm}$) due to external loading result in the modified elements of the actual modified structure. Pipes equates these sets of stresses and strains

$$\underline{P}_{ho} = \underline{P}_{hm} \tag{18}$$

$$\underline{V}_{ho} = \underline{V}_{hm} \tag{19}$$

and consequently determines the fictitous initial strain vector which produces the same effects (stress and strain vectors) as the actual structural modification. Utilizing this vector, formulas for the modified system's stress and displacement vectors, in terms of the altered elements flexibility matrices and the action transfer matrix of the original system, may be easily derived.

Pipes also presents a structural modification procedure utilizing fictitous initial-stresses in conjunction with a stiffness-displacement analysis. The element displacements ($\underline{V}$) are related to the structural displacements ($\underline{X}$) and kinematically indeterminate displacements ($\underline{X}_i$) by

$$\underline{V} = \underline{a}_o\, \underline{X} + \underline{a}_i\, \underline{X}_i \tag{20}$$

The matrices $\underline{a}_o$ and $\underline{a}_i$ are displacement transfer matrices [8]. These matrices are generated a column at a time by applying unit displacements corresponding to unknown joint displacements ($\underline{a}_o$) and to known support movements ($\underline{a}_i$). The modification formulas resulting from the initial stress method are similar to those of the initial strain approach except for the use of displacement transfer matrices and element stiffness matrices. Several interesting cases of structural modifications are examined, including element removal (cut outs), addition of fixed-boundary conditions, arbitrary changes to element properties, making certain elements rigid, and modifications preserving the geometry of an element. The methods of structural analysis on which the initial strain and initial stress modification procedures are based have been largely replaced by the direct stiffness-assembly procedure. For this reason these methods will not be considered further.

Another structural modification procedure based on the flexibility-force approach to structural analysis is outlined in Refs. [10,11]. The derivation in these papers is applicable only to trusses, although it is claimed to apply to any general structural element. The procedure yields the internal forces of the modified structure and does not include formulas for the displacements.

Inverse Adjustment Methods

The first paper utilizing the matrix inverse adjustment formula in the engineering literature appears to be Ref. [12]. In this case, only columns

$$\underline{J} = (j_1 \quad j_2 \quad \cdots \quad j_p)^T \qquad (p \times 1) \tag{21}$$

of the stiffness modification matrix $\Delta\underline{K}$ are nonnull. The modified stiffness matrix may then be represented by

$$\underline{K} = \underline{K}_o + \Delta\underline{K} = \underline{K}_o + \sum_{\ell=1}^{p} \Delta\underline{K}_{j_\ell} \underline{e}_{j_\ell}^T \qquad (N \times N) \tag{22}$$

Here Eq. (10) is implemented in a recursive form as

$$(\underline{K}^i)^{-1} = (\underline{K}^{i-1})^{-1} - [(\underline{K}^{i-1})^{-1} \Delta\underline{K}_{j_i}][\underline{e}_{j_i}^T (\underline{K}^{i-1})^{-1}] / [1 + \underline{e}_{j_i}^T (\underline{K}^{i-1})^{-1} \Delta K_{j_i}] \tag{23}$$

where $(\underline{K}^i)^{-1}$ is the inverse of the modified stiffness matrix including only the first i nonnull columns of ΔK. Note then that

$$\underline{K}^o = \underline{K}_o \tag{24}$$

$$\underline{K}^p = \underline{K} = \underline{K}_o + \Delta\underline{K} \tag{25}$$

After Eq. (23) is solved for i = p the modified system displacement vector is obtained from

$$\underline{Y} = \underline{K}^{-1} \underline{F} \tag{26}$$

Kavlie and Powell [13] improved the numerical efficiency of the Sack, Carpenter, and Hatch approach [12] by noting that only the modified system's displacement vector (and not the modified stiffness matrix inverse) is of importance. The form of the stiffness modification matrix is again that of Eq. (22). Equation (10) is used twice in the approach, which may be summarized by the recursive formula

$$\underline{Y}_i = \underline{Y}_{i-1} - \underline{W}_i^{i-1} \underline{e}_{j_i}^T \underline{Y}_{i-1} / (1 + \underline{e}_{j_i}^T \underline{W}_i^{i-1}) \tag{27}$$

$$\underline{W}_i^K = (\underline{K}^k)^{-1} \Delta \underline{K}_{j_i} \tag{28}$$

$$\underline{Y}_o = \underline{X} = \text{unmodified system displacement vector} \tag{29}$$

where $\underline{Y}_i$ is the system displacement vector after the first i nonnull columns of $\Delta\underline{K}$ are incorporated. Equation (27) follows directly from Eq. (23) upon postmultiplication by the force vector $\underline{F}$. To avoid again the actual computation of a matrix inverse, Eq. (28) is solved by using Eq. (10) as

$$\underline{W}_i^k = \underline{W}_i^{k-1} - \underline{W}_k^{k-1} \underline{e}_{j_k}^T \underline{W}_i^{k-1} / (1 + \underline{e}_{j_k}^T \underline{W}_k^{k-1}) \tag{30}$$

$$\underline{K}_o \underline{W}_i^o = \Delta \underline{K}_{j_i} \qquad i = 1, 2, \ldots p \tag{31}$$

The vector $\underline{W}_i^o$ is calculated by back substitution using the triangularized form of $\underline{K}_o$ from the unmodified system's solution. This recursive process is complete when i = p, i.e.,

$$\underline{Y} = \underline{Y}_p = \text{modified system displacement vector} \tag{32}$$

The procedure is illustrated in Fig. 1 for the simple case p = 4. Przemieniecki [14] utilized Eq. (11) in an approach to the reanalysis of locally modified structures. He assumed that the local modification occurs in only one small zone of the structure. The element stiffness matrices of this zone are also assumed to be positioned in the top left hand corner of the global stiffness matrix.

The results are

$$\underline{K}_o = \begin{bmatrix} \underline{K}_{11} & \vdots & \underline{K}_{12} \\ \cdots & & \cdots \\ \underline{K}_{21} & \vdots & \underline{K}_{22} \end{bmatrix} \qquad \underline{G} = \underline{K}_o^{-1} = \begin{bmatrix} \underline{G}_{11} & \vdots & \underline{G}_{12} \\ \cdots & & \cdots \\ \underline{G}_{21} & \vdots & \underline{G}_{22} \end{bmatrix}$$

$$\Delta\underline{K} = \begin{bmatrix} \Delta\underline{K}_{11} & \vdots & \underline{0} \\ \cdots & & \cdots \\ \underline{0} & \vdots & \underline{0} \end{bmatrix} = \underline{b}\ \Delta\underline{K}_{11}\ \underline{b}^T, \quad \Delta\underline{K}_{11}\ (p x p) \tag{33}$$

$$\underline{b} = [\underline{e}_1 \vdots \underline{e}_2 \vdots --- \vdots \underline{e}_p] \qquad N \times p$$

and from equation (11)

$$\underline{A} = \underline{K}_o , \quad \underline{A}^{-1} = \underline{G}$$

$$\underline{U} = \underline{b} , \quad \underline{V}^T = \Delta\underline{K}_{11}\ \underline{b}^T , \quad \underline{s} = \underline{I}_p$$

$$\underline{K}^{-1} = (\underline{K}_o + \Delta\underline{K})^{-1} = (\underline{K}_o + \underline{b}\ \Delta\underline{K}_{11}\ \underline{b}^T)^{-1} \tag{34}$$

$$= \underline{G} - \underline{G}\ \underline{b}\ (\underline{I}_p + \Delta\underline{K}_{11}\ \underline{b}^T\ \underline{G}\ \underline{b})^{-1}\ \Delta\underline{K}_{11}\ \underline{b}^T\ \underline{G}$$

$$= \underline{G} - \begin{bmatrix} \underline{G}_{11} \\ --- \\ \underline{G}_{21} \end{bmatrix} (\underline{I}_p + \Delta\underline{K}_{11}\ \underline{G}_{11})^{-1}\ \Delta\underline{K}_{11} [\underline{G}_{11} \vdots \underline{G}_{12}]$$

The modified system displacments then may be calculated from

$$\underline{Y} = \underline{K}^{-1}\ \underline{F} \tag{35}$$

Argyris [15] generalized Przemieniecki's approach by allowing the modifications, although sparse, to be scattered throughout the structure. In addition, Argyris improved the computational efficiency of this approach by directly calculating the modified system's displacements, and by utilizing the Cholesky decomposition

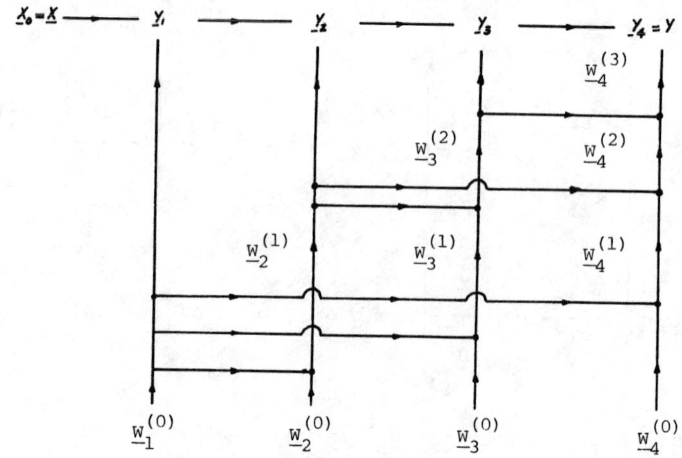

Figure 1 Flow diagram for Kavlie and Powell's successive modification approach, p=4.

of the original stiffness matrix, instead of its inverse His technique can be summarized as

$$\underline{K}_o \underline{X} = \underline{F} \tag{36}$$

$$(\underline{K}_o + \Delta K)\underline{Y} = \underline{F} \tag{37}$$

Only rows (or columns)

$$\underline{J} = (j_1 \quad j_2 \quad \cdots \quad j_p)^T \tag{38}$$

of $\Delta \underline{K}$ are nonnull, hence

$$\Delta \underline{K} = \underline{b} \ \Delta \hat{\underline{K}} \ \underline{b}^T \tag{39}$$

where

$$\underline{b} = [\underline{e}_{j_1} \vdots \ \underline{e}_{j_2} \vdots --- \vdots \ \underline{e}_{j_p}] \qquad (N\text{x}p) \tag{40}$$

$$\Delta \hat{\underline{K}} = (\Delta \underline{K}) \begin{matrix} (j_1 & j_2 & \cdots & j_p) \\ (j_1 & j_2 & \cdots & j_p) \end{matrix} \qquad (p\text{x}p) \tag{41}$$

Utilize Eq. (11) with

$$\underline{A} = \underline{K}_o\ , \quad \underline{U} = \underline{b}$$

$$\underline{V}^T = \Delta\hat{\underline{K}}\ \underline{b}^T\ , \quad \underline{s} = \underline{I}_p \tag{42}$$

This yields

$$(\underline{K}_o + \Delta\underline{K})^{-1} = (\underline{K}_o + \underline{b}\ \Delta\hat{\underline{K}}\ \underline{b}^T)^{-1}$$

$$= \underline{K}_o^{-1} - \underline{K}_o^{-1}\ \underline{b}\ (\underline{I}_p + \Delta\hat{\underline{K}}\ \underline{b}^T\ \underline{K}_o^{-1}\ \underline{b})^{-1}\ \Delta\hat{\underline{K}}\ \underline{b}^T\ \underline{K}_o^{-1} \tag{43}$$

Postmultiply by $\underline{F}$

$$\underline{Y} - \underline{X} = -\underline{K}_o^{-1}\ \underline{b}(\underline{I}_p + \Delta\hat{\underline{K}}\ \underline{b}^T\ \underline{K}_o^{-1}\ \underline{b})^{-1}\ \Delta\hat{\underline{K}}\ \hat{\underline{X}} \tag{44}$$

where

$$\hat{\underline{X}} = (\underline{X})(j_1\ \ j_2\ \ \dots\ j_p) \tag{45}$$

Replace the inverses in Eq. (44) by Cholesky decomposition-triangular factors

$$\underline{K}_o = \underline{L}_k\ \underline{L}_k^T \qquad \text{(Cholesky)}$$

$$\underline{Y} - \underline{X} = -\underline{L}_k^{-T}\underline{L}_k^{-1}\ \underline{b}(\underline{I}_p + \Delta\hat{\underline{K}}\ \underline{b}^T\ \underline{L}_k^{-T}\ \underline{L}_k^{-1}\ \underline{b})^{-1}\ \Delta\hat{\underline{K}}\ \hat{\underline{X}} \tag{46}$$

$$\underline{L}_k\ \underline{Z} = \underline{b}$$

$$\underline{L}_k^T(\underline{Y} - \underline{X}) = -\ \underline{Z}\ (\underline{I}_p + \Delta\hat{\underline{K}}\ \underline{Z}^T\ \underline{Z})^{-1}\ \Delta\hat{\underline{K}}\ \hat{\underline{X}} \tag{47}$$

$$\underline{Q} = \underline{L}_Q\ \underline{L}_Q^T = \underline{Z}^T\ \underline{Z} \qquad \text{(Cholesky)}$$

$$\underline{L}_k^T\ (\underline{Y} - \underline{X}) = -\underline{Z}\ \underline{Q}^{-1}\ (\underline{Q}^{-1} + \Delta\hat{\underline{K}})^{-1}\ \Delta\hat{\underline{K}}\ \hat{\underline{X}} \tag{48}$$

$$= -\underline{Z}\ \underline{L}_Q^{-T}\ \underline{L}_Q^{-1}\ (\underline{Q}^{-1} + \Delta\hat{\underline{K}})^{-1}\ \Delta\hat{\underline{K}}\ \hat{\underline{X}}$$

$$(\underline{Q}^{-1} + \Delta\hat{\underline{K}}) = \underline{L}_{Qk}\ \underline{L}_{Qk}^T \qquad \text{(Cholesky)} \tag{49}$$

$$\underline{L}_k^T\ (\underline{Y} - \underline{X}) = -\underline{Z}\ \underline{L}_Q^{-T}\ \underline{L}_Q^{-1}\ \underline{L}_{Qk}^{-T}\ \underline{L}_{Qk}^{-1}\ \Delta\hat{\underline{K}}\ \hat{\underline{X}} \tag{50}$$

Finally, $(\underline{Y} - \underline{X})$ is calculated from the formulas

$$\underline{r} = \Delta\underline{\hat{K}}\;\underline{\hat{X}} \qquad (p\text{x}1) \qquad (51)$$

$$\underline{L}_{Qk}\;\underline{L}_{Qk}^{T}\;\underline{r}' = \underline{r} \qquad (p\text{x}1) \qquad (52)$$

$$\underline{L}_{Q}\;\underline{L}_{Q}^{T}\;\underline{r}'' = \underline{r}' \qquad (p\text{x}1) \qquad (53)$$

$$\underline{r}''' = -\underline{Z}\;\underline{r}'' \qquad (N\text{x}1) \qquad (54)$$

$$\underline{L}_{k}^{T}\;(\underline{Y} - \underline{X}) = \underline{r}''' \qquad (N\text{x}1) \qquad (55)$$

The computational procedure is then,

1. compute $\underline{r}$, (Eq. 51)
2. evaluate $\underline{Z}$, (Eq. 47) and $\underline{Q}$ (Eq. 48)
3. triangularize $\underline{Q}$, (Eq. 48) and evaluate $\underline{Q}^{-1}$
4. triangularize $(\underline{Q}^{-1} + \Delta\underline{\hat{K}})$, (Eq. 49)
5. compute $\underline{r}'$, (Eq. 52)
6. compute $\underline{r}''$, (Eq. 53)
7. compute $\underline{r}'''$, (Eq. 54)
8. compute $\underline{Y} - \underline{X}$, (Eq. 55)

Kirch and Rubinstein [16] also introduced several methods of exact static reanalysis utilizing the matrix inverse-adjustment formulas. These authors assume that the modification occurs in one isolated zone of the structure, i.e., it is a local but nonscattered alteration. The stiffness modification matrix is represented here by

$$\Delta\underline{K} = \begin{array}{c} \left[\begin{array}{c:c:c} \underline{0} & \underline{0} & \underline{0} \\ \hdashline \underline{0} & \Delta\underline{\hat{K}} & \underline{0} \\ \hdashline \underline{0} & \underline{0} & \underline{0} \end{array}\right]\begin{array}{l} \\ a \\ \\ b \\ \\ \end{array} \\ \qquad c \quad\;\; d \qquad\quad \end{array} = \underline{b}_{ab}\;\Delta\underline{\hat{K}}\;\underline{b}_{cd}^{T} \qquad (56)$$

$$\underline{b}_{ab} = [\underline{e}_{a} \;\vdots\; \underline{e}_{a+1} \;\vdots\; \cdots \;\vdots\; \underline{e}_{b}] \qquad (N\text{x}\ell) \qquad (57)$$

$$\underline{b}_{cd} = [\underline{e}_c \vdots \underline{e}_{c+1} \vdots \cdots \vdots \underline{e}_d] \qquad (N\times\ell) \qquad (58)$$

$$\ell = b - a + 1 = d - c + 1 \qquad (59)$$

<u>Case 1</u>

Substitute Eq. (56) and

$$\underline{A} = \underline{K}_o, \quad \underline{u} = \underline{b}_{ab}, \; \underline{s} = \Delta\underline{\hat{K}}^{-1}, \; \underline{V}^T = \underline{b}_{cd}^T \qquad (60)$$

into Eq. (12)

$$\underline{K}^{-1} = (\underline{K}_o + \Delta\underline{K})^{-1} = (\underline{K}_o + \underline{b}_{ab}\, \Delta\underline{\hat{K}}\, \underline{b}_{cd}^T)^{-1}$$

$$= \underline{K}_o^{-1} - \underline{K}_{ab}^{-1} (\Delta\underline{\hat{K}}^{-1} + \underline{K}_{abcd}^{-1})^{-1} \underline{K}_{cd}^{-1} \qquad (61)$$

$$\Delta\underline{\hat{K}} = (\Delta\underline{K}) \begin{pmatrix} a & a+1 & \cdots & b \\ c & c+1 & \cdots & d \end{pmatrix} \qquad \ell\times\ell \qquad (62)$$

$$\underline{K}_{ab}^{-1} = (\underline{K}_o^{-1}) \begin{pmatrix} 1 & 2 & \cdots & N \\ a & a+1 & \cdots & b \end{pmatrix} \qquad N\times\ell \qquad (63)$$

$$\underline{K}_{abcd}^{-1} = (\underline{K}_o^{-1}) \begin{pmatrix} c & c+1 & \cdots & d \\ a & a+1 & \cdots & b \end{pmatrix} \qquad \ell\times\ell \qquad (64)$$

$$\underline{K}_{cd}^{-1} = (\underline{K}_o^{-1}) \begin{pmatrix} c & c+1 & \cdots & d \\ 1 & 2 & \cdots & N \end{pmatrix} \qquad \ell\times N \qquad (65)$$

$$\underline{Y} = \underline{K}^{-1}\, \underline{F} = \text{modified system displacements} \qquad (66)$$

Numerical difficulties may arise with this case since $\Delta\hat{\underline{K}}$ is frequently singular. This is understood by recalling that element stiffness matrices usually have nonzero degeneracy, i.e., their rank is less than the corresponding matrix order. This problem could have been avoided if the authors had utilizedEq. (11) instead of (12), which would have been similar to Przemieniecki's approach.

Case 2

In this case the authors form $\underline{K}^{-1}$ using Eq. (11) by adding $\Delta\hat{\underline{K}}$ one element at a time. Consider the modification of the stiffness matrix inverse due to the addition of ΔK_{ij}

$$\Delta\underline{K} = \Delta K_{ij}\ \underline{e}_i\ \underline{e}_j^T$$

$$\underline{A} = \underline{K}_o,\ \underline{u} = \underline{e}_i,\ \underline{s} = \Delta K_{ij},\ \underline{V}^T = \underline{e}_j^T$$

$$\underline{K}^{-1} = (\underline{K}_o + \Delta\underline{K})^{-1} = (\underline{K}_o + \Delta K_{ij}\ \underline{e}_i\ \underline{e}_j^T)^{-1}$$

$$= \underline{K}_o^{-1} - \underline{K}_i^{-1}(\underline{K}_j^{-1})^T \frac{1}{\dfrac{1}{\Delta K_{ij}} + (\underline{K})^{-1}_{ij}} \qquad (67)$$

$$\underline{K}_i^{-1} = (\underline{K}_o^{-1}) \begin{pmatrix} 1 & 2 & \cdots & N \end{pmatrix}_{(i)} \qquad (N\mathrm{x}1)$$

$$\underline{K}_j^{-1} = (\underline{K}_o^{-1}) \begin{pmatrix} 1 & 2 & \cdots & N \end{pmatrix}_{(j)} \qquad (N\mathrm{x}1)$$

$$(\underline{K}^{-1})_{ij} = (\underline{K}_o^{-1}) \begin{matrix} (i) \\ (j) \end{matrix} \qquad (1\mathrm{x}1)$$

The formation of the complete modified stiffness matrix inverse requires ℓ^2 applications of Eq. (67) to incorporate $\hat{\Delta \underline{K}}$. All of the quantities in Eq. (67) must be updated for each application when the total inverse has been formed the modified system displacement vector is calculated from

$$\underline{Y} = \underline{K}^{-1} \underline{F} \qquad \text{Nx1}$$

Case 3

In this case the authors form $\underline{K}^{-1}$ using Eq. (11) by adding $\hat{\Delta \underline{K}}$ one column at a time. Consider the modification of the stiffness matrix inverse due to the addition of $\hat{\Delta \underline{K}}_j$ (jth column of $\hat{\Delta \underline{K}}$)

$$\Delta \underline{K} = \Delta K_j \, \underline{e}_j^T$$

$$\underline{A} = \underline{K}_o, \; \underline{u} = \Delta K_j, \; \underline{s} = 1, \; \underline{V}^T = \underline{e}_j^T$$

$$\underline{K}^{-1} = (\underline{K}_o + \Delta \underline{K})^{-1} = (\underline{K}_o + \Delta K_j \, \underline{e}_j^T)^{-1}$$

$$= \underline{K}_o^{-1} - \underline{K}_{ab}^{-1} \Delta \underline{K}_{abj} (\underline{K}_j^{-1})^T / (1 + (K_{abj}^{-1})^T \Delta \underline{K}_{abj}) \qquad (68)$$

$$\underline{K}_{ab}^{-1} = (\underline{K}_o^{-1}) \begin{pmatrix} 1 & 2 & \cdots & N \\ a & a+1 & \cdots & b \end{pmatrix} \qquad (\text{N}x\ell)$$

$$\Delta \underline{K}_{abj} = (\Delta K) \begin{pmatrix} a & a+1 & \cdots & b \\ & (j) & & \end{pmatrix} \qquad (\ell x1)$$

$$\underline{K}_j^{-1} = (\underline{K}_o^{-1}) \begin{pmatrix} 1 & 2 & \cdots & N \\ & (j) & & \end{pmatrix} \qquad (\text{Nx1})$$

$$\Delta \underline{K}_{abj}^{-1} = (K_o^{-1}) \begin{pmatrix} a & a+1 & \cdots & b \\ & (j) & & \end{pmatrix} \qquad (\text{N}x\ell)$$

The formation of the complete modified stiffness matrix inverse requires ℓ applications of Eq. (68) to incorporate $\Delta\hat{K}$. All of the quantities in Eq. (68) must be updated for each application when the total inverse has been formed the modified system displacement vector is calculated from

$$\underline{Y} = \underline{K}^{-1}\,\underline{F} \qquad N\times 1 \qquad (69)$$

<u>Case 4</u>

In this case the explicit calculation of the modified system's matri inverse is bypassed and, instead, the modified system displacement vector is computed directly. The results are derived by post multiplying Eq. (61) by $\underline{F}$

$$\underline{K}\,\underline{X}_o = \underline{F}$$

$$\underline{Y} = \underline{X} - \underline{K}_{ab}^{-1}\,(\Delta\hat{\underline{K}}^{-1} + \underline{K}_{abcd}^{-1})^{-1}\,\underline{X}_{cd} \qquad (70)$$

$$\underline{X}_{cd} = (\underline{X})\ (c \quad c+1 \quad \ldots \quad d)$$

Equation (61) is put into a form identical to that of these authors by noting that

$$(\Delta\hat{\underline{K}}^{-1} + \underline{K}_{abcd}^{-1})^{-1} = (\Delta\hat{\underline{K}}^{-1} + \underline{K}_{abcd}^{-1})^{-1}\,\underline{K}_{abcd}^{-1}\,\Delta\hat{\underline{K}}$$

$$- (\Delta\hat{\underline{K}}^{-1} + \underline{K}_{abcd}^{-1})^{-1}\,\underline{K}_{abcd}^{-1}\,\Delta\hat{\underline{K}} + (\Delta\hat{\underline{K}}^{-1} + \underline{K}_{abcd}^{-1})^{-1} + \Delta\hat{\underline{K}} - \Delta\hat{\underline{K}}$$

$$= \Delta\hat{\underline{K}} - (\Delta\hat{\underline{K}}^{-1} + \underline{K}_{abcd}^{-1})^{-1}\,\underline{K}_{abcd}^{-1}\,\Delta\hat{\underline{K}}$$

$$+ (\Delta\hat{\underline{K}}^{-1} + \underline{K}_{abcd}^{-1})^{-1}\,(\underline{K}_{abcd}^{-1} + \Delta\hat{\underline{K}}^{-1})\Delta\hat{\underline{K}} - \Delta\hat{\underline{K}}$$

or

$$\underline{Y} = \underline{X} - \underline{K}_{ab}^{-1}(\underline{I}_{\ell} - (\Delta\hat{\underline{K}}^{-1} + \underline{K}_{abcd}^{-1})^{-1}\underline{K}_{abcd}^{-1})\Delta\hat{\underline{K}}\,\underline{X}_{cd} \qquad (71)$$

Case 4, although more computationally efficient than case 1, contains the same shortcoming, in that $\Delta\hat{\underline{K}}$ must be nonsingular.

Sparsity Condensation Methods

The third approach to exact static reanalysis exploits the sparsity of the stiffness modification matrix. This results in a condensation of the modified system's static equilibrium equation. In contrast to the preceeding approach, simultaneous modifications to the stiffness matrix and external force vector may be incorporated. Kosko [17] appears to be the first to utilize this approach to structural modifications. This method is implictly applicable to scattered local modification-type problems. By a suitable interchange of rows and columns, or by properly numbering the nodes, the modified stiffness matrix is of the form

$$\underline{K} = \underline{K}_o + \Delta\underline{\underline{K}} = \left[\begin{array}{c:c} \underline{K}_{11} & \underline{K}_{12} \\ \hdashline \underline{K}_{21} & \underline{K}_{22} \end{array}\right] + \left[\begin{array}{c:c} \Delta\underline{K} & \underline{0} \\ \hdashline \underline{0} & \underline{0} \end{array}\right] =$$

$$\left[\begin{array}{c:c} \underline{K}_{11} & \underline{K}_{12} \\ \hdashline \underline{K}_{21} & \underline{K}_{22} \end{array}\right] \left[\begin{array}{c:c} \underline{I}_p & \underline{0} \\ \hdashline \underline{0} & \underline{I}_{M-p} \end{array}\right] + \left[\begin{array}{c:c} \underline{G}_{11} & \underline{G}_{12} \\ \hdashline \underline{G}_{21} & \underline{G}_{22} \end{array}\right] \left[\begin{array}{c:c} \Delta\hat{\underline{K}} & \underline{0} \\ \hdashline \underline{0} & \underline{0} \end{array}\right] \quad (N\text{x}N)$$

where

$$\underline{G} = \left[\begin{array}{c:c} \underline{G}_{11} & \underline{G}_{12} \\ \hdashline \underline{G}_{21} & \underline{G}_{22} \end{array}\right] = \left[\begin{array}{c:c} \underline{K}_{11} & \underline{K}_{12} \\ \hdashline \underline{K}_{22} & \underline{K}_{22} \end{array}\right]^{-1} = \underline{K}_o^{-1} \qquad (73)$$

Kosko, using matrix manipulations explicitly, inverts Eq. (72)

$$\underline{K}^{-1} = \left[\begin{array}{c:c} (\underline{I}_p + \underline{G}_{11}\,\Delta\hat{\underline{K}})^{-1}\underline{G}_{11} & (\underline{I}_p + \underline{G}_{11}\,\Delta\hat{\underline{K}})^{-1}\,\underline{G}_{12} \\ \hdashline -\underline{G}_{21}\Delta\hat{\underline{K}}(\underline{I}_p+\underline{G}_{11}\,\Delta\hat{\underline{K}})^{-1}\underline{G}_{11}+\underline{G}_{21} & -\underline{G}_{21}\Delta\hat{\underline{K}}(\underline{I}_p+\underline{G}_{11}\,\Delta\hat{\underline{K}})^{-1}\underline{G}_{12}+\underline{G}_{22} \end{array}\right] \qquad (74)$$

Subtracting $\underline{K}^{-1}$ yields

$$\underline{K}^{-1} - \underline{K}_o^{-1} = - \left[\begin{array}{c} \underline{G}_{11} \\ \hdashline \underline{G}_{21} \end{array}\right] \Delta\hat{\underline{K}}(\underline{I}_p + \underline{G}_{11}\,\Delta\hat{\underline{K}})^{-1}[\underline{G}_{11} \,\vdots\, \underline{G}_{12}] \qquad (75)$$

Note that only a matrix inverse of order p need be made in Eq. (75), where ΔK is of order p. By utilizing the Householder identity (Eq. (11)) Kosko's formula (75) may be shown to be equivalent to Przemieniecki's (34), i.e.,

$$\underline{A} = \underline{I}_p,\ \underline{s} = \underline{I}_p,\ \underline{u} = \underline{G}_{11},\ \underline{V}^T = \Delta\hat{\underline{K}}$$

$$\Delta\hat{\underline{K}}(\underline{I}_p + \underline{G}_{11}\ \Delta\hat{\underline{K}})^{-1} = \Delta\hat{\underline{K}} - \Delta\hat{\underline{K}}\ \underline{G}_{11}(\underline{I}_p + \Delta\hat{\underline{K}}\ \underline{G}_{11})^{-1}\Delta\hat{\underline{K}} \qquad (76)$$

$$= (\underline{I}_p + \Delta\hat{\underline{K}}\ \underline{G}_{11})^{-1}\ \Delta\hat{\underline{K}}$$

McQuire and Gallagher [18] postmultiply Eq. (75) by $\underline{F}$ and obtain

$$\underline{K}_o\ \underline{X} = \underline{F}$$

$$\underline{K}\ \underline{Y} = \underline{F}$$

$$\underline{Y} = \underline{X} - \begin{bmatrix} \underline{G}_{11} \\ -- \\ \underline{G}_{21} \end{bmatrix} \Delta\hat{\underline{K}}\ (\underline{I}_p + \underline{G}_{11}\ \Delta\hat{\underline{K}})^{-1}\ \underline{X}_1 \qquad \text{Nx1} \qquad (77)$$

$$\underline{X}_1 = (\underline{X})(1 \quad 2 \quad \ldots \quad P) \qquad \text{px1} \qquad (78)$$

which can be rearranged into the form

$$\underline{Y} = \begin{bmatrix} \underline{Y}_1 \\ -- \\ \underline{Y}_2 \end{bmatrix} = \begin{bmatrix} (\underline{I}_p + \underline{G}_{11}\ \Delta\hat{\underline{K}})^{-1}\ \underline{X}_1 \\ ------------------ \\ \underline{X}_2 - \underline{G}_{21}\ \Delta\hat{\underline{K}}\ (\underline{I}_p + \underline{G}_{11}\ \Delta\hat{\underline{K}})^{-1}\ \underline{X}_1 \end{bmatrix} \qquad (79)$$

These authors improve the computational efficiency of Kosko's approach by bypassing the modified matrix inverse computation. The results of Martin's derivation [19] of a structural modification reanalysis method are also identical to Eq. (79).

Case 5 of Kirch and Rubinstein's work [16] is termed a "solution by reduced set of equations." Their results are identical to Eq. (79) with the understanding that $\Delta\underline{K}$ is partitioned as shown in Eq. (56), i.e.,

$$\underline{Y}_1 = (\underline{Y})(c \quad c+1 \quad \ldots \quad d)$$

$$\underline{Y}_2 = (\underline{Y})(1 \quad 2 \quad \ldots \quad c-1 \quad d+1 \quad \ldots \quad N)$$

$$\underline{X}_1 = (\underline{X})(c \quad c+1 \quad \ldots \quad d)$$

$$\underline{X}_2 = (\underline{X})(1 \quad 2 \quad \ldots \quad c-1 \quad d+1 \quad \ldots \quad N)$$

$$\Delta\hat{\underline{K}} = (\Delta\underline{K}) \begin{matrix} (a & a+1 & \ldots & b) \\ (c & c+1 & \ldots & d) \end{matrix}$$

$$\underline{G}_{11} = (\underline{K}_o^{-1}) \begin{matrix} (c & c+1 & \ldots & d) \\ (a & a+1 & \ldots & b) \end{matrix}$$

$$\underline{G}_{21} = (\underline{K}_o^{-1}) \begin{matrix} (1 & 2 & \ldots & c-1 & d+1 & \ldots & N) \\ & (a & a+1 & \ldots & b) & & \end{matrix} \qquad (80)$$

Argyris [20] has developed a very general formula for static reanalysis, utilizing a sparse modification-condensation approach. His results simultaneously incorporate modifications to elements, removal of degrees of freedom by adding supports or suppression, increasing degrees of freedom by removing supports or suppressions, attaching a separate substructure, removing a substructure from the original structure (cut out), and replacing a piece of the original structure, i.e., changing the discretization scheme in the modified zones. An extensive amount of work has been devoted to these areas, and since the focus of this review is only on modifications to elements, just this aspect of Argyris's formula is examined. The equation to be developed here simultaneously incorporates element and external force modifications. The external force alterations are restricted to occur in the modified element zones, i.e., from Eq. (37)

$$(\underline{K}_o + \Delta\underline{K})\underline{Y} = \underline{F} + \Delta\underline{F} \qquad (81)$$

where

$$\Delta F_i = 0 \quad \text{if} \quad i \notin J = (j_1 \quad j_2 \quad \cdots \quad j_p) \qquad (82)$$

The following identity is used in the development; if

$$(\underline{K}_o)\begin{pmatrix}1 & 2 & \dots & N\\ 1 & 2 & \dots & N\end{pmatrix}(\underline{K}_o^{-1})\begin{pmatrix}1 & 2 & \dots & N\\ 1 & 2 & \dots & N\end{pmatrix} = \underline{K}_o\,\underline{K}_o^{-1} = \underline{I}_N \qquad (83)$$

then

$$(\underline{K}_o)\begin{pmatrix}1\ 2..j_1-1\ j_1+1..N\ ,j_1\ j_2..j_p\\ 1\ 2..j_1-1\ j_1+1..N\ \ j_1\ j_2..j_p\end{pmatrix}(\underline{K}_o^{-1})\begin{pmatrix}1\ 2..j_1-1\ j_1+1..N\ j_1\ j_2..j_p\\ 1\ 2..j_1-1\ j_1+1..N\ j_1\ j_2..j_p\end{pmatrix} = I_N \qquad (84)$$

or, in partitioned matrix notation,

$$\begin{bmatrix}\underline{K}_{ii} & \vdots & \underline{K}_{im}\\ - - & \vdots & - - \\ \underline{K}_{mi} & \vdots & \underline{K}_{mm}\end{bmatrix}\begin{bmatrix}\underline{G}_{ii} & \vdots & \underline{G}_{im}\\ - - & \vdots & - - \\ \underline{G}_{mi} & \vdots & \underline{G}_{mm}\end{bmatrix} = \begin{bmatrix}\underline{I}_{N-p} & \vdots & \underline{0}\\ - - - & \vdots & - - - \\ \underline{0} & \vdots & \underline{I}_p\end{bmatrix} \qquad (85)$$

where

$$\underline{K}_{ii} = (\underline{K}_o)\begin{pmatrix}1\ \ 2..j_1-1\ j_1+1..N\\ 1\ \ 2..j_1-1\ j_1+1..N\end{pmatrix},\ \underline{G}_{ii} = (\underline{K}^{-1})\begin{pmatrix}1\ \ 2..j_1-1\ j_1+1..N\\ 1\ \ 2..j_1-1\ j_1+1..N\end{pmatrix} \qquad (86)$$

$$\underline{K}_{im} = \underline{K}^T_{\ i} = (\underline{K}_o)\begin{pmatrix}1\ \ 2..j_1-1\ j_1+1..N\\ j_1\ \ j_2\ ..j_p\end{pmatrix},\ \underline{G}_{im} = \underline{G}^T_{\ i} = (\underline{K}^{-1})\begin{pmatrix}1\ \ 2..j_1-1\ j_1+1..N\\ j_1\ \ j_2\ ..j_p\end{pmatrix} \qquad (87)$$

$$\underline{K}_{mm} = (\underline{K}_o)\begin{pmatrix}j_1 & j_2 & \dots & j_p\\ j_1 & j_2 & \dots & j_p\end{pmatrix},\quad \underline{G}_{mm} = (\underline{K}_o^{-1})\begin{pmatrix}j_1 & j_2 & \dots & j_p\\ j_1 & j_2 & \dots & j_p\end{pmatrix} \qquad (88)$$

Note that $\underline{K}_{ii}$ is formed from $\underline{K}_o$ by striking out rows and columns $j_1, j_2 \dots j_p$. Similar comments apply to the remaining submatrices. Utilizing the relations

$$\underline{K}_{ii}^{-1}\,\underline{K}_{im} = -\,\underline{G}_{im}\,\underline{G}_{mm}^{-1} \qquad (N-p) \times p \qquad (89)$$

$$\underline{K}_{ii}^{-1} = \underline{G}_{ii} - \underline{G}_{im}\,\underline{G}_{mm}^{-1}\,\underline{G}_{mi} \qquad (N-p) \times (N-p) \qquad (90)$$

$$\underline{K}_{mm} - \underline{K}_{mi}\,\underline{K}_{ii}^{-1}\,\underline{K}_{im} = \underline{G}_{mm}^{-1} \qquad p \times p \qquad (91)$$

it is then shown that

$$(\underline{Y})(1\ \ 2\ \ \ldots\ \ N) - (\underline{X})(1\ \ 2\ \ \ldots\ \ N)$$

$$= -\underline{K}_o^{-1}\ \underline{b}\ \underline{G}_{mm}^{-1}\ [\underline{G}_{mm}^{-1} + \Delta\hat{\underline{K}}]^{-1}\ (\Delta\hat{\underline{K}}\ \hat{\underline{X}} - \Delta\hat{\underline{F}}) \tag{92}$$

where

$$\underline{b} = [\underline{e}_{j_1} \ \vdots\ \underline{e}_{j_2} \ \vdots\ --- \ \vdots\ \underline{e}_{j_p}] \qquad \text{Nxp} \tag{93}$$

$$\Delta\hat{\underline{K}} = (\Delta\underline{K})\ \begin{matrix}(j_1 & j_2 & \cdots & j_p)\\(j_1 & j_2 & \cdots & j_p)\end{matrix} \qquad \text{pxp} \tag{94}$$

$$\underline{K}_o\ \underline{X} = \underline{F}$$

$$\hat{\underline{X}} = (\underline{X})(j_1\ \ j_2\ \ \cdots\ \ j_p) \qquad \text{px1} \tag{95}$$

$$\Delta\hat{\underline{F}} = (\Delta\underline{F})(j_1\ \ j_2\ \ \cdots\ \ j_p) \qquad \text{px1} \tag{96}$$

As in his previous paper [15], Argyris now utilizes the Cholesky factorization

$$\underline{K}_o = \underline{L}_k\ \underline{L}_k^T \qquad \text{(Cholesky)}$$

$$\underline{L}_K\ \underline{Z} = \underline{b}$$

$$\underline{Q} = \underline{L}_Q\ \underline{L}_Q^T = \underline{Z}^T\underline{Z} \qquad \text{(Cholesky)}$$

$$\underline{G}_{mm}^{-1} = (\underline{b}^T\ \underline{K}_o^{-1}\ \underline{b})^{-1} = (\underline{b}^T\ \underline{L}_K^{-T}\ \underline{L}_K^{-1}\ \underline{b})^{-1} = (\underline{Z}^T\underline{Z})^{-1} = \underline{L}_Q^{-T}\ \underline{L}_Q^{-1} = \underline{Q}^{-1}$$

$$(\underline{Q}^{-1} + \Delta\hat{\underline{K}}) = \underline{L}_{Qk}\ \underline{L}_{Qk}^T \qquad \text{(Cholesky)}$$

this yields

$$\underline{L}_k^T(\underline{Y}-\underline{X}) = -\underline{Z}\ \underline{L}_Q^{-T}\ \underline{L}_Q^{-1}\ \underline{L}_{Qk}^{-T}\ \underline{L}_{Qk}^{-1}\ (\Delta\hat{\underline{K}}\ \hat{\underline{X}} - \Delta\hat{\underline{F}}) \tag{97}$$

These results are identical to Eq. (50) with the following substitution

$$\Delta\hat{\underline{K}}\ \hat{\underline{X}} \rightarrow \Delta\hat{\underline{K}}\ \hat{\underline{X}} - \Delta\ \hat{\underline{F}} \tag{98}$$

The procedure for solving Eq. (97) is the same as that shown following Eq. (55), with step one replaced by

$$1.\ \text{compute}\ \underline{r},\quad \underline{r} = \Delta\hat{\underline{K}}\ \hat{\underline{X}} - \Delta\hat{\underline{F}} \tag{99}$$

Argyris also developed algorithms for the modified stiffness matrix triangular factors [7] and modifications to elements in substructures, in Ref. [20].

The authors of this chapter have derived an element modification reanalysis formula similar to Argyris's; however, only the desired responses at degrees of freedom not included in $(j_1, j_2, ..j_p)$ are computed, and alterations to the external force vector may occur at degrees of freedom not included in $(j_1, j_2, ..j_p)$. The results are easily derived using a modification sparsity-condensation approach. A summary of these results are as follows:

$$(\underline{I}_p + \underline{G}_{11}\ \Delta\hat{\underline{K}})\ \underline{Y}_1 = \underline{X}_1 + \underline{G}_1^*\ \underline{\Delta F}^* \tag{100}$$

$$\underline{Y}_2 = \underline{X}_2 - \underline{G}_{21}\ \Delta\hat{\underline{K}}\ \underline{Y}_1 + \underline{G}_2^*\ \underline{\Delta F}^* \tag{101}$$

where $\underline{Y}_1$ is the displacement vector connected to the modification, $\underline{Y}_2$ is the desired displacement response vectors, and

$$\underline{K}_o\ \underline{X} = \underline{F}$$

$$(\underline{K}_o + \Delta\underline{K})\underline{Y} = \underline{F} + \underline{\Delta F}$$

$\underline{J} = (j_1\ j_2 ... j_p)$: nonnull rows (or columns) of $\Delta\underline{K}$

$(k_1\ k_2 ... k_v)$: degrees of freedom not in $\underline{J}$ where responses are desired

$(\ell_1\ \ell_2 ... \ell_w)$: degrees of freedom with nonzero ΔF_i (102)

$$\underline{X}_1 = (\underline{X})(j_1\ j_2 ... j_p),\quad \underline{Y}_1 = (\underline{Y})(j_1\ j_2 ... j_p) \tag{103}$$

$$\underline{X}_2 = (\underline{X})(k_1\ k_2 \ldots k_v), \quad \underline{Y}_2 = (\underline{Y})(k_1\ k_2 \ldots k_v) \tag{104}$$

$$\Delta\hat{\underline{K}} = (\Delta\underline{K}) \begin{pmatrix} j_1 & j_2 \ldots j_p \\ j_1 & j_2 \ldots j_p \end{pmatrix} \tag{105}$$

$$\underline{G}_{11} = (\underline{K}_o^{-1}) \begin{pmatrix} j_1 & j_2 \ldots j_p \\ j_1 & j_2 \ldots j_p \end{pmatrix}, \quad \underline{G}_{21} = (\underline{K}_o^{-1}) \begin{pmatrix} k_1 & k_2 \ldots k_v \\ j_1 & j_2 \ldots j_p \end{pmatrix} \tag{106}$$

$$\underline{G}_1^* = (\underline{K}_o^{-1}) \begin{pmatrix} j_1 & j_2 \ldots j_p \\ \ell_1 & \ell_2 \ldots \ell_w \end{pmatrix}, \quad \underline{G}_2^* = (\underline{K}_o^{-1}) \begin{pmatrix} k_1 & k_2 \ldots k_v \\ \ell_1 & \ell_2 \ldots \ell_w \end{pmatrix}$$

$$\underline{\Delta F}^* = (\Delta\underline{F})(\ell_1\ \ell_2 \ldots \ell_w) \tag{107}$$

Operations Count Comparisons

The goal of all reanalysis procedures is to reduce considerably the computational cost for the repeated analysis of a structural model. Arithmetic operation counts for several of the popular direct static reanalysis methods are presented here. A single operation is either a multiplication or a division followed by an addition or subtraction. The lowest numbered degree of freedom at which a response is desired is denoted by (K_1).

A complete solution includes factorization of the current stiffness matrix and forward and back substitution to obtain the current response vector

$$\underline{K}\ \underline{Y} = \tilde{\underline{L}}_k\ \tilde{\underline{L}}_k^T\ \underline{Y} = \tilde{\underline{F}} \qquad (N\mathrm{x}1) \tag{108}$$

$$\tilde{\underline{L}}_k\ \underline{Z} = \tilde{\underline{F}} \tag{109}$$

$$\tilde{\underline{L}}_k^T\ \underline{Y} = \underline{Z} \tag{110}$$

The operations count for q complete solutions in [22]

$$\text{factorization:} \left\{ \frac{Nb^2}{2} + \frac{Nb}{2} - N - \frac{b^3}{3} + \frac{b}{3} \right\} q$$

$$\text{forward substitution:} \left\{ Nb - N - \frac{b^2}{2} + \frac{3b}{2} \right\} q$$

$$\text{back substitution:} \left\{ Nb - k_1 b - \frac{b^2}{2} + \frac{3b}{2} \right\} q$$

$$\text{TOTAL: } q\left\{\frac{Nb^2}{2} + \frac{5}{2}Nb - 2N - \frac{b^3}{3} - b^2 + \frac{7}{3}b - k_1 b\right\} \quad (111)$$

where b is the bandwidth of $\underline{K}$, $K_{ij} = 0$ whenever $|i-j| \geq b$.

Argyris's method is given by Eqs. (50) or (97) and is utilized according to the procedure following Eq. (55). The required operation count for solving the original system and (q-1) modified systems by this method is [21].

$$\text{Original System: } \frac{Nb^2}{2} + \frac{5}{2}Nb - 2N - \frac{b^3}{3} - b^2 + \frac{7}{3}b - k_1 b \quad (112)$$

Step 1: $\underline{r}$, $(q-1)p^2$

Step 2: $\underline{z}$, $p(bN - \frac{b^2}{2} + \frac{3b}{2}) - b\sum_{i=1}^{p} j_i$, $j_i > b$

$\underline{Q}$, $\frac{(N+1)}{2}(p^2 + p) - \sum_{\ell=1}^{p} \ell \cdot j_\ell$

Step 3: $\underline{L}_Q$ and $\underline{Q}^{-1}$, $\frac{p^3}{2} + \frac{3}{2}p^2$

Step 4: $\underline{L}_{QK}$, $(q-1)(\frac{p^3}{6} + \frac{p^2}{2} + \frac{p}{3})$

Step 5: $\underline{r}'$, $(q-1)(p^2 + p)$

Step 6: $\underline{r}''$, $(q-1)(p^2 + p)$

Step 7: $\underline{r}'''$, $(q-1)\{Np + p - \sum_{i=1}^{p} j_i\}$

Step 8: $\underline{Y} - \underline{X}$, $(q-1)(Nb - \frac{b^2}{2} + \frac{3b}{2} - k_1 b)$

Total (original system plus q-1 modified systems):

$$Np\{b+\frac{p}{2}+\frac{1}{2}\} - bp\{\frac{b}{2}-\frac{3}{2}\} + p^3/2 + 2p^2 + p/2 - \sum_{\ell=1}^{p}(b+\ell)\, j_\ell$$

$$+ \frac{Nb^2}{2} + \frac{5}{2}Nb - 2N - \frac{b^3}{3} - b^2 + \frac{7}{3}b - k_1 b + (q-1)\{N_p + p^3/6 + 7p^2/2$$

$$+ Nb - b^2/2 + 3b/2 - K_1 b - \sum_{\ell=1}^{p} j_\ell, \quad j_\ell > b \quad (113)$$

Note that Eq. (113) assumes that the sparsity integer set $(j_1\ j_2 \ldots j_p)$ is the same for each modified system. This implies that the structural parameters of interest are changed in magnitude and not in location. The operations count presented by Argyris [15,20] does not include 2, 3, and 4 above, assumes that on the average changes occur in the middle nodal point numbers, i.e., $j_i = N/2$, assumes that the half bandwidth of $\underline{K}$, $b << N$, and assumes that only one reanalysis occurs $(q=2)$. Considering these assumptions, Eq. (113) reduces to

$$Nbp/2 + Np^2/4 + 2p^3/3 \tag{114}$$

which is identical to Argyris's Eq. (21), Ref. [15], or Eq. (37), Ref. [20].

Argyris's method is directly applicable if the changes to the force vector only occur at the same degrees of freedom which are affected by element modifications. He recommends that if force component changes occur at other degrees of freedom, the displacement vector of the original system resulting from the new force vector be computed before the element modification reanalysis. Since the Cholesky factor of $\underline{K}_o$ is available, the displacement vector computation only requires a forward and backward substitution. It then follows that in this case if $(q-1)$ reanalyses are performed with alterations to the force vector during each cycle, the additional operations count to add with Eq. (113) is

$$(q-1)(2Nb - N - K_1 b - b^2 + 2b) \tag{115}$$

An operations count for the method presented by this chapter's authors, Eqs. (100 and 101), is derived in the following manner. The first consideration is the formation of the submatrices in Eq. (106). Since $\underline{K}_o$ is symmetric, only columns $(j_1\ j_2 \ldots j_{p*})$ of $\underline{K}_o^{-1}$ need be computed for $\underline{G}_{11}$, $\underline{G}_{21}$, or $\underline{G}_1^*$. The submatrix $\underline{G}_2$ may be formed if either columns $(k_1\ k_2 \ldots k_v)$ or columns $(\ell_1\ \ell_2 \ldots \ell_w)$ of $\underline{K}_o^{-1}$ are available. Define

$$u = \min\ (v,w) \tag{116}$$

$$(n_1\ n_2 \ldots n_u) = \begin{cases} (k_1\ k_2 \ldots k_v)\ , & \text{if } u = v \\ (\ell_1\ \ell_2 \ldots \ell_w)\ , & \text{if } u = w \end{cases} \tag{117}$$

then G_2^* requires, at most, u additional columns of K_o^{-1}. The required operations count for solving the original system and $(q-1)$ modified systems by this method is

Original System: $\frac{Nb^2}{2} + \frac{5}{2} Nb - 2N - \frac{b^3}{3} - b^2 + \frac{7}{3} b - k_1 b$ (118)

$\underline{G}_{11}, \underline{G}_{21}, \underline{G}^*_1 : \quad p\{2Nb - b^2 + 2b - N - 1\} - (b-1) \sum_{\ell=1}^{p} j_\ell, \quad j_\ell > b$

$\underline{G}^*_2 : \quad u\{2Nb - b^2 + 2b - N - 1\} - (b-1) \sum_{\ell=1}^{u} n_\ell, \quad n_\ell > b$

$\underline{G}^*_1 \underline{\Delta F}^* : \quad pw(q-1)$

$\underline{G}^*_2 \underline{\Delta F}^* : \quad vw(q-1)$

$\underline{G}_{21} \underline{\Delta \hat{K}} \underline{Y}_1 : \quad (pv + p^2)(q-1)$

$\underline{G}_{11} \underline{\Delta \hat{K}} : \quad p^3(q-1)$

$\underline{Y}_1$, Eq. (100): $(\frac{p^3}{3} + p^2 - \frac{p}{3})(q-1)$

Total (original system plus q-1 modified systems):

$$(u + p)\{2Nb - b^2 + 2b - N - 1\} - (b-1)\{\sum_{\ell=1}^{p} j_\ell + \sum_{\ell=1}^{u} n_\ell\}$$

$$+ \frac{Nb^2}{2} + \frac{5}{2} Nb - 2N - \frac{b^3}{3} - b^2 + \frac{7}{3} b - k_1 b$$

$$+ (q-1)\{pw + vw + pv + \frac{4p^3}{3} + 2p^2 - \frac{p}{3}\}$$

$$j_\ell > b, \; n_\ell > b, \; k_1 < j_1 \qquad (119)$$

Note that Eq. (119) is valid only if the three integer sets $(k_1 \; k_2 \ldots k_v)$, $(\ell_1 \; \ell_2 \ldots \ell_w)$, and $(j_1 \; j_2 \ldots j_p)$ remain constant during all (q-1) reanalyses.

To illustrate the use of the operations counts consider a typical example with the following parameters

$$N = 2000,\ p = 25,\ v = 15,\ w = 10,\ u = 10,\ k_1 = 500$$

$$(j_1 \quad j_2 \ldots j_{25}) = (750 \quad 751 \ldots 774)$$

$$(n_1 \quad n_2 \ldots n_{10}) = (1001 \ldots 1005 \quad 1770 \ldots 1774)$$

The external force vector changes occur at degrees of freedom

$$(\ell_1 \quad \ell_2 \ldots \ell_{10}) = (n_1 \quad n_2 \ldots n_{10})$$

consequently Eq. (115) must be added to Eq. (113) to evaluate the operations count by Argyris's method. Counts for two half bandwidths (b) of $\underline{K}_o$ are given in Tables 1a and 1b

These results clearly indicate that a large reduction in computation time can be achieved by utilizing a reanalysis scheme with sparsely modified structural models. A comparison of columns 3 and 4 in these tables reveals that the present approach may, in some cases, be substantially more efficient than Argyris's approach. Greater efficiency is most probable when force components at degrees of freedom not in $(j_1 \quad j_2 \ldots j_p)$ are altered during each reanalysis cycle, and when the total number of analysis cycles (q) is large. The latter condition may occur in some locally nonlinear structures and in certain optimization schemes.

Table 1a Operations Count Comparison
b = 75. One count equals one x or one ÷

q (No. of Analyses)	Complete Analyses, Eq. (111), (x 10^7)	Argyris Eq. (113) and (115), (x 10^7)	Present Method Eq. (119) (x 10^7)
10	5.812	1.208	1.382
25	14.531	1.809	1.416
50	29.062	2.811	1.473
75	43.593	3.812	1.531
100	58.124	4.814	1.588

Table 1b Operations Count Comparison
b = 150

q (No. of Analyses)	Complete Analyses, Eq. (111),(x 10^7)	Argyris Eq. (113) and (115),(x 10^7)	Present Method Eq. (119) (x 10^7)
10	22.023	3.356	3.748
25	55.060	4.482	3.782
50	110.12	6.358	3.839
75	165.18	8.234	3.896
100	220.24	10.111	3.953

APPROXIMATE METHODS

Approximate static reanalysis techniques are commonly categorized as:

1. truncated Taylor series
2. reduced basis
3. iterative techniques

Since these solution procedures yield approximate results, both accuracy and efficiency are usually considered when comparing them with other approximate or exact methods.

Truncated Taylor Series (TTS)

The static equilibrium equation for the displacement method of structural analysis is expressed by

$$\underline{K}\ \underline{Y} = \underline{F} \qquad (N\text{x}1) \qquad (120)$$

Individual elements of the stiffness matrix ($\underline{K}$) are dependent on a set of design parameters defined by

$$\underline{V} = (V_1 \quad V_2 \ldots V_q)^T \qquad (q\text{x}1) \qquad (121)$$

This set contains, for instance, cross section dimensions, elastic moduli, and element thicknesses. The displacement vector then has the Taylor series representation [23].

$$\underline{Y} = \underline{X} + \sum_{i=1}^{q} \left.\frac{\partial \underline{Y}}{\partial V_i}\right|_o \Delta V_i + \frac{1}{2} \sum_{i=1}^{q} \sum_{j=1}^{q} \left.\frac{\partial^2 \underline{Y}}{\partial V_i \partial V_j}\right|_o \Delta V_i \, \Delta V_j \qquad (122)$$

and higher order terms where

$$\underline{K}_o \underline{X} = \underline{F}$$

and subscript o designates a term evaluated for the "initial" or "base" design values of V_i. Differentiation of Eq. (120), assuming that the load vector $\underline{F}$ is independent of V_i, yields

$$\frac{\partial \underline{K}}{\partial V_i} \underline{Y} + \underline{K} \frac{\partial \underline{Y}}{\partial V_i} = \underline{0}$$

$$\underline{K} \frac{\partial \underline{Y}}{\partial V_i} = -\frac{\partial \underline{K}}{\partial V_i} \underline{Y} \qquad (123)$$

Similarly,

$$\underline{K} \frac{\partial^2 \underline{Y}}{\partial V_i \partial V_j} = - \frac{\partial^2 \underline{K}}{\partial V_i \partial V_j} \underline{Y} + \frac{\partial \underline{K}}{\partial V_i} \frac{\partial \underline{K}}{\partial V_j} + \frac{\partial \underline{K}}{\partial V_j} \frac{\partial \underline{Y}}{\partial V_i} \qquad (124)$$

Since the stiffness matrix of the initial design, $\underline{K}_o$, has been previously decomposed into triangular factors from the solution for $\underline{X}$, Eqs. (122) - (124) indicate that the displacement vector derivatives may be obtained with only forward and backward substitutions. Computational efficiency is enhanced further by considering the sparsity of the derivatives of $\underline{K}$ in the matrix vector products of Eqs. (123) and (124).

Storaasli and Sobieszczanski [24,25] employ the TTS method in the reanalysis of a 600 dof fuselage midsection model. Their reanalysis results include a reduction in computation time by a factor of 39, as compared with an exact solution procedure. They separate both stresses and displacements into 10 decile groups according to absolute magnitudes. The highest decile group contains the largest displacements and stresses and is typically the one of major concern in structural design. Percent errors within each decile group were obtained by comparison of the reanalysis results with solutions from the structural analysis code ELAS. The maximum percent error within the highest decile group is used to judge the accuracy of the TTS method for various structural modifications. Less than 16% error was observed for single element variation of -100% (i.e., element removal) to +500%, and for -50% to 50% change for multielements.

Noor [26] investigated applying the TTS method to the mixed approach of structural analysis. In this approach static equilibrium is expressed by

$$\underline{\hat{K}}\ \underline{\hat{Y}} = \underline{\hat{F}} \tag{125}$$

where $\underline{\hat{K}}$ is a "generalized" stiffness matrix, $\underline{\hat{Y}}$ is a response vector of force and displacment variables, and $\underline{\hat{F}}$ contains external loads. For the simple truss in Fig. 2, Eq. (125) becomes

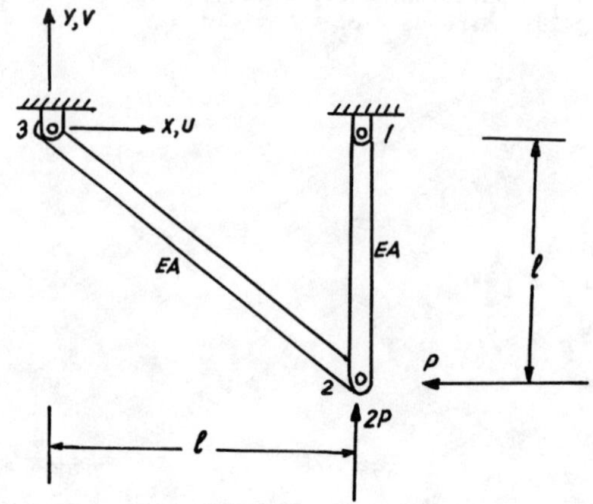

Figure 2 Simple two bar truss for the illustration of mixed method reanalysis

$$\begin{bmatrix} (L^3/EA)_{12} & 0 & 0 & \ell \\ 0 & (L^3/EA)_{32} & -\ell & \ell \\ 0 & -\ell & 0 & 0 \\ \ell & \ell & 0 & 0 \end{bmatrix} \begin{bmatrix} \tilde{N}_{21} \\ \tilde{N}_{23} \\ U_2 \\ V_2 \end{bmatrix} = \begin{bmatrix} 0 \\ 0 \\ 0 \\ -2P \end{bmatrix} \tag{126}$$

where

N_{23} = axial force in bar 23

N_{21} = axial force in bar 21

$\tilde{N}_{23} = N_{23}/L_{23} = N_{23}/(\sqrt{2}\ \ell)$

$\tilde{N}_{21} = N_{21}/L_{21} = N_{21}/\ell$

The TTS reanalysis equations for the mixed method are identical to Eqs. (122), (123), and (124) with $\underline{Y}$ replaced by $\hat{\underline{Y}}$ and $\underline{K}$ replaced by $\hat{\underline{K}}$.

Noor states that the nondiagonal elements of $\hat{\underline{K}}$ are always either linear in the design variables $\underline{V}_i$, or constants. This makes the evaluation of the derivatives of $\hat{\underline{K}}$ much simpler than their counter parts in Eqs. (123) and (124). For this same reason these derivatives of $\underline{K}$ are usually very sparse, consequently the efficiency of the reanalysis procedure may be substantially increased.

The approach of Romstad, Hutchinson, and Runge to static reanalysis [27] is based on the Maclaurin series expansion. The series is expressed in terms of the perturbation parameter ϵ where

$$\underline{K}_o\ \underline{X} = \underline{F}_o \tag{127}$$

$$\underline{K} = \underline{K}_o + \epsilon\ \underline{K}_1 = \underline{K}_o + \Delta\underline{K} \tag{128}$$

$$\underline{F} = \underline{F}_o + \epsilon\ \underline{F}_1 = \underline{F}_o + \Delta\underline{F} \tag{129}$$

$$\underline{K}\ \underline{Y} = \underline{F} \tag{130}$$

The modified system's displacement vector is then computed from

$$\underline{Y}\ (\epsilon) = \underline{X} + \sum_{i=1}^{\infty} \epsilon^i\ \underline{Y} \tag{131}$$

where

$$\underline{K}_o\ \underline{Y}_1 = \underline{F}_1 - \underline{K}_1\ \underline{X} \tag{132}$$

$$\underline{K}_o\ \underline{Y}_2 = -\underline{K}_1\ \underline{Y}_1 \tag{133}$$

$$\vdots$$

$$\underline{K}_o\ \underline{Y}_i = -\underline{K}_1\ \underline{Y}_{i-1} \tag{134}$$

Here it is assumed that the triangular factorization of $\underline{K}_o$ has been performed for the original system, and consequently each $\underline{Y}_i$ is computed with only a forward and backward substitution.

The authors state that the above series converges if and only if all eigenvalues of $\epsilon\, \underline{K}_o^{-1}\underline{K}_1$ lie within the unit circle. Since the eigenvalues of $\epsilon\, \underline{K}_o^{-1}\underline{K}_1$ are ϵ times the eigenvalues of $\underline{K}_o^{-1}\underline{K}_1$ this may provide an upper bound on ϵ.

Reduced Basis Method (RB)

This approximate approach to static reanalysis is employed to substantially decrease the dimension of the system of equations needed to solve for the displacements of the modified system. An approximation to the actual response vector is computed from a selected subspace of N-vectors. This subspace is defined by a given set of basis vectors that span the subspace. The particular vector in this subspace which results in a minimum value for the total potential energy [28] is chosen to be the best approximation of the actual response vector. The static equilibrium equation of the modified system is

$$\underline{K} \cdot \underline{Y} = \underline{F} \qquad (N\text{x}1) \tag{135}$$

Restricting $\underline{Y}$ to an r-dimensional subspace spanned by a selected set of basis vectors

$$\underline{Y} \approx \underline{\tilde{Y}} = \sum_{i=1}^{\tilde{r}} h_i\, \underline{\rho}_i = \underline{\Phi}\, \underline{H} \tag{136}$$

where

$$\underline{\Phi} = [\underline{\rho}_1 \;\vdots\; \underline{\rho}_2 \;\vdots\; --- \;\vdots\; \underline{\rho}_r\,] \qquad (N\text{x}r) \tag{137}$$

$$\underline{H} = (h_1 \quad h_2 \ldots h_r)^T \qquad (r\text{x}1) \tag{138}$$

Considering the total potential energy when evaluated for any vector in the given subspace

$$\tilde{E} = (\text{internal strain energy}) + (\text{potential energy due to external loads})$$

$$= \frac{1}{2}\, \underline{\tilde{Y}}^T\, \underline{K}\, \underline{\tilde{Y}} - \underline{\tilde{Y}}^T\, \underline{F} \tag{139}$$

Utilizing Eq. (136), $\tilde{E}$ becomes

$$\tilde{E} = \frac{1}{2} \underline{H}^T \underline{\tilde{K}} \underline{H} - \underline{H}^T \underline{\tilde{F}} \tag{140}$$

in which

$$\underline{\tilde{K}} = \underline{\Phi}^T \underline{K} \underline{\Phi} \qquad (r \times r) \tag{141}$$

$$\underline{\tilde{F}} = \underline{\Phi}^T \underline{F} \tag{142}$$

setting the partial derivative of $\tilde{E}$ with respect to each h_i to zero

$$\frac{\partial E}{\partial h_i} = \frac{1}{2} \underline{e}_i^T \underline{\tilde{K}} \underline{H} + \frac{1}{2} \underline{H}^T \tilde{K} \underline{e}_i - \underline{e}_i^T \underline{\tilde{F}} = \frac{1}{2}(\underline{\tilde{K}}_i^T \underline{H} + \underline{H}^T \underline{\tilde{K}}_i) - \tilde{F}_i$$

$$= \underline{\tilde{K}}_i^T \underline{H} - \tilde{F}_i = 0 \qquad i = 1, 2, \ldots r \tag{143}$$

where

$\underline{e}_i$ = null vector except for 1 in column 1

$\underline{\tilde{K}}_i$ = ith column of symmetric matrix $\underline{K}$

When written for all i, Eq. (143) implies

$$\underline{\tilde{K}} \underline{H} = \underline{\tilde{F}} \qquad (r \times 1) \tag{144}$$

The procedure of the reduced basis method is then

1. to form $\underline{\tilde{K}}$ and $\underline{\tilde{F}}$ with Eqs. (141) and (142)
2. to solve the r-dimensional system of equations in Eq. (144)
3. to obtain the approximate response vector from the transformation in Eq. (136).

Since r (dimension of the subspace) is chosen to be much less than N, a considerable computation time savings usually results. The questions of which and how many basis vectors to employ in this method have been addressed by several investigators.

Fox and Miura [29] selected "basic or typical design" response vectors as basis vectors in the RB approach. These basic design vectors are exact solutions of the static equilibrium equation for a set of typical, potential designs. The results for a 96-degree-of-freedom space-truss example showed high accuracy and computational efficiency. The subspace dimension of this example was r = 5. Although no systematic procedure for choosing a "basic design" was presented, the use of the corresponding response vectors in the RB approach has a definite intuitive appeal.

Noor and Lowder [30] have presented a systematic means for computing the basis vectors in the RB method. The basis vectors employed are

$$\underline{\rho}_1 = \underline{X} \tag{145}$$

$$\underline{\rho}_{i+1} = \left.\frac{\partial \underline{Y}}{\partial V_i}\right|_o \qquad i = 1,2,\ldots q \tag{146}$$

where $\underline{X}$ and $\partial\underline{Y}/\partial V_i$ are defined as in Eq. (122). The dimension (r) of the subspace containing the approximate response vector is the number (q) of independent design variables (V_i), plus one. These authors repeated Fox and Miura's 96-dof space truss example, with the basis vectors of Eqs. (144) and (146), and obtained a substantial increase in accuracy. In this example, the subspace dimension was again set equal to q = 5 by considering r = 4 design variables.

Eigenvectors of the unmodified system's stiffness matrix are utilized as RB method basis vectors in the paper by Sobieszczanski and Hajela [31]. This procedure provides a set of linearly independent, orthogonal vectors and also provides guidelines for determining how many and which eigenvectors should be included as basis vectors. The eigenvectors of $\underline{K}_o$ are computed from

$$(\lambda_i \underline{I} - \underline{K}_o)\underline{q}_i = \underline{0} \qquad (N\text{x}1) \tag{147}$$

The basis vectors are then initially selected as

$$\underline{\Phi} = [\underline{\rho}_1 \vdots \underline{\rho}_2 \vdots --- \vdots \underline{\rho}_m] = [\underline{q}_1 \vdots \underline{q}_2 \vdots --- \vdots \underline{q}_m] \qquad (N\text{x}m) \tag{148}$$

The exact solution of the unmodified system is obtained from

$$\underline{K}_o \underline{X}_j = \underline{F}_j \qquad j = 1,2,\ldots p \qquad (N\text{x}1) \tag{149}$$

where $\underline{F}_j$ = is the jth external load vector of interest.

The selection criterion for the number of modes (m) to utilize as basis vectors in the RB subspace is based on the contribution of this set of modes to the total internal strain energy of the original system. In addition, examination of the relative strain energy contributions between modes in this set (q_1 $q_2 \ldots q_m$) reveals which modes are of little importance and may therefore be disregarded.

The exact, total internal strain energy of the original system, subjected to load vector $\underline{F}_j$, is expressed by

$$S_{jo} = \frac{1}{2}\underline{X}_j^T \underline{K}_o \underline{X}_j = \frac{1}{2}\underline{X}_j^T \underline{F}_j \tag{150}$$

Consider a solution of the original system, $\tilde{\underline{Y}}_{jo}$, obtained by employing the RB method with the first m eigenmodes of $\underline{K}_o$

$$\tilde{\underline{K}}_o \underline{H}_{jo} = \tilde{\underline{F}}_j \qquad \text{mx}1 \tag{151}$$

where

$$\tilde{\underline{K}}_o = \underline{\Phi}^T \underline{K}_o \underline{\Phi} \qquad m \times m \tag{152}$$

$$\tilde{\underline{F}}_j = \underline{\Phi}^T \underline{F}_j \qquad m \times 1 \tag{153}$$

$$\tilde{\underline{Y}}_{jo} = \underline{\Phi} \underline{H}_{jo} \qquad N \times 1 \tag{154}$$

The strain energy of the original system with the approximate RB method displacement vector is expressed as

$$\tilde{S}_{jo} = \frac{1}{2} \tilde{\underline{Y}}_{jo}^T \underline{K}_o \tilde{\underline{Y}}_{jo} = \frac{1}{2} \underline{H}_{jo}^T \underline{\Phi}^T \underline{K}_o \underline{\Phi} \underline{H}_{jo}$$

$$= \frac{1}{2} \sum_{n=1}^{m} (h_{jo}^{(n)})^2 \underline{q}_n^T \underline{K}_o \underline{q}_n \tag{155}$$

Equation (155) is derived by using the orthogonality relationships

$$\underline{q}_i^T \underline{q}_j = \delta_{ij} \tag{156}$$

$$\underline{q}_i^T \underline{K}_o \underline{q}_j = \delta_{ij} \lambda_j \tag{157}$$

An alternate expression for $\tilde{S}_{jo}$ is

$$\tilde{S}_{jo} = \frac{1}{2} \underline{H}_{jo}^T \tilde{\underline{K}}_o \underline{H}_{jo} = \frac{1}{2} \underline{H}_{jo}^T \tilde{\underline{F}}_j$$

$$= \frac{1}{2} \sum_{n=1}^{m} h_{jo}^{(n)} \underline{q}_n^T \underline{F}_j \tag{158}$$

A quantitative measure of whether the lowest m eigenmodes of $\underline{K}_o$ are sufficient basis vectors in the RB reanalysis is if

$$(S_{jo} - \tilde{S}_{jo})/S_{jo} \leq \delta_1 \tag{159}$$

for all load vectors $\underline{F}_j$, j = 1,2,...p. The constant δ_1 is selected so that $\delta_1 \ll 1$.

Sobieszczanski and Hajela also implement a second criterion to discard the modes among the lowest m which do not contribute significantly to S_{jo}. This further reduces the dimension of the subspace, and in turn the number of simultaneous linear equations in the RB reanalysis. Define

$$\tilde{S}'_{jo} = \frac{1}{2} \sum_{n=1}^{r} [h_{jo}^{(\ell_n)}]^2 \, \underline{q}_{\ell_n}^T \, \underline{K}_o \, \underline{q}_{\ell_n} = \frac{1}{2} \sum_{n=1}^{r} h_{jo}^{(\ell_n)} \, \underline{q}_{\ell_n}^T \, \underline{F}_j \tag{160}$$

where

$$\mathcal{L} = (\ell_1 \quad \ell_2 \ldots \ell_r) \tag{161}$$

Set $\mathcal{L}$ contains r integers which form a subset of $\mathcal{M} = (1 \quad 2 \quad 3 \ldots m)$. By comparison of Eqs.(160,161) to Eqs. (155,158), S_{jo} is the portion of the internal strain energy of the original system contained in the eigenmodes of $\mathcal{L}$. The second criterion for selection of the eigenmodes is then

$$(\tilde{S}_{jo} - \tilde{S}'_{jo})/\tilde{S}_{jo} \leq \delta_2 << 1 \tag{162}$$

for all load vectors $\underline{F}_j$, j = 1,.2,...p. The selection of the integer set $\mathcal{L}$ is obviously facilitated by plotting the contribution of each mode in $\mathcal{M}$, i.e.,

$$S_{jo}^{(n)} = \frac{1}{2} (h_{jo}^{(n)})^2 \, \underline{q}_n^T \, \underline{K}_o \, \underline{q}_n = \frac{1}{2} h_{jo}^{(n)} \, \underline{q}_n^T \, \underline{F}_j \tag{163}$$

$$n = 1,2,\ldots m \text{ and } j = 1,2,\ldots p$$

versus the total internal strain energy of the original system.

Both criteria, Eqs. (159) and (162), must be simultaneously satisfied for all load cases, $\underline{F}_j$, j = 1,2,...p. The final set of basis vectors to use in the RB static reanalysis of modified systems are then

$$\underline{\Phi} = [\underline{q}_{\ell_1} \vdots \underline{q}_{\ell_2} \ldots \vdots \underline{q}_{\ell_r}] \qquad (N\text{x}r) \tag{164}$$

Reanalysis of the modified system, represented by $\underline{K}$, proceeds as in Eq. (144), i.e.,

$$\tilde{\underline{K}} = \underline{\Phi}^T \, \underline{K} \, \underline{\Phi} \qquad (r\text{x}r) \tag{165}$$

$$\tilde{\underline{F}}_j = \underline{\Phi}^T \, \underline{F}_j \qquad (r\text{x}1) \tag{166}$$

$$\tilde{\underline{K}} \, \underline{H}_j = \tilde{\underline{F}} \qquad (r\text{x}1) \tag{167}$$

$$\tilde{\underline{Y}}_j = \underline{\Phi} \, \underline{H}_j \qquad (N\text{x}1) \tag{168}$$

The formation of K for each trial design may require a considerabble amount of numerical computation, by the definition in Eq. (165). These authors propose to evaluate K with a perturbation technique described by

$$\tilde{\underline{K}} = \tilde{\underline{K}}_o + \sum_{i=1}^{q} \frac{\partial \underline{K}}{\partial V_i} \Delta V_i \tag{169}$$

$$\frac{\partial \tilde{\underline{K}}}{\partial V_i} = \Phi^T \frac{\partial \tilde{\underline{K}}}{\partial V_i} \Phi \tag{170}$$

where V_i are design variables and the symbol "0" indicates evaluation for the original system.

The three numerical examples considered include a 270-dof trapezoidal wing, a 444 dof arrow wing, and a 490 dof fuselage. The corresponding subspace dimensions are respectively r = 5, r = 7, and r = 17. These examples demonstrate the excellent accuracy obtained by utilizing this approach to RB static reanalysis. Numerical efficiency of the RB method is shown to increase as the number of modification cases increase. A minimum of 4 to 6 cases must be performed before the RB method becomes more efficient than an exact solution approach. This number is frequently exceeded for optimization and nonlinear problems.

Iterative Methods (IM)

This approach to approximate static reanalysis may be explained by examining a standard iterative technique for solving systems of linear equations, i.e.,

$$\underline{A}\,\underline{X} = \underline{b} \tag{171}$$

The Jacobi approach [32] decomposes $\underline{A}$ into the form

$$\underline{A} = \underline{L} + \underline{D} + \underline{u} \tag{172}$$

in which

$$\underline{D} = \underline{\text{diag}}\ (A_{jj}) \tag{173}$$

and

$$\underline{L} + \underline{u} = \underline{A} - \underline{D} \tag{174}$$

Substitute Eq. (172) into (171) and premultiply by $\underline{D}$-1

$$(\underline{I} + \underline{D}^{-1} [\underline{L} + \underline{u}])\underline{X} = \underline{D}^{-1} \underline{b} \tag{175}$$

or

$$\underline{X} = (\underline{I} + \underline{D}^{-1} [\underline{L} + \underline{u}])^{-1} \underline{D}^{-1} \underline{b} \tag{176}$$

Consider the infinite series representation

$$(\underline{I} + \underline{B})^{-1} = \underline{I} - \underline{B} + \underline{B}^2 - \underline{B}^3 + \underline{B}^4 - + \ldots \tag{177}$$

A necessary and sufficient condition for this series to converge is that the spectral radius of $\underline{B}$ be less than unity [23, pg. 155] i.e.,

$$|\lambda_i(\underline{B})| < 1 \qquad i \in (1,2,\ldots N) \tag{178}$$

where $\lambda_i(B)$ are the eigenvalues of the NxN matrix B.

Comparison of Eqs. (176) and (177) implies

$$\underline{X} = [\underline{I} - \underline{D}^{-1}(\underline{L} + \underline{u}) + \{\underline{D}^{-1}(\underline{L} + \underline{u})\}^2 - + \ldots]\underline{D}^{-1} \underline{b} \tag{179}$$

This series converges if and only if

$$|\lambda_i[\underline{D}^{-1}(\underline{L} + \underline{u})]| < 1 \qquad i \in (1,2,\ldots N) \tag{180}$$

The Jacobi iterative solution generates Eq. (177) via the recursion formula

$$\underline{X}_{(i+1)} = -\underline{D}^{-1}(\underline{L} + \underline{u})\underline{X}_{(i)} + \underline{D}^{-1} \underline{b} \tag{181}$$

$$\underline{X}_{(o)} = \underline{b} \qquad \text{(arbitrary)} \tag{182}$$

In order to see that Eq. (181) does yield (179), consider the first several iterations

$$\underline{X}_{(1)} = [\underline{I} - \underline{D}^{-1}(\underline{L} + \underline{u})\underline{D}]\underline{D}^{-1}\underline{b}$$

$$\underline{X}_{(2)} = [\underline{I} - \{\underline{D}^{-1}(\underline{L} + \underline{u})\} + \{\underline{D}^{-1}(\underline{L} + \underline{u})\}^2\underline{D}]\ \underline{D}^{-1}\ \underline{b} \tag{183}$$

$$\underline{X}_{(3)} = [\underline{I} - \{\underline{D}^{-1}(\underline{L} + \underline{u})\} + \{\underline{D}^{-1}(\underline{L} + \underline{u})\}^2$$

$$- \{\underline{D}^{-1}(\underline{L} + \underline{u})\}^3\underline{D}]\underline{D}^{-1}\underline{b}$$

The reanalysis equations are

$$\underline{K}_o \underline{X} = \underline{F}$$

$$(\underline{K}_o + \Delta\underline{K})\underline{Y} = \underline{F} \tag{184}$$

From Eqs. (181) and (182) the Jacobi approximate static reanalysis technique [33] becomes

$$\underline{Y}_{(i+1)} = -\underline{\text{diag}}(\beta_j^{-1})[\underline{K}_o + \Delta\underline{K} - \underline{\text{diag}}(\beta_i)]Y$$

$$+ \underline{\text{diag}}(\beta_j^{-1})\underline{F} \tag{185}$$

where

$$\beta_j = (\underline{K}_o + \Delta\underline{K})_{jj} \tag{186}$$

$$\underline{Y}_{(o)} = \underline{F} \tag{187}$$

Kirsch and Rubinstein [33] have developed a generalized iterative approach to static structural reanalysis by considering the equations

$$\underline{K}_o \underline{X} = \underline{F}$$

$$(\underline{K}_o + \underline{G} - \underline{G} + \Delta\underline{K})\underline{Y} = \underline{F} \qquad (N\text{x}1) \tag{188}$$

The matrix $\underline{G}$ is chosen to accelerate convergence of the iteration. As with Eq. (175), premultiplication of Eq. (188) by

$$(\underline{K}_o + \underline{G})^{-1} = (\underline{I}_N + \underline{K}_o^{-1} \underline{G})^{-1} \underline{K}_o^{-1} \tag{189}$$

yields

$$[\underline{I}_N - (\underline{I}_N + \underline{K}_o^{-1} \underline{G})^{-1}(\underline{K}_o^{-1} \underline{G} - \underline{K}_o^{-1} \Delta\underline{K})]\underline{Y} = (\underline{I}_N + \underline{K}_o^{-1} \underline{G})^{-1} \underline{X} \tag{190}$$

By employing Eq. (177), the series solution of (190) becomes

$$\underline{Y} = \underline{A}\{\underline{I}_N + \underline{C}\,\underline{A} + (\underline{C}\,\underline{A})^2 + (\underline{C}\,\underline{A})^3 + \ldots\}\underline{X} \tag{191}$$

where

$$\underline{A} = (\underline{I}_N + \underline{K}_o^{-1} \underline{G})^{-1} \tag{192}$$

$$\underline{C} = (\underline{K}_o^{-1} \underline{G} - \underline{K}_o^{-1} \Delta\underline{K}) \tag{193}$$

This series representation of $\underline{Y}$ converges if and only if

$$|\lambda_i(\underline{A}\ \underline{C})| < 1 \qquad i \in (1,2,\ldots N) \tag{194}$$

The series in Eq. (191) may be generated by the recursion formulas

$$(\underline{K}_o + \underline{G})\underline{Y}_{(i+1)} = \underline{F} - (\Delta\underline{K} - \underline{G})\underline{Y}_{(i)} \tag{195}$$

$$\underline{Y}_{(o)} = \underline{X}$$

Equations (195) then comprise the iterative solution of Eq. (188).

The first case considered by these authros [33] is referred to as the "simple iteration method." In this case, $\underline{G} = 0$ and the iteration formula becomes

$$\underline{K}_o\ \underline{Y}_{(i+1)} = \underline{F} - \Delta\underline{K}\ \underline{Y}_{(i)} \tag{196}$$

$$\underline{Y}_{(o)} = \underline{X} \tag{197}$$

This formula will converge if and only if

$$|\lambda_i(\underline{K}_o^{-1}\ \Delta\underline{K})| < 1 \qquad i \in (1,2,\ldots N) \tag{198}$$

It is assumed here that the triangular factors of $\underline{K}_o$ are available from the unmodified system solution, hence, computation for each $\underline{Y}_{(i)}$ requires only a forward and back substitution. This method of iterative reanalysis was also proposed in the paper by Kaulie and Powell [13].

A second case examined is called the "improved vector iteration" method [33]. Set the matrix $\underline{G}$ equal to

$$\underline{G} = \underline{K}_o\ \underline{B}_d \tag{199}$$

where B_d is a diagonal matrix with a principal diagonal defined by

$$(\underline{B}_d)_{jj} = (\underline{K}_o^{-1}\ \Delta\underline{K})_{jj} \tag{200}$$

The recursion formula is obtained by substituting Eq. (199) into (195) and premultiplying by $\underline{K}_o^{-1}$

$$\underline{Y}_{(i+1)} = (\underline{I} + \underline{B}_d)^{-1}\{\underline{X} + (B_d - \underline{K}_o^{-1}\underline{\Delta K})\underline{Y}_{(i)}\} \tag{201}$$

$$\underline{Y}_{(o)} = \underline{X}$$

Although the inversion of the diagonal matrix $(\underline{I} + \underline{B}_d)$ is trivial, the computation of $\underline{B}_d$ necessitates additional numerical computations. Phansalkar [34] shows that $\underline{B}_d$ can be calculated by inverting the Cholesky factor of $\underline{K}_o$.

Improved vector iteration can be shown to be a form of Jacobi iteration. The modified system is defined as

$$(\underline{K}_o + \Delta\underline{K})\underline{Y} = \underline{F}$$

or

$$(\underline{I} + \underline{K}_o^{-1} \Delta\underline{K})\underline{Y} = \underline{X}$$

Compare this equation with Eq. (171)

$$\underline{A} \rightarrow \underline{I} + \underline{K}_o^{-1} \Delta\underline{K}$$

$$\underline{X} \rightarrow \underline{Y}$$

$$\underline{b} \rightarrow \underline{X}$$

$$\underline{D} \rightarrow \underline{I} + \underline{B}_d$$

$$\underline{L} + \underline{u} = \underline{A} - \underline{D} \rightarrow \underline{K}_o^{-1} \Delta\underline{K} - \underline{B}_d$$

Substitute these expressions into Eq. (181)

$$\underline{Y}_{(i+1)} = (\underline{I} + \underline{B}_d)^{-1}\{\underline{X} + (\underline{B}_d - \underline{K}_o^{-1} \Delta\underline{K})\underline{Y}_{(i)}\}$$

This result is identical to Eq. (201).

A third case examined by Kirsch and Rubinstein [33] is called "separate iteration of components." The matrix $\underline{G}$ is set equal to

$$\underline{G} = \alpha \underline{K}_o \tag{202}$$

Substitute Eq. (202) into Eqs. (191), (192), and (193)

$$\underline{Y} = (1 + \alpha)^{-1}\{\underline{I}_N + [(1 + \alpha)^{-1}(\alpha\ \underline{I}_N - \underline{K}_o^{-1}\ \Delta K)]$$

$$+ [(1 + \alpha)^{-1}(\alpha\ \underline{I}_N - \underline{K}_o^{-1}\ \Delta\underline{K})]^2 + \ldots\}\underline{X} \tag{203}$$

From Eq. (194), this series will converge if and only if

$$|\lambda_i\ ([1 + \alpha]^{-1}[\alpha\ \underline{I}_N - \underline{K}_o^{-1}\ \Delta\underline{K}])| < 1, \qquad i \in (1,2,\ldots N) \tag{204}$$

Equation (203) may be rewritten as

$$\underline{Y} = (1 + \alpha)^{-1}\{\underline{X} + (1 + \alpha)^{-1}(\alpha\ \underline{X} - \underline{T}_1)$$

$$+ (1 + \alpha)^{-2}(\alpha^2\ \underline{X} - 2\alpha\ \underline{T}_1 + \underline{T}_2)$$

$$+ (1 + \alpha)^{-3}(\alpha^3\ \underline{X} - 3\alpha^2\ \underline{T}_1 + 3\alpha\ \underline{T}_2 - \underline{T}_3)\ldots\} \tag{205}$$

where

$$\underline{T}_1 = \underline{K}_o^{-1}\ \Delta\underline{K}\ \underline{X} \qquad \text{or} \qquad \underline{K}_o\ \underline{T}_1 = \Delta\underline{K}\ \underline{X}$$

$$\underline{T}_2 = (\underline{K}_o^{-1}\ \Delta\underline{K})^2\underline{X} \qquad \text{or} \qquad \underline{K}_o\ \underline{T}_2 = \Delta\underline{K}\ \underline{T}_1 \tag{206}$$

$$\underline{T}_3 = (\underline{K}_o^{-1}\ \Delta\underline{K})^3\underline{X} \qquad \text{or} \qquad \underline{K}_o\ \underline{T}_3 = \Delta\underline{K}\ \underline{T}_2$$

The N-vectors $\underline{T}_1$, $\underline{T}_2$, and $\underline{T}_3$ are each calculated with only a single forward and back substitution when K_o has already been decomposed into triangular factors, from the solution to the original system. From Eq. (205), the jth component of the modified system's displacement vector is

$$Y_j = (1 + \alpha)^{-2}\{X_j + (1 + \alpha)^{-1}(\alpha\ X_j - T_{1j})$$

$$+ (1 + \alpha)^{-2}(\alpha^2\ X_j - 2\alpha\ T_{1j} + T_{2j})$$

$$+ (1 + \alpha)^{-3}(\alpha^3\ X_j - 3\alpha^2\ T_{1j} + 3\alpha\ T_{2j} - T_{3j})\ldots\} \tag{207}$$

Each displacement component, Y_j, will converge at a different rate, depending on the value of α in Eq. (207). Since α is an arbitrary constant it may be chosen independently for each Y_j, i.e., α_j. These authors choose α_j so as to eliminate the second term in the series of Eq. (207).

$$\alpha_j = \frac{T_{1j}}{X_j} \tag{208}$$

Substitute (208) into (207)

$$Y_j = X_j^2 (X_j + T_{1j})^{-3} \{ (X_j + T_{1j})^2 + (-T_{1j}^2 + T_{2j} X_j) - (X_j + T_{1j})^{-1} (X_j^2 T_{3j} - 3X_j T_{1j} T_{2j} + 2T_{1j}^3) \ldots \} \tag{209}$$

One and two term solutions are defined from this series by

$$Y_j = \frac{X_j^2}{X_j + T_{1j}} \quad \text{(one term)} \tag{210}$$

$$Y_j = \frac{X_j^3 (X_j + 2T_{1j} + T_{2j})}{(X_j + T_{ij})^3} \quad \text{(two term)} \tag{211}$$

The "separate iteration of components" approach is shown to be applicable also to the original system solution. Expressions corresponding to Eqs. (210) and (211) are

$$X_j = \frac{F_j^2}{\tilde{\underline{K}}_{oj} \; \underline{F}} \quad \text{(one term)} \tag{212}$$

$$X_j = \frac{F_j^3 (\tilde{\underline{K}}_{oj} \underline{K}_o \underline{F})}{(\tilde{\underline{K}}_{oj} \underline{F})^3} \quad \text{(two term)} \tag{213}$$

where

$\tilde{\underline{K}}_{oj}$ = jth row vector of $\underline{K}_o$

X_j = jth component of $\underline{X}$

Formulas (209-213) comprise a complete approximate solution procedure providing a means for computing both the original and modified system displacements.

These authors [33] consider two numerical examples utilizing the same structure, a 5 element, 4 dof Euler-Bernoulli beam model, in each. Modifications consist of alterations to the cross-sectional area moments of inertia in each element. The results show (1) very poor or no convergence with the simple iteration method, equations (196,197), (2) good convergence characteristics with the improved vector iteration method, Eq. (201), and (3) excellent results when utilizing the separate iteration of components method, Eq. (210,211).

Noor [30] has combined the simple iteration method, Eq. (196), with the Taylor series method, Eq. (122). This combined Taylor - iterative technique computes the initial-guess vector

$$\underline{Y}_{(o)} = \underline{X} + \sum_{i=1}^{q} \left. \frac{\partial Y}{\partial V_i} \right|_{o} \Delta V_i \tag{214}$$

with Eqs. (122) and (123) and then employs Eq. (196)

$$\underline{K}_o \, \underline{Y}_{(i+1)} = \underline{F} - \Delta\underline{K} \, \underline{Y}_{(i)} \tag{215}$$

Noor reports a significant improvement in accuracy obtained by this combined approach.

Phansalkar [34] has presented an excellent summary of iterative static reanalysis methods, including simple and Jacobi iterations. he has also examined the use of point and block Guass-Seidel iteration for static reanalysis.

Summary of Reanalysis Methods

The various exact and approximate reanalysis methods in static reanalysis are summarized in Tables 2 and 3, respectively. For each, five modified-inverse approaches and five modified-displacement approaches are summarized. These equations, along with detailed definitions of the nomenclature defined in appropriate equations of this paper can be used as a standing point for the implementation of reanalysis methods. Additionally, sources of the various methods are indicated for further references.

Choice of a Reanalysis Method

The choice of a reanalysis method depends on the need for accuracy and efficiency. When using the exact method, the accuracy is, theoretically, the same as that of the direct solution. In this case, the decision to employ reanalysis depends solely on whether it is more efficient than a direct solution. According to Argyris [15], if the number of dof connected to the modification is less than 0.75B, where B is the bandwidth of the system, the exact reanalysis method will be more efficient.

When the modification is connected to more dof than 0.75B, then either a direct solution or an approximate method should be used from the standpoint of efficiency. For the approximate method, it would be advisable to frequently update the "original" system solution to ensure the accuracy of the subsequent approximate solutions.

Table 2 Exact Methods of Static Reanalysis

General: $K_0 X = F$, $KY = (K_0 + \Delta K) Y = F$, $G = K_0^{-1}$

	Reference		
MODIFIED INVERSE	Sack [12]	$K = K_0 + \Delta K = K_0 + \sum_{\ell=1}^{P} \Delta K_{j_\ell} e_{j_\ell}^T$, $K^0 = K_0$, $K^P = K$, $Y = K^{-1} F$ $(K^i)^{-1} = (K^{i-1})^{-1} - [(K^{i-1})^{-1} \Delta K_{j_i}][e_{j_i}^T (K^{i-1})^{-1}]/(1 + e_{j_i}^T (K^{i-1})^{-1} \Delta K_{j_i})$	Column Modifications (21-26)
	Kirsch [16]	$K^{-1} = K_0^{-1} - K_{ab}^{-1} \Delta K_{abj} (K_j^{-1})^T / (1 + (K_{abj}^{-1})^T \Delta K_{abj})$, $Y = K^{-1} F$	Column Modifications (68)
	Kirsch [16]	$K^{-1} = K_0^{-1} - K_i^{-1} (K_j^{-1})^T / (\Delta K_{ij}^{-1} + (K)_{ij}^{-1})$, $Y = K^{-1} F$	Element Modifications (67)
	Przemieniecki [14], Kosko [17]	$K^{-1} = G - \begin{bmatrix} G_{11} \\ G_{21} \end{bmatrix} (I_p + \Delta K_{11} G_{11})^{-1} \Delta K_{11} [G_{11} \vdots G_{12}]$, $\Delta K_{11} = (\Delta K) \begin{pmatrix} 1 & 2 \ldots P \\ 1 & 2 \ldots P \end{pmatrix}$, $Y = K^{-1} F$	Submatrix Modification (35)
	Kirsch [16]	$K^{-1} = K_0^{-1} - K_{ab}^{-1} (\Delta \hat{K}^{-1} + K_{abcd}^{-1})^{-1} K_{cd}^{-1}$, $Y = K^{-1} F$	Submatrix Modification (60-66)
MODIFIED DISPLACEMENT	Kavlie and Powell [13]	$K = K_0 + \Delta K = K_0 + \sum_{\ell=1}^{P} \Delta K_{j_\ell} e_{j_\ell}^T$, $Y_i = Y_{i-1} - W_i^{i-1} e_{j_i}^T Y_{i-1} / (1 + e_{j_i}^T W_i^{i-1})$ $Y_0 = X$, $Y = Y_p$, $W_i^k = W_i^{k-1} - W_k^{k-1} W_i^{k-1} / (1 + e_{j_k}^T W_k^{k-1})$, $K_0 W_i^0 = \Delta K_{j_i}$	Column Modification (27-32)
	Argyris [15], [20]	$\Delta \hat{K} = (\Delta K) \begin{pmatrix} j_1 & j_2 \ldots j_p \\ j_1 & j_2 \ldots j_p \end{pmatrix}$, $r = \Delta \hat{K} \hat{X}$, $L_{Qk} L_{Qk}^T r' = r$ $L_Q L_Q^T r'' = r'$, $r''' = -Z r''$, $L_k^T (Y - X) = r'''$, $K_0 = L_k L_k^T$	Submatrix Modification (51-55), (81-89)
	Kirsch [16]	$Y = X - K_{ab}^{-1} (\Delta \hat{K}^{-1} + K_{abcd}^{-1})^{-1} X_{cd}$	Submatrix Modification (70)
	McQuire [18], Martin [19], Kirsch [16]	$Y = \begin{bmatrix} Y_1 \\ Y_2 \end{bmatrix} = \begin{bmatrix} (I_p + G_{11} \Delta \hat{K})^{-1} X_1 \\ X_2 - G_{21} \Delta \hat{K} (I_p + G_{11} \Delta \hat{K})^{-1} X_1 \end{bmatrix}$	Submatrix Modification (79)
	Present Authors	$(I_p + G_{11} \Delta \hat{K}) Y_1 = X_1 + G_1^* \Delta F^*$, $Y_2 = X_2 - G_{21} \Delta \hat{K} Y_1 + G_2^* \Delta F^*$	Submatrix Modification (100-101)

Table 3 Approximate Methods of Static Reanalysis

General: $\underline{K}_0\underline{X} = \underline{F}$, $\underline{K}\underline{Y} = (\underline{K}_0 + \Delta\underline{K})\underline{Y} = \underline{F}$

	Reference	Description	(Equation Numbers)
TAYLOR SERIES	Storasli, Sobieszczanski [24,25],	$\underline{Y} = \underline{X} + \sum_{i=1}^{8} \frac{\partial \underline{Y}}{\partial V_i}\Big\vert_{\mathbf{o}} \Delta V_i + \frac{1}{2}\sum_{i=1}^{8}\sum_{j=1}^{8} \frac{\partial \underline{Y}}{\partial V_i \partial V_j}\Big\vert_{\mathbf{o}} \Delta V_i \Delta V_j$ + higher order terms — Displacement Formulation	(122-124)
	Noor [26]	$\underline{K}\frac{\partial \underline{Y}}{\partial V_i}\Big\vert_o = -\frac{\partial \underline{K}}{\partial V_i}\Big\vert_o \underline{X}, \quad \underline{K}\frac{\partial^2 \underline{Y}}{\partial V_i \partial V_j}\Big\vert_o = -\frac{\partial^2 \underline{K}}{\partial V_i \partial V_j}\Big\vert_0 \underline{X} + \frac{\partial \underline{K}}{\partial V_i}\Big\vert_o \frac{\partial \underline{Y}}{\partial V_j}\Big\vert_o + \frac{\partial \underline{K}}{\partial V_j}\Big\vert_o \frac{\partial \underline{Y}}{\partial V_i}\Big\vert_o$ — Mixed Formulation	(125-126
	Romstad	$\underline{K} = \underline{K}_o + \varepsilon \underline{K}_1, \quad \underline{F} = \underline{F}_o + \varepsilon \underline{F}_1, \quad \underline{Y} = \underline{X} + \sum_{i=1}^{\infty} \varepsilon^i \underline{Y}_i$ $\underline{K}_o \underline{Y}_1 = \underline{F}_1 - \underline{K}_1\underline{X}, \quad \underline{K}_o \underline{Y}_i = -\underline{K}_1\underline{Y}_{i-1}, \quad i = 1,2,3...$ Taylor Series-Iteration	(124-134)
REDUCED BASIS	General	$\tilde{\underline{Y}} = \sum_{i=1}^{r} h_i \underline{\phi}_i = \underline{\Phi}\,\underline{H}, \quad r << N, \quad \frac{\partial \vec{E}}{\partial h_i} = 0 \rightarrow \tilde{\underline{K}}\,\underline{H} = \tilde{\underline{F}}, \quad \tilde{\underline{K}} = \underline{\Phi}^T \underline{K}\,\underline{\Phi}, \quad \tilde{\underline{F}} = \underline{\Phi}^T \underline{F}$	
	Fox [29]	$\underline{\phi}_i$ = "basic or typical" design displacement vectors	(135-144)
	Noor [30]	$\underline{\phi}_1 = \underline{X}, \quad \underline{\phi}_{i+1} = \frac{\partial \underline{Y}}{\partial V_i}\Big\vert_o, \quad i = 1,2,...8$	(145-146)
	Sobieszczanski [31]	$(\lambda_i \underline{I} - \underline{K}_o)\underline{\phi}_i = \underline{0}, \quad (S_{jo} - \tilde{S}_{jo})/S_{jo} \leq \delta_1, \quad (\tilde{S}_{jo} - \tilde{S}'_{jo})/S_{jo} < \delta_2$	(147-170)
ITERATIVE	Kirsch and Rubenstein [33]	$\underline{Y}_{(i+1)} = -\underline{diag}(\beta_j^{-1})[\underline{K}_o + \Delta\underline{K} - \underline{diag}(\beta_j)]\underline{Y}_{(i)} + \underline{diag}(\beta_j^{-1})\underline{F}, \quad \underline{Y}_{(o)} = \underline{F}, \quad \beta_j = (\underline{K}_o + \Delta\underline{K})_{jj}$ Jacobi Iteration	(184-187)
		$\underline{K}_o \underline{Y}_{(i+1)} = \underline{F} - \Delta\underline{K}\,\underline{Y}_{(i)}, \quad \underline{Y}_{(o)} = \underline{X}$ Simple Iteration	(196-197)
		$\underline{Y}_{(i+1)} = (\underline{I} + \underline{B}_d)^{-1}\{\underline{X} + \underline{B}_d - \underline{K}_o^{-1}\,\Delta\underline{K})\underline{Y}_{(i)}\}, \quad \underline{Y}_{(o)} = \underline{X}$ Improved Vector Iteration	(201)
		$Y_j = X_j^2(X_j + T_{1j})^{-3}\{(X_j + T_{1j})^2 + (-T_{1j}^2 + T_{2j}X_j) - (X_j + T_{1j})^{-1}(X_j^2 T_{3j} - 3X_j T_{1j} T_{2j} + 2T_{ij}^3)...\}$ Separate Iteration of Components $\underline{K}_o\underline{T}_1 = \Delta\underline{K}\,\underline{X}, \quad \underline{K}_o\underline{T}_2 = \Delta\underline{K}\,\underline{T}_1, \quad \underline{K}_o\underline{T}_3 = \Delta\underline{K}\,\underline{T}_2$	(209)
	Noor [30]	$\underline{K}_o\underline{Y}_{(i+1)} = \underline{F} - \Delta\underline{K}\,\underline{Y}_{(i)}, \quad \underline{Y}_{(o)} = \underline{X} + \sum_{i=1}^{8} \frac{\partial \underline{Y}}{\partial V_i}\Big\vert_o \Delta V_i$ Combined Taylor Series Iteration	**(214-215)**

REFERENCES

1 Sherman, J., and Morrison, W. J., "Adjustment of An Inverse Matrix Corresponding to Changes in the Elements of A Given Column or a Given Row of the Original Matrix," Ann. Math. Stat., Vol. 20, 1949, p. 621.

2 Sherman, J., and Morrison, W. J., "Adjustment of An Inverse Matrix Corresponding to a Change in One Element of a Given Matrix," Ann. Math. Stat., Vol. 21, 1950, pp. 124-127.

3 Woodbury, M., "Inverting Modified Matrices," Memorandum Report 42, S.R.G., Princeton, 1950.

4 Bartlett, M. S., "An Inverse Matrix Adjustment Arising in Discriminant Analysis," Ann. Math. Stat., Vol. 22, 1951, pp. 107-111.

5 Householder, A. S., Principles of Numerical Analysis, McGraw Hill, 1953, p. 79.

6 Householder, A. S., "A Survey of Some Closed Methods for Inverting Matrices," SIAM Journ., Vol. 5, No. 3, Sept. 1957, pp. 155-169.

7 Bennett, J. M., "Triangular Factors of Modified Matrices," Numerische Mathematik, Vol. 7, 1965, pp. 217-225.

8 Vanderbilt, M. D., Matrix Structural Analysis, Quantum Publishers, Inc., 1974, Ch. 4 and 7.

9 Pipes, L. A., Matrix Methods for Engineering, Prentice Hall, Englewood Cliffs, New Jersey, 1963, Ch. 6.

10 Melosh, R. J., and Luik, R., "Multiple Configuration Analysis of Structures," ASCE Journal of the Structural Division, ST11, Nov. 1968, pp. 2581-2596.

11 Fenves, S. T., and Erias, R., "Multiple Configuration Analysis of Structures," ASCE Journ. Struct. Div., Vol. 95, No. ST7, July 1969, pp. 1586-15 .

12 Sack, R. L., Carpenter, W. C., and Hatch, G. L., "Modification of Elements in the Displacement Method," AIAA Journ., Vol. 5, No. 9, Sept. 1967, pp. 1708-17 .

13 Kaulie, D., and Powell, G. H., "Efficient Reanalysis of Modified Structures," ASCE Journ. Struc. Div., Vol. 97, No. ST1, Jan. 1971, pp. 377-39 .

14 Przemieniecki, J. S., Theory of Matrix Structural Analysis, McGraw Hill, 1968, pp. 426-427.

15 Argyris, J. H., Bronlund, O. E., Roy, J. R., and Scharpf, D. W., "A Direct Modification Procedure for the Displacement Method," AIAA Journal, Vol. 9, No. 9, Sept. 1971, pp. 1861-1864.

16 Kirch, U., and Rubinstein, M. F., "Reanalysis for Limited Structural Design Modifications," ASCE Journ. of the Engr. Mech. Div., Vol. 98, No. EM1, Feb. 1972, pp. 61-70.

17 Kosko, E., "Effect of Local Modifications in Redundant Structures," Journ. of the Aero. Sciences, March 1954, pp. 206-207.

18 McQuire, W., and Gallagher, R. H., Matrix Structural Analysis, 1st ed., John Wiley and Sons, 1979, p. 348.

19 Martin, H. C., Introduction to Matrix Methods of Structural Analysis, 1st ed., McGraw Hill, 1966, p. 182.

20 Argyris, J. H., and Roy, J. R., "General Treatment of Structural Modifications," ASCE Journ. of the Struct. Div., Vol. 98, No. ST2, Feb. 1972, p. 465-492.

21 Fox, L., An Introduction to Numerical Linear Algebra, 1st ed., Oxford University Press, New York, 1965.

22 Franklin, J. N., Matrix Theory, 1st ed., Prentice Hall, Englewood Cliffs, New Jersey, 1968.

23 Brogan, W. L., Modern Control Theory, 1st ed., Quantum Publishers, Inc., New York, N.Y., 1974.

24 Storaasli, O. O., and Sobieszczanski, J., "On the Accuracy of the Taylor Approximation for Structure Resizing," AIAA Journal, Vol. 12, No. 2, Feb. 1974, pp. 231-233.

25 Storaasli, O. O., and Sobieszczanski, J., "Design Oriented Structural Analysis," AIAA/ASME SAE 14th Struc., Struc. Dyn., and Materials Conference, Williamsburg, Va., March 20-22, 1973.

26 Noor, A., "Multiple Configuration Analysis Via Mixed Methods," ASCE Journal of the Structural Division, ST9, Sept. 1974, pp. 1991-1997.

27 Romstad, K. M., Hutchinson, J. R., and Runge, K. A., "Design Parameter Variation and Structural Responses," Int. Journal Num. Meth. in Engr., Vol. 5, 1973, pp. 337-34 .

28 Desai, C. S., and Abel, J. F., Introduction to the Finite Element Method, 1st ed., Van Nostrand Reinhold, 1972.

29 Fox, R. L., and Miura, H., "An Approximate Analysis Technique for Design Calculations," AIAA Journal, Vol. 9, No. 1, Jan. 1971, pp. 177-179.

30 Noor, A. K., and Lowder, H. E., "Approximate Techniques of Structural Reanalysis," Computers and Structures, Vol. 4, 1974, pp. 801-812.

31 Sobieszczanski-Sobienski, J., and Hajela, P., "Accuracy of an Approximate Static Structural Analysis Technique Based on Stiffness Matrix Eigenmodes," AIAA/ASME/ASCE/AHS 20th Struc., Struc. Dyn., and Mat. Conf., St. Louis, Mo., April 4-6, 1979.

32 Goult, R. J., Hoskins, R. F., Milner, J. A., and Pratt, M. J., Computational Methods in Linear Algebra, 1st ed., Halsted, Great Britain, 1974.

33 Kirsch, U., and Rubinstein, M. F., "Structural Reanalysis by Iteration," Computers and Structures, Vol. 2, 1972, pp. 497-510.

34 Phansalkar, S. R., "Matrix Iterative Methods for Structural Reanalysis," Computers and Structures, Vol. 4, 1974, pp. 779-800.

35 Arora, J. S., "Survey of Structural Reanalysis Techniques," ASCE Journal of the Structural Division, April 1976, pp. 783-8 .

36 Kirsch, U., Optimum Structural Design, McGraw Hill, 1980, Ch. 5.

Subject Index

Index of Programs